the teaching
of
secondary
mathematics

mcgraw-hill series in education

The late HAROLD BENJAMIN   *Consulting Editor-in-Chief*

ARNO A. BELLACK   *Teachers College, Columbia University*
Consulting Editor, Supervision, Curriculum, and Methods in Education

The late HAROLD BENJAMIN   *Emeritus Professor of Education*
George Peabody College for Teachers
Consulting Editor, Foundations in Education

PHILIP M. CLARK   *Ohio State University*
Consulting Editor, Psychology and Human Development in Education

WALTER F. JOHNSON   *Michigan State University*
Consulting Editor, Guidance, Counseling, and Student Personnel in Education

supervision curriculum and methods in education

ARNO A. BELLACK   *Consulting Editor*

BATCHELDER, McGLASSON, AND SCHORLING   *Student Teaching in Secondary Schools*

BENT, KRONENBERG, AND BOARDMAN   *Principles of Secondary Education*

BROWN, LEWIS, AND HARCLEROAD   *AV Instruction: Media and Methods*

BUTLER, WREN, AND BANKS   *The Teaching of Secondary Mathematics*

LEFEVRE   *Linguistics and the Teaching of Reading*

LUCIO AND McNEIL   *Supervision: A Synthesis of Thought and Action*

MACKENZIE   *Toward a New Curriculum in Physical Education*

MARKS, PURDY, AND KINNEY   *Teaching Elementary School Mathematics for Understanding*

MASSIALAS AND COX   *Inquiry in Social Studies*

MICHAELIS, GROSSMAN, AND SCOTT   *New Designs for the Elementary School Curriculum*

PHENIX   *Realms of Meaning*

STOREN   *The Disadvantaged Early Adolescent: More Effective Teaching*

STRANG, McCULLOUGH, AND TRAXLER   *The Improvement of Reading*

WINGO AND SCHORLING   *Elementary School Student Teaching*

the teaching
of
secondary
mathematics

CHARLES H. BUTLER
Professor of Mathematics, Emeritus
Western Michigan University

F. LYNWOOD WREN
Professor of Mathematics
San Fernando Valley State College

J. HOUSTON BANKS
Professor of Mathematics
George Peabody College for Teachers

FIFTH EDITION

McGRAW-HILL BOOK COMPANY
New York, St. Louis, San Francisco, Düsseldorf
London, Mexico, Panama, Sydney, Toronto

the teaching of secondary mathematics

Library of Congress Catalog Card Number 79-105421

09330

1 2 3 4 5 6 7 8 9 0   M A M M   7 9 8 7 6 5 4 3 2 1 0

This book was set in Palatino by Progressive Typographers,
and printed on permanent paper and bound by The Maple Press
Company. The designer was Barbara Ellwood; the drawings
were done by B. Handelman Associates, Inc. The editors
were Eliza Little and Susan Gamer. Matt Martino supervised
the production.

preface

The cordial reception given the four previous editions of this book and the new emphases which continue to remold the program of secondary mathematics created a challenge to prepare this fifth edition.

The revision has been extensive. Two chapters which were carried by each of the previous editions have been dropped. In two different areas three chapters have been reduced to two; and one completely new chapter, "The Teaching of Probability and Statistics," has been added. Each of the retained chapters has been subjected to appropriate revision when this was suggested by careful analysis. In all cases the exercises have been revised to make them more effective as learning and teaching aids. Also all bibliographies have been updated to provide supplementary resource references which report the most recent developments in secondary mathematics.

Like the fourth edition, this book is divided into two parts. Part I directs its attention to the discussion of those traditional and current educational problems, practices, and issues which give significant character to effective teaching of secondary mathematics. Part II concerns itself with giving prospective and active teachers of secondary mathematics a more informed understanding of the basic subject matter to be taught and of ways to help students learn it effectively.

As in each of the previous editions, the purpose in writing this edition has been to bring together in one volume the substance of the best contemporary thought on the most significant issues relevant to the teaching and learning of secondary-school mathematics. There is an advantage in having such a presentation within the covers of a single book. We believe that our book is useful both as a basic textbook in undergraduate or graduate classes for prospective or in-service teachers of mathematics, and as a helpful source of suggestions and supplementary references for the more intensive study of particular ideas.

For their kind permission to quote from published sources, we wish to express our appreciation to those authors, publishers, organizations, and journals from whose works such quotations have been taken. Also, we wish to express to Eliza Little, Susan Gamer, Robert R. Laffler, and Alleyne I. Wren our sincere appreciation of their valuable assistance in the preparation of this manuscript.

CHARLES H. BUTLER
F. LYNWOOD WREN
J. HOUSTON BANKS

contents

PREFACE v

**PART I THE PROGRAM OF INSTRUCTION IN
SECONDARY MATHEMATICS 1**

INTRODUCTION

1 The Evolving Program of Secondary Mathematics 4
2 Mathematics in General Education 41
3 The New Program in Mathematics 54
4 Modern Curriculum Problems in Mathematics 91
5 A Theory of Mathematical Learning 116
6 Means to Effective Learning and Teaching of
Mathematics 137
7 Evaluation of Instruction in Mathematics 172

**PART II THE TEACHING OF SELECTED TOPICS IN
SECONDARY MATHEMATICS 189**

INTRODUCTION

8 The Teaching of Arithmetic 192
9 The Teaching of Further Topics in Arithmetic 236
10 The Teaching of Junior High School Algebra 271
11 The Teaching of Senior High School Algebra 322
12 The Teaching of Geometry in the Junior High School 363
13 The Teaching of Geometry in the Senior High School 390
14 The Teaching of Geometry in the Senior High School (continued) 423
15 The Teaching of Trigonometry 453
16 The Teaching of Analytic Geometry 493
17 The Teaching of Calculus 531
18 The Teaching of Probability and Statistics 566

INDEX 587

the teaching
of
secondary
mathematics

1

**the program
of
instruction
in
secondary
mathematics**

INTRODUCTION

The program of mathematics in the secondary school is a composite of many diverse aspects, each characterized by distinct professional singularities. During recent years the selection, grade placement, and organization of the subject-matter content of the curriculum possibly have received the greater amount of interested attention and careful study. Equally important, however, are two other major components of the total program of secondary mathematics, namely (1) the planning for effective instruction by the teacher and perceptive learning by the student, and (2) the formulation of a functional program for the evaluation of instruction.

The subject-matter of secondary mathematics has evolved from a rigid set of reckoning rules demanded by the philosophy of mental discipline of pioneer days, through the activity-oriented pattern of selected units of environment experiences imposed by the pragmatic philosophy of the first half of the twentieth century, into the challenges of basic mathematical structure raised by the demands of the amazing technology of the second half of the twentieth century. In the course of this evolution much of the former subject matter has been rendered passé, and outmoded manipulative techniques have been replaced by more refined and sophisticated procedures. These developments have resulted in a revision in the grade placement of traditional content, a modified emphasis and approach in dealing with traditional subject matter retained in the curriculum, and an introduction of new ideas and content where they can be most helpful in shaping the new program in secondary mathematics.

While the textbook and the chalkboard remain important teaching tools, the modern teacher has the benefit of new teaching aids which he can utilize in meeting the varied new demands of the schoolroom. These require that teachers become familiar with the possibilities of television and other audio-visual aids, manipulative devices, programmed materials, and computerized procedures now available. Within the scope of such extended media of information a truly effective system can be formulated for solving the basic problems of instruction in secondary mathematics, which may be categorized as (1) teaching for understanding, (2) teaching for assimilation, (3) teaching for transfer, and (4) teaching for permanence.

Evaluation of instruction has in recent years evolved into a significant multiphase component of the mathematics program. It is no longer restricted to sparse written tests for measuring achievement. The total evaluation program must involve inventory, prognostic, and diagnostic tests, as well. Tests may be either written or oral; anecdotal or mere observation; teacher-made or standardized; the problem or the short-answer type. Each kind of test has its advantages and its shortcomings. Tests may be used as aids in proper classification of students and as warning signals to students. These are but some of the more important aspects of a really functional evaluation program as it relates to the student's understanding, assimilation, and retention. In such a capacity it serves as a measure of performance and progress. Another important function of an evaluation program is to appraise the relative effectiveness of the teaching techniques employed in the instructional program.

It is the purpose of Part One to examine each of these major areas of the teaching of secondary mathematics in the context of its historical background and present trend, and to acquaint the reader with some of the important past and continuing experimentation in the revision of subject matter and the modification of instructional patterns.

one | the evolving program of secondary mathematics

In the three centuries of American secondary education many significant changes have taken place. The early aristocratic policy of selecting students from among a favored few has been replaced by the modern democratic policy of opening the doors of educational opportunity to students from all levels of society. The fundamental philosophy has changed from one which demanded an institution whose principal function was preparation for a single profession to one which calls for an institution whose chief aim is twofold in nature, namely, the provision of terminal training that is functional for all students and the provision of propaedeutic training for those who can, and desire to, pursue their study in institutions of higher learning.

Change in philosophy

MATHEMATICS AND THE CHANGING EDUCATIONAL CURRICULUM

In the early frontier days the need for mathematics and the motivation for its development were rather limited. The farmer and the ordinary worker needed little beyond the ability to add and subtract. Boys who wanted to go into trade needed to know something of simple computation and of common measure, a few simple fractions, and the use of English and other European moneys. The seafaring man needed to know the basic principles of navigation; the clergyman found astronomy necessary in fixing the dates of religious festivals; and the public official needed knowledge of surveying to fix territorial boundaries. From this meager source flowed the shallow stream of mathematics in sixteenth-century America. Consequently, it is not surprising that mathematics received little attention in the early elementary schools, which were established for the primary purpose of teaching writing and reading, with an occasional reference to ciphering.

Mathematics before the twentieth century

It was not until the latter part of the nineteenth century that real progress began to take place in the development of mathematics in

America. By that time there was a fair-sized group of native talent working in the field of mathematics, and there were major influences shaping up to promote significant development both in mathematical research and in the improvement of instruction in mathematics.

EARLY ARITHMETIC

Rote memory and mechanical manipulation

Arithmetic, the only mathematical study of importance in the secondary schools of the United States during the colonial period, made its entrance into the curriculum of the Latin grammar school through the early writing school. The subject matter of the course was logical in arrangement and consisted primarily of a series of rules to be memorized and dogmatically applied according to rather definite classifications. No attempt was made to adapt the instruction to the pupil, and very little change was made in the nature or content of the subject matter. Under such a system of instruction, the only arithmetic studied was ciphering, which consisted largely of the manipulation of integers.

Text books were not generally used until the latter part of the eighteenth century. The master dictated the problems to be solved and stated the rule or rules to be used. No special directions or explanations were given. The rules and problems were recorded in cipher books. In describing two such books used in the study of arithmetic in the state of Illinois between 1804 and 1808, Breslich states that the subject taught was but little more than a mechanical manipulation of figures and a study of rules dogmatically applied.[1]

By the methods of colonial times each problem was solved as being one of a certain type or as belonging to a particular case, and few pupils were able to solve a problem unless they knew under which case it came. This system and these methods were applied to problems on a variety of subjects. Such an instructional program placed the emphasis almost entirely on the rote memorization of rules and paid little attention, if any, to basic understanding of concepts and techniques or to the significant characteristics of effective reasoning.

MENTAL DISCIPLINE

The curriculum of the academy was much broader in its scope than was that of the Latin grammar school and, in general, was less dominated by college-entrance requirements. An examination of

[1] E. R. Breslich, Arithmetic One Hundred Years Ago, *Elementary School Journal*, **25** (1924–1925), 664–674.

the annual reports made to the Regents of the University of the State of New York reveals that many different subjects appeared in various academy curriculums during the period from 1787 to 1870; among them were arithmetic, algebra, astronomy, book-keeping, conic sections, civil engineering, plane geometry, analytic geometry, leveling, logarithms, mapping, mensuration, navigation, nautical astronomy, statistics, surveying, and trigonometry.[2] The particular attention which was given to mathematics during this period was due in part to the possibility of practical applications, but principally to the idea of mental discipline, which occupied a very prominent place in educational thought during the early years of American education and exerted a profound influence upon curriculum making and methods of teaching.

The more extreme views on mental discipline did not go unchallenged, especially in the Middle West. The pioneer life made it necessary for the individual to rely upon his ability to develop the natural resources of this new country, and this called for a type of education which placed more emphasis on the utilitarian values than on the disciplinary or the cultural values. Although the number of mathematical subjects in the curriculum remained fairly uniform throughout the life of the academy, the nature and purpose of instruction underwent considerable change.

FOREIGN INFLUENCES

English influence

The English influence predominated in the American schools from the time of the Revolution until 1820. Many of the instructors in the American colleges and academies had received their training in England, and the majority of the texts were either English editions or were copied rather closely from English authors. Hutton's "Mathematics," Bonnycastle's "Algebra," and Playfair's "Euclid" are three of the most frequently mentioned texts of this early period.[3]

French influence

The period of French influence may be dated from the appointment of Claude Crozet, who had been trained in the École Polytechnique of Paris, as professor of mathematics at the United States Military Academy in 1817. For a period of approximately fifty years from this date texts by French authors were the most popular for general use, although they never entirely displaced the older English texts.

Contemporaneous with the influx of French mathematics was

[2] From Paul Monroe, "Principles of Secondary Education" (New York: The Macmillan Company, 1914), p. 54. By permission of The Macmillan Company, publishers.
[3] F. Cajori, "The Teaching and History of Mathematics in the United States" (Washington, D.C.: Government Printing Office, 1890), pp. 55–56.

the revival of interest in elementary education under the influence of the Pestalozzian school. The first incorporation of Pestalozzian ideas in the preparation of an arithmetic text was in Warren Colburn's "Intellectual Arithmetic upon the Inductive Method of Instruction," otherwise known as the "First Lessons."[4] This text, published first in 1821, marked the beginning of a new epoch in arithmetic and the teaching of arithmetic. The pupil, instead of studying and memorizing rules that he did not always fully understand, now was expected to set up his own rules as generalizations of his actual experiences. He was introduced to new topics by means of practical problems and questions, the order of presentation always being from the concrete to the abstract.[5] Colburn published a more advanced book in 1822 as a "sequel" to his "First Lessons." This text was designed as a practical arithmetic to be studied after the more elementary text. It consisted of topics usually found in the earlier advanced arithmetics except for certain omissions—in particular, the rule of three, rule of position, and powers and roots. The method of presentation was the same in the two texts.[6]

The period from 1821 to 1857 was one of rapid development for the study of arithmetic. One hundred ninety-five texts on the subject were published during that time; of that number, forty-six were designed for use in colleges and academies and four were direct translations from the French.[7] During the period from 1860 to 1892 there was no essential change in aim or content and there were few modifications in the methods of teaching.[8] In contrast with the previous period, however, there was significant change in the organization and presentation of subject matter. The arithmetics of the latter period were combinations of the old, as found in colonial arithmetics, and the new, as found in the works of Colburn. The old arithmetics generally rejected reasoning; Colburn's arithmetics rejected rules and encouraged reasoning; the texts of the period 1860 to 1892 gave rules but at the same time gave demonstrations and encouraged pupils to think.

The Pestalozzian influence for reform in content selection and instructional technique was felt in algebra and geometry as well as in arithmetic. Colburn, who published his "Introduction to Algebra upon the Inductive Method of Instruction" in 1832, advanced new ideas on methods of instruction in algebra. His idea was to

---

[4] *Ibid.*, p. 106.
[5] Walter S. Monroe, "Development of Arithmetic as a School Subject" (U.S. Office of Education Bulletin 10, 1917), pp. 63–70, 80–88.
[6] Walter S. Monroe, Analysis of Colburn's Arithmetics, *Elementary School Teacher*, **13** (1912–1913), 239–246.
[7] J. M. Greenwood, "American Textbooks on Arithmetic," *Annual Report of the Commissioner of Education* (Washington, D.C.: Government Printing Office, 1897–1898), vol. I, pp. 796–868.
[8] Walter S. Monroe, *op. cit.*, Development of Arithmetic as a School Subject, p. 90.

make the transition from arithmetic to algebra as gradual as possible. Because the student was expected to derive most knowledge from solving the problems himself, the explanations were made as brief as was consistent with giving what was required. The problems were designed to exercise the student in reasoning, instead of making him a mere listener.[9] Geometry, before the nineteenth century, was taught dogmatically, and the students merely memorized and worked by rule. Although there still remain traces of the dogmatic method of instruction, during the first half of the twentieth century there was a definite increase in emphasis on original exercises, with less rote memorization of theorems. In more recent years this new trend toward greater geometric understanding has been augmented by a marked emphasis on more careful and specific attention to the postulational structure of geometry, more intelligent recognition of the relative educational values of both three-dimensional and two-dimensional geometry, and more thoughtful evaluation of the relative significance and effectiveness of the synthetic and analytic techniques of geometric proof.

THE PUBLIC HIGH SCHOOL

By 1860 the educational philosophy which was to shape the program of the public high school had begun to predominate over that which had fostered both the Latin grammar school and the academy. There was now a strong tendency toward expansion in both number and content of courses offered, as well as an attempt to blend intellectual and practical training in the same school. Curriculums were organized and expanded rapidly with no particular plan or definite educational objective in view. By 1890 this unrest had reached its highest point.[10] This unsystematic expansion of the curriculum offered a sufficient reason for a demand for reform, and mathematics received its share of the attack.

THE COMMITTEE OF TEN

The Committee of Ten on Secondary School Subjects agreed that a radical change in the teaching of mathematics was necessary. The Subcommittee on Mathematics recommended that a course in concrete geometry, with numerous exercises, be introduced into

[9] H. G. Meserve, Mathematics One Hundred Years Ago, *Mathematics Teacher*, **21** (1928), 339.
[10] I. L. Kandel: "History of Secondary Education" (Boston: Houghton Mifflin Company, 1930), p. 461.

the grammar school and that systematic algebra should be begun at the age of fourteen. The committee suggested that demonstrative geometry should follow the first year of algebra, that it should be taught along with algebra for the next two years, and that work in solid geometry might be incorporated. Formal algebra was to be studied for 5 hours a week during the first year and for 2½ hours a week for the two following years, during which time it was to parallel work in geometry. Special emphasis was to be placed on literal as well as numerical coefficients. The committee also suggested that those who did not expect to go to college might, after the first year of algebra, turn to bookkeeping and the technical parts of arithmetic, while students planning to attend scientific schools might profitably spend a year on trigonometry and some more advanced topics of algebra. A hope was expressed by the committee that a place might be found in the high school or college course for at least the essentials of modern synthetic or projective geometry.[11]

THE COMMITTEE ON COLLEGE
ENTRANCE REQUIREMENTS

In order to bring about a better articulation between the secondary schools and colleges, the Committee on College Entrance Requirements in 1899 recommended the following course:

Seventh Grade: Concrete Geometry and Introduction to Algebra; Eighth Grade: Introduction to Demonstrative Geometry and Algebra; Ninth and Tenth Grades: Algebra and Plane Geometry; Eleventh Grade: Solid Geometry and Plane Trigonometry; Twelfth Grade: Advanced Algebra and Mathematics reviewed.

Algebra for the seventh and eighth grades was to begin with literal arithmetic, which was to be followed by simple polynomials and fractional expressions, equations of the first degree with numerical coefficients in one and two unknowns, the four fundamental operations for rational algebraic expressions, and simple factoring. One-half of the time of the seventh grade was to be devoted to concrete geometry, while in the eighth grade one-half of the time was to be spent on demonstrative geometry. The important objective of such work was to awaken an interest in demonstrative geometry. The committee recommended that an equal amount of time be devoted to algebra and geometry in the ninth and tenth grades.[12]

[11] "Report of the Committee of Ten on Secondary School Subjects" (New York: American Book Company, 1894), pp. 105–116.
[12] A. F. Nightingale, "Report of the Committee on College Entrance Requirements," *Proceedings and Addresses of National Education Association*, 38th Annual Meeting, 1899, pp. 648–651.

THE INTERNATIONAL COMMISSION

Another influence for change in the curriculum of secondary mathematics was due to the reports of the International Commission on the Teaching of Mathematics, which were published by the U.S. Bureau of Education between the years 1911 and 1918. Committee III of the commission, in its study of "Mathematics in the Public General Secondary Schools of the United States," found that every high school offered algebra and geometry for at least one year each. One-half of the schools gave algebra for an extra half year, and less than twenty percent gave algebra for the full two years. There were very few schools that offered algebra for two and one-half years, and only the larger high schools had courses in solid geometry, plane trigonometry, and advanced algebra.[13]

The prevailing program in algebra and geometry

The sequence in practically all the textbooks in geometry was that of Legendre. Geometrical constructions by the euclidean method[14] were usually given a logical place among other propositions. The original exercises, which ranged from 600 in one text to 1,200 in another, were rigidly confined to the subject matter of the text.

In addition to subjects usually recognized as secondary school subjects, several high schools offered a course in commercial arithmetic similar to the course frequently given in the elementary school, except that the problems were somewhat more difficult and more closely related to commercial life.[15]

Two main needs for reform

After their general survey of the field of secondary mathematics, the commission felt that there were two main needs which were dominant, namely,

> The need for the better preparation of teachers and the need to reduce, if not eliminate, the waste of effort involved in independent and often inadequate treatment of fundamental and broad questions by separate schools, colleges, or local systems.[16]

---

[13] Report of Committees III and IV of the International Commission, "Mathematics in the Public and Private Secondary Schools of the United States" (U.S. Office of Education Bulletin 16, 1911), pp. 17–22.

[14] The first three postulates stated by Euclid in his famous "Elements" are: "Let it be granted,
  "*a*. That a straight line may be drawn from any one point to any other point:
  "*b*. That a terminated straight line may be produced to any length in a straight line:
  "*c*. And that a circle may be described from any centre, at any distance from that centre."
  The first two of these postulates enable us to draw a straight line, but not lines of a prescribed length except insofar as a line might be drawn to connect two given points. In other words, these two postulates permit all operations possible with an unmarked straightedge. The third postulate allows the use of the compass for the drawing of a circle with a given center and passing through a given point, i.e., with a fixed radius.
  Thus "geometrical constructions by the euclidean method" are those constructions which can be performed by using only the unmarked straightedge and compass.
  For further discussion see Richard Courant and Herbert Robbins, "What is Mathematics?" (Fair Lawn, N.J.: Oxford University Press, 1941), pp. 117–140.

[15] Report of Committees III and IV of the International Commission, *op. cit.*, p. 22.

[16] "Report of the American Commissioners of the International Commission on the Teaching of Mathematics" (U.S. Office of Education Bulletin 14, 1912), pp. 39–40.

In their study of elementary mathematics in the college tne commission found that calculus had become primarily a sophomore study and that it was serving somewhat as "a boundary line between two styles of teaching," the recitation method and the lecture or lecture-quiz method. This difference in the educational problem before and after calculus was further emphasized by the proposal, on the part of some, to relegate the first two years of college work to the high school and, on the part of others, to take up this work in "a junior college leading to an appropriate degree." The organization of subject matter was still largely compartmentalized, but a tendency toward fusion was developing, with more emphasis on practical applications. The general outline of material was algebra, trigonometry, analytic geometry, and calculus, with a prerequisite of elementary algebra through quadratics, plane geometry, and sometimes solid geometry. The changing composition of the school population was recognized as a cause for readjustment of content and instructional technique in the freshman year.[17]

THE NATIONAL COMMITTEE OF FIFTEEN ON GEOMETRY SYLLABUS

In 1908 the Mathematics Round Table of the Secondary Department of the National Education Association unanimously called for a committee to study and report upon the problem of a syllabus for geometry. During the same year the American Federation of Teachers of the Mathematical and Natural Sciences authorized the appointment of such a committee, and in 1909 the Secondary Department of the National Education Association authorized the committee to proceed as a joint committee of the association and federation.

In its report[18] the committee recommended that reasonable attention be given to concrete exercises but with no diminishing attention to the logical structure of geometry. It suggested that there be "a quickening of the logical sense" through a distribution of emphasis designed to economize on the time and energy spent in the mastery of theorems and to provide more time and opportunity for the study of geometry in its more concrete relations. It pointed out that there are some terms in geometry which it is best to accept as undefined, and recommended that definitions be

Need for more emphasis on the concrete in geometry

[17] *Ibid.*, pp. 41–47.

Report of Committee XII of the International Commission, "Graduate Work in Mathematics in Universities and in Other Institutions of Like Grade in the United States" (U.S. Office of Education Bulletin 6, 1911), pp. 45–47.

[18] Committee of Fifteen, "Provisional Report on Geometry Syllabus," *School Science and Mathematics*, **11** (1911), 330.

introduced when needed rather than massed at one place in the text or course of study. The desirability of the use of certain informal proofs was mentioned, as well as the advisability of excluding limits and incommensurables from the requirements for entrance to college. It was recommended that between one and one and one-half years be given to plane geometry and that it be taught simultaneously with algebra or preceded by at least one year of algebra.

In the treatment of exercises the committee recommended that careful thought be given to their distribution and gradation; it seemed to feel that the tendency has been to overemphasize difficult abstract applications of various theorems in the exercises. It therefore suggested concrete exercises, along with "a judicious selection of a reasonable number of abstract originals." Material for exercises was to be found in other subject fields, such as architecture, natural design, indirect measurement, and any other source available to the individual teacher. A great deal of emphasis was given to the nature and importance of the concept of locus.[19]

THE NATIONAL COMMITTEE ON MATHEMATICAL REQUIREMENTS

In 1916 the National Committee on Mathematical Requirements was organized under the auspices of the Mathematical Association of America, Inc., "for the purpose of giving national expression to the movement for reform in the teaching of mathematics, which had gained considerable headway in various parts of the country, but which lacked the power that coordination and united effort alone could give."[20]

Need for reform in the teaching of mathematics

The committee was instructed to concern itself with making a comprehensive study of the whole problem of mathematical education on the secondary and collegiate levels. One of the major problems was thus to make proper provision for the comparatively new, yet fairly well-established, junior and senior high school programs of instruction. In its final report the aims of mathematical instruction were formulated into three general classes (practical, disciplinary, and cultural),[21] and instead of a detailed syllabus for the junior high school, there was a proposal for a general outline by topics, accompanied by a statement that further experimentation was necessary before a standardized syllabus

Aims of mathematical instruction

---

[19] *Ibid.*, pp. 434–460, 509–531.
[20] The National Committee on Mathematical Requirements, "The Reorganization of Mathematics in Secondary Education" (Boston: Houghton Mifflin Company, 1923), p. vii.
[21] *Ibid.*, pp. 6–13.

could be determined. Although the committee refused to take a definite stand on the arrangement of topics, it did suggest five plans for distribution of this material, hoping that they might prove helpful in the organization of mathematics curriculums for the junior high school. It further recommended that the mathematics proposed for the grades of the junior high school be required of all students.[22]

Mathematics in the junior high school

The committee recommended that provision be made for the specific aims of the mathematics of the senior high school through a body of elective material which should be open to all pupils who had satisfactorily completed the required work of the junior high school. Realizing that the method of organization of this material could be more elastic than that for grades 7 to 9, and in consideration of the fact that no one best plan had been determined, the committee suggested four different plans, any one of which might be used for the purpose of more efficiently organizing the instructional content of the mathematics of grades 10 to 12.

Mathematics in the senior high school

Additional electives, such as elementary statistics, mathematics of investment, shop mathematics, surveying and navigation, and descriptive or projective geometry, were suggested for schools where there was a need for such work and where the conditions warranted their inclusion in the curriculum. It was also recommended that extensive use be made of historical and biographical material in the entire teaching program to lend interest and significance to the subject matter studied.[23]

INTEGRATED COURSES

The arrangement of subject matter has always been a problem at least as difficult as its selection. The early tendency was simply to follow the compartment system of organization, and that has continued to be probably the most familiar pattern of the senior high school course. However, in this century there has been increasing significance in the attention and effort directed toward the integration of related subject matter. The initial impetus in shaping the underlying philosophy of this new pattern of instruction in mathematics can be traced largely to the efforts of the Committee of Ten and the Committee on College Entrance Requirements during the latter part of the nineteenth century. Although there had been a few scattered instances of such treatment of mathematical subject matter prior to that time, the reports of the two committees seem to carry the first evidence of any concentrated thought devoted to

Committee influence

[22] *Ibid.*, pp. 29–42.
[23] *Ibid.*, pp. 48–57.

its consideration. In an address before the National Education Association (1902), Newhall expressed the hope that a time would come when the secondary school course would comprise six years and mathematics would not be limited by artificial boundaries, as was the case in the study of algebra, geometry, and trigonometry.[24]

Influence of
leading
mathematicians

Contemporaneous with this address, the influence of Klein in Germany, Tannery and Borel in France, Perry and Nunn in England, and Moore in America made the conditions more favorable for a fairly rapid growth of more general interest in the integration of instructional materials in mathematics.

The effort to present the mathematics of even the junior high school in a fused course has not been without its rather severe critics. There are those who feel that it is too much of a hodgepodge of superficialities that tends to general weakening of the subject content. Some critics have felt that too much emphasis is given to fusion of subject matter and not enough attention is paid to the significance of the individuality of different topics. Nevertheless, the fact that two of the fundamental services of the junior high school have been to provide for exploration and for contact with minimum essentials has helped to concentrate interest in integrated mathematics courses in its curriculum.

Criticism of
integration

The effort to evolve a functional mathematics program well adapted to the education of the masses has also brought about significant changes in the content and instructional techniques of senior high school mathematics. The mathematical content for the later years of secondary instruction is more specialized than that of the three previous years and, as a consequence, has not been so readily adapted to a fused method of organization. One of the most difficult problems which confront the teachers of senior high school mathematics is that of so organizing and presenting subject content as to preserve its intrinsic characteristics and yet to introduce the desired continuity.

In recent years there has been a great deal of experimentation in the use of different types of instructional materials arranged in varying course patterns by such groups as the School Mathematics Study Group (SMSG), the University of Maryland Mathematics Project (UMMaP), the University of Illinois Committee on School Mathematics (UICSM), the Ball State Teachers College Experimental Program, the Boston College Mathematics Institute, the Southern Illinois University–Comprehensive School Mathematics Project (SIU-CSMP), the Madison Project of Syracuse University and Webster College, the Minnesota Mathematics and Science Teaching Project (Minnemast), and the Greater Cleveland Mathematics Program (GCMP). These efforts have resulted not only in the

Experimental
groups

[24] Charles W. Newhall, Correlation of Mathematical Studies in Secondary Schools, *Proceedings of the National Education Association*, 1902, pp. 488–492.

introduction of new material, but also in an emphasis on integrated organization and treatment of subject matter at both junior and senior high school levels of instruction.

Mathematics in the junior college

In the development of the mathematics curriculum of the junior college there are definite indications of a trend toward a more integrated pattern of content organization in these first two years of the college program. The best evidence of this is to be found in the many different types of integrated texts now in use, in particular, texts on "Unified Algebra and Trigonometry" and "Analytic Geometry and Calculus," and also in the recommendations of the Committee on the Undergraduate Program in Mathematics (CUPM) of the Mathematical Association of America.[25] Many teachers feel that students taking such courses get a deeper appreciation of the fundamental interrelationships of mathematical material, and consequently have a better idea of the real meaning of mathematics than do those who take the traditional compartmentalized type of course. They also claim that such a student will attain just as satisfactory a mastery of the fundamentals, if not better.

COLLEGE ENTRANCE EXAMINATION BOARD

The problem of the curriculum of secondary mathematics has always been closely related to the question of college-entrance requirements. The entire program of the Latin grammar school was defined in terms of preparation for college. The academy, however, early expanded its program to include not only preparation for college, but also a terminal type of program for the non-college-bound student. In meeting the demands of this new function of secondary education, the academy gradually encroached upon the educational program of the colleges. The natural consequence of this was a material increase in college-entrance requirements.

Change in college entrance requirements

At the close of the eighteenth century the only mathematics required for admission to college was "a knowledge of the rules and processes of vulgar arithmetic." The statutes of 1807 prescribed that the requirements for admission to Harvard should include the rules of arithmetic dealing with simple and compound notation, addition, subtraction, multiplication, division, reduction, and the single rule of three. In 1820 these requirements were extended to include the algebra of simple equations, roots and powers, and arithmetical and geometrical progressions. Columbia

---

[25] Report of the Committee on the Undergraduate Program in Mathematics, *American Mathematical Monthly*, **63** (1955), 511–520. Also see subsequent reports and bulletins distributed through the central office of the committee, P.O. Box 1024, Berkeley, Calif.

added algebra to her entrance requirements in 1821; Yale, in 1847; and Princeton, in 1848. In 1844, candidates for admission to Harvard College were examined in arithmetic, algebra, and geometry (up to the book on proportion). Geometry was made an entrance requirement at Yale in 1865; at Princeton, Michigan, and Cornell in 1868; and at Columbia in 1870. By 1870 the admission requirements at Harvard had been extended to include higher arithmetic, algebra through quadratic equations, logarithms, and the elements of plane geometry. Yale and Princeton specified only to quadratic equations in algebra. While Yale specified the first two books of Playfair's "Euclid" (or an acceptable equivalent), Princeton specified only the first book. Similar requirements existed at the other leading universities of that period.[26]

The National Committee on Mathematical Requirements in its 1923 report recognized the far-reaching influence of college entrance requirements upon the teaching of secondary mathematics. It criticized the prevailing type of examination as overemphasizing "the candidate's skill in formal manipulation." In an effort to make desirable modifications in the prevailing type of college-entrance examination, members of the national committee met with members of a committee from the College Entrance Examination Board and drew up a list of recommendations which were incorporated in the 1923 report. While attention was paid to the problem of reducing the excessive "difficulty and complexity of the formal manipulative questions," two of the most significant recommendations were as follows:

1. An effort should be made to devise [algebraic] questions which will fairly test the candidate's understanding of principles and his ability to apply them, while involving a minimum of manipulative complexity.
2. The examinations in geometry should be definitely constructed to test the candidate's ability to draw valid conclusions rather than his ability to memorize an argument.[27]

Recommendations of the College Entrance Examination Board

Early in 1921 the College Entrance Examination Board appointed a commission to study the problem of college entrance requirements and make recommendations for desirable revisions in the definitions of requirements in elementary mathematics. In their reports[28] published in 1923 the commission eliminated from the list of requirements in algebra the extended and useless manipulation of polynomials, reduced factoring to three types, and simplified the requirements in fractions. Increased recognition was given to the formula and the graph, and two notable changes were made in the simplification of the material dealing with surds and

[26] E. C. Broome, "A Historical and Critical Discussion of College Admission Requirements" (New York: The Macmillan Company, 1903), pp. 41–53.
[27] The National Committee on Mathematical Requirements, *op. cit.*, pp. 76–77.
[28] College Entrance Examination Board, *Documents* 107 and 108 (New York: College Entrance Examination Board, 1923).

in the introduction of numerical trigonometry. For plane geometry only eighty-nine theorems were included in the syllabus, and of these only thirty-one were starred to be used for purposes of proofs. In the case of the unstarred propositions the candidate was expected to be familiar with content so that he might answer questions related to their substance or use the propositions in solving originals. Similar provisions were made for solid geometry. A new type of examination was one designed to take care of a one-year course in plane and solid geometry. The committee made the effort to reorganize the examination material in such a way that the demands on the candidate's memory would be lightened, and increased opportunity for the development of geometrical understanding would be given. These examinations served to set up more definite goals of instruction, as well as to provide a principal pattern of textbook construction. The work of the board has helped to clarify the problem of entrance requirements and provide for better articulation between the work of the senior high school and that of the freshman year of college.

In 1935 the Commission on Examinations in Mathematics, a commission of the College Entrance Examination Board, completely revised the examinations in mathematics. In the new ones, known as alpha, beta, gamma, the effort was made "to combine the advantages of the longer essay-type, multiple-step question with those of the single-step question."[29] Two of the significant differences between the new and the old form of entrance examinations were the increased objectivity in scoring and the reduced emphasis upon the traditional compartmentalized treatment of subject matter.

Alpha, beta, gamma examinations

The commission postulated that "the examinations should be such as to determine: (a) the candidate's understanding and appreciation of the fundamental principles and characteristic modes of approach of mathematics; (b) his technical equipment and his knowledge of mathematical facts."[30] Furthermore, in recognition of the different interpretations of the meaning of "fitness for college," the commission attempted to provide examinations for the three following groups:

(α) Those who are not ready to carry on in college the study of mathematics or natural science, but who base their claim to be admitted to college in part upon the study of mathematics in the secondary schools

(β) Those who intend to fulfill at least the minimum college requirement in mathematics or natural science

(γ) Those who look forward to more advanced undergraduate work in mathematics and science.[31]

---

[29] College Entrance Examination Board, "Description of Examination Subjects" (New York: College Entrance Examination Board, 1940), pp. 34–37. An earlier draft of this document, later edited, was published in *Mathematics Teacher*, **28** (1935), 154–166.

[30] *Ibid.*

[31] *Ibid.*

Soon after the introduction of these examinations, schools began to voice a rather general demand that an examination be provided suitable for candidates whose first two years had been devoted primarily to the study of algebra. In response to this demand the Committee of Examiners in Mathematics of the College Entrance Examination Board introduced in June, 1942, Mathematics 2A (Alternative Alpha).

After the discontinuance in 1943 of the alpha, beta, and gamma tests, the board went through five distinct but unsatisfactory phases of testing. Each phase represented a definite effort to work out a satisfactory combined use of the Scholastic Aptitude Test and various types of achievement tests in mathematics. The final plan, which was put into use in 1950, called for two distinct phases:

(1) the Scholastic Aptitude Test, taken by mathematics candidates along with all candidates during the morning session, and (2) two 1-hour achievement tests in mathematics (Intermediate Mathematics and Advanced Mathematics) in the afternoon.

In 1955 the board assumed the responsibility for continuing the

work on the Advanced Placement Program which originated in 1952 in the School and College Study of Admission with Advanced Standing, a project sponsored by the Fund for the Advancement of Education. The first administration of the program was held in May, 1956, and the program has since continued to be administered yearly by the Educational Testing Service. Advanced placement is defined by the board to mean:

(1) Exemption from prescribed courses and placement in an advanced college course instead of in an elementary course which would otherwise have been required, or
(2) the award of college credit in recognition of achievement in covering the work ordinarily required in a course of college level, or
(3) both advanced placement and college credit.[32]

In 1955 another important action was taken by the board in the

interest of improved instruction in mathematics. The Commission on Mathematics was appointed

. . . (1) to study the present secondary school mathematics curriculum with a view toward the recommendation of a realignment of the entire secondary mathematics program to provide adequate preparation for the study of present-day college and advanced mathematics; and (2) . . . to investigate the Board's activities in the testing of mathematics and to recommend any possible improvement therein.[33]

Believing that "the improvement of secondary school mathe-

[32] College Entrance Examination Board, "Fifty-third Annual Report of the Director" (New York: College Entrance Examination Board, 1955), p. 20.
[33] College Entrance Examination Board, "Fifth-fifth Annual Report of the Director" (New York: College Entrance Examination Board, 1957), p. 10. The report of the commission was published in April, 1959.

matics instruction . . . would be greatly facilitated and the colleges in nowise handicapped," the commission strongly recommended that the traditional requirements in elementary algebra, intermediate algebra, advanced algebra, plane and solid geometry, and trigonometry be replaced by a new formulation of entrance requirements in mathematics. The new program would designate the new requirements in terms of length of time spent in study. The titles suggested for courses to be given in four successive high school years were Elementary Mathematics I, Elementary Mathematics II, Intermediate Mathematics, and Advanced Mathematics. The group then proceeded to define in rather specific detail the subject-matter content of each year's program,[34] and in order to help implement the recommendations for revised and renewed emphases in the content of instruction, a separate volume of appendixes was published concurrent with the report.

The commission, recognizing the need for a "context of reference" for the proper interpretation of its recommendations, closed its report with the following brief summary of all the commission's recommendations:

Summary of the commission's recommendations

College preparatory mathematics should include topics selected from algebra, geometry (demonstrative and coordinate), and trigonometry—all broadly interpreted. The point of view should be in harmony with contemporary mathematical thought; emphasis should be placed upon basic concepts and skills and upon the principles of deductive reasoning regardless of the branch of mathematics from which the topic is chosen. In every case, the standard of substance and content should be commensurate with that of the courses outlined in Chapter 4 [on pages 20–47]. Courses designed for other purposes (e.g., consumer mathematics, business mathematics, shop mathematics) are not acceptable.[35]

The commission did not overlook the importance of the well-prepared teacher; a considerable portion of the report is devoted to the discussion of both preservice and in-service training of both elementary school and secondary school teachers of mathematics.[36]

In the light of these and other impending recommendations for change in the college and high school mathematics programs, the Educational Testing Service, in the spring of 1958, began initial planning for a new series of end-of-course Cooperative Mathematics Tests.[37] These plans culminated in the 1962 announcement of "new-course-oriented achievement tests in arithmetic (grades 7, 8, and 9), elementary algebra, intermediate algebra, and high school geometry."[38]

Cooperative Mathematics Tests

---

[34] "Report of Commission on Mathematics" (New York: College Entrance Examination Board, 1959), pp. 20–47.
[35] *Ibid.,* pp. 60–61.
[36] *Ibid.,* pp. 48–58.
[37] Sheldon S. Myers, Cooperative Mathematics Tests: A Progress Report, *American Mathematical Monthly,* **69** (1962), 223–225.
[38] New Cooperative Mathematics Tests, *American Mathematical Monthly,* **69** (1962), 917.

NATIONAL ORGANIZATIONS

No discussion of the forces that have had significant influence in the evolution of the program in secondary mathematics would be complete without mention of the Mathematical Association of America, the National Council of Teachers of Mathematics, and the Central Association of Science and Mathematics Teachers.

The Mathematical Association of America (MAA)

This group was organized at Columbus, Ohio, in December, 1915, and incorporated under the laws of the state of Illinois on Sept. 8, 1920. In the interest of improved instruction in collegiate mathematics the association has sponsored:

Activities of MAA

1 The publication of the *American Mathematical Monthly,* a high-grade mathematical magazine devoted to the interests of collegiate mathematics.
2 The organization of a large number of sections in which papers in mathematical research are presented and instructional problems in collegiate mathematics are discussed.
3 The organization of many undergraduate clubs in colleges and universities. These clubs have been very effective in motivating interest in mathematics.
4 The appointment of many committees for the study of problems related to the content and methods of mathematical instruction and the better training of teachers of mathematics. Some of the committees have been independent committees of the association; others have been joint committees with representation from other interested groups.
5 Since 1961, the publication of the *Mathematics Magazine* (formerly the *National Mathematics Magazine*). The policy of this "Journal of Collegiate Mathematics" is to "publish a wide variety of mathematical material that will be of interest to undergraduate students and to teachers at both the college and secondary levels."[39]
6 The promotion, with other organizations, of joint meetings, committees, and conferences in the interest of improved instruction in junior college mathematics.

Each year, in addition to the sectional meetings, the association holds two regular national meetings at which papers are read and instructional problems are discussed. Further evidences of the interest of the association in the promotion of mathematics are (1) annual subsidies paid to journals that are interesed in the publication of mathematical research; (2) the publication in December, 1929, of the Rhind Mathematical Papyrus; (3) the publication of the *Carus Monograph Series* and the *Slaught Papers;* (4) the awarding of the $100 Chauvent prize, the purpose of which is to stimulate expository contributions in mathematical journals; (5) the sponsoring of various committee studies of secondary

[39] Statement by the editor in the January, 1961, issue of the magazine.

school and college mathematics programs; (6) the sponsoring of competitive tests at the college and high school levels; (7) the promotion, under grants from the National Science Foundation, of two programs of visiting lectures, one at the college level and one at the high school level; (8) the sponsoring of summer institutes and conferences for college teachers; and (9) the holding of symposia on problems related to improved instruction in mathematics.[40]

The National Council of Teachers of Mathematics (NCTM)

This group was organized at Cleveland, Ohio, on Feb. 24, 1920, and incorporated under the Illinois laws on Apr. 28, 1928. The purpose of the council is to promote interest in mathematics, especially in the elementary and secondary fields, by the following means:[41]

Activities of NCTM

1 Holding of meetings for presentation and discussion of papers. The annual meeting is usually held during the month of April. Ten other national meetings called "name-of-site" meetings are held each year. During the summer a meeting is held in conjunction with the National Education Association, of which the council, while retaining its identity and independent status, became a department on July 8, 1950. Meetings are held in conjunction with the American Association for the Advancement of Science during the Christmas season, and with the Mathematical Association during January of odd-numbered years. The council assists local groups through its policy of cosponsored meetings with affiliated groups.

2 Publication of three journals and of books, pamphlets, monographs, and reports for the purpose of vitalizing and coordinating the work of local organizations of teachers of mathematics and of bringing the interests of mathematics to the attention and consideration of the educational world. There are two official journals, the *Mathematics Teacher*, the only magazine in the United States whose interests are devoted entirely to the improvement of instruction in mathematics at the secondary level, and the *Arithmetic Teacher*, the only magazine in the United States whose interests are devoted entirely to the improvement of instruction in arithmetic. The council also publishes the *Mathematics Student Journal*, for high school students, and the *Journal for Research in Mathematics Education*. A further significant contribution to the literature of better instruction in mathematics is

---

[40] A. A. Bennett, Brief History of the Mathematical Association of America before World War II, *American Mathematical Monthly* (50th Anniversary Edition), **74**, part II (1967), 1–11; R. A. Rosenbaum, History of MAA since World War II, *ibid.*, 12–22.

[41] Frank B. Allen, The Council's Drive to Improve School Mathematics, *Mathematics Teacher*, **56** (1963), 386–393; *Arithmetic Teacher*, **10** (1963), 368–375.

Bruce E. Meserve, The NCTM, Its Growth and Growing Pains, *ibid.*, **58** (1965), 490–495; Mathematics Teachers, On Guard!, *ibid.*, **59** (1966), 522–530.

Julius H. Hlavaty, Toward the Golden Jubilee Year—1970, *Mathematics Teacher*, **61** (1968), 661–664; *Arithmetic Teacher*, **16** (1968), 342–345.

Donovan Johnson, President's Report, *Mathematics Teacher*, **60** (1967), 661–664; *Arithmetic Teacher*, **14** (1967), 523–526; President's Report of the State of the Council, *Mathematics Teacher*, **61** (1968), 644–648; *Arithmetic Teacher*, **15** (1968), 571–575.

the *Yearbook*, published at intervals since 1926 by the council, which is devoted to the discussion of important aspects of the teaching of elementary and secondary mathematics. There is a continuing Yearbook Planning Committee which gives a great deal of thought to the planning of the yearbook program.

A new venture in the interest of mathematics and its place in the modern educational program is the series of supplementary publications. The purpose of this series of publications is to enrich the instructional background of the teacher of elementary and secondary mathematics and to provide supplementary instructional aids and enrichment materials for students.

3   Promotion of the affiliation of local organizations of teachers of mathematics with the council and of close cooperation with other professional organizations. Recently, the council has become somewhat international in nature through such affiliation with groups from certain provinces of Canada.

4   Promotion of investigations for the purpose of improving the teaching of elementary school and secondary school mathematics.

5   Participation with the Mathematical Association of America (MAA), the American Mathematical Society (AMS), the Association for Symbolic Logic (ASL), the Association for Computing Machinery (ACM), the Institute of Mathematical Statistics (IMS), and the Society for Industrial and Applied Mathematics (SIAM) in a cooperative effort to improve instruction in mathematics in American and Canadian Schools and colleges. This unified effort is directed by the Conference Board of the Mathematical Sciences.

6   Promotion and study of the use of new educational media in the teaching of mathematics in the elementary and secondary schools.

The Central Association of Science and Mathematics Teachers (CASMT)

Activities of CASMT

Although it is a sectional organization, this group has exerted a national influence over the teaching of secondary school mathematics. The Central Association was organized in April, 1903, and incorporated in July, 1928. Since its organization, it has sponsored a very active program in the interest of improved teaching of science and mathematics in the secondary schools of our nation. Its program has been carried forward through annual meetings, held during the Thanksgiving holiday season, and the publication of *School Science and Mathematics*, "a journal for all science and mathematics teachers." The programs of the annual meetings are inspirational and informative, as well as pedagogical.

THE JOINT COMMISSION TO STUDY THE PLACE OF MATHEMATICS IN SECONDARY EDUCATION

In the fall of 1933 a Commission to Study the Place of Mathematics in Secondary Education was appointed by the Mathematical Association of America; later this commission was incorporated into a

Joint Commission of the Mathematical Association and the National Council of Teachers of Mathematics. In its final report[42] the commission undertook to define the place of mathematics in the modern educational program and then organize a mathematical curriculum for grades 7 to 14 (secondary education was defined to include the junior college) in terms of the major mathematical fields which would provide for continuity of development and flexibility of administration.[43]

Program proposed by the Joint Commission

The proposed program was based upon an assumed "normal mathematical equipment of the American pupil who has satisfactorily completed the work of the sixth grade," which was defined as follows:

1. A familiarity with the basic concepts, the processes, and the vocabulary of arithmetic
2. Understanding of the significance of the different positions that a given digit may occupy in a number, including the case of a decimal fraction
3. A mastery of the basic number combinations in addition, subtraction, multiplication, and division
4. Reasonable skill in computing with integers, common fractions, and decimal fractions
5. An acquaintance with the principal units of measurement, and their use in everyday life situations
6. The ability to solve simple problems involving computation and units of measurement
7. The ability to recognize, to name, and to sketch such common geometric figures as the rectangle, the square, the circle, the triangle, the rectangular solid, the sphere, the cylinder, and the cube
8. The habit of estimating and checking results[44]

In recognition of existing differences in educational philosophies and practices and in an effort to make "a definite step toward educational harmony," the commission set up a tentative list of guiding principles to be followed in organizing the mathematical program for grades 7 to 12.

In the light of these principles two classifications of the materials of mathematical instruction were made.

1. *The subdivision according to major subject fields*
   I. The field of numbers and computation
   II. The field of geometric form and space perception
   III. The field of graphic representation
   IV. The field of elementary analysis
   V. The field of logical (or "straight") thinking
   VI. The field of relational thinking
   VII. The field of symbolic representation and thinking

---

[42] Joint Commission of the Mathematical Association of America, Inc., and the National Council of Teachers of Mathematics, "The Place of Mathematics in Secondary Education," *Fifteenth Yearbook* (Washington, D.C.: National Council of Teachers of Mathematics, 1940). (Hereafter referred to as the Joint Commission.)
[43] *Ibid.,* p. 53.
[44] *Ibid.,* p. 54.

2. *The subdivision according to certain broad categories enumerated as follows:*
    I. Basic concepts, principles, and terms
    II. Fundamental processes
    III. Fundamental relations
    IV. Skills and techniques
    V. Applications[45]

In chapters V and VI of the report the commission proposes and discusses in considerable detail two alternative curriculum plans. The two differ somewhat in detail and emphasis, but both give recognition to the guiding principles enumerated and are consonant with the foregoing dual classification of subject matter. For one of these plans a grade-placement chart displays a suggested allocation and organization of the subject matter in each year for grades 7 to 12.[46]

The report contains suggestions for modification of the program to give flexibility to the curriculum, and it also contains a discussion of the problems of both retardation and acceleration in their bearing upon the program of mathematical instruction. In this connection a second grade placement chart is presented which gives a proposed selection and grade allocation of subject matter for slow students in grades 7 to 9.[47]

In the discussion of the mathematics program for grades 13 and 14 (the junior college) the commission points out that the preparatory type of student is in the minority and that the mathematical needs of this type of student are adequately provided for in the traditional courses. Accordingly, the discussion deals mainly with the problem of providing for the terminal type of student. Two programs, somewhat different in nature, are proposed as possible terminal courses for students who do not plan to pursue the study of mathematics further. These courses are based on the commission's belief that the junior college curriculum should make provision for a mathematical course of at least one year for all students.

The commission emphasized that in no sense was this recommended program of mathematical instruction to be regarded "as a final unchanging yardstick inhibiting personal initiative and further experimentation." The intention was, rather, that it might prove to be a step forward in securing "for mathematics the place in education it so richly deserves" and a safe standard for comparison in the program of curriculum experimentation and change.

[45] *Ibid.*, p. 61.
[46] *Ibid.*, pp. 72–119, 246–251.
[47] *Ibid.*, pp. 120–148, 252–253.

THE PROGRESSIVE EDUCATION ASSOCIATION COMMITTEE ON THE FUNCTION OF MATHEMATICS IN GENERAL EDUCATION

In 1932 the Executive Board of the Progressive Education Association established the Commission on Secondary School Curriculum. This commission subsequently established several committees to explore the respective contributions of various subject fields to general education at the secondary level; among them was the Committee on the Function of Mathematics in General Education. The complete report of this committee was issued in tentative (mimeographed) form in 1938 and published in final form in 1940.[48]

Basic philosophy of the Progressive Education Committee

The report is in four parts. The first of these presents the educational philosophy which guided the committee in the formulation of the report. Central in this philosophy is the premise that mathematics, in order to justify its place in the secondary school curriculum, must contribute to the satisfaction of the needs of the students. These needs are enumerated in terms of the following four "basic aspects of living":

1. Personal living
2. Immediate personal-social relationships
3. Social-civic relationships
4. Economic relationships[49]

This part of the report closes with a discussion of the role of mathematics in satisfying the needs of people with respect to these four aspects of living.

Part II is the most extensive section of the report. It consists of an elaborate discussion of certain broad concepts or understandings which find application in problem solving, whether in situations that are peculiarly mathematical or not. In the discussion of these concepts an effort is made to show applications to situations encountered in ordinary living, as well as to strictly mathematical situations. In other words, much emphasis is placed upon the *generality* of the concepts and upon various broad aspects involved in their understanding.

Part III is concerned with an explanation of the nature and development of mathematics.

Part IV considers the problem of understanding the student and stresses the need for considering not only overt behavior, but also the various influences which have operated to shape the student's

---

[48] Maurice Hartung and others, Commission on Secondary School Curriculum of the Progressive Education Association, "Mathematics in General Education," *Report of the Committee on the Function of Mathematics in General Education* (New York: Appleton-Century-Crofts, Inc., 1940).

[49] *Ibid.*, p. 20.

personality. It contains a section on implications for teaching. The report closes with a chapter on the evaluation of student achievement. This chapter discusses the purposes of evaluation and contains some interesting suggestions of new and unique means and devices for organizing an evaluation program in terms of instructional objectives previously set up.

THE AAAS CO-OPERATIVE COMMITTEE ON THE TEACHING OF SCIENCE AND MATHEMATICS

Concomitant with the great increase in size in the program of secondary education in the United States during the last three centuries there has been a vast expansion of purpose. Modern educational problems are rooted in the context of mass education, which seems to nurture extensive, and at times seemingly excessive, curriculum design. These problems will always remain complex; there is no way to simplify them. The only hope for an intelligent approach to their solution is through the cooperative effort of duly organized groups who are interested in the formulation and promotion of that program in our schools which will be most significant when evaluated in terms of the educational needs of a school population that is highly heterogeneous as to abilities, aptitudes, and interest.

An important step in this direction was made in 1941 when the representatives of several scientific societies created the Co-operative Committee on Science Teaching "to work on educational problems the solution of which can be attained better by co-operative action than by any single scientific group working alone." The Mathematical Association of America was one of the societies represented on the original committee before its reorganization, in 1944, as a committee of the American Association for the Advancement of Science (AAAS). As presently constituted, the committee consists of representatives from fourteen national scientific societies, three of which are the Mathematical Association of America, the National Council of Teachers of Mathematics, and the Central Association of Science and Mathematics Teachers.

Since its organization, the committee has given attention to the problem of the preparation of teachers of science and mathematics. In 1946 it published its recommendations relative to this important problem in a report on "The Preparation of High School Science and Mathematics Teachers," in which the following proposals were made:

Recommendations
of the AAAS
Cooperative
Committee

(1) A policy of certification in closely related subjects within the broad area of the sciences and mathematics should be established and put into practice.
(2) Approximately one-half of the prospective teacher's four-year college program should be devoted to courses in the sciences.

(3) Certificates to teach general science at the 7th-, 8th-, or 9th-grade level should be granted on the basis of not less than forty-two semester hours of college courses in the subjects covered in general science.

(4) Colleges and certification authorities should work toward a five-year program for the preparation of high-school teachers.

(5) Curriculum improvements in the small high school should go hand in hand with improvement in teacher preparation.[50]

The committee not only has directed its attention to many other problems and projects but also has projected a rather active future program of study and service.[51] Among the most important projects undertaken was the study of the effectiveness of the teaching of science and mathematics at all levels, which served as the basis for a report incorporated as Appendix II of Volume 4 of the report on *Science and Public Policy* made by the President's Scientific Research Board.[52] In this study appraisals of the science and mathematics programs from grades 1 to 12 were made. These served as the basis for certain recommendations for improvement in type of curriculum and pattern of instruction.

The report also included many pertinent recommendations for the recruitment and training of teachers of science and mathematics in the elementary and secondary schools.[53]

In 1959 a second report on the preparation of teachers of science and mathematics was published. This report concerned itself with the problems inherent in the new curriculums and patterns of instruction in secondary schools. One of its primary concerns was with the many types of demands made on the beginning teacher. Several typical curriculums, in both science and mathematics, were outlined and presented as highly desirable basic training programs.[54]

THE EMERGENCY OF WORLD WAR II

The inadequacy of the mathematics program in our schools became very conspicuous in the light of the deficiencies in mathe-

---

[50] Report of the AAAS Co-operative Committee on the Teaching of Science and Mathematics, The Preparation of High School Science and Mathematics Teachers, *School Science and Mathematics*, **46** (1946), 107–118.

[51] The Co-operative Committee on the Teaching of Science and Mathematics: Its Organization and Program, *Science*, **106** (July 11, 1947), 28–30.

AAAS Co-operative Committee Effort Spans Quarter Century, *Mathematics Teacher*, **59** (1966), 741–743.

Louis Panush: Twenty-five Years of the AAAS Co-operative Committee on the Teaching of Science and Mathematics, *School Science and Mathematics*, **67** (1967), 395–400.

[52] "Science and Public Policy" (Washington, D.C.: President's Scientific Research Board, 1947), pp. 4, 47–149.

[53] *Ibid.*, pp. 107–109.

[54] Alfred B. Garrett, Recommendations for the Preparation of High School Teachers of Science and Mathematics, *School Science and Mathematics*, **59** (1959), 281–289; Preparation of High School Science Teachers, *Science*, **131** (Apr. 8, 1960), 1024–1029.

War emergency
committees

matics discovered among the inductees into the war training program of World War II. To meet the emergency of the situation, the U.S. Office of Education, in cooperation with the National Council of Teachers of Mathematics, appointed two committees to give the problem careful study. The first committee worked in close cooperation with the Army, Navy, and Civil Aeronautics Administration. Its report[55] was based on a detailed analysis of approximately fifty unit courses used in the federal-state program of Vocational Training for War Production Workers, twenty Navy training manuals, and fifty Army instructional manuals. The committee gave attention to the entire program of secondary mathematics and made specific recommendations for a Special One-year Course and a Special One-semester Course designed as an emergency refresher course for high school students near graduation or induction but not studying mathematics.

The report[56] of the second committee served as an extension of that of the first committee in that it was designed to supplement the earlier report "by amplifying the suggestions offered for the *lower* levels of mathematics as represented in the Special One-year Course." The procedure used by this committee consisted of conferences "with Army officers directly in charge of training enlisted men" and observation of "the basic training process itself during the first thirteen weeks of the inductee's Army life." A rather detailed outline of minimum essentials was given, along with a presentation of "general suggestions with respect to instruction."

These two reports are given special prominence because of their specific and important implications concerning the teaching of mathematics in the elementary and secondary schools. The War Preparedness Committee (appointed in 1940) and the War Policy Committee (appointed in 1943) were joint committees of the American Mathematical Society and the Mathematical Association of America. Their interests were primarily in the organization and direction of manpower in mathematical research for most efficient and effective service to the war effort. A similar committee was the National Committee of Physicists and Mathematicians, appointed in 1943. Some of the reports of these committees had significant import for mathematics at the secondary level.[57]

---

[55] National Council of Teachers of Mathematics, Report on Pre-induction Courses in Mathematics, *Mathematics Teacher*, **36** (1943), 114–124.

[56] National Council of Teachers of Mathematics, Report of the Committee on Essential Mathematics for Minimum Army Needs, *Mathematics Teacher*, **36** (1943), 243–282.

[57] William L. Hart, On Education for Service, *American Mathematical Monthly*, **48** (1941), 353–362. Also published in *Mathematics Teacher*, **34** (1941), 297–304.

Marston Morse and William L. Hart, Mathematics in the Defense Program, *Mathematics Teacher*, **34** (1941), 195–202.

William L. Hart et al., Universal Military Training in Peace Time, *Mathematics Teacher*, **39** (1946), 17–23.

THE COMMISSION ON POST-WAR PLANS

At its annual meeting in February, 1944, the Board of Directors of the National Council of Teachers of Mathematics created the Commission on Post-War Plans for the purpose of planning for effective programs in secondary mathematics in the postwar period. As originally constituted, the commission consisted of five members. This number was expanded later to include thirteen members from eleven widely scattered states. The commission found significant background for its thinking and planning in the work of the first two of the above-mentioned committees of the war period.

In its first report[58] the commission announced its plan of organization and solicited help from the interested public. With the hope of crystallizing thinking and "in order to promote discussion . . . in workshops and professional courses," the commission proposed, and discussed briefly, five recommendations which it felt "should be carefully considered in planning for the postwar years."

Report of the Commission on Post-War Plans

The commission's second report[59] contained its recommendations for the improvement of mathematics in grades 1 to 14. These recommendations were presented in the form of thirty-four theses. The first thesis stated that "The school should guarantee functional competence in mathematics to all who can possibly achieve it." To make explicit the implications of "functional competence in mathematics," the commission delineated its essentials in the form of a checklist of twenty-eight items, later expanded to twenty-nine. The remaining theses were directed to problems of instruction in mathematics and the education of teachers in accordance with this outline:

1 *Theses 2–8:* Mathematics in grades 1 to 6
2 *Theses 9–11:* Mathematics in grades 7 and 8
3 *Theses 12–13:* Mathematics in grade 9
4 *Theses 14–20:* Mathematics in grades 10 to 12
5 *Theses 21–23:* Mathematics in the junior college
6 *Theses 24–32:* Education of teachers of mathematics
7 *Theses 33–34:* Multisensory aids in mathematics

Mathematics in Consumer Education

In 1945, in conjunction with the Consumer Education Study, the commission published a pamphlet entitled "The Role of Mathematics in Consumer Education."[60] In this report the commission first analyzed the nature and purposes of consumer education in general. It then pointed out the relation of elementary school and secondary school mathematics to this total program, and also

[58] Commission on Post-War Plans, First Report, *Mathematics Teacher*, **37** (1944), 226–232.
[59] Commission on Post-War Plans, Second Report, *Mathematics Teacher*, **38** (1945), 195–221.
[60] Commission on Post-War Plans, "The Role of Mathematics in Consumer Education" (Washington, D.C.: The Consumer Education Study, National Association of Secondary School Principals, 1945).

suggested to administrators and teachers a form for organization of materials, as well as methods of instruction.

One of the recognized major problems in modern secondary education is that of intelligent guidance of students as they plan their school programs. It is a well-established fact that in no subject-matter area have high school students suffered more from erratic and unwise guidance than in mathematics. The Commission on Post-War Plans made a significant attempt to correct this unfortunate situation in the publication of a "Guidance Pamphlet,"[61] in the preparation of which they were aided materially by the counsel of representatives from the U.S. Office of Education, men of wide experience in the problems and techniques of educational guidance. The commission then proceeded to present to the high school student significant information in simple style within the framework of which he might find answers to his questions. This pamphlet, through subsequent revisions, has continued to guide young people in charting their educational course through the secondary school and college.

The Guidance Pamphlet

MATHEMATICS IN GENERAL EDUCATION

During the early 1950s, the demands of a program of "general education" began to make their imprint upon the curriculum from the elementary school through the junior college. This new emphasis in educational philosophy was in essence a reaction against the emphases of an age of specialism. The claim was made that the college graduate was educated in the sense that he had acquired competencies in some particular occupation yet fell short of the demands of active citizenship in his community.[62] There were many who felt that the graduate of the secondary school could be characterized similarly. The trend toward specialization had led to the introduction of many courses and varied curriculums in both the secondary school and the college. The net result of such emphases had been a decreasing opportunity for the student to participate in a program from which he might derive an "integrated view of human experience." As an antidote to the trend toward specialization there evolved a plan of general education which emphasizes a program designed to develop the abilities, attitudes, understandings, and behavior patterns which should be the common experience of all educable men and women.

Reaction against specialization

Within the context of such a philosophy there has evolved a

---

[61] Commission on Post-War Plans, Guidance Report, *Mathematics Teacher*, **40** (1947), 315–339. Later published as the "Guidance Pamphlet in Mathematics."
[62] "Higher Education for American Democracy," vol. I, "Establishing Goals" (Washington, D.C.: President's Commission on Higher Education, 1947), p. 48.

continuing problem to which individual teachers of mathematics and committees of the council, the association, and other professional organizations have given persistent attention. There does exist a body of mathematical content which can be used to make the field comprehensible to the general student, and hence can be made significant to every individual capable of intelligent participation in the educational program. What is this mathematical subject matter, how should it be organized and presented, and what basic training can be most effective to prepare teachers for participation in the program? These are the three major aspects of the problem confronting those interested in providing our schools with the most significant mathematics program possible.

Three major problems

The fact that this program should be designed for the general student, and not the student interested in specialization, does not imply that it should be a watered-down treatment of computational techniques or a memorization of formulas and rules. There are mathematical concepts and procedures which are of importance to the educated individual. It would seem that, in a technological age, no person is well-informed without at least some fundamental knowledge of the nature of proof; the basic concepts of the structure of our number system; algebraic and geometric structures; the nature of measurement; the concepts of relation and function; and basic statistical measures.

Basic mathematics for general education

OTHER ORGANIZATIONAL ACTIVITIES

Secondary School Curriculum Committee

At its meeting in December, 1956, the Board of Directors of the National Council of Teachers of Mathematics appointed the Secondary School Curriculum Committee (SSCC) with the commission "to make a comprehensive and critical study of the curriculum and instruction in mathematics in secondary schools with relation to the needs of contemporary society." The membership of the committee was selected from secondary school and college teachers of mathematics, research workers in pure and applied mathematics, and personnel from business and industry. The committee work was carried out by subcommittees appointed to make intensive studies in each of the following areas:[63]

1 The place of mathematics in a changing society and the implications of contemporary mathematics
2 The aims of mathematics education and the pedagogy of mathematics
3 The nature of mathematical thought in grades 7 to 12
4 How geometry should be introduced and developed
5 Content and organization of junior high school mathematics

[63] The report of the Secondary School Curriculum Committee was published in the May, 1959, issue of *Mathematics Teacher*, pp. 389–417.

6 Foreign mathematics programs
7 Adjustment of the mathematics program to students of average and below-average ability
8 Aids to teaching
9 The organization of the mathematics program
10 The administration of the mathematics program
11 Programs of instruction for the mathematically gifted pupil

The Committee on the Undergraduate Program (CUP) of the Mathematical Association of America was appointed in January, 1953.[64] This committee was directed "to consider the problems of making available in our society the values of modern mathematics" and "to attack the problem with broader scientific and cultural objectives than could be expressed through another mere study of curriculum revision."

Under this mandate the following books have been published: *Universal Mathematics, Elementary Mathematics of Sets with Applications,* and *Modern Mathematical Methods and Models* (volumes I and II, designed primarily for biology and social science majors). The committee also sponsored the publication of a paperback edition of the notes used by Emil Artin in a freshman honors course at Princeton University, Polya's *Mathematical Discovery* (Vol. I), two or three *Carus Monographs,* and preliminary writing on other books.

Sensitive to its inability to keep abreast of the rapid changes in mathematics, the committee asked to be dismissed so that a new committee might be formed, with a much broader program. In

Committee on the Undergraduate Program in Mathematics

January, 1959, the Committee on the Undergraduate Program in Mathematics (CUPM) was constituted. The new organization called for the establishment of a central office with an executive director, a change in basic policy to recognize that any change in college curriculums must take into account pedagogy as well as content, and the establishment of four panels: the Panel on Teacher Training; the Panel on Mathematics for the Physical Sciences and Engineering; the Panel on Mathematics for the Biological, Management, and Social Sciences; and the Panel on Pre-graduate Training. Each panel, whose membership was augmented by the addition of invited experts from its respective area of interest, has the assigned responsibility of making recommendations for curricular change in its particular area and of making consistent effort to implement these recommendations.

These assignments have resulted in the publication of reports and the holding of conferences to promote the implementation of the recommendations made.[65] The committee, which operates on

---

[64] For a complete history of this important committee see W. L. Duren, Jr., CUPM, the History of an Idea, *American Mathematical Monthly* (50th Anniversary Edition), **74**, part II (1967), 23–37.
[65] *Ibid.,* pp. 31–32, 35.

grants from the National Science Foundation and the Ford Foundation, also has established a Consultants Bureau and a Library Committee to assist colleges in updating their curriculums and improving their library holdings.[66] The committee proposes to write completely new materials for experimental tryouts, with the hope that from these there will ultimately evolve an undergraduate program in mathematics which will retain from the traditional and introduce from the new a mathematical content of established significance. This significance is to be evaluated in the context of the extended mathematical needs of engineering, physical science, biological science, social science, and high-speed digital automata.

Educational media Both the National Council of Teachers of Mathematics and the Mathematical Association of America have appointed a Committee on Educational Media. The recognition of the many different facets of their assigned problem and its tremendous importance has resulted in the coordination of the activities and responsibilities of the two committees to prevent any unnecessary duplication of effort. Among the most important of such media are the sound film, filmstrips, programmed texts, radio, television, and the use of computer technology. Computer-based instruction is very new and quite expensive; it seems to have exciting possibilities, as well as real disadvantages, both in classroom instruction and in education of teachers.[67] Television is another of the new media which offers many interesting possibilities as well as vexing problems in mathematics education. According to a report from the National Center for School and College Television,[68] there is a great deal of room for improvement in the use of this medium for instruction and teacher education in mathematics. There is a need for the development of a better television presence for the teacher, as well as an improvement in the use of teaching aids before the camera. The use of television should serve as motivation for various topics in mathematics, as a means for effective teaching of troublesome topics, and as a technique for enrichment. This means that the teacher must be more than merely a transplanted classroom teacher, since the potential of appeal is to an audience of much greater diversity of interest and ability than that of the normal classroom. There is a need for a de-emphasis of the purely lecture type of instruction and for more student presence

[66] The activities of the committee and its panels are publicized through a series of reports and pamphlets which are available from the central office of the Committee on the Undergraduate Program in Mathematics, P.O. Box 1024, Berkeley, Calif.

[67] Walter Dick, The Development and Current Status of Computer-based Instruction, *American Educational Research Journal,* **2** (1965), 41–54.

   C. Alan Riedesel and Marilyn N. Suydam, Computer-assisted Instruction: Implications for Teacher Education, *Arithmetic Teacher,* **14** (1967), 24–29.

[68] National Center for School and College Television, Television in Mathematics Education, *Arithmetic Teacher,* **14** (1967), 596–602.

and participation. In spite of these criticisms of the present status of this new educational medium, the panel which was responsible for the report agreed that there do exist four significant principal uses of television, namely: "(a) in-service teacher training, (b) classroom instruction, (c) enrichment, and (d) provision of a course in mathematics not otherwise available."

Four basic uses of educational television

Attention has previously been called to the fact that certain foreign influences played an important role in the early history of mathematics education in this country. Again, approximately one hundred years later, it is becoming increasingly evident that current professional thinking and curriculum development in the Soviet Union, as well as in certain European and South American countries, may have implications of significance to mathematics education in the United States. This is particularly true in certain areas of teacher education, mathematics in the elementary school, and the total program in geometry.[69]

Foreign influence

The American Association for the Advancement of Science, in 1955, inaugurated its Science Teaching Improvement Program (STIP). This was to be "an action program to increase the number of well-qualified science and mathematics teachers at the secondary-school level." In January, 1957, a plan for regional consultants in science and mathematics was inaugurated. The purpose of this plan was to stimulate regional efforts to recognize problems related to improved instruction and to initiate plans and programs designed to solve these problems on a regional basis. The program, made possible under a grant from the General Electric Educational and Charitable Fund, was in effect for eighteen months and was instrumental in shaping the plans of the American Association for a continuing program in the interest of improved instruction in science and mathematics. This program was extended in 1959 by a new three-year grant from the Carnegie Corporation of New York. One of the major activities of the extended program was the Study on the Use of Special Teachers of Science and Mathematics in Grades 5 and 6.

Science Teaching Improvement Program

Another grant in 1959 from the Carnegie Corporation of New York to the AAAS was for a study of certification requirements for teachers of secondary school science and mathematics. The study was to be made in cooperation with the National Association of

Certification requirements

---

[69] Robert B. Davis, "The Changing Curriculum: Mathematics" (Washington, D.C.: Association for Supervision and Curriculum Development, 1967).

Howard F. Fehr et al., "New Thinking in Mathematics" (Washington, D.C.: Organization for European Economic Co-operation, 1961).

Howard F. Fehr (Editor), "Mathematical Education in the Americas" (New York: Bureau of Publications, Teachers College, Columbia University, 1962).

James M. Moser, Mathematics Education in the Secondary Schools of the Soviet Union, *Mathematics Teacher,* **60** (1967), 885–892.

Attention is also called to the articles which appear regularly in the section entitled "International Mathematics Education" of the *Mathematics Teacher.*

State Directors of Teacher Education and Certification (NASDTEC). The report of this study was published in 1961.[70] A second grant from the Carnegie Corporation was made in 1961 for the extension of the study and use of the guidelines for secondary school programs and for a study of programs in mathematics and science for elementary school teachers. The program received strong support and professional contribution from the Committee on the Undergraduate Program in Mathematics, and additional financial support from the National Science Foundation. The final report was made through the medium of these publications.

Guidelines for teacher education

1 Guidelines for Preparation Programs of Teachers of Secondary School Science and Mathematics
2 Guidelines for Science and Mathematics in the Preparation Program of Elementary School Teachers
3 New School Science: A Report of Regional Conference of School Administrators
4 Secondary School Science and Mathematics Teachers: Characteristics and Service Loads

National Science Foundation

The National Science Foundation was authorized by an Act of Congress in 1950. It has two distinct sets of functions: (1) the support of research and education through grants, fellowships, and other means, and (2) the development of national science policy and the evaluation and correlation of the research activities of the federal government, as well as the correlation of its own program with those of other agencies, both public and private.[71]

This organization has rendered, and still renders, a tremendous service in improving and strengthening the programs of science and mathematics in the secondary schools and colleges of our country.

Cambridge conferences

In June, 1963, a group of professional mathematicians and mathematics users gathered in Cambridge, Massachusetts, under the auspices of Educational Services, Incorporated, and the National Science Foundation. The purpose of this meeting was to consider problems of curricular reform in the mathematics program for grades K to 12 in the context of "exploratory thinking with a view to a long-range future." The principal results of their deliberations, as presented in the report of the conference,[72] are divided into two major categories: Curriculum for Elementary School (K–6) and Curriculum for Grades 7–12. It was the consensus of the group that this thirteen-year program should provide a level of training for the student comparable with a current three-year

[70] NASDTEC-AAAS Studies, "Guidelines for Preparation Programs of Teachers of Secondary School Science and Mathematics" (Washington, D.C.: The American Association for the Advancement of Science, 1961).

[71] Alan T. Waterman, National Science Foundation: A Ten-year Resumé, *Science,* **131** (May 6, 1960), 1341–1354.

[72] Report of the Cambridge Conference on School Mathematics, "Goals for School Mathematics" (Boston: Houghton Mifflin Company, 1963).

college program which would contain two years of calculus and one semester each of modern algebra and theory of probability.

The curriculum proposed for the elementary school is designed to make each student of the elementary grades familiar with the structure of the real-number system and the basic ideas of both synthetic and analytic geometry. Also, significant attention is to be given to inequalities in the program of the elementary school after a very early introduction: "immediately after learning to count." The outline for the early grades is separated into two parts: one outline of topics for grades K to 2, with great emphasis on very informal treatment, and one for grades 3 to 6, continuing the informal pattern but with more direct concern for fundamental preparation for the mathematics program of the high school. The content of both programs is outlined under the following broad topics: the real-number system, geometry, logic, and applications, with the additional topic area of "theory of real functions" for grades 3 to 6.

For the development of this program a great deal of "premathematics" and spiral treatment is recommended. The term "premathematics" is defined to mean "general heuristic cognitive patterns."

It is hoped that the student graduating from the sixth grade of such a program as that proposed will be so thoroughly grounded in arithmetic and intuitive geometry that he will be prepared to undertake a strong program in algebra, deductive geometry, calculus, linear algebra, and probability when he enters high school. With this in mind the report presents two proposed outlines for grades 7 to 12. The similarities and dissimilarities of the two programs are discussed at length. The two outlines in broad-topic form are presented here in separate columns.

Outline for grades K to 6

Outlines for grades 7 to 12

Grade	Proposal I	Proposal II
7 and 8	Algebra	Algebra
	Probability	Geometry
		Probability
9	Geometry	Algebra
		Geometry
		Calculus
10	Geometry	Analysis
	Topology	Probability
	Linear Algebra	Linear Algebra
11 and 12	Analysis	Analysis

The Cambridge Conference on School Mathematics (CCSM) has continued its activities in the interest of improved teaching of mathematics. This has been accomplished through conferences, publication of reports and experimental materials, and the sponsoring of specifically designed classroom experimentation. In particular, CCSM cosponsored, with the School Mathematics Study Group (SMSG), during March, 1965, a conference on teacher training. Out of this conference there emerged the resolve to tackle the teacher-training problem at a later conference, in 1966.[73]

This conference was held during the summer months of 1966 at the Pine Manor Junior College in Brookline, Massachusetts, under the auspices of the Educational Development Center, Inc. The report contained "two curriculum proposals for the generalist elementary school teacher," each of which was outlined in a two-year sequence for a total of twelve semester hours.[74] In considerably less detail, the report also contained suggestions for the training of specialists. The conference closed its report with the recommendation that the Educational Development Center be advised to set up a writing program to prepare materials for experimentation both in curriculums for the schools and in programs for the training of teachers. While the emphasis of this report is entirely on the program and problems of the elementary school, it contains definite implications for the mathematics program of the secondary school.

One should not pass judgment, positive or negative, on the programs proposed by these two conferences without making a very careful study not only of the content of the different programs proposed, but also of the intent of the recommendations made. Each conference emphasized that its ideas were exploratory and should not be taken as prescriptive. In its report the first conference stated: "We propose an ambitious program, aware that it may be impossible, but still convinced that it is worth shooting toward." The second conference was slightly more positive in saying that "this report represents, in an admittedly tentative manner, the exploratory efforts of one group to anticipate an apparently inevitable trend."

Along with other efforts and movements in the interest of improved instruction in secondary mathematics should be mentioned the increasing interest in television as an instructional medium, the use of films and other types of audio-visual materials, teaching machines and programmed instruction, the "Continental Classroom," the national and state contests in mathematics, and the intensive programs in curriculum improvement and teacher

National Defense Education Act

training being promoted in several states. The National Defense Education Act of 1958, which is administered by the U.S. Office of

[73] Peter Hilton, The Continuing Work of the Cambridge Conference on School Mathematics, *Arithmetic Teacher*, **13** (1966), 145–149.

Educational Development Center, Inc., "Goals for Mathematical Education of Elementary School Teachers" (Boston: Houghton Mifflin Company, 1967), p. 7.

[74] Educational Development Center, Inc., *op. cit.*, pp. 14–24, 49–94.

Education, provides funds to be used by the schools of the country in the purchase of equipment for aid in teaching science, mathematics, and foreign languages. The act also makes provision for financial assistance to state departments of education in the employment of supervisors in these three areas of the school program.

This is indeed an era of revived and concerned interest in the real import of mathematics as an integral part of the American program of education, from the early elementary grades through the total program. It is the sincere hope of all concerned that the study now being given to the problem of improved instruction will be sufficiently intensive and extensive to produce curriculums and patterns of teaching that will offer to the boys and girls of our land unexcelled opportunities to become significantly informed in the field of mathematics.

EXERCISES

1 What have been some of the more important aspects of the evolving philosophy of education in the United States?

2 How did the mathematics curriculum of the academy differ from that of the Latin grammar school?

3 Briefly trace the influence of college-entrance requirements in mathematics on the secondary school mathematics curriculum.

4 What were some of the more important causes of change in the mathematics program of the Latin grammar school and the academy?

5 In what way did the Pestalozzian movement affect the teaching of mathematics?

6 Name the early texts that most clearly reflected the Pestalozzian influence.

7 What was the purpose and what were the main recommendations of the Committee of Fifteen on Geometry?

8 Briefly outline the recommendations for secondary mathematics made in the report "The Reorganization of Mathematics in Secondary Education."

9 What classification of aims was given in the report "The Reorganization of Mathematics in Secondary Education"?

10 Point out the distinguishing characteristics of each group of aims called for in exercise 9. Also indicate the extent to which the groups overlap.

11 Briefly outline the recommendations of the Joint Commission concerning the program of secondary mathematics.

12 Contrast the recommendations of the Joint Commission with those of the National Committee on Mathematical Requirements.

13 What do you understand by the general mathematics movement? By what other names has this movement been designated?

14 Compare the value of general mathematics in the senior high school with its value in the junior high school and in the junior college.

15 In what ways has the junior college movement affected the curriculum of secondary mathematics?

16 What is your evaluation of the Joint Commission's discussion of the role of mathematics in civilization and the place of mathematics in the educational program?

17 What are some of the more significant aspects of the nature and work of the Commission on Mathematics of the College Entrance Examination Board?

18 Briefly outline the work of the Commission on Post-War Plans.

19 Briefly summarize the most important of the implications of the thirty-four theses of the second report of the Commission on Post-War Plans.

20 What are some of the more significant aspects of the Report of the Secondary School Curriculum Committee (SSCC)?

21 What are some of the more important recommendations of the Committee on the Undergraduate Program in Mathematics (CUPM)?

22 What have been some of the more important activities of the experimental groups mentioned on page 14?

23 Outline the more significant aspects of the reports of the Cambridge Conference on School Mathematics.

24 What is your evaluation of the timeliness and significance of the Cambridge reports?

BIBLIOGRAPHY

AAAS Co-operative Committee Effort Spans Quarter Century, *Mathematics Teacher,* **59** (1966), 741–743.

Adler, Irving: The Cambridge Conference Report: Blueprint or Fantasy, *Mathematics Teacher,* **59** (1966), 210–217.

Allen, Frank B.: The Council's Drive to Improve School Mathematics, *Mathematics Teacher,* **56** (1963), 370–378; **57** (1964), 370–378.

Allendoerfer, Carl B.: The Second Revolution in Mathematics, *Mathematics Teacher,* **58** (1965), 640–645.

"An Analysis of New Mathematics Programs" (Washington, D.C.: National Council of Teachers of Mathematics, 1963). (Pamphlet.)

Baird, George H.: The Greater Cleveland Program, *Mathematics Teacher,* **54** (1961), 31.

Beberman, Max: "An Emerging Program of Secondary School Mathematics" (Cambridge, Mass.: Harvard University Press, 1958).

Bennett, A. A.: A Brief History of the Mathematical Association of America before World War II, *American Mathematical Monthly,* **74,** part II (January, 1967), 1–11.

Blyth, John W.: Teaching Machines and Logic, *American Mathematical Monthly,* **67** (1960), 285–287.

Brumfiel, Charles, Robert Eicholz, and Merrill Shanks: The Ball State Experimental Program, *Mathematics Teacher,* **53** (1960), 75–84.

Cambridge Conference on School Mathematics, Report of: "Goals for School Mathematics" (Boston: Houghton Mifflin Company, 1963).

Commission on Mathematics, Report of: "Program for College Preparatory Mathematics" (New York: College Entrance Examination Board, 1959).

Commission on Post-War Plans, Second Report, *Mathematics Teacher,* **38** (1945), 195–221.

Davis, Robert B.: The Syracuse University "Madison Project," *American Mathematical Monthly,* **67** (1960), 178–180.

———: Madison Project Activities for 1965–1966: Report on Unfinished Business, *American Mathematical Monthly,* **73** (1966), 301–304.

Duren, W. L., Jr.: CUPM, The History of an Idea, *American Mathematical Monthly,* **74,** pt. II (January, 1967), 23–37.

Educational Development Center, Inc.: "Goals for Mathematical Education of Elementary School Teachers" (Boston: Houghton Mifflin Company, 1967).

Forbes, Jack E.: Programmed Instructional Materials: Past, Present, and Future, *Mathematics Teacher,* **56** (1963), 224–227.

Hale, William T.: UICSM's Decade of Experimentation, *Mathematics Teacher,* **54** (1961), 613–618.

Hilton, Peter: The Continuing Work of the Cambridge Conference on School Mathematics, *Arithmetic Teacher,* **13** (1966), 145–149.

Hlavaty, Julius H.: Mathematics in Transition, *Mathematics Teacher,* **54** (1961), 21–22, 26–30.

———: Towards the Golden Jubilee Year—1970, *Mathematics Teacher,* **61** (1968), 661–664; *Arithmetic Teacher,* **16** (1969), 342–346.

Johnson, Donovan: President's Report, *Mathematics Teacher,* **60** (1967), 661–664; *Arithmetic Teacher,* **14** (1967), 523–526.

———: President's Report: The State of the Council, *Mathematics Teacher,* **61** (1968), 644–648; *Arithmetic Teacher,* **15** (1968), 571–575.

Joint Commission of the Mathematical Association of America and the National Council of Teachers of Mathematics: "The Place of Mathematics in Secondary Education," *Fifteenth Yearbook* (Washington, D.C.: National Council of Teachers of Mathematics, 1940).

Jones, Phillip S.: The History of Mathematical Education, *American Mathematical Monthly,* **74,** pt. II (January, 1961), 38–55.

Kemeny, John G.: Report to the International Congress of Mathematicians, *Mathematics Teacher,* **56** (1963), 66–78.

May, Kenneth O.: "Programmed Learning and Mathematical Education" (San Francisco: Mathematical Association of America, Committee on Educational Media, Box 2310, 1964). (Pamphlet.)

Meserve, Bruce E.: The NCTM: Its Growth and Growing Pains, *Mathematics Teacher,* **58** (1965), 490–495.

———: Mathematics Teachers, On Guard!, *Mathematics Teacher,* **59** (1966), 522–530.

Monroe, W. S.: A Chapter in the Development of Arithmetic Teaching in the United States, *Elementary School Teacher,* **13** (1912–1913), 17–24.

———: Analysis of Colburn's Arithmetics, *Elementary School Teacher,* **13** (1912–1913), 239–246, 294–302.

Moore, E. H.: On the Foundations of Mathematics, *First Yearbook* (Washington, D.C.: National Council of Teachers of Mathematics, 1926), pp. 32–57.

National Committee on Mathematical Requirements: "The Reorganization of Mathematics in Secondary Education" (Boston: Houghton Mifflin Company, 1923).

On the Mathematics Curriculum of the High

School, *American Mathematical Monthly*, **69** (1962), 189–193.

Panush, Louis: Twenty-five Years of the AAAS Co-operative Committee on the Teaching of Science and Mathematics, *School Science and Mathematics*, **67** (1967), 395–400.

Perry, John: The Teaching of Mathematics, *Educational Review*, **23** (1902), 158–181.

Pieters, Richard S., and E. P. Vance: The Advanced Placement Program, *Mathematics Teacher*, **54** (1961), 201–211.

"The Revolution in School Mathematics" (Washington, D.C.: National Council of Teachers of Mathematics, 1961). (Pamphlet.)

Rising, Gerald R.: Research and Development in Mathematics and Science Education at the Minnesota School Mathematics and Science Center and the Minnesota National Laboratory, *School Science and Mathematics*, **65** (1965), 811–820.

Rosenbaum, R. A.: History of the MAA Since World War II, *American Mathematical Monthly*, **74**, pt. II (January, 1967), 12–22.

Secondary School Curriculum Committee of the National Council of Teachers of Mathematics, Report of: The Secondary Mathematics Curriculum, *Mathematics Teacher*, **52** (1959), 389–417.

Smith, D. E., and Jekuthiel Ginsburg: "A History of Mathematics in America before 1900," *Carus Monograph* 5, The Mathematical Association of America, Inc. (La Salle, Ill.: The Open Court Publishing Company, 1934).

Stone, Marshall: The Revolution in Mathematics, *American Mathematical Monthly*, **68** (1961), 715–734.

———: Review of Goals for School Mathematics: Report of the Cambridge Conference on School Mathematics, *Mathematics Teacher*, **58** (1965), 353–360.

Teaching Machines and Mathematics Programs, *American Mathematical Monthly*, **69** (1962), 552–565.

Wagner, John: The Objectives and Activities of the SMSG, *Mathematics Teacher*, **53** (1960), 454–459.

Willoughby, Stephen S.: "Contemporary Teaching of Secondary Mathematics" (New York: John Wiley & Sons, Inc., 1967), pp. 1–57.

Wills, Herbert: The UICSM Programmed Instruction Project, *American Mathematical Monthly*, **69** (1962), 804–806.

Wooten, William: "SMSG: The Making of a Curriculum" (New Haven, Conn.: Yale University Press, 1965).

Young, G. S.: The NASDTEC-AAAS Teacher Preparation and Certification Study, *American Mathematical Monthly*, **67** (1960), 792–797.

two | mathematics in general education

The total education program may be considered as composed of two distinct, yet complementary, patterns. One pattern is for *special education* and is designed to provide the student with those qualifications needed for excellence of performance in some specific area of service to mankind. The other pattern is for *general education*, which is concerned with preparation of the student for life as a trustworthy human being and responsible citizen. This does not imply that the general-education program is not for the specialist as well as for the nonspecialist; both are human beings who should be aspiring to active citizenship. Neither does it imply that subject content and instructional procedures must be the same for both. There are basic distinctions in each area, and they lie in point of view, sophistication of treatment, and challenge of subject matter. At all levels, general education should attempt to develop those abilities, understandings, and behavior patterns which should be within the common experience of all educable people. On the other hand, special education, at appropriate levels, should attempt to fashion programs leading to the development of competencies in special areas of interest and endeavor.

Basic distinctions

A BASIC PHILOSOPHY OF GENERAL EDUCATION

One of the motivating forces behind the evolution of a basic philosophy of general education has been the sense of a need to protect against the threatened narrowness of an educational program designed primarily for specialization. Within this context two essentially distinct philosophies have evolved: one with the more formal flavor of a liberal arts program, and the other with the more informal pattern of preparation for social adjustment. The former probably is best represented by the recommendations of the Harvard Report. Such a program should be designed to provide the abilities "to think effectively, to communicate thought, to make relevant judgments, and to discriminate among values."[1] In con-

**Two distinct
philosophies of
general education**

**The Harvard
Report**

---

[1] Report of the Harvard Committee, "General Education in a Free Society" (Cambridge, Mass.: Harvard University Press, 1962), p. 65.

Ten imperative
needs of youth

trast, possibly the best representation of the less formal program is to be found in the *"Ten Imperative Needs of Youth"* proposed by The National Association of Secondary School Principals.[2] These needs were identified as (1) individual skills, (2) health and physical fitness, (3) rights and duties of citizenship, (4) appreciation of the significance of family life, (5) purchasing of goods and services, (6) understanding of the influence of science, (7) appreciation of nature and the arts, (8) use of leisure time, (9) ethical values and principles, and (10) basic skills.

The nature of the
education process

Education is the process of deriving from past experience and from present opportunity that fund of information, those guidelines of action, and that demeanor of performance necessary and sufficient for effective confrontation with the challenge of the future. Some of the objectives of this process can be best attained through the formal program offered by our schools, colleges, and universities. It is just as significantly true that some of them can be attained through those informal experiences which occur outside our halls of learning. Whether the program of general education should have its major orientation within the formal context of the liberal arts or in the informal context of social adjustment is a debatable question. Whatever its principal orientation might be, it would seem that the major purposes of general education are fourfold: (1) to contribute to the preparation for life needs, not only those which the student realizes but also those he must be taught to realize; (2) to establish basic relevance between knowledge and everyday experience; (3) to provide a nonspecialized type of training characterized by wide application, universal value, and great intellectual appeal; and (4) to lay the foundation of basic information essential to later intelligent pursuit of individual interests and special aptitudes.

Purposes of
general education

Objectives of
general education

The objectives of a program provided to meet such educational responsibilities should be designed to help the student (1) think effectively, (2) communicate thought, (3) discriminate among values, (4) make relevant judgments, (5) improve and maintain health, (6) do his part as an active and responsible citizen, (7) choose a vocation intelligently, (8) gain skill in adding to his previous knowledge, (9) find self-expression in, and create an appreciation for, things of beauty, (10) make sound emotional and social adjustments, (11) choose avocational interests wisely, (12) realize and appreciate his cultural heritage, and (13) understand his physical environment.

Contributions from
mathematics

The program in mathematics can and must make significant contribution toward the attainment of these basic objectives of

[2] National Association of Secondary School Principals, "Planning for American Youth," rev. ed. (Washington, D.C.: National Association of Secondary School Principals, 1951), pp. 9, 62–63.

general education. It must make provision for:

1 Competence in the basic skills and understandings for dealing with number and form
2 Habits of effective thinking—a broad term involving analytical, critical, and postulational thinking, as well as reasoning by analogies and the development of intellectual curiosity
3 Communication of thought through symbolic expression and graphs
4 Development of the ability to make relevant judgments through the discrimination of values
5 Development of the ability to distinguish between relevant and irrelevant data
6 Development of intellectual independence
7 Development of aesthetic appreciation and expression
8 Cultural advancement through a realization of the significance of mathematics in its own right and in its relation to the total physical and social structure

In this context there does exist a body of mathematical subject matter that is of significance to every educable individual at all levels of instruction.

THE JUNIOR HIGH SCHOOL

It is true that the primary force behind the demand for a program of general education was a revolt against the elective system which characterized for many years the instructional program of our schools and colleges. However, it is of interest to note that the basic philosophy of the evolving pattern for the contribution of mathematics to general education is fundamentally the same as that expressed in 1923 by the National Committee on Mathematical Requirements as a guide for the general mathematics program of the junior high school. As witness to the truth of this statement compare the purposes of general education, as stated by the Harvard Committee[3] (see above), and their implications for mathematics education, with the following statement from the National Committee's report.

The primary purposes of the teaching of mathematics should be to develop those powers of understanding and of analyzing relations of quantity and of space which are necessary to an insight into and a control over our environment and to an appreciation of the progress of civilization in its various aspects, and to develop those habits of thought and of action which will make these powers effective in the life of the individual.[4]

To implement this stated purpose, the National Committee recommended a body of subject matter to be required of all students

[3] Harvard Committee, *loc. cit.*
[4] National Committee on Mathematical Requirements, "The Reorganization of Mathematics in Secondary Education" (Boston: Houghton Mifflin Company, 1927), pp. 13–14.

entering the junior high school. The basis for this requirement was the conviction that its content included the mathematical knowledge and skills likely to be needed by every citizen. The members of the committee seem to have conceived of the program of mathematics in general education as performing two basic functions: (1) to give the students a broad view of the field of elementary mathematics in order to explore their interests and test their abilities and (2) to give the students the mathematical information and skills most likely to be useful to them in their vocational pursuits.

Two basic functions
of mathematics in
general education

While no effort was made to recommend grade levels for the treatment of specific topics, several optional plans of organization which did have certain implications for grade placement were presented. Basically, these recommended patterns of subject-matter organization have prevailed through the intervening years. Support of the fundamental philosophy and specific recommendations of grade content were included in the 1940 report of the Joint Commission of the Mathematical Association of America and the National Council of Teachers of Mathematics.[5] The major modification found in this second report consisted of a recommended two-track program in which the basic differentiation consisted of a possibility of two distinct patterns in grade 9: algebra for some and general mathematics for others. Both committees agreed in their recommendation that the mathematics program through grade 9 be required of all pupils. These recommendations were given further confirmation in the report of the Commission on Post-War Plans.[6]

Two-track program

The basic philosophy underlying the program of mathematics in general education has not undergone any great change under the pressure of the demands for a more modern program of mathematics in our schools. There have been, however, some very marked changes in the interpretation of the implications of this philosophy for attaining the fundamental objectives of the program. In particular this is true at the junior high school level of instruction. The modern program is laying much more emphasis than was done in former years on such basic concepts as relation, function, structure, mathematical systems, precise terminology and definition, significance of the nature and techniques of induction and deduction, the need for study of inequalities as well as equations, and the construction of mathematical models. It is laying much less emphasis on the learning of rules, mere manipulation of formulas and equations, development of computational skills, and the measurement of geometric configurations. This

The modern
program

---

[5] Joint Commission of the Mathematical Association of America, Inc., and the National Council of Teachers of Mathematics, "The Place of Mathematics in Secondary Education," *Fifteenth Yearbook* (Washington, D.C.: National Council of Teachers of Mathematics, 1940).
[6] Commission on Post-War Plans, Second Report, *Mathematics Teacher,* **38** (1945), 204–207.

change in emphasis has not only affected the algebra program of the junior high school but has also tended to revise the program of the general-mathematics track.

Criticism of the
mathematics
program

In the past, a great deal of the criticism of the mathematics program of the junior high school was that there was too much emphasis on those quantitative concepts and procedures which belong to the sort of informal experience that takes place outside the classroom. Such topics as insurance, discount, commission, various home and farm activities, banking, and taxation offer opportunities for the application of mathematical information and procedures, but should not serve as criteria for selection of curriculum content. Mathematics is a study of order and form abstracted from the specifics of concrete realities. It is the responsibility of general education to recognize this fact in its program and

Applications in the
instructional
program

seek the challenge of pertinent applications only after basic competence in mathematics has been attained. The modern emphasis on structure and form underscores the need for a program which provides proficiency in the mathematical concepts, principles, and skills needed in intelligent approach to problem situations. Whatever the ability of an educable person may be, the general education program in mathematics must provide him with a background

Responsibilities of
the general
education program
in mathematics

of information and skills to enable him to compute with facility; to understand, appreciate, and construct a simple valid argument; to recognize and analyze a problem situation; to discriminate between known and unknown elements; to distinguish between relevant and irrelevant data; to determine the need for additional data; to recognize basic relationships; to detect fundamental restrictions and possibilities; to make intelligent guesses and estimates; and to evaluate and interpret results. A program so designed would tend to meet the prescription of the Commission on Mathematics that the mathematics of general education should provide a medium for teaching secondary school students "the basic mathematical ideas and concepts that every citizen needs to know, and to explain the essential character of mathematics."[7] Furthermore, it would provide a solid foundation upon which to build an effective program designed to meet the needs of the terminal students, who constitute a rather large segment of the secondary school population and who present a wide range of ability and interest.[8] Given such a foundation on which to build, the individual student's mathematical success would be limited only by his ability to deal intelligently and persistently with abstractions.

Although the philosophy in the report of the National Com-

---

[7] "Report of the Commission on Mathematics" (New York: College Entrance Examination Board, 1959), p. 11.

[8] Sol Weiss, Innovations and Research in the Teaching of Mathematics to the Terminal Student, *Mathematics Teacher*, **60** (1967), 611–618.

mittee on Mathematical Requirements (1923) calling for change is pretty much the same as the modern philosophy demanding reform, there is one important difference, at least in implication. The basic emphasis on general mathematics (better said, mathematics in general education) of the 1923 report, the report of the Joint Commission (1940), and that of the Commission on Post-War Plans (1945) is reflected in this quotation from the Commission on Post-War Plans: ". . . general mathematics is *organized* differently, . . . it offers a greater *variety* of topics and . . . it is related *more directly* with immediate application."[9] As stated previously, the

Differentiation in treatment rather than content

basic emphasis of the modern demand for a program in general education is that general education and special education are not to be distinguished from each other so much in subject matter as in point of view and method of treatment. This implies that, while there may be differentiation in tracks, in the two-track program of the junior high school there will not be any differentiation in basic subject matter or basic preparation of teachers. The appropriate development of relevant basic mathematical skills, concepts, and principles will be the first responsibility of teachers regardless of track. The differentiation will come in the interpretation, supplementation, and enrichment of this development. For one track this aspect of the program will be oriented in the context of the user of mathematics; in the other it will assume the point of view of a forward look toward more advanced work in mathematics.

Three-track program

There are some who are proposing still a third track to provide for a still slower-paced mathematics program for students of very low-level competence. Regardless of track, the teachers of mathematics in the junior high school will have to be equally well informed in mathematical subject matter, in the history of mathematics, in the psychology of individual differences, and in effective techniques of presentation of materials and evaluation of results.

THE SENIOR HIGH SCHOOL

The inception of the idea of dividing the six-year secondary education program of grades 7 to 12 into the junior high school and the senior high school dates from the early 1900s. Since that time, the primary function of the senior high school has been defined in terms of providing opportunities for the beginning of content specialization and the pursuance of aptitudes and special interests. While this has been generally accepted as the basic philosophy in the formulation of the senior high school program in mathematics, there have been those who have argued for the need to provide for

---

[9] Commission on Post-War Plans, *op. cit.* The italics are in the original, and the comparisons are made with the algebra program of the ninth grade.

continuing emphasis on general education into the senior high school. It has been their contention that young people are graduating from high school with tragic inadequacies in the fundamentals

Minimum content

of elementary mathematics. The minimum content of such a program should be concerned with the basic structure of our decimal-numeral system; the basic structure of algebra; the nature of proof; the concepts of relation and function, with particular attention to the linear and quadratic functions and their graphs; the solution of linear and quadratic equations; the concept of measurement and its approximate nature; computation involving approximation; and the fundamentals of probability and statistics.

The Secondary School Curriculum Committee took the position

Recommendations of Secondary School Curriculum Committee

that it is desirable for all graduates from the high school to have attained at least a certain minimal degree of mathematical competency, and recommended that some means should be provided to determine whether or not prospective graduates have done so. Further, it recommended that, possibly, grade 11 is the best place to subject the candidate to this check, in order that a required program might be pursued in grade 12 by those who fail to measure up to the basic mathematics requirements of general education.[10] Here again the pattern of individual differences can well

Multiple-track program

call for a multiple-track program. If it is to have significance to the student, the general-education program should not be allowed to degenerate into one of remedial efforts, but must be designed to challenge the hidden potential of low achievers[11] as well as provide that mathematics which is essential to meet the vocational and nonacademic needs of terminal students.[12] It is quite possible that current experimentation in the use of programmed materials and computer-assisted instruction (CAI)[13] will result in significant contributions to these problems of curriculum and instruction in mathematics. Furthermore, the mathematically gifted should be given the opportunity to work in an atmosphere of full challenge and maximum interest. There should be differentiation on the basis of need and ability without "burdening with a stigma" or "investing with a halo" any one group as compared with another.

[10] Secondary School Curriculum Committee, The Mathematics Curriculum, *Mathematics Teacher*, **52** (1959), 413.

[11] Herbert Fremont and Neal Ehrenburg, The Hidden Potential of Low Achievers, *Mathematics Teacher*, **59** (1966), 551–557.

Sarah Greenholz, Successful Practices in Teaching Mathematics to Low Achievers in Senior High School, *Mathematics Teacher*, **60** (1967), 329–335.

[12] Weiss, *loc. cit.*

[13] Ralph T. Heimer: Designs for Future Explorations in Programmed Instruction, *Mathematics Teacher*, **59** (1966), 110–114.

Kenneth O. May, "Programmed Learning and Mathematical Education" (San Francisco: Committee on Educational Media, Mathematical Association of America, 1965).

Patrick Suppes, Computer Based Mathematics Instruction, *Bulletin of the International Study Group for Mathematics Learning* III (1965).

Conant's
recommendations

After an intensive study of the American high school, James Bryant Conant recommended a teaching program structured in three categories, as follows:

> First, there are the courses that should be *required* of *all* students, irrespective of their academic ability or their vocational goals. Then, there are two types of elective programs—the nonacademic and the academic.
>
> The required program should occupy about half of every student's time. It should include four years of English, three or four years of social studies including two of history, at least one year of mathematics and one year of science. These courses are intended to provide the groundwork for citizenship in a democracy. . . .
>
> The nature of the nonacademic elective program will depend almost entirely on the community. There may be a considerable number of parents who are interested in having their children whose talents are nonacademic, take vocational courses geared to employment opportunities in the community. In that case, such courses should be offered. . . .
>
> I am convinced . . . that, on a national basis, something like 15 per cent of the youth of high-school age have the ability to study effectively and rewardingly advanced mathematics, science, and a foreign language. And I think those academically talented students should be urged by the counselors to elect a minimum academic elective program that includes four years of mathematics, four years of *one* foreign language, and three years of a science.[14]

These recommendations are directed toward four-year high school programs, but they have important implications for those programs which are on a 3-3 pattern of junior high school and senior high school.

Attributes of a
good teacher

The success of any such program of mathematics education will depend to a very great extent upon the preparation and experience of the teacher. Whether his instructional responsibilities are directed toward general education or toward the more specialized nonacademic and academic programs, he should have a strong mathematical background, be acquainted with the demands of individual differences, and be informed on the relative merits of appropriate teaching techniques. These more highly specialized attributes of a good teacher should be supported by the cultural, disciplinary, and practical qualities of a sound program in general education.

THE JUNIOR COLLEGE

The name "junior college" is used here to apply to grades 13 and 14, whether they are attached to the high school, organized as a separate two-year unit, or constitute the first two years of a four-year college program. At this level of instruction, somewhat as at the junior high school level, there is need for concern with at least two large groups of students. There are those who, for various reasons, will desire to terminate their college program at the end of

Varied
responsibilities of
the college
program

[14] James Bryant Conant, A Hard Look at Our High Schools, *Look*, **23** (Feb. 3, 1959), 31–32.

the two years, and there are those who will plan to go on to more advanced work. Also, from the point of view of mathematics, there are those who, even though they continue for four years or more of college and university work, do not have any special interest in and aptitude for mathematics. These statements are supported by the report on "Aspects of Undergraduate Training in Mathematics."[15] According to this report, of the 348,000 junior college students enrolled in mathematics classes, 42.8 percent were in courses generally recognized as bona fide college classes (college algebra, analytic geometry, calculus, finite mathematics, differential equations, and linear algebra); 38.2 percent were in classes generally considered as elementary or high school courses (arithmetic, algebra, geometry); and 19.0 percent were in various types of vocational courses. From this evidence it is apparent that junior college instruction also is confronted with the problems of the low achiever, the terminal student, and other students who have no particular interest in an academic program. At this level of instruction there are still the same problems of differences in ability, interest, and emotional stability as characterize the curriculum and instruction in the elementary school and in the junior high school. Recognition of this fact, and of the fact that in our modern technological society mathematics has a responsible contribution to make to the program of general education, has given concern to educators and mathematicians alike. What is the most effective contribution that mathematics can make to the program of general education at the college level? There is not as yet any real agreement on the answer. Committees are still giving concentrated attention to the problem of finding the most appropriate answer. In particular, the work of the Committee on the Undergraduate Program in Mathematics[16] and the Secondary School Curriculum Committee[17] is to be noted. The professional journals have also carried many articles expressing individual points of view on the content of such a program. Despite the wide differences of opinion, there seems to be universal agreement on

Fundamental characteristic of the program

one fundamental characteristic of the program: *the content of the course must be mathematics, not just about mathematics.*

Students who terminate their mathematics program at the junior college level have three types of mathematical needs. Some need mathematics as part of their vocational training. Courses that satisfy this need are properly special education. Many terminating students have need for remedial mathematics. But for a significant segment of the junior college population, the final formal course in

---

[15] John Jewett and Clarence Lindquist, "Aspects of Undergraduate Training in Mathematics" (Washington, D.C.: Conference Board of the Mathematical Sciences, 1967).
[16] Report of the Committee on the Undergraduate Program in Mathematics, *American Mathematical Monthly,* **63** (1955), 511–520.
[17] Secondary School Curriculum Committee, *loc. cit.*

mathematics affords the opportunity to experience the true nature of mathematics within the context of familiar material. Although he is not a future mathematician, the student has the opportunity to discover the kinds of things that concern the mathematician.

Texts that reflect different points of view have begun to appear. The most generally accepted program seems to be developed around the broad areas of the basic notion of number, measurement, probability and statistics, function, and the nature of proof. The discussion of number seems to be concerned with (1) the historical background of our numeration system, paying special attention to the concepts of one-to-one correspondence, place value, and order; (2) numeration systems with nondecimal bases; (3) the basic properties of real numbers; (4) extension of number systems from natural numbers to complex numbers, including the concepts of sets, groups, and fields; (5) congruences and modular number systems; (6) the number line; and (7) rectangular coordinates. The approximate nature of measurement is developed, along with the concepts of precision and accuracy, significant digits, and standard notation; linear, area, volume, and capacity measurements; direct and indirect measurement; and computation involving approximations. The introduction to probability and statistics is restricted to the basic patterns of probability and the simpler measures of central tendency and variability. There is some consideration of basic characteristics of a normal distribution and the product-moment correlation. Sets, relations, and functions form an important part of the language and the subject matter of this program. More precise definitions of constant, variable, and function are given. Simple algebraic and trigonometric functions are introduced, and appropriate techniques, including graphs, are used for deriving their properties. The study and use of the basic rules of logic and simple truth tables are introduced as a foundation for a clearer understanding of the nature of proof as it applies to various mathematical areas. The importance of intuition and the necessity of deduction are developed. Contrasts are drawn between the algebraic and the purely geometric types of proof, as well as between direct and indirect methods. Careful attention is also paid to the basic nature of postulates, with some extensions to Boolean algebra being made.

This rough outline of topics can be considered an indication of what might be thought of as a required program in mathematics for a general-education program at the college level. An analysis of the outline will disclose an implementation of the generally accepted basic assumption upon which such courses are to be built, as stated above; namely, the course must be mathematics, not just about mathematics.

There is no doubt that mathematical content for such a course

The most
generally accepted
mathematics
program

The need for a
well-prepared
teacher

can be developed in a meaningful manner that is quite compatible with the scholastic aptitude of all college students. As in any instructional area, the final responsibility for the effectiveness and value of any such course is the teacher's. No course designed for the program of general education should be relegated to the apprentice teacher or the graduate assistant.

When staffing is a problem, one competent teacher, with the aid of graduate assistants, can adequately care for a large number of students. If closed-circuit television is available, the basic presentation can be supplemented in a variety of ways. But in any event the principal teacher should have a deep interest in the program and a conviction of its worth. Teachers of such courses must be prepared specifically for the job. The preparation program must provide learning experiences in advanced subject matter which will help the prospective teacher see more elementary content in the rich context of the more advanced, and to interpret the more advanced in the language and understanding of the more elementary. It must help the prospective teacher to see the profession of teaching as an opportunity to make a valuable contribution, no less genuine than that which lies open to the person trained for research in pure or applied mathematics. Such a program of preparation must be carried out with advanced courses in mathematics and related areas which have been designed to develop basic interrelationships as well as specific properties, and it must emphasize the necessity of recognizing the limitations of individual aptitudes as well as encouraging high standards of endeavor. In the hands of a teacher so prepared, the mathematics course in the general-education program can make a truly significant contribution to the intellectual growth of every educable person.

EXERCISES

1 Distinguish between general education and special education.

2 What are the basic purposes of a program in general education?

3 What general abilities should a program in general education be designed to help students develop?

4 In what ways can the program in secondary mathematics contribute toward the attainment of the objectives of general education?

5 What should be the basic objectives in mathematics for a general-education program at the level of the junior high school? The senior high school? The junior college?

6 Contrast the relative merits of a general-education program based on the philosophy of the report of the Harvard Committee and the one based on the philosophy of the report of the National Association of Secondary School Principals.

7 To what extent do you agree or disagree with the thirteen objectives (listed on page 42) as responsibilities of a program in general education?

8 To what extent do you agree or disagree with the eight contributions (listed on page 43) that mathematics should make to the general-education program?

9 What are some of the major modifications which the modern philosophy of mathematics instruction has introduced into the program of general education?

10 How important as a fundamental principle for a sound mathematics program for

general education is the thesis that the content and instructional emphasis of the program must be mathematics, and not just about mathematics?

11   What implications for the general-education program in mathematics do you think can be derived from research and experimentation in curriculum content and instructional procedures for the low achiever? For the terminal student?

12   Do you think that research and experimentation in the areas of programmed learning or computer-assisted instruction have any implications for the program of mathematics in general education?

13   What part, if any, should the use of computers play in shaping the program of general education?

14   Give some of the arguments both for and against placing emphasis on each of these content areas in a mathematics program for general education: the number concept, measurement, the nature of proof, functionality, statistics, structure of number systems, structure of algebra, structure of geometry, computation involving approximations.

15   Are there content areas other than those listed in exercise 14 which should be included in a mathematics program for general education?

BIBLIOGRAPHY

Adler, Henry L.: Mathematics for Liberal Arts Students, *American Mathematical Monthly*, **72** (1965), 60–66.

Alberty, Elsie J.: Mathematics in General Education, *Mathematics Teacher*, **59** (1966), 426–431.

Alexander, Doyle F.: "An Experiment in Teaching Mathematics at the College Level by Closed Circuit Television," *Contribution to Education*, 587 (Nashville, Tenn.: George Peabody College for Teachers, 1961).

Beckmann, Milton W.: Ninth Grade Mathematical Competence 15 Years Ago and Now, *School Science and Mathematics*, **69** (1969), 315–319.

Breslich, E. R.: Importance of Mathematics in General Education, *Mathematics Teacher*, **59** (1966), 464–469.

Bryan, J. C.: Mathematics in General Education, *School Science and Mathematics*, **58** (1958), 249–255.

Davis, Robert B.: "The Changing Curriculum in Mathematics" (Washington, D.C.: Association for Supervision and Curriculum Development, 1967).

Easterday, Kenneth E.: An Experiment with Low Achievers in Arithmetic, *Mathematics Teacher*, **57** (1964), 462–468.

Fehr, Howard F.: Goal Is Mathematics for All, *School Science and Mathematics*, **56** (1956), 109–120.

Fremont, Herbert, and Neal Ehrenburg: The Hidden Potential of Low Achievers, *Mathematics Teacher*, **59** (1966), 551–557.

Green, L. W.: From Knowledge into Power: A Philosophy of General Education, *Journal of General Education*, **11** (1958), 151–156.

Greenholz, Sarah: Successful Practice in Teaching Mathematics to Low Achievers in Senior High School, *Mathematics Teacher*, **60** (1967), 329–335.

Hannon, H. H.: Mastery of Certain Aspects of Mathematics for General Education, *Journal of Educational Research*, **50** (1957), 363–371.

Hartung, M. L.: Mathematics in the Total School Program, *Mathematics Teacher*, **51** (1958), 336–343.

Harvard Committee, Report of: "General Education in a Free Society" (Cambridge, Mass., Harvard University Press, 1945).

Heimer, Ralph T.: Designs for Future Explorations in Programmed Instruction, *Mathematics Teacher*, **59** (1966), 110–114.

"Higher Education for American Democracy," vol. I, "Establishing the Goals" (Washington, D.C.: President's Commission on Higher Education, 1947).

Holtan, Boyd De Vere: A Comparison of Motivational Vehicles in Teaching General Mathematics, unpublished doctoral dissertation (Urbana, Ill.: University of Illinois, 1963).

Horton, George W.: HOBLADIC, *Mathematics Teacher*, **54** (1961), 212–216.

Johnson, Donovan A., and Gerald R. Rising: "Guidelines for Teaching Mathematics" (Belmont, Calif.: Wadsworth Publishing Company, Inc., 1967), pp. 149–209.

Lane, Bennie R.: "An Experiment with Programmed Instruction as a Supplement to Teaching College Mathematics by Closed Circuit Television," *Contribution to Education*, 618 (Nashville, Tenn.: George Peabody College for Teachers, 1962).

Layton, W. I.: Mathematics in General Education, *Mathematics Teacher*, **50** (1957), 493–497.

Littlefield, D. G.: Computer Programming for High Schools and Junior Colleges, *Mathematics Teacher*, **54** (1961), 220–223.

Matchett, Margaret S.: Teaching Mathematics or What? *Mathematics Teacher*, **55** (1962), 351–355.

Mathematics in the Modern World, *Scientific American*, **211** (1964), entire issue.

May, Kenneth O.: "Programmed Learning and Mathematical Education" (San Francisco: Committee on Educational Media, Mathematical Association of America, 1965).

Mires, K. C.: General Mathematics for College Freshmen, *Mathematics Teacher*, **50** (1957), 513–516.

National Council of Teachers of Mathematics: "Computer Oriented Mathematics" (Washington, D.C.: The Council, 1963).

————: "Preliminary Report of the Conference on the Low Achiever in Mathematics," co-sponsored by the Office of Education (Washington, D.C.: The Council, 1964).

Pixley, Loren W.: Mathematics in the Community Junior College, *Mathematics Teacher*, **57** (1964), 313–316.

Rees, Mina: The Impact of the Computer, *Mathematics Teacher*, **51** (1958), 162–168.

Riedesel, Alan C., and Marilyn N. Suydam: Computer-assisted Instruction: Implications for Teacher Education, *Arithmetic Teacher*, **14** (1967), 24–29.

Rowe, Jack L.: General Mathematics for Terminal Students in California Junior Colleges, *Mathematics Teacher*, **52** (1959), 105–106.

School Mathematics Study Group: "Conference on Mathematics Education for Below Average Achievers" (Stanford, Calif.: Stanford University, 1964).

Simpson, T. M.: Mathematics in the College General Education Program, *Mathematics Teacher*, **50** (1957), 155–159.

Smith, David Eugene: Mathematics in the Training for Citizenship, *Mathematics Teacher*, **60** (1967), 140–148.

Spencer, Donald D.: Computers: Their Past, Present, and Future, *Mathematics Teacher*, **61** (1968), 65–75.

Stone, D. R., and H. C. Bateman: Basic Elements in Defining General Education, *Junior College Journal*, **27** (1956), 90–92.

Summerer, K. C.: College Mathematics for the Non-science, Non-mathematics Major, *School Science and Mathematics*, **56** (1956), 39–43.

Suppes, Patrick: Computer-based Mathematics Instruction, *Bulletin of the International Study Group for Mathematics*, **3** (1965).

Tillett, Harley E.: Computer Programming for Young Students, *Journal of the Association for Computing Machinery*, **5** (1958), 309–318.

Trimble, H. C.: Mathematics in General Education, *Mathematics Teacher*, **50** (1957), 2–5.

Trowbridge, H.: Forty Years of General Education, *Journal of General Education*, **11** (1958), 161–169.

Weiss, Sol: Innovations and Research in the Teaching of Mathematics to the Terminal Student, *Mathematics Teacher*, **60** (1967), 611–618.

Whitehead, A. N.: Mathematics and Liberal Education, *Mathematics Teacher*, **61** (1968), 509–516.

Williams, Horace E.: "A Study of the Effectiveness of Classroom Teaching Techniques Following a Closed Circuit Television Presentation in Mathematics," *Contribution to Education*, 610 (Nashville, Tenn.: George Peabody College for Teachers, 1962).

three | the new program in mathematics

In recent years the efforts of writing groups and experimental programs have been directed toward shaping a new program for mathematics in elementary and secondary education. Prior to this era the emphasis on mathematics instruction, both in the elementary and secondary school, had been almost entirely on the "how" of manipulation, with very little, if any, attention being paid to the "what" and the "why" of understanding. No longer is this true. Rather than being designed primarily to establish a mere catalog of rules and formulas for mechanical performance, the instructional program now evolving is designed to develop not only operational facility but also comprehension of and appreciation for basic concepts and an understanding of the purpose and function of operational techniques.

Shift in instructional emphasis

This new program in mathematics is not due to any desire to present at the elementary and secondary levels any great amount of newly invented or discovered subject matter. Rather, it is an attempt to make the mathematics curriculum consistent with the demands for intelligent living in the changing culture of our modern era. The implementation of this program is being accomplished through the use of at least three distinct, yet complementary, media, namely:

Three complementary media

1 *A new point of view* which attempts to redirect the emphasis in instruction to the "what" and "why" of understanding as well as to the "how" of manipulation. Attention is paid to the basic structure of fundamental mathematical systems as an effective means for developing a background of understanding along with a facility in manipulation.

2 *New subject matter* which provides not only desirable and appropriate updating of the content of the mathematics program in both the elementary school and the secondary school, but also ways and means of clarifying, simplifying, and enriching its presentation.

3 *New recognition of the significance of application* which directs attention to the basic structure of theorems to be proved or

problems to be solved. The use of guesses, conjectures, estimates, and other methods of intuition and induction is encouraged as aids in approach to theorem or problem situations. Furthermore, the appropriate techniques of deduction are carefully developed, and emphasis is given to the necessity for their use in the development of a valid argument, whether in the proof of a theorem or the solving of a problem.

The full significance of this trifocal nature of the new program in mathematics can be understood and appreciated only in the historical perspective of its evolution.

A NEW POINT OF VIEW

Origin of the modern point of view

The origin of what might be called the modern point of view in mathematics can be traced to the pioneering efforts of Gauss, Bolyai, Lobachevski, and Riemann in the creation of noneuclidean geometries. By daring to challenge that which for two millennia had been accepted as absolute, they freed the intellect to reject the evidence of the senses for the sake of what the mind might produce. The modern postulational method of mathematics finds its source in the publication by Lobachevski (1830) and Bolyai (1832) of a seemingly self-consistent geometric system which contradicted the euclidean fifth postulate of parallelism while keeping all other postulates intact. It was further enhanced through the

Noneuclidean geometries

publication by Riemann (1854) of still another such noneuclidean geometry, based upon a still different contradiction of the fifth postulate and the noneuclideanism of "curvature of space." Subsequent refinements by Pasch, Peano, and Hilbert succeeded in establishing the purely hypothetico-deductive nature of geometry. In fact, it has been said that Hilbert's work "firmly implanted the postulational method, not only in the field of geometry, but also in nearly every other branch of mathematics of the twentieth century."[1]

The nature of postulates

This new method no longer recognizes postulates (axioms) as "self-evident truths," but merely as "acceptable assumptions." They are individual creations of the investigator's mind and are to be used as the basic hypotheses for some type of intellectual venture. The investigator may or may not be concerned about their material truth or falsity; he is concerned with their consistency and is curious about their implications. After he is convinced of the validity of his conclusions, he may become interested in the pos-

[1] Howard Eves and Carroll V. Newsom, "An Introduction to the Foundations and Fundamental Concepts of Mathematics," rev. ed. (New York: Holt, Rinehart and Winston, Inc., 1965), p. 94.

sibility of existence of physical or social situations which would provide a context of "truth" for his assumptions. In such cases the same aura of usefulness would encompass his conclusions. The validity and consistency of results rather than the practicality of results, however, are the major concerns of the mathematician.

The need for undefined elements

The new method also places emphasis on the necessity for clear distinctions between that which is defined and that which must remain undefined. It is recognized that concepts and terms are defined through the use of other concepts and terms. Therefore, to avoid undesirable circuity of definition, the necessity for undefined, or irreducible, elements is created. The experience of the individual usually serves as the basic orientation for the specification of such undefined elements and the selection of fundamental postulates. Thus the modern point of view concerning geometry is that it is a creation of man's intellect, its distinctive structure being delineated by the basic postulates, the undefined elements, the dimensionality of the space of orientation, and the techniques of investigation.

The modern concept of geometry

In essentially contemporaneous development with geometry, algebra too was being freed from the shackles of authoritative tradition. The English mathematician George Peacock was the first, in about 1835, to think of algebra as a hypothetico-deductive system. This concept of algebra as an abstract science was developed further, in England, by D. F. Gregory and Augustus DeMorgan and, in Germany, by Hermann Hankel. The central thought of this development had its origin in the recognition and abstraction of the fundamental properties which characterize the algebra of positive integers (natural numbers). Such abstraction provided the symbolization which led to the realization that these same properties could very well characterize operations with elements other than the positive integers. If the operations are addition and multiplication and if a, b, and c represent positive integers, distinct or not, then the properties may be stated in the following manner:

The modern concept of algebra

Closure: If a and b are positive integers, then $a + b$ and $a \times b$ are positive integers.
Associative: $a + (b + c) = (a + b) + c$
$a \times (b \times c) = (a \times b) \times c$
Commutative: $a + b = b + a$ $a \times b = b \times a$
Distributive: $a \times (b + c) = (a \times b) + (a \times c)$

Noncommutative algebra

Sir William Rowan Hamilton, a British mathematician, did for algebra what Lobachevski and Bolyai did for geometry. In 1834 he made known his new quaternion algebra, in which he had dared to contradict the commutative property of multiplication. Other noncommutative algebras followed, notably Grassmann's (1844) classes of algebras of still greater generality than Hamilton's quaternion algebra and Cayley's (1857) matrix algebra. Of more recent date are the nonassociative algebras, such as those of Jordan and Lie.

From such considerations of algebraic structure there have evolved postulate sets for groups, rings, integral domains, and fields, each of which has great potential for significant contribution at the level of the secondary school to the better understanding of the essential nature of algebra as a body of mathematical subject matter.

CHARACTERISTICS OF A POSTULATE SYSTEM

In any hypothetico-deductive system the question of *consistency* is the problem of major concern. How can one be assured that, among all the implications derivable from the basic postulates, there can never occur conflicting statements? Consistency can be of two types: *relative* and *absolute*. In the previous statements concerning the consistency of lobachevskian and riemannian geometries the only implication is that, at the time of publication, no internal inconsistencies had been discovered. This, of course, did not rule out the possibility of the eventual detection of contradictory theorems implied by the basic postulates. Since 1868 there has been the added significance of relative consistency. This was established in rather brilliant fashion by E. Beltrami, who demonstrated that

Consistency of a set of postulates

. . . plane hyperbolic [lobachevskian] geometry can be interpreted as that of the geodesics [curves of shortest length] on a surface of constant negative curvature [pseudosphere or tractoid], and likewise for spherical geometry [plane riemannian geometry] and a surface of constant positive curvature [sphere]. Since pseudospheres and spheres are familiar surfaces in Euclidean space, it was felt that the consistency of the classical non-Euclidean geometries had been demonstrated.[2]

Relative consistency

Of course, the implication is merely that the geometries of Lobachevski and Riemann are just as consistent as is that of Euclid, no more and no less. Euclidean geometry merely serves as a mathematical model of the noneuclidean geometries, since it was found possible to find unique representation in euclidean geometry of the postulates and undefined terms of the noneuclidean geometries. For example, the controversial fifth postulate of Euclid was represented in each noneuclidean geometry by its respective substitute: point was identified with point and the straight lines of euclidean geometry with the geodesics of noneuclidean; two straight lines (geodesics) intersect in one point in euclidean and

[2] E. T. Bell, "The Development of Mathematics," 2d ed. (New York: McGraw-Hill Book Company, 1945), p. 307.

lobachevskian geometry but in two points in riemannian geometry. (Arcs of great circles on the surface of a sphere intersect in the two poles.)

When a mathematical system contains an infinite number of primitive elements, no better than relative consistency can be established. This is not always as nebulous as it may seem. For example, since the points of euclidean plane geometry can be identified with ordered pairs of real numbers, and algebraic meanings can be assigned to the five primitive terms (point, line, on, between, and congruent), it follows that euclidean geometry, and hence the noneuclidean geometries mentioned above, are as consistent as the real-number system.[3] Similarly, the consistency of many mathematical systems can be checked against that of the real-number system.

Absolute consistency

When a mathematical system contains only a finite number of primitive elements, concrete representation can be found in the domain of reality, and thus absolute consistency of the system can be established.[4]

Since finite postulational systems can be checked for consistency against the concrete expectations of reality, the basic problem of consistency of postulational systems is that of infinite systems and, therefore, primarily that of the consistency of the real-number system. Through the inspirational researches of Peano, Dedekind, and G. Cantor the consistency of the real-number system has in turn been related to that of the system of natural numbers, thus giving

> . . . the mathematician a considerable feeling of security concerning the consistency of most of mathematics. This attitude follows from the fact that the natural number system seems to have an intuitive simplicity lacking in most other mathematical systems, and the natural numbers have been very extensively handled over a long period of time without producing any known inner contradictions.[5]

The quest for a solution of the problem of consistency of infinite mathematical systems may be analyzed into five significant phases:

1 The study of the absolute consistency of finite systems. An exhaustive examination of all elements in a model of such a system can detect inconsistencies or establish consistency.

2 The relative proofs of consistency, for example, Beltrami's use of the techniques of differential geometry to establish the relative con-

---

[3] Eves and Newsom, *op. cit.,* pp. 105–111.
[4] See, for example, Burton W. Jones, Miniature Number Systems, *Mathematics Teacher,* **51** (1958), 226–231, and Miniature Geometries, *ibid.,* **52** (1959), 66–71. Also see Eves and Newsom, *op. cit.,* pp. 158–161, 164.
[5] Eves and Newsom, *op. cit.,* p. 208. The authors present a very interesting discussion on The Postulational Approach to the Real Number System, pp. 203–225.

sistency of euclidean, lobachevskian, and riemannian geometries and Hilbert's use of cartesian coordinate geometry to draw the conclusion that his geometry was as consistent as algebra.

3 Hilbert's efforts to construct "absolute" proofs for which he stipulated that there should be no reference to the consistency of other systems, to an infinite number of structural properties of formulas, or to an infinite number of operations with formulas. The thought behind these stipulations was that if every mathematical system could be exhibited as a pattern of formulas linked together in a finite structure, an exhaustive analysis could establish whether or not contradictory theorems could be deduced from the accepted postulates of each respective system.

4 The 1931 paper by Gödel, which established that it is quite unlikely that an absolute proof of consistency, satisfying Hilbert's conditions, can ever be found for all deductive systems, particularly arithmetic; also that there are an infinite number of arithmetical truths which can never be deduced from a given set of postulates within the restrictions of a finite set of rules of inference.[6] This means that if the arithmetic of real numbers is consistent, this fact cannot be established within its own formal structure.

5 Proofs of the consistency of arithmetic by Gerhard Gentzen, of the Hilbert school, and others. Although these proofs were not accomplished in accordance with Hilbert's stipulations, they are of logical significance.

From a logician's point of view it is also desirable that any set of postulates be independent, complete, and categorical, as well as consistent. From a pedagogical point of view these three properties are not necessary at all and, at times, they can be undesirable. The only essential property of a set of postulates, whether from a logical or a pedagogical point of view, is consistency.

Independence of a set of postulates

A set of postulates is said to be *independent* if it is impossible to derive any particular postulate of the system as a logical consequence from the remaining postulates. Probably the most famous of all investigations of the independence of a postulate system is the centuries-long investigation of Euclid's fifth postulate (the postulate of parallelism). Certainly this is the most significant study when evaluated in terms of its contribution to the modern point of view in the teaching of secondary mathematics. Actually, the number of postulates in a system is immaterial provided there exist no inconsistencies within the set. Logically, a minimum list of assumptions is desirable in order to provide the maximum number of derivable theorems. Pedagogically, it is frequently desirable to postulate a needed theorem whose proof is too advanced for the student's experience with the subject. Later, at a more appropriate time, the proof of such a theorem may be estab-

[6] Ernest Nagel and James R. Newman, "Gödel's Proof" (New York: New York University Press, 1960), p. 98.

lished with understanding. Such a system is said to be *redundant*. The set of postulates most generally stated, at least at the more elementary levels, for the natural numbers is a redundant system.

THE NATURAL-NUMBER SYSTEM

Given the set of all natural numbers, $N = \{1,2,3, \ldots\}$, and the

two familiar well-defined operations of addition (+) and multiplication (×), for which the following postulates hold:

N1 *Closure.* If, for a and b in N, $a + b = c$ and $a \times b = d$, then c and d are elements of N.
N2 If a and b are in N, then $a + b = b + a$.
N3 If a and b are in N, then $a \times b = b \times a$.
N4 If a, b, c are in N, then $(a + b) + c = a + (b + c)$.
N5 If a, b, c are in N, then $(a \times b) \times c = a \times (b \times c)$.
N6 If a, b, c are in N, then $a \times (b + c) = (a \times b) + (a \times c)$.
N7 There exists a natural number 1 such that $a \times 1 = a$ for all a in N.
N8 If a, b, c are in N and if $c + a = c + b$, then $a = b$.
N9 If a, b, c are in N and if $c \times a = c \times b$, then $a = b$.
N10 For given a and b in N, one and only one of the following holds: $a = b$, $a + x = b$, $a = b + y$, where x and y are in N.
N11 If M is a set of natural numbers such that (1) M contains the natural number 1 and (2) M contains the natural number $k + 1$ whenever it contains the natural number k, then M contains all the natural numbers.

This system is redundant since postulates N2, N3, N5, N8, and N9 are theorems provable as consequences of the remaining six postulates, which can be shown to be independent.[7] The proofs for N2, N3, and N5 require the use of the Principle of Finite induction, as stated in N11, while the proofs of N8 and N9 require the method of indirect proof known as *reductio ad absurdum.* Each of these techniques of proof is fairly sophisticated and advanced. On the other hand, each of the five properties is essential for intelligent work in elementary arithmetic and algebra. For this reason, it is desirable to list them among the basic postulates of the natural-number system in spite of their redundant nature.

Attention was called earlier to Hamilton's contradiction of the commutative property of multiplication. While he was concerned with the properties of an algebraic system other than those of the real number system, he did retain the postulates of that system. By thinking of the complex number $a + bi$ ($i^2 = -1$) as the ordered pair (a,b) of real numbers, he was able to relate the algebra of the complex numbers to the geometry of simple rotations in the plane. By his definitions of equality, addition, and multiplication, and

---

[7] Eves and Newsom, *op. cit.,* pp. 314–317.

using the field properties of real numbers, he established the fact that complex numbers conform to all the field properties, in particular, the commutative law for multiplication. Furthermore, he was able to show that there exists an isomorphic relation between the set of all ordered pairs of the form (a,0) and the set of all real numbers. In order to extend the same algebraic pattern to the study of simple rotations in space, he was led to consider ordered quadruples of real numbers (a,b,c,d). He called these numbers *quaternions.*

Retaining the postulates of the real-number system, he defined equality, addition, and multiplication for quaternions in such a way that they conformed to all the field properties but one. In this system multiplication is not commutative. In spite of this fact, quaternions of the form (a,b,0,0) behave just as complex numbers, and those of the form (a,0,0,0) behave just as real numbers. While the definitions of multiplication for complex numbers and for quaternions are well-defined operations within the context of the field properties of real numbers, they lead to results which seemingly are in contradiction to each other. This situation, of course, is not an example of redundancy, independence, or inconsistency of a system of postulates. Rather, it is an illustration of the importance of definition in the structure of mathematical systems.

A consistent set of postulates is said to be a *complete* set if it is impossible to add another consistent independent postulate without increasing the number of the primitive terms. In any pattern of postulational thinking there is a set of primitive terms (defined or undefined); defined terms; a consistent set of assumed statements (postulates) about the primitive terms; rules for combining terms, definitions, and postulates to form statements; patterns for combining such statements into a valid argument (proof); and theorems which can be established as logical consequences of the postulates. In the structure of such a system the primitive terms are selected, and then the process of structuring the set of consistent postulates is undertaken. It is in this process that the problem of completeness arises. For example, the first four postulates of euclidean and lobachevskian geometries are the same, namely:

Completeness of a set of postulates

1 A straight line may be drawn connecting two points.
2 A finite straight line may be produced continuously in a straight line.
3 A circle may be drawn with any point as center and any length as a radius.
4 All right angles are congruent to one another.

As a postulational system for either geometry this set would not be complete since it would not permit any conclusion to be drawn concerning the sum of the angle measures of a triangle. In euclidean geometry this angle sum has the same measure as two right angles. In lobachevskian geometry this same angle sum is always less than two right angles. Each respective theorem which establishes the angle sum in its geometry is a direct consequence of the appropriate fifth postulate concerning parallelism. Pedagogically, we might say that only relative attention to completeness is desirable. At the elementary and secondary levels of instruction there certainly can be no desire to strive for logical completeness of any of the different mathematical systems studied. On the other hand, there is a need that the set of postulates be sufficiently complete, so as to rule out the necessity for resorting to some unacceptable pattern of tacit assumptions in order to build the theorem structure desired, in any particular system considered pertinent to a proper understanding of mathematics and an appreciation of its place in our culture.

Categoricalness of a set of postulates

A set of postulates is *categorical* if the elements of any two models, P and Q, of the system can be placed in one-to-one correspondence in such a way that all relations, whether postulated or derived, between elements are preserved under the correspondence. For example, it is possible to place the set of all positive integers into one-to-one correspondence with the natural numbers in such a manner that all postulates and provable theorems for natural numbers are also true for positive integers. In usage we rely on this fact when, frequently, we speak of natural numbers or positive integers without being much concerned as to which interpretation is used. An immediate illustration of this fact is the situation in elementary mathematics where we say that, when a numeral has no sign associated with it, it may be considered, if desirable, as representing a positive integer. The numeral 3 (without the sign) is the usual symbol for the natural number where the positive integer symbol is $+3$. From the point of view of instruction in elementary mathematics, the interest in the property of categoricalness is informal. With the appropriate definitions of addition and multiplication such isomorphic relationship exists not only between natural numbers and positive integers, but also between the set of all integers and the set of common fractions (rational numbers) with 1 as a denominator, and between the set of all real numbers and the set of complex numbers of the form $a + 0i$, where a is a real number and $i^2 = -1$. The only references that are usually made to these isomorphisms are more or less casual, through statements that such interchanges of usage can be made when and if they are found to be helpful. This casualness of reference can be, and frequently is, a much more appropriate instructional procedure than careful formal treatment would be.

However, such casual attention to the property of categoricalness does not detract from its significance as an important property of a set of postulates. From a logician's point of view one of its most positive values as a basic property of a set of postulates is the fact that it can be used as an effective test for completeness of the set. It is not too difficult to prove that if a postulate system is categorical, then it is complete.

The basic substance of the modern point of view in mathematics supports the philosophy that no longer is the teaching of mathematics at the elementary and secondary levels of instruction to be designed to result in merely shaping a tool kit of rules, formulas, techniques, and assorted mnemonics. Rather, it is to recognize that each mathematical system studied is characterized by its own individual structure, and that basic understanding of this structure can serve effectively as a background for building for the students not only greater facility in the mechanics of mathematics, but also more informed comprehension of, and appreciation for, basic concepts and deeper understanding of the purpose and function of the operational procedures. Such a philosophy recognized that to teach mathematics within the context of the immediate demands of the present environment is, most likely, to leave the student quite unprepared for future change. On the other hand, to place the emphasis on the basic structure of appropriate mathematical systems should lay the foundation for intelligent coping with environmental demands, present or future.

NEW SUBJECT MATTER

The effectiveness of any program of instruction is dependent not only on the point of view, but also on the subject matter to which it is adapted. The basic philosophy which directs the shaping of the curriculum in secondary mathematics recognizes that there are different geometries, different algebras, and different number systems, each with its individual postulational structure and techniques of investigation. Also, it is cognizant of the fact that the demands of a changing technological environment continually emphasize the necessity for modifications in the traditional content within any instructional program, as well as for adaptations of newly developed subject matter for appropriate introduction into the program. Out of the history of mathematical thought there have evolved significant patterns for desirable modification of the traditional in the curriculum of secondary mathematics, as well as for pertinent introduction of the new.

Demands of technology

GEOMETRY

The etymology of the word "geometry" (earth measure) indicates the primitive association with the concept of measurement. This concept of geometry, identified by the term *metric,* is concerned fundamentally with the properties of shape and size, which are characterized by measures such as those of angles, lengths, areas, and volumes. Even within the somewhat restricted domain of metric geometry, there exist at least four distinct, though not mutually exclusive, postulational structures: the *absolute geometry* of Saccheri, Legendre, and Bolyai (the geometry in which the postulate of parallelism plays no part, also called *neutral geometry*); the *unique parallelism geometry* of Euclid; the *nonunique parallelism geometry* of Bolyai and Lobachevsky; and the *nonparallelism geometry* of Riemann.

Four distinct metric geometries

Up to the middle of the seventeenth century the techniques of study and discovery in geometry were *synthetic* (purely geometric) in nature. In 1637 Descartes, in an appendix to his *"Discours de la méthode,"* introduced the *analytic* technique as a powerful instrument for use not only in geometry but in other areas of mathematics as well. In this work he systematized the method of applying algebra to geometry, introduced the notion of variables and constants into the study of geometric relations, and conceived of curves as generated by a moving point, and referred these curves to two intersecting lines and represented them by equations involving two variables, the relation of these variables being determined by the distances from the two lines of reference. It was this notion of expressing curves by algebraic equations that made possible the step from geometry to analysis and thus paved the way for calculus. A few years later Leibniz introduced the word "function" to designate magnitudes involved in Descartes' idea of curves generated by a moving point. The researches of Newton and Leibniz made extensive use of this new concept of the locus of a moving point, and by application of the techniques of infinitesimal analysis gave new significance to the implications of functional dependence.

Descartes' contribution

It is interesting to note that cartesianism also provided the basis for the modern refinement of the concept of function which subordinates the idea of dependence to the more fundamental idea of relation. The cartesian frame of reference, composed of two intersecting number lines, provides the machinery, and the language of sets provides the terminology, for more precise descriptions of many fundamental mathematical concepts. While relation and function are not necessarily restricted to dealing with numbers, the associations expressed through the cartesian pairing of numbers in graphs provides a basis for a more precise description of

Relation and function

Ordered pairs

the correspondence existing between different sets of elements. This is accomplished through the mechanism of *ordered pairs* such as (x,y), where x is the first element and y the second element of the ordered pair. A *relation*, then, is merely a set of ordered pairs, and a *function* is a relation in which there is associated with each first element one and only one second element. Thus the set $\{(1,-1),(1,1),(4,-2),(4,2),(9,-3),(9,3)\}$ would be a relation, while the set $\{(-1,1),(1,1),(-2,4),(2,4),(-3,9),(3,9)\}$ would be a function.[8]

It is true that the cartesian technique derives a great deal of its importance from its power as a most effective method for the study of the properties of the configurations of 2-space. Of even greater significance, however, is its remarkable flexibility of adaptation, which invests it with no lesser degree of effectiveness in the investigation of the generalities of n-space and the specifics of 1-space and 3-space than it possesses in dealing with the problems of 2-space.

Projective geometry

Contemporaneous (1639) with Descartes, the French architectural engineer Desargues published an original treatise in which he developed the geometric techniques of perspective and projection as effective methods for the study of conic sections. Although this effort was supported through further contemporaneous work by Pascal (1623–1662), it was so completely overshadowed by the contribution of Descartes that this new projective geometry was temporarily buried in pure metric geometry. There it remained until revived by the publications of Carnot (1803, 1806) and Poncelet (1822). Further impetus was given to this area of investigation through the announcement (1825–1827) by Gergonne of the principle of duality, "which, with its generalizations, left as substantial a residue of new and useful methods in geometry, algebra, and analysis as any mathematical invention of the nineteenth century."[9]

From these efforts there evolved an entirely new and distinct area of geometry, known as *projective*, or *nonmetric, geometry*, in which the fundamental concern is with those descriptive properties of geometric configurations which deal with position and union of points, lines, and planes.

Impact on the modern geometry program

As a result of the critical evaluation of these discoveries of noneuclidean and nonmetric geometries, the modern program of instruction in the secondary school is designed to build a more carefully patterned logical structure of geometry. Such a program recognizes the existence of noneuclidean geometries, and studies, along with metric properties, some of the nonmetric properties of

---

[8] For a good presentation of the more modern concept of function see Kenneth D. May and Henry Van Engen, Relations and Functions, *Twenty-fourth Yearbook* (Washington, D.C.: National Council of Teachers of Mathematics, 1959), pp. 65–110.
[9] Bell, *op. cit.*, p. 316.

geometric configurations of 1-, 2-, and 3-space. While the analytic technique of cartesianism has not completely replaced the traditional synthetic technique of investigation, and probably never should, it is recognized as an important method for the careful study of geometric configurations.

Klein's definition
of geometry

In 1872 Felix Klein announced his famous Erlanger program. In the address announcing this program he incorporated a definition of geometry which served to restore order, as it were, to the existing confusion. He appealed to algebra to give him the concept needed and defined a geometry as "the system of definitions and theorems invariant under a *group* of transformations." While this synthesis of geometrical thinking no longer seemed adequate after the advent of the general relativity theory, it does still serve to provide an effective approach to the better understanding of the real significance of geometry at the level of the secondary school. Invariance is an extremely important property of geometrical configurations, which is of sufficiently simple structure to be comprehensible at the secondary level of instruction, yet sufficiently abstract to open up new vistas of mathematical endeavor of challenging interest.

PROBABILITY

The first mechanical
computer

In addition to his contribution to nonmetric geometry, Pascal's invention of the adding machine laid the foundation for the modern era of the computer. He also combined his talents with those of Fermat (1601–1665) to lay the foundation for the theory of probability in the joint solution of a game-of-chance problem proposed to Pascal by Chevalier de Méré. In this episode of 1654 the mathematics of chance had its beginning; since then it has attained such stature that it has become basic in many areas of modern living and scientific investigation. Something of its significance is implied by the fact that the Commission on Mathematics of the College Entrance Examination Board published an experimental text for high school use entitled "Introductory Probability and Statistical Inference for Secondary Schools." This work served as the introduction into the secondary curriculum of a new and growing interest in the elementary theory of probability.

TRIGONOMETRY AND CALCULUS

Along with the study of analytic geometry, the study of trigonometry and differential calculus affords unlimited opportunities for coming into contact with the fundamental principles that are

New emphases in trigonometry

essential to an appreciative and intelligent comprehension of the basic interrelationships which give structure to mathematics as a field of thought. For this reason trigonometry has been lifted from the restrictions of indirect measurement of triangles and numerical computation, and the fundamental calculus techniques of differentiation and integration are developed and used to provide at least a more complete treatment of polynomial, logarithmic, exponential, and trigonometric functions.

Wrapping function

Through the use of the concept of a wrapping function, the domain and range of trigonometric functions have been extended to the set of all real numbers of which the measurement numbers constitute a subset. A somewhat intuitive concept of limit is introduced and applied in an elementary consideration of sequences and series, and is used, as well, in a fundamental development of

Concept of limit

differentiation and integration. This introduction of concepts, techniques, and topics from analytic geometry, trigonometry, and calculus, along with the rapid developments of pertinent significance to secondary mathematics, has resulted in necessary adaptations and revisions in curriculum placement of many of the traditional topics from arithmetic, algebra, and geometry.

ALGEBRA

The word "algebra" is derived from an Arabic word which gave to the content of algebra an identification with the theory of equations. In 1801 a relation between subsets of the set of rational integers was discovered by Gauss.[10] This relation, which he called

Congruence relation

the *congruence relation*, was defined as follows: *The rational integers a, b are said to be congruent modulo m ($a \equiv b$, mod m) if and only if a and b have the same remainder when divided by the rational integer m, or equivalently, if and only if a − b is divisible by m.* This concept provided a technique and the motivation for the study of relations between integers and sets of integers rather than merely the results of operations with integers. The door was now opened to further abstractions in the theory of number, to the drawing of analogies between arithmetic and algebra, and to the investigation of the general properties which describe relations between numbers and sets of numbers. This work, along with the work of Abel and Galois in the theory of equations and of Hamilton in the postula-

The new concept of algebra

tional structure of algebraic systems, caused mathematicians to direct their efforts to the study of the basic structure of algebra and the investigation of the existence of different systems, rather than restrict their efforts to the contemplation of the specifics within any one system.

[10] *Ibid.,* pp. 175–176.

In its modern framework algebra has lost none of its original character as a theory of equations, but, through its laws of operations upon symbolic forms, expands further into a systematic method for the expression and examination of existing relationships. According to Nesselmann,[11] the history of algebra divides itself into three periods: (1) the rhetorical, (2) the syncopated, and (3) the symbolic. The rhetorical period was characterized by the fact that words were written out in full and no symbols were used.

Three periods in the history of algebra

The oldest Egyptian, Babylonian, Arabian, Persian, and Italian algebraists represent this period. In the syncopated period the presentation was similar in literary type to that of the rhetorical period, but abbreviations were used. This period began with Diophantus (ca. 275) and extended up to the middle of the seventeenth century. In the symbolic period abbreviations gave way to signs and symbols.

The following examples show this transition from pure rhetorical algebra to that of modern compact symbolism; they show how the same equation would have been written by several medieval and Renaissance mathematicians:[12]

Regiomontanus, A.D. 1464:
   3 Census et 6 demptis 5 rebus aequatur zero
Pacioli, A.D. 1494:
   3 Census p. 6 de 5 rebus ae 0
Vieta, A.D. 1591:
   3 in A quad -5 in A plano $+6$ aequatur 0
Stevinus, A.D. 1585:
   3② $-$ 5① $+$ 6⊙ $= 0$
Descartes, A.D. 1637:
   $3x^2 - 5x + 6 = 0$

There are, of course, no clear-cut lines of demarcation between the three periods. Diophantus, in fact, used certain features of all three.[13]

Basic algebraic structure

With this freedom of symbolic abstraction it is possible to define many different algebras and their companion arithmetics. The concept of a basic algebraic structure arises from the recognition of the fact that, with the ordinary definition of addition and multiplication, the properties of associativity, commutativity, and distributivity characterize these operations not only with natural numbers, rational numbers, real numbers, irrational numbers, and complex numbers, but also with polynomials and even more general types of functions and with many other sets of elements. Even with slight modifications in the definitions of the basic operations, these properties continue to be the basic laws as the

[11] G. H. F. Nesselmann, *"Die Algebra der Griechen"* (Berlin: G. Reimer, 1842), pp. 301–305.
[12] L. Hogben, "Mathematics for the Million" (New York: W. W. Norton & Company, 1936), p. 303.
[13] D. E. Smith, "History of Mathematics," vol. II (Boston: Ginn and Company, 1925), p. 379.

operations are applied to more general sets of elements. Thus the concept of algebra is extended beyond a mere symbolization of arithmetic. It becomes a definitive structure with specified elements, defined operations, and basic postulates. Such abstractions identify algebra as a truly hypothetico-deductive system, and there come into existence algebras of many different types, such as the algebra of matrices, the algebra of symmetry, the algebra of transformations, and the algebra of sets. The new program in algebra of the secondary school recognizes these facts by paying careful attention to the algebraic systems of group and field, additional attention being given on occasion to the concepts of ring and integral domain. Furthermore, more careful and detailed attention to some of the fundamental properties and techniques of the algebra of inequalities is one of the important innovations of the revolution in mathematics that is effecting such great change in the high school curriculum. It has been recognized that a basic understanding of inequalities and a facility in their use are desirable goals of instruction in mathematics. Students whose programs have been so fortified will not only be stronger students of algebra but also better able to cope with problems from geometry, analysis, approximation procedures, linear programming, and many other areas of mathematical endeavor.

THE CONCEPT OF SET

Collection of elements

Probably the most significant and most basic of all the newer concepts of modern mathematics is that of *set*. An aggregate, ensemble, assemblage, class, or set is merely a collection of elements which are thought of as having some characteristic coherence. Some examples of sets are a set of dishes, a swarm of bees, a flock of sheep, a herd of cows, the fingers on one hand, the letters of the alphabet, all the positive integers, all the integers, the rational numbers, the real numbers, the points of a line, the points of a plane. The symbol used to indicate a set is illustrated by

Equivalence of sets

$A = \{a,b,c,d,e\}$, which is a set of five elements. A basic relation existing between sets is that of *equivalence,* or *one-to-one correspondence* between elements. For example, the set A above is equivalent to the set of fingers on a normally shaped hand because to each finger there corresponds one and only one element of the set A and, conversely, to each element of the set A there corresponds one and only one finger. This basic concept of equivalence of classes (sets) was recognized by Galileo. In 1638 he published a work in which he not only recognized this basic principle of equivalence of sets containing finite numbers of elements, but also announced the fundamental distinguishing characteristic of in-

Infinite set

finite sets; namely, an infinite set is one whose elements can be placed in one-to-one correspondence with only a portion of the elements of the set. Stated in clearer language, an infinite set is a set which is equivalent to a *proper subset* of itself. The set B is a proper subset of the set C if every element of B is an element of C and there is at least one element of C which is not an element of B. Galileo exhibited a one-to-one correspondence between the set of all positive integers and the proper subset of positive integers which are perfect squares. Thus the set of all positive integers was exhibited as an infinite set.

Finite set

In contrast, a finite set is a set for which a one-to-one correspondence cannot be established with any of its proper subsets. For example, the set S of all the letters of the English alphabet is a finite set. A bit of thought should make it evident that a one-to-one correspondence cannot be established between the set S and the set $A = \{a,b,c,d,e\}$ or any other proper subset of S.

The significance attached to the concepts of set and equivalence of sets was relatively incidental until toward the latter part of the nineteenth century. Although Bolzano (1850) had earlier postulated the basic distinction between finite and infinite sets and Boole (1847, 1854) had made an algebraic approach to the study of the theory of sets, it was G. Cantor (1895) who recognized the nonintuitive character of the concept of set and proceeded through the structure of a theory of sets of points to make significant contributions toward the modernization of the field of mathematical analysis.

Following in close sequence, Fréchet (1906) generalized the riemannian (1854) point-set approach to the study of geometry through his introduction of a theory of abstract spaces. Such a space consisted merely of a set of undefined elements, usually points, and a set of relations involving these elements. The geometries which evolved as distinct theories of such spaces served to provide effective techniques for the development of Einstein's general relativity theory. It was this type of geometry which did not adapt necessarily to effective classification under Klein's transformation theory.

Further evidence of the fundamental significance of set theory lies in the fact that it is possible to define natural numbers in terms of sets. Such definition not only reduces the number of undefined terms necessary for the structure of mathematical systems, but also relates the consistency of such systems to the problem of the possibility of the structure of the theory of sets as a consistent postulational system.[14]

---

[14] For an excellent discussion of some of the basic concepts of set theory see E. J. McShane, Operating with Sets, *Twenty-third Yearbook* (Washington, D.C.: National Council of Teachers of Mathematics, 1957), pp. 36–64.

It is not through these many avenues of fundamental research, which the general theory of sets has made available to mathematicians, that the concept of set has made its major contribution to the program in secondary mathematics. Rather, it is through its simplicity of idea and precision of language that it makes its contribution alike to curriculum content and instructional program.

TECHNIQUES OF DEDUCTION

Patterns of deductive thinking

The new emphasis on the postulational structure of mathematical subject matter calls attention to the need for clearer understanding of the basic techniques used in valid patterns of deductive thinking.[15] Such a pattern of argumentation is essentially one of combining statements, or propositions, into still other propositions.

Proposition

The word "proposition" is used to mean a sentence which is so clearly stated, and for which the context is so clearly defined, that it can be declared unequivocally to be either true or false. It should be evident that, while propositions may be of many different types, not all sentences are propositions. Consider, for example, these sentences:

1 Washington, D.C., is the capital city of the United States.
2 Nashville is the capital city of California.
3 Today is Wednesday.
4 Christmas day will come on Wednesday.
5 a is b.

The first three sentences are propositions, since the first one is true and the second one is false, while the third may be true or false, depending on when it is read. The fourth sentence is not a proposition since its truth or falsity cannot be determined. The fifth sentence has the form of a proposition but has no potential for truth or falsity until words or phrases are used to replace the symbols a and b. It is called a *propositional form*. The symbols may

Propositional form

be replaced in such a manner that it is a true proposition or a false proposition or, indeed, a sentence of pure nonsense would result.

Valid argument

A valid argument consists of a sequence of propositions, each implied by some previously assumed or derived proposition. The last proposition of the sequence is, of course, the conclusion derived from the argument. The statement that a proposition p implies another proposition q may be written in the form "If p, then q," or symbolically, $p \rightarrow q$. It means that if p is accepted as true (whether assumed or derived), then it follows that q is true. In other words, it is impossible for q to be false if p is true. An *im-*

[15] For an excellent discussion of such techniques see Carl B. Allendoerfer, Deductive Methods in Mathematics, *Twenty-third Yearbook* (Washington, D.C.: National Council of Teachers of Mathematics, 1957), pp. 65–99.

plication, thus, is a relation between two propositions p and q, where p is the *conditional* clause and q the *consequence* clause of the *conditional proposition* $p \rightarrow q$, or "if p, then q." The "if," or conditional, clause is frequently called the *hypothesis,* and the "then," or consequence, clause the *conclusion.* The importance to deductive reasoning of the conditional proposition is that it is the foundation of the *Simple Inference Rule,* or *Law of Detachment.*

Law of detachment

SIMPLE INFERENCE RULE

If it has been established that proposition p implies proposition q and proposition p is known to be true, then the truth of proposition q follows immediately.

Symbolically: $p \rightarrow q$, $p \therefore q$.

In the use of the Simple Inference Rule it is important to keep in mind what it states and what it does not state. It does not establish that q is true, but only that the truth of q follows as a consequence of the truth of p; in other words, that p is a sufficient condition to justify the statement of the truth of q, or that q is a necessary consequence of the truth of p. The *Law of the Syllogism* follows as a direct consequence of the Simple Inference Rule.

LAW OF THE SYLLOGISM

If it has been established that proposition p implies proposition q and, in turn, that proposition q implies proposition r, then it follows that proposition p implies proposition r.

Deductive principle

These two principles, with the Deductive Principle,[16] permit the inclusion of any established theorem among those properties derivable from the basic postulates of a particular mathematical system. For the use of the Law of the Syllogism it is extremely important to recognize the fact that the conclusion of the first proposition must be the hypothesis of the second proposition in any such sequential chain, and not the hypothesis of the converse proposition. The failure to recognize this fact is an error which is dangerous to the neophyte. A *converse* of any proposition may be obtained from the original proposition by the interchange of any number of hypotheses with the same number of conclusions. The fact that a theorem has been established never implies the truth of any of its converse theorems. It simply presents another proposition to be established as either true or false. There do exist true propositions whose converses are also true. Such a pair would be

Converse proposition

[16] Robert M. Exner and Myron F. Rosskopf, "Logic in Elementary Mathematics" (New York: McGraw-Hill Book Company, 1959), pp. 88–90.

an example of two *equivalent propositions,* that is, two propositions p and q so related to each other that each implies the other. Any such statement of equivalence between two propositions p and q is called a *biconditional proposition,* and is indicated symbolically by $p \leftrightarrow q$. To establish this biconditional relationship between two propositions it is necessary to prove the two independent conditional propositions $p \rightarrow q$ and $q \rightarrow p$. The biconditional relationship is independent of the truth or falsity of either proposition, except that, in either implication, a true hypothesis can be followed only by a true conclusion. An important consequence of the equivalence relation between two propositions is that either may be substituted for the other in any effort to build a valid argument. The double-arrow symbol may be read in any of several ways, all of which carry the same meaning. Among the more important translations of the symbol are "p if and only if q," or "q is the necessary and sufficient condition for p"; "q if and only if p," or "p is a necessary and sufficient condition for q"; or, for simplicity purposes, "p double arrow q." Note that in such translations the conditional clause is the one introduced by either "if" or "only if."

Biconditional proposition

There are other techniques of logic which may be used to derive new propositions from other propositions. The four that are of significance here are (1) from two or more propositions by *conjunction* or by *disjunction* and (2) from one proposition by *negation* or by *contraposition.* The *conjunction of two propositions,* which is formed simply by use of the connective "and," *is true if and only if each of the two propositions is true.* The hypothesis of the Law of the Syllogism is an illustration of such a conjunction.

Conjunction

The connective "or" is used to form a new proposition from two given propositions by *disjunction.* For example, a familiar proposition in dealing with integers is "if $a = 0$ or $b = 0$, then $a \times b = 0$." The hypothesis in this conditional proposition is formed by the disjunction of the two propositions $a = 0$ and $b = 0$. From what is known about integers we know that the only way the conclusion can be false is for *both* propositions of the hypothesis to be false. This is a simple illustration of the fact that, in logical usage, *the disjunction of two propositions is false only if the two component propositions are both false.*

Disjunction

The *negation* of the proposition p is customarily indicated by *not-p.* Since the basic characteristic of any proposition is that it is either true or false but not both, it follows that the negation of a true proposition must be false and the negation of a false proposition must be true. For example, the negation of "$b = 0$" is "not-$(b = 0)$," and *only* one of the two propositional forms will be a true proposition when b is replaced by an integer. As in this case, the customary symbolic wording can frequently be replaced

Negation

by a simpler symbol and a smoother-sounding translation into words. The better form here is "$b \neq 0$," which is read "b is not equal to zero."

Contrapositive

The *contrapositive* is related only to the implication, or conditional, proposition. It is most easily understood when stated in symbolic form. The contrapositive of the implication $p \rightarrow q$ is the conditional proposition not-$q \rightarrow$ not-p. Note that the hypothesis and the conclusion of the original proposition have each been negated and then interchanged. Thus the contrapositive of "If the the triangle *ABC* is isosceles, then it has at least two sides congruent" is the proposition "If the triangle *ABC* does not have at least two sides congruent, then it is not isosceles." An analysis of these two theorems reveals that they are stating exactly the same information about triangle *ABC*. This illustrates a very important characteristic relationship which exists between any conditional proposition and its contrapositive proposition: they are equivalent.

The processes of conjunction, disjunction, implication, negation, and contraposition are the fundamental techniques of logic used at the secondary level of teaching to structure a valid argument, whether in the proof of a theorem or in the solution of a problem.

THE NATURE OF PROOF

When a mathematical system has been clearly structured by the selection of the undefined elements, the definition of basic terms, and the acceptance of a fundamental set of assumptions, then the proving of theorems, i.e., derivable propositions, becomes the major concern. Every theorem has two characteristic properties, a hypothesis and a conclusion. The hypothesis is a statement, simple or compound, of the accepted relationships existing between elements of the given structure which are to be used in the search for the new relationships that are summed up in the conclusion, again

Proof of a theorem

a simple or compound statement. The *proof* of the theorem consists in the establishment of the truth of the conclusion through implications and inferences that find their original source of justification in the hypothesis. There are three distinct processes to be used in establishing the proof of any given theorem.

Synthetic Process

Basic pattern of a
synthetic argument

The synthetic process consists in drawing a series of necessary conclusions until the desired conclusion is reached. The hypothesis implies, as a necessary consequence, the hypothesis of some axiom, postulate, or previously established theorem; these hypotheses imply the conclusions associated with them, which in turn make further implications, and this chain of necessary deductions is pursued until the desired conclusion is reached. Although the simplicity, elegance, and rigor of this form of argument make it highly desirable, it is far from desirable as a sole procedure to be followed in deriving mathematical proofs. As a technique it makes no provision for the student to understand the reason for making significant constructions or applying auxiliary theorems. As a simple illustration let us consider a synthetic proof for the following theorem from geometry.

Theorem.   If two sides of a triangle are congruent, the angles opposite these sides are congruent.

Hypothesis: $\triangle ABC$, in which $\overline{AC} \cong \overline{AB}$ (Fig. 3-1)

Conclusion: $\angle B \cong \angle C$

Proof

Statements	*Reasons*
1 Bisect $\angle BAC$	1 *To bisect an angle*
2 Produce the bisector until it meets $\overline{BC}$ in D	2 *Postulate*
3 $\angle BAD \cong \angle CAD$	3 *Construction*
4 $\overline{AB} \cong \overline{AC}$	4 *Hypothesis*
5 $\overline{AD} \cong \overline{AD}$	5 *Identity*
6 In $\triangle BAD$ and CAD if $\angle BAD \cong \angle CAD$, $\overline{AB} \cong \overline{AC}$ and $\overline{AD} \cong \overline{AD}$, then $\triangle BAD \cong \triangle CAD$	6 *Two triangles are congruent if two sides and the included angle of the one are congruent, respectively, to two sides and the included angle of the other*
7 $\triangle BAD \cong \triangle CAD$	7 *Steps 3 to 6 and the Simple Inference Rule*

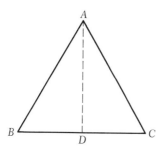

Figure 3-1

8 Two triangles, in this case BAD and CAD, are congruent if and only if their corresponding parts are congruent	**8** *Definition*
9 $\angle B \cong \angle C$	**9** *Steps 7 and 8 and the Simple Inference Rule*

The hypothesis of the given theorem, *through the auxiliary construction*, implies the conditions of the hypothesis of the congruence theorem (side, angle, side), which in turn implies through its conclusion the desired conclusion of the theorem: the angles opposite the congruent sides are congruent. The inexperienced student who has had no more insight into this theorem than that pictured here is likely to become quite confused with the content of the very first step. How did the author know to bisect the angle BAC? Many questions such as these are likely to arise, and they are certain indicators of a lack of understanding and self-confidence in the pursuit of geometric information. The neophyte in the techniques of deductive thinking needs more exercise of his intuition and opportunity for discovery than such a procedure provides.

Diagrammatically, the chain of reasoning may be written $H_1 \rightarrow H_2 \rightarrow C_2 \rightarrow C_1$, where the symbol $\rightarrow$ is to be read "implies" and H_i and C_i represent hypotheses and conclusions, respectively.

Attention is called to the fact that the "postulate" cited as a reason in step 2 of the proof may be a stated modified form of Pasch's Postulate, or in fact it could be a theorem derivable as a consequence of the postulate, which may be stated in this form: *If a straight line, in the plane of the triangle ABC, contains a point of the segment $\overline{AB}$, then it also contains a point either of the segment $\overline{AC}$ or of the segment $\overline{BC}$.* This postulate, along with Dedekind's Postulate of Continuity, is now included among the basic postulates of euclidean geometry in order to take care of some of the tacit assumptions of intersection which characterized Euclid's presentation. In the proof of any theorem it is important to make clear to the student just what has been proved. For example, in the theorem proved here, the conclusion is not that two angles "of a triangle are 'congruent,'" but that under the conditions of the hypothesis they are congruent.

Analytic-synthetic Process

Combining discovery with proof

The analytic-synthetic process is not only a principal research tool in the hands of a mature mathematician, but also an effective technique for guiding the immature student in the ways of discovery and validation of results. The analysis is the process of discovery of ways and means of arriving at desired results. The investigator considers the desired conclusion and raises the question: What relation or property is *sufficient* to justify the use of this conclusion as a true statement? Once this relation or property is found, he analyzes it for the same purpose, with the hope that ultimately he will arrive at the hypothesis of the theorem as the source of the chain of sufficient reasons. This provides one with the information and understanding necessary to construct a valid argument for the proof of the theorem. It can be accomplished by the simple reversal of the steps of the analysis. This reverse argument is called the *synthesis*. The analytic approach to the theorem given above would be as follows:

1 By what methods can two angles be proved congruent?	1 *Among other methods, two angles can be proved congruent if they can be shown to be corresponding angles of congruent △.*
2 It is possible to introduce two congruent △ into the figure?	2 *Since $\overline{AB} \cong \overline{AC}$ by hypothesis, I see that by drawing the bisector of $\angle BAC$ I shall have the two congruent △BAD and CAD.*

Analytic Process

In a sense the analytic process is a condensed form of the analytic-synthetic process. The investigator considers the desired conclusion and reasons that *it is implied* by the conclusion of some proposition. He follows such a chain of reasoning back to the hypothesis of the unproved theorem, thus closing the logical chain necessary to establish the validity of the desired conclusion. Diagrammatically, this type of proof may be written $C_1 \leftarrow C_2 \leftarrow H_2 \leftarrow H_1$, where the symbol $\leftarrow$ is read "is implied by." Of course, the chain of implications can become much more complex than that indicated here, but the basic pattern remains the same regardless of the degree of complexity.

Another important type of analytic argumentation in geometry is that which places its orientation in a cartesian coordinate system. This enables one to make use of the properties and techniques of algebra and, at more advanced levels, those of calculus as methods of study and investigation, instead of using geometric intuition and deduction. In the ordinary geometry of two or three dimensions, points are represented by ordered pairs or ordered triples, respectively, of real numbers; lines (whether curved or straight), planes, and surfaces are represented by equations and formulas involving independent and dependent variables whose common domain is the set of all real numbers. Concepts such as "angle," "on," "between," and "congruent" are given algebraic meanings. Within such a context the interrelationships between

Two forms of analytic proof

points, lines, and planes which shape and characterize significant geometric configurations become subject to the laws and techniques of the field of real numbers. The proving of geometric theorems becomes transformed into the proving of corresponding algebraic theorems or the deriving of valid implications contained in systems of equations.

The two most important types of proof are *direct proof* and *indirect proof*. Direct argumentation takes place when we try to prove a truth as stated. The attempt is made to start with a hypothesis and proceed through a chain of syllogistic reasoning to the implication of the desired conclusion. As pointed out above, it is frequently the case that a critical analysis of possible chains of sufficient conditions is *necessary* before an appropriate chain of necessary conclusions can be constructed.

Direct proof

Indirect reasoning (or indirect proof) is a method of reaching a desired conclusion through the process of investigation and elimination of *all other mutually exclusive possibilities.*

Indirect proof

A basic characteristic of indirect proof is the use of contradictory possibilities and the gradual elimination of those that can be established as inconsistent with conditions which are known or can be shown to exist. Such pairs of contradictory propositions have the following characteristics:

1   They cannot both be true at the same time.
2   They cannot both be false at the same time.
3   If one of them is false, the other must be true.
4   If one of them is true, the other must be false.

If we wish, then, to prove one of two contradictory propositions true, it is sufficient to prove that the other one is false. This, in brief, is the essence of indirect proof in its simplest form.

In summary, when a proposition to be proved is in the form of an implication ($p \rightarrow q$), it may be proved in the most appropriate of three patterns:

Three basic patterns of proof

1   Assume p and follow the pattern of direct argumentation to derive q.
2   Assume not-q and follow the pattern of direct argumentation to derive not-p.
3   Assume p and not-q and follow the pattern of indirect argumentation either (a) to derive a contradiction of p, some other accepted assumption of the system, or some previously proved proposition, or (b) to derive two contradictory propositions. It then follows that $p \rightarrow q$.

Two other forms of proof, which are of limited significance, are the *existence proof* and the *enumeration proof.* The existence proof consists in setting up an example which establishes the truth of the proposition. For example, suppose the statement is that every quadratic equation with complex coefficients has two roots of the form $a + bi$, where a and b are real numbers. The general quadratic equation in its simplest form is $x^2 + px + q = 0$, with p and q both

Existence proof

Enumeration proof

real. The two values $(-p + \sqrt{p^2 - 4q})/2$ and $(-p - \sqrt{p^2 - 4q})/2$ can be verified as solutions, and they are of the form $a + bi$. The enumeration proof, which has application in a situation involving only a small number of cases, consists in checking each case for the truth of a given proposition. For example, it would not be difficult to verify that multiplication is commutative for the positive integers modulo 4.

Counterexample

The mathematician frequently is involved in efforts to disprove a proposition rather than prove it. The use of *counterexamples* is an effective method for disproving statements. For example, the statement "$p = n^2 - n + 41$, for n a positive integer, will always produce a prime number" can be disproved by the fact that, when $n = 41$, $p = (41)^2$, which is not prime. Unfortunately, this technique is of no value in the proof of the truth of a general statement.

Contradiction

Another effective method for disproof is that of *contradiction*. This technique involves assuming the truth of some statement and then showing that a chain of logical deductions from this assumed truth leads to the contradiction of some previously established truth. This is, of course, quite similar to the method of indirect proof.

THE NATURE AND SIGNIFICANCE OF INDUCTION[17]

Although the deductive process provides the technique for drawing valid conclusions and deriving necessary consequences, the inductive process provides the means for imaginative inquiry and daring discovery. The investigation of specific cases and the observation of characteristic behavior can lead to conjectured generalizations. Such induction has played a very significant role in the history of mathematical research. Euler is credited with having said:

> The properties of the numbers known today have been mostly discovered by observation, and discovered long before their truth has been confirmed by rigid demonstration. There are even many properties of the numbers with which we are well acquainted, but which we are not yet able to prove; only observations have led us to this knowledge.[18]

Conjectures of Fermat and Goldbach

Two of the most famous illustrations of the lasting truth of the above statement are Fermat's last theorem, "The equation $a^n + b^n = c^n$ is not solvable in integers for any $n > 2$," and Goldbach's conjecture, "Every even number greater than 2 is the sum of two prime numbers." Neither of these statements has been either proved or disproved, but each has challenged many mathe-

---

[17] For a very helpful and enlightening treatment on the significance of induction as a mathematical process see G. Polya, "Mathematics and Plausible Reasoning" (Princeton, N.J.: Princeton University Press, 1954), vols. I and II.

[18] *Ibid.*, vol. I, p. 3.

maticians to engage in significant research. The immature student needs guidance in learning how to profit from considered guesses and significant hunches. He needs to be taught to search experience and experimentation for basic information upon which to base pertinent inductions.

When a student measures the interior angles of several triangles and finds that in each case the sum of their measures approximates two right angles, or when he cuts out these angles and fits them together and finds that they make a straight angle, he has the background for the induction that the sum of the measures of the interior angles of any triangle is the same as that of two right angles. If a student had two containers, one conical in shape and the other cylindrical but of the same height and diameter, it would be a very simple experiment to show that the conical container held only one-third as much as the one which was cylindrical in shape. The induction might possibly follow for this student that such a relationship between the contents of a cone and a cylinder of the same dimensions would always hold. Such inductions are important in the discovery of mathematical truths, regardless of the area of interest.

Dangers of induction

On the other hand, there are many dangers involved in making use of the inductive process. It is always dangerous to make generalizations from specific cases. In the case of the above-mentioned formula $p = n^2 - n + 41$, each of the values of n from 1 to 40 will produce a value for p which is a prime number. The one counterexample, however, when $n = 41$, is sufficient to destroy the generalization one might be tempted to make. Discoveries by induction are in the realm of probable truths. Thus, by induction, the student who experiments with the angles of a triangle or the relationship between a cone and cylinder of like dimensions can only say, in the respective cases, that (1) it is probably true that the sum of the measures of the interior angles of any triangle is the same as that of two right angles, and that (2) the volume of a cone is probably equal to one-third the volume of a cylinder of the same dimensions.

Such experiments as these lay the foundations for inductive generalizations, which in turn call for deductive demonstrations to establish validity and universality of application.

NEW RECOGNITION OF THE SIGNIFICANCE OF APPLICATION

Meaningful learning evolves from efforts to seek verifiable answers to questions inspired by thought-provoking situations. In not all such situations can mathematical principles and techniques be applied in order to determine the answers. However, in this technological age, many conjectures arise for which one desires valid proofs or convincing disproofs, and many problems challenge one to determine the possibility or impossibility of solution. Attention has already been paid to the characteristics of a valid argument in the proof of theorems whether concerned with arithmetic, algebraic, or geometric properties. Also, the significance of counterexample and authoritative negation as effective methods of disproof was emphasized. In problem situations counterexample and negation retain their effectiveness as methods for demonstrating the impossibility of solution.

Proof and problem solving

While proof of a theorem and solution of a problem have many procedural similarities, there are differences of great significance, particularly to problem solving. A conjecture is stated in the context of a particular mathematical system, which places at one's disposal the basic postulates, definitions, and derived properties of the system. The same is true for any given problem with mathematical orientation. The same techniques of deduction may be used in the building of a valid argument, and, where numerical computations are involved, the same operational procedures are available. The connectives of logic may be used to cast a proposed conjecture in the framework of a conditional statement of implication. Once this has been done, the building of the argument calls, first, for a clear enunciation and understanding of the hypothesis and conclusion and, second, for the use of the techniques of deduction within appropriate patterns of proof to build a valid argument. The statement of a problem is usually in some verbal form which requires a careful analysis to determine what the problem is, what the pertinent data are, and within what mathematical system one is to work. The proof of a theorem requires the building of a sequential chain of necessary conditions, with the hypothesis as the first link and the conclusion as the final link. After the equation, or equations, have been derived from the data of a problem, the same pattern of building a sequential chain is followed, with the equation as the first link in the chain, and the final link being a necessary conclusion as to what the solution must be if one exists. There still remains one very important step to be taken before the problem-solving process can be considered complete. The necessary conclusion must be tested to see whether or not it is sufficient. If it is, then the solution set can be identified; if it is not, then it can be stated that the problem has no solution within the context of its statement.

Consider the fractional equation

$$\frac{2x}{x-5} - 4 = \frac{10}{x-5}$$

within the field of real numbers. We may use this equation to frame a theorem to be proved or a problem to be solved.

Theorem.   If x is a real number such that

$$\frac{2x}{x-5} - 4 = \frac{10}{x-5} \qquad \text{then} \qquad x = 5$$

Problem.   Find the solution set within the field of real numbers such that

$$\frac{2x}{x-5} - 4 = \frac{10}{x-5}$$

The hypothesis and conclusion of the theorem are:

Hypothesis: x is a real number, *and* $\dfrac{2x}{x-5} - 4 = \dfrac{10}{x-5}$

Conclusion: $x = 5$

In the usual process of solving the problem as stated, the first step would be to assume the hypothesis of the theorem. The principles of deduction would then reveal that the conclusion, $x = 5$, follows. In the proof of the theorem this would be the end of the investigation. In the solution of the problem all we have at this point is that, if the equation is *assumed* to be true, then x must have the value 5. In other words, $x = 5$ is a necessary condition for the equation to have a solution. When this condition is tested for sufficiency, it is discovered that $x = 5$ is an impossible value since, in two of the terms of the equation, there would be a division by zero. In the solution of any problem the work should never be considered as completed until such questions of consistency have been investigated carefully.

Difficulties in problem solving

The difficulties inherent in problem solving fall into four distinct categories: *comprehension, structure, operation,* and *judgment.* The *flowchart for problem solving* in Fig. 3-2 presents an analysis of the sources of each type of difficulty and instructional patterns for dealing with them. In each case, key references (1*a*, 1*b*, etc.) connect the chart with the more detailed discussions found in the following paragraphs. Row 1, reading down, shows types; row 2, sources; row 3, instructional techniques; and row 4, diagnosis. Comprehension problems are always identified *a*; structure, *b*; operation, *c*; and judgment, *d.*

Comprehension difficulty

The first type of difficulty which one confronts in the attempt to determine whether a given problem has a solution or not is that of *comprehension* (1*a*). Is there a clear understanding of just what the problem is? What data are to be used in seeking a solution? Within what context, or restrictions, is the solution to be sought? And, what type of information is to be furnished by the solution, if and when it is found? These are types of questions to which the answers must be known before an intelligent attack can be made on any problem.

If a student is confronted with any such difficulty, his troubles very likely are due to vocabulary weakness, inefficient reading habits, inability to concentrate on details, inability to distinguish known from unknown, inability to phrase the essential part of the problem in one's own words, or inability to detect hidden questions, interpretations, and implications (2*a*). Instructional techniques (3*a*) which might be used in an effort to remove such sources of difficulty are specific training in the use of a dictionary; questions and answers to discover hidden questions and meanings; training in asking oneself pertinent questions; emphasis on slow, careful, and critical reading; attention to problem patterns; and practice in telling in one's own words what he has read. After such a program of instruction a carefully designed diagnostic test (4) should be administered. If the test results indicate success in removing this difficulty, attention may be directed to other types of problem-solving difficulty which may be present; otherwise further individual attention and remedial procedures will be necessary.

Structure difficulty

The next type of difficulty likely to cause trouble is that of determining the *structure* of the solving process (1*b*). Some readily identifiable sources (2*b*) of such difficulty are inability to distinguish between essential and nonessential data, inability to recognize basic relationships, inability to identify pertinent operational processes, absence of systematic procedure, poor study habits, and unwillingness to persist in effort. Among the techniques of instruction (3*b*) which might be used to overcome such stumbling blocks are:

1   Direct attention to the selection of pertinent data with such questions as: What is given? What are you required to find? What do you need to know in order to answer the questions raised? Is any additional information needed? If so, what is its nature? Why do you need to use certain data and not other data supplied in the statement of the problem?
2   Identify basic relationships, pertinent formulas, hidden questions which need to be answered, and significant implications to be followed.
3   Require the drawing and labeling of pertinent diagrams.
4   Emphasize the function and basic characteristics of each of the fundamental operations.
5   Have students construct verbal problem situations from given data.
6   Have students practice translating from English sentences to mathematical symbols and from mathematical symbols to English sentences, expressed in good grammatical structure.
7   Insist on neatness in all work.
8   Discourage haphazard guessing, but encourage thoughtful and careful appraisals and estimates.

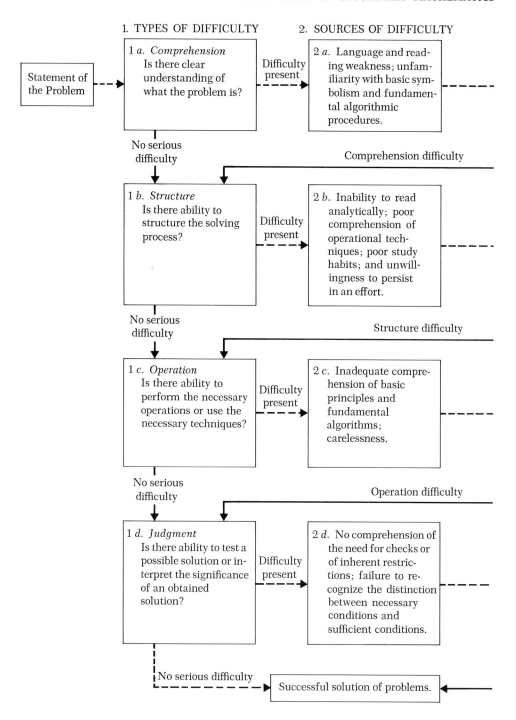

Figure 3-2
Flowchart for problem solving.

3. INSTRUCTIONAL TECHNIQUES 4. DIAGNOSIS

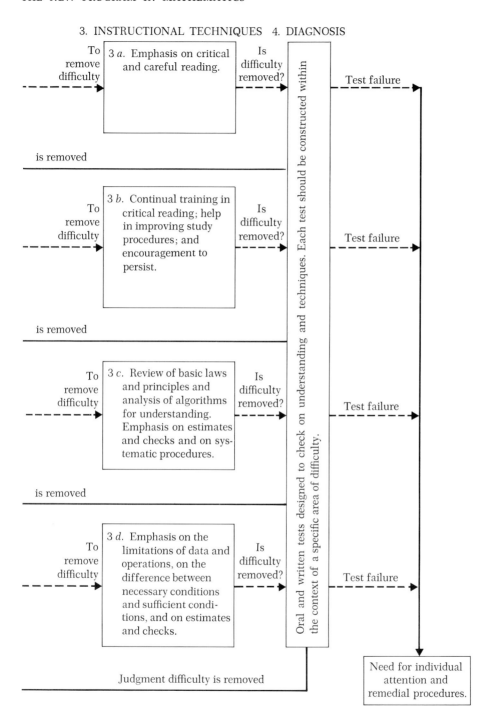

9 Emphasize and help develop good study habits and systematic patterns of work.

10 Insist on persistent effort and on concentrated and sustained attention.

11 Help students acquire the ability to formulate similar problems which are of the same basic pattern but not so difficult to solve.

Such a concentrated instructional program to overcome the problems of structure should be followed by a diagnostic test (4) such as that suggested previously in connection with the difficulties of problem comprehension. The same procedures should be followed in the construction of the test and in the use made of the information which it provides.

The third type of difficulty associated with problem solving is that of being able to perform the *operation* needed to accomplish the solution (1c). Among the sources (2c) of this type of difficulty are inadequate comprehension of basic principles, poor understanding of the fundamental laws of the mathematical system within which the problem is stated, unfamiliarity with the implications of the basic algorisms and formulas of the system, and carelessness in working procedures. The more helpful instructional procedures (3c) are review of basic laws and principles for clearer understanding, practice in the operational mechanics, analysis of algorisms and formulas for better comprehension of the structure of the mathematical system which provides the context of effort, instruction in the techniques of significant estimation and careful checking, and emphasis on systematic procedures and careful work.

Again, the pattern of diagnostic testing (4) should be used to evaluate the success of the instructional efforts and serve as a guide to subsequent procedure.

The fourth, and final, category of difficulty in problem solving is that of proper *judgment* of the significance of the obtained results and in the use made of them (1d). The most serious sources (2d) of such difficulty are lack of recognition of the need for systematic and careful checks of any obtained results, unfamiliarity with the most appropriate techniques for checking, inability to make "educated" estimates, and inability to diagnose and interpret restrictions imposed by the data and the domain of operation. The corrective instructional program (3d) should emphasize the distinction between the basic significance of necessary and sufficient conditions in a problem situation, the techniques of making estimates, the need for checking against the original problem situation, and the nature and significance of physical and operational restrictions. The results of this instructional program, as in the case of all others, should be evaluated by means of a careful pattern of diagnosis (4).

Operation difficulty

Judgment difficulty

In any program like the one outlined here, a student who requires additional individual attention or remedial procedures should be allowed to re-enter the program at a point indicated by appropriate follow-up diagnosis.

Solvable, unsolvable, and unsolved problems

The present new emphasis on applications of mathematics recognizes the fact that a great deal of the significant mathematics of today has developed from beginnings motivated by the desire and need to solve problems. This is true whether we are dealing with the myriad of *solvable* problems such as those which our environment creates daily, the *unsolvable* problems such as the three famous problems of antiquity (the trisection of an angle, the duplication of a cube, and the squaring of a circle), or the *unsolved* problems such as the discovery of proofs for Fermat's theorem and Goldbach's conjecture or a formula to yield all the prime numbers. New emphasis in instruction and new adaptations of subject-matter content will continue to pay attention to the motivation and direction of new applications as important instruments in giving shape to the new program in secondary mathematics.

EXERCISES

1 Give two illustrations of how the new point of view in mathematics is affecting the secondary school program.

2 Give two illustrations of the use of new subject-matter content in the mathematics program of the secondary school.

3 Give two illustrations of the importance of mathematical applications in the teaching of secondary mathematics.

4 What are the differences in the implications of the concept of a postulate as a "self-evident truth" and an "accepted assumption"?

5 As a mathematical system, what is the definition of a group? A ring? An integral domain? A field?

6 What is the significance of Klein's definition of geometry in terms of a group of transformations?

7 What is meant by the basic structure of arithmetic? Of algebra? Of geometry?

8 What are the basic postulates of lobachevskian geometry? Of riemannian geometry? Of euclidean geometry?

9 What are the implications of this statement: One man's postulate may be another man's theorem?

10 What is meant by the consistency of a system of postulates?

11 Distinguish between relative and absolute consistency.

12 What is meant by the independence of a set of postulates?

13 Discuss the relative significance of independence, completeness, and categoricalness as contrasted with the consistency of a set of postulates. Draw your contrasts from both a logical and a pedagogical point of view.

14 What were some of the tacit assumptions which Euclid made in his geometry? In what ways are precautions taken in the new program in mathematics to avoid such errors?

15 Give three illustrations of how cartesianism has affected the subject matter of the geometry of the secondary school.

16 What are some of the major differences in the subject matter of trigonometry as taught in the traditional manner and in the pattern of the new program in secondary mathematics?

17 What do we mean when we speak of different algebras and their arithmetics?

18 In what ways is the concept of a number field of significance in the study of algebra?

19 Use the concept of ordered pairs to construct an illustration of a relation which is not a function and also of a relation which is a function.

20 How can the concept of relation be used in building a definition of a function?

21 Use the concept of a group to build the definition of a number field.

22 Give a definition of each of these logic terms: proposition, conjunction, disjunction, negation, contrapositive, implication, conditional proposition, biconditional proposition.

23 Construct an example to illustrate the use of the Simple Inference Rule.

24 Construct an example to illustrate the use of the Law of the Syllogism.

25 In each of the following cases two statements are given, one labeled "condition" and the other "situation." First, determine whether the condition is necessary, sufficient, or necessary and sufficient for the given situation; and second, use the two statements in a grammatically correct English sentence with the proper connective "if," "only if," or "if and only if."
   a. Condition: A triangle is isosceles.
   Situation: A triangle is equilateral.
   b. Condition: $x^n - y^n$ is divisible by $x - y$.
   Situation: n is an even integer.
   c. Condition: A number is divisible by 15.
   Situation: A number is divisible by 3.

26 What is meant by the deductive process?

27 Distinguish between induction and deduction; synthesis and analysis.

28 Why, in a deductive science, must there be undefined terms and accepted assumptions?

29 Distinguish between direct and indirect proof.

30 Distinguish between an indirect proof and a proof by contraposition.

BIBLIOGRAPHY

Adler, Irving: "The New Mathematics" (New York: The John Day Company, Inc., 1958).

———: The Changes Taking Place in Mathematics, *Mathematics Teacher,* **55** (1962), 441–451.

———: What Shall We Teach in High School Mathematics?, *Mathematics Teacher,* **61** (1968), 226–238.

Allendoerfer, Carl B.: The Narrow Mathematician, *American Mathematical Monthly,* **69** (1962), 461–469.

Andree, Richard V.: Modern Trigonometry, *Mathematics Teacher,* **48** (1955), 82–83.

Barnett, I. A.: "Some Ideas about Number Theory" (Washington, D.C.: National Council of Teachers of Mathematics, 1961.) (Pamphlet.)

Barry, Edward H.: "Introduction to Geometrical Transformations" (Boston: Prindle, Weber & Schmidt, Incorporated, 1966).

Beckenbach, Edwin, and Richard Bellman: "An Introduction to Inequalities" (New York: Random House, Inc., 1961).

Bergamini, David: "Mathematics," Life Science Library (New York: Time Inc., 1963).

Blumenthal, L. H.: "A Modern View of Geometry" (San Francisco: W. H. Freeman and Company, 1961).

Botts, Truman, and Leonard Pikaart: Mathematics from the Modern Point of View, *Mathematics Teacher,* **54** (1961), 498–504.

Bruck, R. H.: Recent Advances in the Foundations of Euclidean Plane Geometry, *American Mathematical Monthly,* **62** (1955), 2–17.

Buck, Charles: An Alternative Definition for Equivalence Relations, *Mathematics Teacher,* **60** (1967), 124–125.

Cogan, Edward J.: The Handmaiden Becomes of Age, *American Mathematical Monthly,* **70** (1963), 554–560.

Commission on Mathematics of College Entrance Examination Board: "Introduction to Algebra from the Point of View of Mathematical Structure" (Princeton, N.J.: Educational Testing Service, 1958). (Pamphlet.)

Duren, W. L., Jr.: The Maneuvers in Set Thinking, *Mathematics Teacher,* **51** (1958), 322–335.

Eves, Howard, and Carroll V. Newsom: "An Introduction to the Foundations and Fundamental Concepts of Mathematics," rev. ed. (New York: Holt, Rinehart and Winston, Inc., 1965).

Exner, Robert M., and Myron F. Rosskopf: "Logic in Elementary Mathematics" (New York: McGraw-Hill Book Company, 1959).

George, F. H.: "Computer Arithmetic" (New York: Pergamon Press, Inc., 1966).

———: "An Introduction to Digital Computing" (New York: Pergamon Press, Inc., 1966).

Goldstein, M.: Computer Languages, *American Mathematical Monthly,* **72**, part II (1965), 141–146.

Graves, Lawrence M.: The Postulates of Algebra, and Non-Archimedean Number Systems, *Mathematics Teacher,* **52** (1959), 72–77.

Hamilton, Norman T., and Joseph Landin: "Set Theory, the Structure of Arithmetic" (Englewood Cliffs, N.J.: Allyn and Bacon, Inc., 1961).

Hammel, Arnold: Verifying the Associative Property for Finite Groups, *Mathematics Teacher*, **61** (1968), 136–139.

Hamming, R. W.: Impact of Computers, *American Mathematical Monthly*, **72**, part II (1965), 1–7.

Henkin, Leon W., Norman Smith, Verne J. Varican, and Michael J. Walsh: "Retracing Elementary Mathematics" (New York: The Macmillan Company, 1962).

Johnson, Donovan R., and Gerald R. Rising: Guidelines for Teaching Mathematics (Belmont, Calif., Wadsworth Publishing Company, Inc., 1967).

Johnson, Richard E.: "Vector Algebra" (Boston: Prindle, Weber & Schmidt, Incorporated, 1966).

Jones, Burton, W.: Miniature Number Systems, *Mathematics Teacher*, **51** (1958), 226–231.

———: Miniature Geometries, *Mathematics Teacher*, **52** (1959), 66–71.

———: "Modular Arithmetic" (New York: Blaisdell Publishing Company, 1964).

Kane, Robert B.: Linear Programming: An Aid to Decision Making, *Mathematics Teacher*, **53** (1960), 177–179.

Kelley, John L.: "Introduction to Modern Algebra" (Princeton, N.J.: D. Van Nostrand Company, Inc., 1960).

Kemeny, John G.: Rigor vs. Intuition in Mathematics, *Mathematics Teacher*, **54** (1961), 66–74.

Levi, Howard: "Foundations of Geometry and Trigonometry" (Englewood Cliffs, N.J.: Prentice-Hall, Inc., 1960).

May, Kenneth O.: What Does "If" Mean?, *Mathematics Teacher*, **48** (1955), 10–12.

Meder, Albert E., Jr.: Modern Mathematics and Its Place in the Secondary School, *Mathematics Teacher*, **50** (1957), 418–424.

———: What Is Wrong with Euclid?, *Mathematics Teacher*, **51** (1958), 578–584.

Meserve, Bruce E.: New Trends in Algebra and Geometry, *Mathematics Teacher*, **55** (1962), 452–461.

———: Euclidean and Other Geometries, *Mathematics Teacher*, **60** (1967), 2–11.

——— and Max Sobel: "Mathematics for Secondary Schools" (Englewood Cliffs, N.J.: Prentice-Hall, Inc., 1962).

Miller, Norman: "Limits: The Concept and Its Role in Mathematics" (New York: Blaisdell Publishing Company, 1964).

Modenov, P. S., and A. S. Parkhomenko: "Geometric Transformations," vols. I and II (New York: Academic Press Inc., 1965).

Mosteller, F., R. E. K. Rourke, and G. B. Thomas, Jr.: "Probability and Statistics" (Reading, Mass.: Addison-Wesley Publishing Company, Inc., 1962).

Mueller, Francis J.: The Public Image of "New Mathematics," *Mathematics Teacher*, **59** (1966), 618–623.

National Council of Teachers of Mathematics: "Insights into Modern Mathematics," *Twenty-third Yearbook*, and "The Growth of Mathematical Ideas," *Twenty-fourth Yearbook* (Washington, D.C.: The Council, 1957 and 1959).

———: "Experiences in Mathematical Discovery" (Washington, D.C.: The Council, 1966). (Five pamphlets.)

Niven, Ivan: "Numbers, Rational and Irrational" (New York: Random House, Inc., 1961).

Northrop, E. P.: Modern Mathematics and the Secondary School Curriculum, *Mathematics Teacher*, **48** (1955), 386–393.

Oettinger, A. G.: Computational Linguistics, *American Mathematical Monthly*, **72**, part II (1965), 147–150.

Pedley, Arthur H.: Complex Numbers and Vectors in High School Mathematics, *Mathematics Teacher*, **53** (1960), 198–201.

Pólya, G.: "Mathematical Discovery," vol. I (1962), vol. II (1965) (New York: John Wiley & Sons, Inc.).

Rees, Mina: The Nature of Mathematics, *Mathematics Teacher*, **55** (1962), 434–440.

Richtmyer, R. D.: The Post-war Computer Development, *American Mathematical Monthly*, **72**, part II (1965), 8–14.

Robinson, George A.: Useful Generalizations of the Concept of Function, *Mathematics Teacher*, **52** (1959), 444–448.

Rosenberg, Herman: The Changing Concept of Trigonometry as a School Subject, *Mathematics Teacher*, **51** (1958), 246–252.

Selby, Samuel M., and Leonard Sweet: "Sets—Relations—Functions: An Introduction," 2d ed. (New York: McGraw-Hill Book Company, 1963).

Spencer, Donald D.: Computers: Their Past, Present, and Future, *Mathematics Teacher*, **61** (1968), 65–75.

Szabo, Steven: Several Ways of Translating a Conditional Sentence: A Dialogue, *Mathematics Teacher*, **61** (1968), 22–24.

Tierney, John A.: Trigonometric Functions of a Real Number, *Mathematics Teacher*, **50** (1957), 38–39.

Tierney, John A.: The Law of Contraposition, *Mathematics Teacher*, **53** (1960), 189–190.

Troyer, Robert: Rotations, Angles, and Trigonometry, *Mathematics Teacher*, **61** (1968), 123–129.

Weisert, C. H.: Computer Systems, *American Mathematical Monthly*, **72,** part II, 150–156.

Wiebe, Arthur J.: "Foundations of Mathematics"

(New York: Holt, Rinehart and Winston, Inc., 1962).

Wiseman, John D., Jr.: Introducing Proof with a Finite System, *Mathematics Teacher*, **54** (1961), 251–352.

Wren, F. Lynwood: The "New Mathematics" in Historical Perspective, *Mathematics Teacher*, **62** (1969).

modern curriculum problems in mathematics

The revolution
answers some
questions, poses
others

The curriculum
change springs
from four sources

Widespread
concern over the
mathematics
program

The advent of the recent so-called "revolution" in secondary school mathematics produced on a broad front a concerted attack on many curriculum problems in mathematics. Good research usually poses more questions than it answers. So it is with the recent curricular upheaval—it has created more curriculum problems than it has solved. Other persistent problems have been untouched by recent activity.

The movement sprang from four clearly defined sources: (1) the great hiatus existing between the mathematics curriculum of the past and the spirit and genius of modern mathematical thought, (2) the misdirected emphases in instructional patterns, (3) the mathematical inadequacies of so many high school graduates, and (4) the increased mathematical needs of high school graduates who enter college. Some have argued that in spite of the fact that mathematics is one of the fastest-growing of all the sciences, it is being taught in our schools as though nothing new had happened in at least three centuries. Others have felt that the program of instruction has tended to overemphasize the manipulative aspects of mathematics, with entirely too little attention being paid to the conceptual and structural aspects of the subject. Expressions of concern over the mathematical inadequacies of high school graduates have been heard for many years, but they are given new point and urgency because of the increased and growing proportion of high school graduates who go to college and the greater mathematical demands made upon them when they get there.

Concern over the mathematical program in our schools is both widespread and acute. It is found among laymen as well as among professional people. The significance of this current educational problem is emphasized by the work of committees representing the thinking of prominent professional organizations and by extensive experimentation being carried on for the purpose of discovering appropriate modification of curriculum content and instructional procedures.

The new programs have had no dearth of critics. One of the more legitimate complaints against the traditional program is that it had many shortcomings from the mathematical standpoint.

Efforts at revising the secondary school mathematics curriculum have been cooperative efforts between mathematicians and educators. The results bear the mark of the mathematicians to a much greater extent than that of the educators. Yet the most severe attacks on the new program have come from professional mathematicians.[1]

The new program has its critics

Criticisms of the new program, in general, have been aimed at two weaknesses: (1) lack of regard for applications and (2) lack of concern for pedagogical principles. To these a third should be added: lack of proper orientation on the part of teachers.[2]

Shortcomings of the new program

GRADES SEVEN AND EIGHT

The mathematics program of grades 7 to 9 has been a problem of great concern for many years. The varying patterns of administrative organization (6-3-3, 6-6, 7-5, and 8-4) contribute confusion to the basic educational philosophy which should underlie the program of the junior high school; distorted interpretations of educational values becloud the objectives of instruction; unrealistic standards of competency for promotion from lower grades tend to temper the challenge of instruction; and inadequate preparation of teachers restricts the depth of understanding in presentation of materials. It is a well-known fact that, during these impressionistic years, many boys and girls lose interest in mathematics. Some observers feel that this is due, in large measure, to the overemphasis on "socialized arithmetic" in the seventh and eighth grades. The Secondary School Curriculum Committee states:

Special problems of junior high school

> In grades seven and eight much of the time is given to so-called social applications, some of which seem inappropriate at this level. Few new mathematical ideas are introduced. Teachers often report that the traditional courses at this level offer little challenge to the upper 50 per cent of the pupils, and that review and maintenance provided for the lower 50 per cent usually serve only to deaden their interest because emphasis usually is on drill, with little provision for bringing out deeper insight and understanding.[3]

Others feel that adverse conditioning in the home, among their peers, and by their teachers is a prime cause for poor attitudes of students toward mathematics.[4]

The Commission on Mathematics of the College Entrance Examination Board recommends a program for grades 7 and 8 which it

[1] On the Mathematics Curriculum of the High School, *American Mathematical Monthly*, **69** (1962), 189–193.
[2] Herbert Fremont, New Mathematics and Old Dilemmas, *Mathematics Teacher*, **60** (1967), 715–719.
[3] Report of the Secondary School Curriculum Committee, *Mathematics Teacher*, **52** (1959), 403.
[4] Henry S. Dyer, Robert Kalin, and Frederick M. Lord, "Problems in Mathematical Education" (Princeton, N.J.: Educational Testing Service, 1956).

feels the college-capable can cover in 1½ years. The outline of this program is as follows:

(1) *Fundamental operations and numeration*—whole numbers and fractions (common and decimal), place value in the decimal system and other systems (particularly the binary), arithmetic mean, and a knowledge of square root including methods of approximating square roots of whole numbers.

(2) *Ratio*—making comparisons and scale drawings, per cent with moderate treatment of applications.

(3) *Measurement*—English and metric systems, geometric measurements, use of ruler and protractor, indirect measurement of lengths, areas, volumes, etc.

(4) *Relationships among geometric elements*—parallel, perpendicular, intersecting, and oblique lines (in a plane and in space), various types of angles and triangles, Pythagorean relation, sums of interior angles of polygons, symmetry about a point and a line.

(5) *Graphs and formulas*—reading and construction of bar graphs, line graphs, pictograms, circle graphs, and continuous line graphs, meaning of a scale, basic formulas.[5]

Recommendations of the Commission

The content and pattern of instruction in the eighth grade have created a problem of greater concern than has that of the seventh grade. There are many who feel rather strongly that, particularly in this grade, the mathematics program is seriously impaired because of its incidental relationship to the analysis and solution of social problems which, at best, are of questionable interest and value to immature boys and girls. Mathematics cannot be taught effectively at any grade level when presented only in such incidental fashion. The programs of both grades 7 and 8 thus constitute a fundamental curriculum problem of current interest and significance. The newer programs are now including units from such areas as nondecimal numeration, factoring and primes, nonmetric geometry, techniques of deductive reasoning, averages, finite systems, measurement, approximations, and probability and statistics.

Some feel that the first course in algebra should become the program for the eighth grade. Others would rather extend the instruction in this grade to more advanced properties of number and more general treatment of graphs. Many feel that, whatever the curriculum content of the mathematics program for grades 7 and 8 might be, it must be mathematics, with the emphasis on adaptation to social usage held incidental and used only as an instructional aid in the systematic development of the fundamental mathematical concepts and principles of pertinent concern.

It is generally agreed that mathematics through grade 9 should be required of all students. It does not follow that all should be studying the same mathematics, at the same rate, with the same emphasis. Experience with formal algebra in the eighth grade has

[5] "Report of the Commission on Mathematics of the College Entrance Examination Board" (New York: College Entrance Examination Board, 1959), p. 19.

not been consistent. The evidence seems to indicate that carefully selected students under a competent teacher have a high probability of success with formal algebra in the eighth grade; but the use of formal algebra as the normal eighth-grade program has not been too successful.

Role of algebra

The two ideas that, on the one hand, junior high school mathematics should be a part of the common course for all students and, on the other, that alternative tracks of instruction should be provided are not incompatible.

The need for junior high school work that is exploratory and required of all is an accepted principle. There seems reason to believe that content roughly agreeing with that recommended by the Commission on Mathematics[6] can be covered by the normally progressing students in two years, with formal algebra in grade 9. For some accelerated students the same work can be condensed into a year, with formal algebra in grade 8. The same work can be covered in three years by the slower students, with formal algebra an option in grade 10. Courses of one, two, and three years' duration, but covering the same basic material with appropriate variations, seem to provide a promising approach to a solution for the problem of ability levels in the junior high school, as well as for the vexing problem of general mathematics in grade 9.

Core program in variable time

GRADE NINE

The philosophy of the junior high school has been defined in terms of four fundamental principles or broad objectives: (1) better articulation between the elementary school and the secondary school; (2) exploration, revelation, and guidance; (3) interpretation and control of environment; and (4) motivation. Under the influence of this philosophy and the inspiration of such men as Felix Klein of Germany, John Perry of Scotland, and E. H. Moore of the United States, there developed early in this century a demand for a noncompartmentalized form of organization of subject matter in the mathematics program of the secondary school.

Objectives

General mathematics

Through the early pioneering efforts of a few individuals, a start in this direction had been made for the courses in the junior high school by 1920. This movement was strengthened and given great impetus by the 1923 Reorganization Report of the National Committee on Mathematical Requirements. Within a few years noncompartmentalized courses called "General Mathematics" had come to represent the typical offering in grades 7 and 8, and had also gained a firm foothold as an alternative to elementary algebra

[6] *Ibid.*

in a two-track program for the ninth grade. The recommendations of the Committee on Mathematical Requirements (1923), the Joint Commission (1940), and the Commission on Post-War Plans (1945), all gave support to the significance of such a program in general mathematics for grade 9. The basic purposes of such a program, as designed by its original proponents, were to show the interrelationships between the fundamental structure and techniques of the major areas of mathematical endeavor and to build for the student an understanding and competence in mathematics essential for intelligent living amid the quantitative demands of a technological environment. It was thus designed as a second-track program for those pupils who had neither aptitude nor interest to justify their pursuing the course in first-year algebra.

While the two-track approach has continued to characterize the program of the ninth grade in most schools, it is unfortunately true that narrow interpretations of some of the implications of the pragmatism which has predominated in our educational philosophy of recent years succeeded in seriously misdirecting the emphasis in presentation of the program in general mathematics. This diversion of basic purpose has followed two patterns: (1) The mathematical content has been made incidental to the social situation, and (2) the content has been allowed to degenerate in many areas into that of a refresher program of drill, trivial problem solving, and repetition of the mechanics of operation. This fact has caused great concern among those interested in a bona fide program in mathematics which can be of distinct benefit to educable boys and girls of ninth-grade stature.

Misdirection of second track

One possible solution to the problem of differentiation among ability levels in the ninth grade is to provide algebra for all, but with varying degrees of emphasis and levels of attainment. The Secondary School Curriculum Committee predicted that:

Algebra for all

> All students may eventually study the same algebra, but not at the same depth of understanding, at the same time and rate, with the same application, nor necessarily in the same sequence. Thus, for example, in the ninth school year, one group may be doing a development of the number system from an axiomatic point of view, another group may be studying positive and negative numbers as usually presented in an inductive manner, while a third less able group may be making use of the basic concepts of algebra to help strengthen their understanding of arithmetic processes.[7]

In any event, mathematics for the slow learner remains a nagging problem throughout the junior high school years, and in the ninth grade in particular.

In recent years the algebra program has been subjected to a critical analysis and revision, principally in the direction of modernization of content and treatment. Set terminology and con-

---

[7] Secondary School Curriculum Committee, *op. cit.*, pp. 408–409.

cepts are used for refinement of basic definitions and principles. There has been a marked shift of emphasis away from learning merely to follow stipulated rules of manipulation. Instead, major emphasis is placed on learning the structure of mathematical systems, with the hope that the correct manipulative techniques will evolve from an understanding of this structure. There has been wide acceptance of the recommendations of the Commission on Mathematics embodied in the following statement:

Changes in the algebra curriculum

> In the proposed program, the mechanics or formal manipulations in algebra are the same as hitherto taught, and the subject matter is largely the same. The difference is principally in concept, in terminology, in some symbolism, and in the introduction of a rather large segment of new work dealing with inequalities, treated both algebraically and graphically. Solution sets of inequalities involving two variables are also studied.

> The new emphasis in the study of algebra is upon the understanding of the fundamental ideas and concepts of the subject, such as the nature of number systems and the basic laws for addition and multiplication (commutative, associative, distributive). The application of these laws in various number systems, with emphasis on the generality of the laws, the meanings of conditional equations and identities and inequalities, is stressed. The nature of a function—in particular, the linear, the quadratic, exponential, and logarithmic functions—is also discussed.[8]

Emphasis on understanding

In spite of the sweeping changes that have come about in recent years, many questions remain to be answered, and many problems of curriculum content and instructional procedure in the mathematics program of grades 7 to 9 remain a challenge. Neither the mathematically disadvantaged nor the mathematically gifted are being served very well. Only through considered deliberation and careful experimentation of interested and informed groups can effective solutions be found. There is need for massive longitudinal studies.

A continuing challenge

THE SENIOR HIGH SCHOOL

One of the major criticisms directed against the mathematics program of the senior high school is that it has consisted largely of unrelated specialties and manipulative procedures. Artificial barriers have existed between arithmetic, algebra, geometry, and trigonometry. The needed extensions of our number system from the domain of the positive rational numbers of the elementary school have been made mostly by rule and rote rather than by discovering and understanding. Algebra still has had the ring of the seventeenth-century pattern of learning the proper tricks to perform in order to arrive at the solution of problems. Geometry, when compared with Euclid's "Elements," of 300 B.C., has pre-

Curricular defects

[8] Commission on Mathematics, *op. cit.*, pp. 21–22.

sented basically the same subject content but a psychologically thinned presentation, which too frequently has removed significant challenge rather than providing better motivation and learning conditions. Trigonometry continued to emphasize computation and triangle solving and to give too little attention to the analytic aspects and behavior of the circular functions.

Contemporary thinking seeks ways of correcting these defects by stressing broad, pervasive unifying concepts which thread through all the branches of mathematics and which can give coherence and structure to the whole subject.

The modern emphasis

The modern emphasis in mathematics points out that the true essence of mathematics lies in logic, decision making, and systematic search for the underlying structure of any given system or situation. Instruction in mathematics formerly tended toward the search for the solutions of various types of quantitative problems as they arose. There were some who even recommended the grouping of problems by types and adapting the solution techniques to the individual characteristics of respective types. Now the emphasis is directed toward the search for underlying principles and basic structure as guides to fundamental generalizations and abstractions. "Technology is subject to rapid change. Training in specifics can, and may, soon become obsolete. On the other hand, a person with fundamental training in mathematics will have the background for making adaptations to applications, even to those not now foreseen."[9] This quotation may very well be considered the basic theme directing the thinking and activity of those interested in essential revision of the mathematics curriculum of the secondary school. This should not be taken to imply that applications and the techniques of problem solving are to be abandoned. These should and will continue to be very significant parts of all the courses, but relatively, the structural aspects of mathematics should be the main focus of instructional efforts.

The purpose of applications

Those who criticize the modern program for its indifference to applications may be right for the wrong reason. The secondary school mathematics program cannot become handmaid to any one type of application, whether it be physical science or behavioral science. The crucial focus is, and should remain, the mathematical system as opposed to the applications that may ultimately be made. Applications in mathematical instruction are a means to an end. The applications should serve as motivation for new learning, and more importantly, they should serve to illuminate, to clarify, and to aid in retaining the mathematics.

Mathematical structure

The content of algebra is no longer defined largely in terms of manipulative skills; rather, the emphasis is placed on mathematical structure. Attention is directed to the postulational bases for

[9] Secondary School Curriculum Committee, *op. cit.*, pp. 411–412.

algebraic systems and to the use of deductive techniques in development of the basic properties of such a system. Such concepts as group, integral domain, and field are used to clarify and simplify algebraic language.

The language of sets has been absorbed into the language of secondary school mathematics. For example, a *variable* may be defined as a symbol which represents any one of a set of elements.

New terminology

The *set of elements* is called the domain of the variable. Similarly, a *relation* may be defined as a set of ordered pairs (x,y) such that, to each value of the first element x, there corresponds at least one value for the second element. The domain of the first element is called the domain of the relation, and that of the second element, the range of the relation. If to each value of the first element there corresponds one and only one value of the second element, then the relation is called a *function*.

Equations and inequalities may be thought of as sentences which make statements about the variables included. These statements may be thought of as *set selectors*, in that they select values of the variables for which the sentence is true. Thus, if the *universal set*, the set from which all usable values are to be selected, is the set of all integers, the sentence $x + 1 = 5$ selects the value 4; the sentence $y = x^2$, when x is assigned arbitrary values, selects all integral squares. To each first element x there corresponds one and only one second element y. Thus $y = x^2$ defines a function, although there are two distinct first elements which produce the same second element. For example, $(2,4)$ and $(-2,4)$ both make $y = x^2$ a true statement. The sentence $y > x^2$ also selects values of y for any given x, but in this case, to each first element x there correspond infinitely many values of the second element y. For example, if $x = 2$, then y can be any integer greater than 4. Thus $y > x^2$ defines a relation, and not a function.

Inequalities should receive the recognition they are due. Simultaneous systems involving both equations and inequalities should be treated, and careful attention should be given to the graphical solution of such systems. For example, in Fig. 4-1 the point $(-2,3)$ is the graph of the *solution set*, or truth set, of the system of equations

$$x + 2y = 4$$
$$3x - 2y = -12$$

The shaded portion of Fig. 4-1 represents the graph of the infinite set which is the solution set of the system of inequalities

$$x + 2y > 4$$
$$3x - 2y > -12$$

All this represents a change in emphasis, a change in attitude

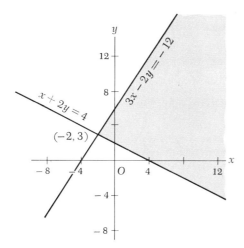

Figure 4-1

*Graphical solution of system involving equations
and inequalities.*

A problem for
teachers

and approach, more than a change in content. These changes
represent a curriculum problem for two reasons. First, teachers
must become accustomed to these changes, and this involves more
than mere mastery on the teacher's part. Long-established habits
do not die easily. Teachers must constantly be on guard lest
habits from their past that are not consistent with present usage
rise up to confuse their students.

The second reason why recent changes constitute a curriculum
problem is the dearth of information on how best to develop the
new ideas, vocabulary, and points of view.

Another problem involving the second course in algebra is in
part an outgrowth of the "revolution." Attempts are being made
to include in the year of algebra a good introduction to analytic
geometry and a fairly comprehensive coverage of trigonometry.
There is serious question as to whether the average student can
master so much material in that length of time.

The program in geometry has been of growing concern for many
years. The basis for this concern has been sixfold: (1) the recognition of the existence of logical defects in the euclidean structure,
Shortcomings of the
geometry program
(2) the failure to make appropriate adaptations of cartesianism to
simplify and enrich geometric study, (3) the failure to emphasize
the postulational nature of euclidean geometry and the possibility
of the existence of noneuclidean geometries, (4) the failure to
emphasize the basic projective properties of geometric configurations, (5) the possible overemphasis on the restriction of geometric
constructions to only those possible by straightedge and compass
alone, and (6) the inadequate attention paid to three-dimensional
geometry.

How to make corrections for these inadequacies in the high school geometry program has created a curriculum problem of no mean consequence. The Commission on Mathematics has proposed a year's program in geometry for grade 10.[10] This program is summarized in the following words:[11]

The Commission's recommendations for geometry

The program proposed by the Commission envisages an informal and intuitive introduction to geometric ideas, followed by an informal discussion of the nature of deductive reasoning. The course would then take up a short but important sequence of theorems, studied deductively, culminating in the Pythagorean Theorem. In the treatment of this sequence, both the geometric and the logical ideas previously introduced informally would be illustrated, consolidated, and confirmed by more formal study. Specific postulates, including in addition to the usual assumptions the congruence properties of triangles, would be introduced.

With the Pythagorean Theorem and theorems about similar triangles established, it is possible to proceed with coordinate geometry. The essential topics to cover are:

1. Location of points by coordinates
2. Length and slope of a line segment
3. Division of a segment in a given ratio
4. Equation of a line
5. Equation of a circle

The remainder of plane geometry can now be developed by using both synthetic and analytic methods. Emphasis should be placed on the development of skill in analyzing a situation and a valid proof of either kind.[11]

This summary fails to indicate that the proposed program is designed as "a course in plane and solid geometry." The outline includes suggestions concerning the drawing of three-dimensional figures and basic definitions, theorems, and formulas related to solid figures.

SSCC recommends more emphasis on synthetic geometry

The report of the Secondary School Curriculum Committee supports a stronger emphasis on synthetic geometry than does that of the Commission on Mathematics. It, too, recommends a combined treatment of solid geometry with the plane, the principal emphasis being directed to the configurations of the plane. Suggestions are made of "elements of geometry [which] are regarded as appropriate at the various grade levels." The point of view of the committee with reference to the total geometry program of the high school is summarized in these words:

Recommendations of the SSCC for geometry

It is the considered opinion of this committee that elements of geometry should be taught throughout the secondary sequence (grades seven to twelve) and that one year should be devoted to synthetic geometry with particular emphasis on the geometry of the plane. This does not imply any desire to minimize the importance of co-ordinate geometry. Indeed the study of co-ordinate systems should permeate the entire secondary sequence beginning with the idea of one-to-one correspondence between numbers and points on a line in grade seven. The year devoted to

---

[10] Commission on Mathematics, *op. cit.*, pp. 38–39. Also see report appendices 11, 12, and 14 to 16 for additional discussion of specific aspects of the proposal.
[11] *Ibid.*, pp. 27–28.

synthetic geometry should be no exception. For example it is instructive to extend the study of loci to the co-ordinate plane. . . . It is also desirable to use analytic methods, on occasion, to provide alternative proofs for certain theorems which have been proved synthetically. Such proofs give pupils confidence in their ability to use analytic methods.

During the year course some teachers with superior classes may find it possible to include a considerable amount of solid geometry along with the plane geometry without sacrificing the essential values of the latter. Indeed some references to space geometry do much to enhance the pupils' understanding of relations which were first considered in the plane. The first consideration should be the presentation of a thorough course in plane geometry in which pupils receive intensive training in the solution of a large number of miscellaneous problems. In this situation the pupil needs time for contemplation, time for the formulation of conjectures, and time to test these conjectures for consistency with known facts. On the other hand, there is no point in pursuing an endless elaboration of originals which are confined to the plane. At some point during the year the good student will find it both natural and profitable to consider solid geometry in a systematic manner and not merely as counterpoint for plane geometry.[12]

Comparison of the two reports

Both committees agree that a full half-year program in solid geometry is no longer justified. Also, both committees agree that it is highly desirable that more careful attention be given to deductive techniques and to the possibilities of other geometries than the metric geometry of the euclidean plane.

Thus, despite some differences in the details of their recommendations, it is clear that both of these committees took the position that euclidean geometry must continue to hold a prominent place in the mathematical program of the senior high school. This position is further supported by the action taken in three important experimental projects[13] in preparing trial courses and textbooks in euclidean geometry. While these, too, differ in details of organization, and while the treatment of the subject in all three cases has a strongly modern orientation, their participation in these experimental projects implies general agreement that the traditional content of euclidean geometry deserves the prominent place which it has held and now holds in the high school curriculum.

Changes in trigonometry

In trigonometry the primary objective has shifted away from the numerical aspects of the subject and toward its analytic aspects. There is still value in the use of trigonometric techniques to acquaint the immature student with the basic characteristics of indirect measurement, and the solution of triangles will still have some importance as a medium for introducing the more elementary techniques of computing with approximate data and as training in the use of tables. But these are ideas which some feel belong to the junior high school. In the senior high school emphasis

---

[12] Secondary School Curriculum Committee, *op. cit.*, pp. 404–405.
[13] The School Mathematics Study Group, the University of Illinois Committee on School Mathematics, and the Ball State Experimental Program in Mathematics.

should be placed on the contribution which the analytic aspects of this subject can make to subsequent work in mathematics. For most students, trigonometry can no longer be properly regarded as a terminal course. The variation and the periodic nature of the trigonometric functions, the relations among the functions, properties of the inverse trigonometric functions, the solution of trigonometric equations, the representation of complex numbers as vectors and their treatment by trigonometric methods, and the circular functions of real numbers are among the topics which henceforth should receive important emphasis in the study of trigonometry. The proposed modifications of this course create curriculum problems demanding careful study. There is much merit in the idea of integrating trigonometry with the second course in algebra. But successful integration within the imposed limitations of time and space constitutes a challenge of major proportions.

Twelfth-year program

The twelfth-year course of study offers almost limitless possibilities and poses many significant curriculum problems. The program for this year is more of an elective program than those of previous years. It is also true that the tight sequence of mathematical study begins to break down a bit at this level. These two facts make it both possible and desirable that the planning of the mathematics curriculum for grade 12 should provide for variation in interests and aptitudes for mathematically capable students. Furthermore, the twelfth grade should make provision for potential graduates who do not yet meet the minimum requirements in mathematics to have the opportunity to meet such requirements.[14]

The literature carries descriptions of experiments and suggestions for topics to be used as instructional units in the program for this grade. Possibly the most carefully considered and the most authoritative recommendation of a program for the mathematically capable is that given by the Commission on Mathematics. Their recommendation is for "a course to be called Elementary Functions," for the first semester, to be followed by a second semester "devoted either to introductory probability with statistical applications or to an introduction to modern algebra (fields and groups)."[15] These recommendations have met with only limited success. Trigonometry as a separate course continues to be offered in many schools. Probability and statistics, a very promising innovation, is used as a semester course only sparingly.[16] The Commission on Mathematics recommends that calculus in the high school be restricted to the Advanced Placement Program;[17] yet calculus is one of the more popular twelfth-year subjects.

---

[14] Secondary School Curriculum Committee, *op. cit.*, p. 413.
[15] Commission on Mathematics, *op. cit.*, pp. 30–33, 42–47.
[16] Frederick Mosteller, What Has Happened to Probability in the High School?, *Mathematics Teacher*, **60** (1967), 824–831.
[17] Commission on Mathematics, *op. cit.*, pp. 14–15.

The Cambridge Conference report

The curriculum problems of the junior and senior high school that are by-products of the "revolution" are insignificant compared with those that would necessarily follow adoption of the curriculum outlines suggested by the Cambridge Conference on School Mathematics.[18] Although the conference itself considers its report "a discussion document, and not a prescription," in Adler's view[19] it is a portent of things to come. The type of thinking underlying the report will doubtless have its effect on the shape of the curriculum of the future.

THE JUNIOR COLLEGE[20]

Varied objectives

From one point of view, at least, the program of the junior college is analogous to that of the junior high school. For many students the two years of junior college will be the final years of their formal educational careers. Others, though they continue in college, are not interested in further work in mathematics. On the other hand, a fairly large and increasing proportion of students who enter college do plan to specialize in fields of study which require an extensive program in mathematics for which a strong background in analytic geometry and calculus is only a prerequisite.

These facts combine to present a curriculum problem which is both important and complicated. Should all junior college students be expected to take some work in mathematics? If not, who should be excused from this requirement, and for what reasons? If so, how much mathematics should be required of all, and what should be the content of this minimum course? What should be the content and arrangement of the regular systematic freshman and sophomore courses for those who plan to continue their work in mathematics through or beyond the junior college? These are a few of the questions that have to be considered. They are not new, but they are becoming ever more acute and more important.

Although the wise determination of a minimum curriculum in mathematics is of major concern, it is but one of several critical problems which have challenged the best thinking of professional groups interested in improved instruction in mathematics. Also calling for careful study are the demands for change in character of content and for increased intensity of application of the mathematics prerequisite to the natural sciences and engineering. Too, there are increasing demands for pertinent prerequisite training in mathematics from less technical areas, such as the social sciences

---

[18] Report of the Cambridge Conference on School Mathematics, "Goals for School Mathematics" (Boston: Houghton Mifflin Company, 1963).

[19] Irving Adler, The Cambridge Report: Blueprint or Fantasy?, *Mathematics Teacher,* **59** (1966), 210–217.

[20] In this section the term "junior college" is used to denote the first two years of college, whether it be a separately organized institution or the lower division of a four-year institution.

and psychology, as well as from business and industry. Furthermore, there is an urgent need for the establishment of a closer affinity between the mathematics of these first two college years and that which serves as the foundation of modern scientific research.

Background for engineers

The Joint Committee of the American Society for Engineering Education and the Mathematical Association of America recommended that colleges should raise standards for mathematics performance, pay more attention to the fundamentals of probability and statistics, and provide for pre-engineering students more course electives in mathematics, as well as a more intensive program of problem solving.[21]

While the Commission on Mathematics was interested in the college-capable students of the high school and directed its report entirely in the direction of such students, it did not overlook the fact that "the colleges have contributed to the high school curriculum problem by their inertia." The report further states that

Response to high school changes

"the Commission sees no hope of effective curriculum reform at the secondary level unless this reform is supplemented by a related effort at the college level."[22] There is gratifying evidence that many colleges now are taking steps in this direction. This is reflected to some degree in the large and increasing number of textbooks that have appeared since about 1960 which exhibit innovations in the organization of the courses or in the treatment of the subject matter.

The most concentrated effort toward modification of the junior college program has been that of the Committee on the Undergraduate Program in Mathematics (CUPM). In assessing the need

Work of CUPM

for revision, it not only called attention to the widespread dissatisfaction with existing programs, but also pointed out that any program of revision must take into account the expanding needs of engineering and the physical sciences and also of the biological and social sciences and the relatively new field of numerical analysis.[23]

As a part of its work, this committee established certain writing groups of mathematicians charged with the responsibility of preparing some new experimental courses for the freshman and sophomore years. This work culminated in the publication by the committee of four experimental textbooks. Taken in pairs, these four books were designed to represent two different courses for the two semesters of the freshman year, each of which would be quite unlike the traditional courses. One of these was thought to be ap-

---

[21] Report of the Joint Committee of the American Society for Engineering Education and the Mathematical Association of America, *American Mathematical Monthly*, **62** (1955), 385–392.
[22] Commission on Mathematics, *op. cit.*, p. 62.
[23] Report of the Committee on the Undergraduate Program in Mathematics, *American Mathematical Monthly*, **62** (1955), 511–520.

propriate for all students. The other was designed with a view to meeting the special needs of students planning to major in the biological or social sciences. Although the experimental books never enjoyed widespread use, their influence is discernible in more conventional textbooks and course offerings.

Much of the work which has been done and is being done toward improvement of the freshman and sophomore courses in mathematics has undoubtedly been initiated directly or indirectly as a result of the activities of the CUPM. Through its activities colleges have been made aware of their teacher-training obliga-

Training of elementary school teachers

tions. A sequence of mathematics courses designed specifically for training of elementary school teachers, and with accompanying outlines, have been proposed by CUPM as minimum training for elementary school teachers. The resolution of many curriculum problems of the junior and senior high school will be greatly eased if the CUPM recommendations for elementary school teachers are followed.

The implementation of this program creates additional curriculum problems at the college level of instruction. While the committee's recommendations give clear specifications as to con-

Difficulties of implementation

tent for the program, there still remain problems of effective organization, proper "grade placement," and appropriate credit recognition. The junior college cannot be expected to assume total responsibility for their solution. Nevertheless, the nature of its program is such that it cannot avoid becoming greatly involved.

EXPERIMENTAL CURRICULUM AND COURSE PROJECTS

Changes in curriculums and in courses originate in the minds of individuals or in the collective thinking of groups. Every textbook for a course in mathematics reflects the ideas of its author as to what content and plan of organization are most appropriate, what things should be emphasized, and what kind of presentation will contribute most effectively to learning. Reports of course or curriculum committees reflect the collective opinions of groups of persons about these things.

Recommendations before 1950

While the recommendations of certain committees and commissions in the past have had far-reaching influence in reshaping curriculums and courses in mathematics, most of those made before the middle of this century were characterized by two things. For the most part they looked toward the rearrangement and adaptation of traditional subject matter, and they were based largely upon collective opinion rather than upon experimental evidence of their validity.

The impact of modern **mathem**atics, however, brought into the picture concepts, terminology, notation, and emphases which hitherto had been lacking in the secondary school courses. Hence the validity, propriety, and feasibility of these innovations for the secondary school curriculum could not be evaluated on the basis of long years of experience and mature observation. As a result, a

Current recommendations

number of significant experimental projects, aimed at producing, trying out, and appraising new courses and methods, have come into being since 1950. These projects have varied both in extent and in their detailed objectives and activities, but they have all aimed at providing new and basic information which could be helpful in curriculum revision.

The following list of such experimental projects related to the improvement of mathematics curriculums and courses was reported, with brief descriptions of the projects, by the National Science Foundation in October, 1962,[24] and gives some idea of the scope and nature of these experimental projects.

Syracuse University–Webster College Madison Project (elementary and secondary); Coordinated Science and Mathematics Curriculum for Grades K–9 (elementary and secondary); Survey of Recent East European Literature in School and College Mathe-

Experimental projects

matics (elementary, secondary, and college); School Mathematics Study Group (SMSG) (elementary and secondary); Regional Orientation Conferences in Mathematics (elementary and secondary); University of Illinois Committee on School Mathematics (UICSM) (elementary and secondary); Evaluation of Secondary School Mathematics Curricula (secondary); Experimental Films in Mathematics (secondary and college); Films for Mathematics Teachers (secondary); Committee on the Undergraduate Program in Mathematics (CUPM) (college); Experimental Teaching Program in Algebra (college); Experimental Pregraduate Programs in Mathematics (college); New Undergraduate Courses in Mathematics (college); Mathematics Courses for Prospective Elementary School Teachers (two separate projects) (college); Power Series and the Elementary Functions (secondary and college); Coordinated Program for Mathematics and Physics Majors in Freshman and Sophomore Years (college); Films in Mathematics for Elementary School Teachers (elementary); Introductory Course in Probability, Matrices, and Calculus for Students in the Biological and Social Sciences (college); Course in Mathematics for Prospective Junior High School Teachers (college).

The foregoing list includes only projects which have received financial support from the National Science Foundation. In addi-

---

[24] "Science Course Improvement Projects," 1, Courses, Written Materials, Films, Studies Supported by the National Science Foundation, NSF 62–38, October, 1962.

tion to these, any list of significant experimental projects should surely include reference to a number of others, such as the Boston College Mathematics Institute (BCMI), the Greater Cleveland Mathematics Program (GCMP), the University of Maryland Mathematics Project (UMMaP), the Ontario Mathematics Commission (OMC), the Ball State Mathematics Project, and the Southern Illinois University–Comprehensive School Mathematics Project (SIU-CSMP). All these are extensive undertakings aimed at the common goal of improving the mathematics curriculum. Of course, there are also many experimental studies of mathematics curriculums and courses which have been and are being conducted at local levels within individual school systems.

Program evaluation In 1959 the National Council of Teachers of Mathematics set up the Committee on the Analysis of Experimental Mathematics Programs. This committee was given responsibility for investigating ways in which the National Council could be of help to teachers or schools in considering changes in their mathematics programs. The first report[25] of this committee was published in 1963. In this report the following eight experimental programs are considered:

Boston College Mathematics Institute, the Greater Cleveland Mathematics Program, the Syracuse University–Webster College Madison Project, the University of Maryland Mathematics Project, the Ontario Mathematics Commission, the School Mathematics Study Group, the Southern Illinois University Comprehensive School Mathematics Project, and the University of Illinois Committee on School Mathematics. For each of these programs a brief description is given, and this is followed by a concise analysis (not evaluation) of the program with respect to eight different criteria: "Social Applications," "Placement," "Structure," "Vocabulary," "Methods," "Concepts vs. Skills," "Proof," and "Provision for Evaluation."

Of all these experimental projects perhaps the UICSM and the SMSG projects, because of their impressive scope and massive scale, seem likely to have the greatest impact upon impending course and curriculum revision in school mathematics. Both are continuing projects. Under each of these projects numerous experimental courses have been written, tried out on a large scale, and extensively revised and rewritten before being released in textbook form; and large numbers of teachers who were to use these experimental materials in participating schools have been given special training for this work. Efforts have also been made to evaluate the experimental courses with respect to both their feasibility and their desirability.

---

[25] "An Analysis of New Mathematics Programs" (Washington, D.C.: National Council of Teachers of Mathematics, 1963).

To provide continuing information on experimental programs and research projects, *The Mathematics Teacher* carries, as a regular feature, a section entitled "Experimental Programs," and *The Arithmetic Teacher* carries a similar section, entitled "Focus on Research."

INDIVIDUAL CAPABILITY LEVELS

The recognition of, and the making of proper provision for, individual differences in learning potential and performance through the years has been, and will continue to be, a major curriculum

The wide range of ability creates problems

problem in the shaping of the secondary school program in mathematics. It is a well-known fact that this problem intensifies at the level of the secondary school. Here there are to be found wide variations in ability, ranging from the academically gifted to the very slow learner. It is indeed a problem of serious concern which confronts teachers as they attempt to deal with individual students and with groups in accordance with their ability to learn. The classification of students (slow learner, average, academically talented) should be the result of cooperative effort on the part of the administrator, the guidance personnel, the teacher, and the parents. It should be based on information from a cumulative record begun in the elementary school and containing results from intelligence and achievement tests, interest and aptitude inventories, and other types of information pertinent to social adjustment and school progress.

There are certain distinguishing characteristics which should be helpful in recognizing the slow learner in mathematics and the mathematically gifted in contradistinction to each other and to

The slow learner

the average group. Although there are many possible exceptions to any given pattern, the following might be safely listed as characteristics of the slow learner:

1 Has intelligence quotient below 90
2 Has little drive
3 Has short span of attention
4 Has weak association memory
5 Is a poor reader
6 Has difficulty with abstractions
7 Is not logical
8 Lacks imagination
9 Is unable to detect his own errors
10 Has little power to transfer training
11 Is not creative in his thinking[26]

In contrast, the Secondary School Curriculum Committee gives

[26] Mary Potter and Virgil Mallory, "Education in Mathematics for the Slow Learner" (Washington, D.C.: National Council of Teachers of Mathematics, 1958), pp. 11–12.

the following lists of general and special characteristics which mark the mathematically gifted:

1 General characteristics

The gifted student

    a. Makes associations readily and retains them indefinitely

    b. Recognizes similarities and differences quickly

    c. Has excellent memory, good vocabulary, broad attention span, and high reading ability

    d. Has a relatively mature sense of values

    e. Pursues interests with tremendous energy and drive

    f. Uses his spare time productively

2 Special characteristics

    a. Recognizes patterns readily and enjoys speculating on generalizations

    b. Prefers to think on higher levels of abstraction

    c. Classifies particular cases as special cases of more general situations with relative ease

    d. Follows a long chain of reasoning, frequently anticipating and contributing

    e. Frequently asks profound questions

    f. May be reading mathematics books years ahead of his class

    g. Is frequently impatient with drill and details that he thinks are not important[27]

Though the identification of the relative-ability groups is a problem of tremendous responsibility, there remain other problems of just as great concern and difficulty. What mathematics program is the most significant for each of the three groups (slow learner, average, and mathematically gifted)? Is there a close similarity or a wide variation in the content of the program for each group? There seems to be rather general agreement that the basic content must be the same for all three groups but must vary in amount, pattern of organization, manner of presentation, and intensity of attention. For the slow learner the manner of presentation must emphasize the approach to abstractions through a large amount of concrete experience, bolstered by frequent reviews and intensive practice. Furthermore, the abstractions must be kept in simple form. The minimum program must be carefully defined to protect the boys and girls against the demands of an age that is becoming more and more technological in nature.

The same basic content for all students

From the point of view of greatest potential for service to our society, the academically talented students are the ones who place the most serious demand on curriculum designers for careful thinking and imaginative planning. The College Entrance Examination Board has taken cognizance of this fact in the report of its Commission on Mathematics[28] and in the sponsoring of the Advanced Placement Program for admission to college with advanced

Talented students must not be slighted

---

[27] Secondary School Curriculum Committee, *op. cit.,* p. 410.

[28] Commission on Mathematics, *op. cit.*

standing.[29] Other groups have studied the problem and made recommendations for solution.[30]

The Secondary School Curriculum Committee seems to have summarized and underscored the best thought on this extremely important problem in these words:

> All schools should provide opportunities for the gifted. Ability grouping is a widely acceptable and desirable practice, and special classes for the able are recommended where organizational and staff facilities permit. Honors classes, seminars, and special projects provide excellent means for challenging the gifted. A policy of acceleration is followed in some areas. Two basically different patterns are used: (1) A narrow type, or "mere speed-up" plan, in which pupils are allowed to "cover" the requirements of one year's program to get into that of the next year, for example: two years of algebra in one year; and (2) a broad type or "faster growth-in-depth" plan, where more mature understandings and procedures are expected sooner.

> There is some question about the advisability of the "mere speed-up plan." A sophomore pupil, for example, who is undertaking senior mathematics could easily be a triple loser. He could be so completely out of step with the educational pattern that he would be confronted with unnecessary confusion in planning for the future; secondly, he could have lost material benefits by not having had the opportunity to make significant explorations below the surface of mere satisfactory accomplishment; and thirdly, he could have missed the inspiring challenge that can come from inquisitive search into the rationale of procedures, the foundations of concepts, and the implications of principles. On the other hand, a carefully planned acceleration program of the "faster-growth-in-depth" type can benefit the able pupil very materially through the provision of opportunities for deeper investigation of foundations, broader contact with related areas of cultural and utilitarian value, and more significant appreciation of basic interrelationships as well as advancement in grade-level accomplishment.

> Any program of enrichment for the mathematically gifted not only should provide real challenge to excellent accomplishment but also should provide basic information essential to top-level performance in mathematics, both for the present and for the future. This can be accomplished in better fashion by less emphasis on drill and on delineation of applications, in order to provide more opportunity for discovery of significant patterns and formulation of generalizations. Under informed guidance such pupils should be encouraged to read widely, to investigate significant topics which offer them challenge, participate in competitive endeavors, and seek occasion to meet with other mathematically gifted pupils both within their own school and from other schools.

> Since the purpose of ability grouping in mathematics is to increase the efficiency of learning, it behooves teachers to adjust their methods of teaching in order to take maximum advantage of homogeneity of the several groups and to gear instruc-

"Growth in depth" versus "speed up"

Enrichment should provide a challenge

[29] College Entrance Examination Board, "Fifty-third Annual Report of the Director" (New York: College Entrance Examination Board, 1955), p. 20.

[30] Report of the Joint Conference of the Cooperative Committee on the Teaching of Science and Mathematics of the American Association for the Advancement of Science and the United States Office of Education, "Education for the Talented in Mathematics and Science" (U.S. Office of Education Bulletin 15, 1952, reprint 1953).

E. P. Vance (Editor), "Program Provisions for the Mathematically Gifted Student in the Secondary School" (Washington, D.C.: National Council of Teachers of Mathematics, reprint 1959).

Report of the Joint Conference of the National Education Association and the National Council of Teachers of Mathematics, "Mathematics for the Academically Talented Student" (Washington, D.C.: National Council of Teachers of Mathematics, 1959).

Efficiency of
learning should be
increased
tion to the learning level of the students in each group. Furthermore, administrators should strive (1) to develop in their staffs an understanding of the basic purposes of ability grouping and the desirability of taking advantage of it, (2) to adjust class size for optimum benefits from such grouping, and (3) to reduce non-teaching duties so that all teachers will have better opportunity for taking care of individual differences at all levels of instruction.[31]

Regardless of the extent to which ability grouping is carried, individual differences will remain a fact and a problem. Opportunities for remedial instruction, differentiated goals, and enriched and challenging assignments are some of the strategies that can be **The role of programmed instruction** employed to provide for individual differences within a class. Some advocates of programmed instructional material claim for it a means of providing for the slow learner. Others with equal vigor claim it solves the problem of providing for the gifted. Both extreme positions may have some merit, but programmed learning is not a panacea. It is a teaching aid which, with proper use, can be quite valuable.

There is on the horizon a much more sophisticated version of the basic idea of programmed-learning material, namely, com-**Computerized instruction** puter instruction. Although the obstacles are presently quite formidable, it remains to be seen what will be the ultimate impact of this innovation.

[31] Secondary School Curriculum Committee, *op. cit.*, pp. 410–411.

EXERCISES

1 To what factors do you attribute the intensity of the recent demand for reshaping the mathematics curriculum of the secondary schools? Be as explicit as you can.

2 What, in your opinion, are the chief problems associated with the improvement of the mathematics curriculum for grades 7 and 8? Discuss at least one of these in some detail.

3 Give a somewhat detailed report on the content and nature of the experimental courses for grades 7 and 8 which were developed in the Maryland Study or one of the other major experimental projects, and point out ways in which these courses differ from the traditional courses for these grades.

4 Examine several commercially published seventh- and eighth-grade textbooks of recent date to see to what extent and in what ways they have been oriented toward modern mathematics.

5 Compare the recommendations of the Secondary School Curriculum Committee and

those of the Commission on Mathematics with respect to the mathematics programs for grades 7 and 8. Point out any similarities and any major differences that you find.

6 Discuss the possibility of offering Algebra I in the eighth grade.

7 What special problems are associated with the mathematics program for grade 9?

8 The double-track program in mathematics for grade 9 has been widely adopted. Discuss the theoretical justification of such a program, and point out some safeguards that should be set up in conducting it.

9 Discuss the special importance of wise counseling of students in the administration of a double-track program in mathematics for grade 9.

10 Discuss the advisability of providing a triple-track program for grades 7 to 9. Give the pros and the cons.

11 Compare some recent textbooks in beginning algebra with others published before 1950, noting any differences in the

major topics included and the ways in which the subject is developed. Report on these differences.

12 Compare the recommendations of the Commission on Mathematics with those of the Secondary School Curriculum Committee with respect to the course in geometry for the high school. What significant differences, if any, do you find?

13 Examine with some care the experimental textbook on geometry prepared and published by the SMSG. What differences do you find between this and some conventional textbooks in geometry published before 1950?

14 Repeat exercise 13, but this time with reference to the experimental textbook on geometry prepared and published by the UICSM.

15 What similarities and what differences do you find between the experimental courses in geometry published by the SMSG and the UICSM?

16 Compare an Algebra II textbook published before 1955 with one published after 1965. List differences both in content and in method of development.

17 Select two trigonometry textbooks published since 1960 and two that were published before 1950. Compare the more recent books with the earlier ones as to the topics included and the relative emphasis given to logarithms and the solution of triangles.

18 Discuss the problems that arise in connection with the program in mathematics for grade 12. What do you think would be the most desirable program? Justify your choice.

19 Give the pros and cons of offering calculus as a high school subject.

20 Find out all you can about the history, objectives, and activities of the UICSM, and make a report.

21 Find out all you can about the history, objectives, and activities of the SMSG, and make a report.

22 Find out all you can about the Maryland and the Ball State experimental projects in mathematics, and make a report.

23 Enumerate some of the problems that must be faced in modernizing the junior college curriculum in mathematics. Discuss one of these.

24 Many colleges offer trigonometry and intermediate algebra (essentially high school courses) and allow college credit for them, while others do not allow college credit for these courses. Discuss whether this presents a curriculum problem to the high schools.

25 Some colleges offer analytic geometry and calculus as a single course. List advantages and disadvantages of this.

26 What curriculum problems in mathematics are presented by the students who are "slow learners"?

27 Describe some of the recommended patterns of instruction designed to challenge mathematically gifted students.

28 What is the Advanced Placement Program sponsored by the College Entrance Examination Board? (See Pieters and Vance in the Bibliography for this chapter.)

29 Assuming ample staff and facilities, what are some of the arguments for and against ability grouping of mathematics students in the high school?

30 Give arguments for and against the use of programmed material in teaching high school mathematics.

BIBLIOGRAPHY

Adler, Irving: Some Changes Taking Place in Mathematics, *Mathematics Teacher*, **55** (1962), 441–451.

———: The Cambridge Report: Blueprint or Fantasy?, *Mathematics Teacher*, **59** (1966), 210–217.

Allendoerfer, Carl B.: The Case against Calculus, *Mathematics Teacher*, **56** (1963), 482–485.

———: The Dilemma in Geometry, *Mathematics Teacher*, **62** (1969), 165–169.

Baker, Russel R.: Program Provisions in Michigan Junior High Schools for Superior Students in Mathematics, *Mathematics Teacher*, **55** (1962), 556–559.

Barker, I. C.: Not What Can Be Taught, but What Should Be Taught, *American Mathematical Monthly*, **69** (1962), 426–428.

Begle, E. G.: A Study of Mathematical Abilities, *American Mathematical Monthly*, **69** (1962), 1000–1002.

_____: SMSG: The First Decade, *Mathematics Teacher*, **61** (1968), 239–245.

Bernstein, Allen L.: Recent Research in Mathematics Teaching, *Michigan Education Journal*, **60** (1962), 262, 273.

Biggs, Edith E., and James R. MacLean: "Freedom to Learn: An Active Approach to Mathematics" (Reading, Mass.: Addison-Wesley Publishing Company, Inc., 1969).

Brown, Robert S.: Survey of Ohio College Opinions with Reference to High School Mathematics Programs, *Mathematics Teacher*, **52** (1959), 245–247.

Brumfiel, Charles, Robert Eicholz, and Merrill Shanks: The Ball State Experimental Program, *Mathematics Teacher*, **53** (1960), 75–84.

Buchanan, O. Lexton, Jr.: Opinions of College Teachers of Mathematics Regarding Content of the Twelfth-year Course in Mathematics, *Mathematics Teacher*, **58** (1965), 223–225.

Cairns, Stewart Scott: Mathematical Education and the Scientific Revolution, *Mathematics Teacher*, **53** (1960), 66–74.

Commentary on the Mathematics Curriculum of the High School, *Mathematics Teacher*, **55** (1962), 191–198. (Three short articles, which should be read together.)

Commission on Mathematics, Report (New York: College Entrance Examination Board, 1959).

Dader, Irving Allen: Numerical Analysis as a Twelfth-year Elective, *Mathematics Teacher*, **55** (1962), 334–336.

Dyer, Henry S., Robert Kalin, and Frederick M. Lord: "Problems in Mathematical Education" (Princeton, N.J.: Educational Testing Service, 1956).

Experimental Programs (a regular continuing department of the *Mathematics Teacher*).

Fehr, H. F.: Mathematics Curriculum for the High School of the Future, *Teachers College Record*, **59** (1958), 258–267.

_____: Breakthrough in Mathematical Thought, *Mathematics Teacher*, **52** (1959), 15–19.

_____: New Thinking in Mathematical Education, *Mathematics Teacher*, **53** (1960), 424–429.

Fisher, L. B.: How Curriculum Builders View New Math Ideas, *School Science and Mathematics*, **64** (1964), 31–36.

Fraser, Dorothy M.: "Current Curriculum Studies in Academic Subjects" (Washington, D.C.: National Education Association, 1962).

Fremont, Herbert: New Mathematics and Old Dilemmas, *Mathematics Teacher*, **60** (1967), 715–719.

Gabai, Hyman: An Experimental Twelfth-grade Mathematics Course, *Mathematics Teacher*, **60** (1967), 375–380.

Grossman, George: Advanced Placement Mathematics: For Whom?, *Mathematics Teacher*, **55** (1962), 560–566.

Hale, William T.: UICSM's Decade of Experimentation, *Mathematics Teacher*, **54** (1961), 613–619.

Hegstrom, William J., and Donald E. Riffle: A Two-year Study of Eighth Grade Algebra I, *Mathematics Teacher*, **56** (1963), 419–423.

Hilton, P.: Continuing Work of the Cambridge Conference on School Mathematics (CCSM), *Arithmetic Teacher*, **13** (1966), 145–149.

Jones, Burton W.: Silken Slippers and Hobnailed Boots, *Mathematics Teacher*, **52** (1959), 322–327.

Keedy, M. L.: The University of Maryland Project, *Mathematics Teacher*, **52** (1959), 281–282.

Kemeny, John G.: Report to the International Congress of Mathematicians, *Mathematics Teacher*, **56** (1963), 66–78.

Kenner, Morton R.: The Developmental Project in Secondary Mathematics, *American Mathematical Monthly*, **68** (1961), 797–798.

Kline, Morris: The Ancient versus the Moderns: A New Battle of the Books, *Mathematics Teacher*, **51** (1958), 418–427.

_____: A Proposal for the High School Mathematics Curriculum, *Mathematics Teacher*, **59** (1966), 322–330.

Kucinski, Romuald A.: An Introduction to Calculus for Junior High School Students, *Mathematics Teacher*, **52** (1959), 250–255.

Leissa, Arthur W., and Robert C. Fisher: A Survey of Teachers' Opinions of a Revised Mathematics Curriculum, *Mathematics Teacher*, **53** (1960), 113–118.

Malerich, Sister Autone, O.S.B.: A New Look at Enrichment, *Mathematics Teacher*, **57** (1964), 349–351.

Marlin, Lillian: SMSG: One Point of View, *Mathematics Teacher*, **55** (1962), 476–478.

Mayor, John, and John Brown: New Mathematics in the Junior High School, *Educational Leadership*, **18** (1960), 166.

Meder, A. E.: The Ancients versus the Moderns: A Reply, *Mathematics Teacher*, **51** (1958), 428–433.

_____: Current Experimental Programs in Mathematics, *Theory in Practice*, **3** (1964), 54–56.

_____: Sets, Sinners, and Salvation, *Mathematics Teacher*, **59** (1966), 358–363.

Merriell, D. M.: College Mathematics in the High School, *Mathematics Teacher*, **51** (1958), 556–557.

Meserve, Bruce E.: New Trends in Algebra and Geometry, *Mathematics Teacher*, **55** (1962), 452–461.

Meyer, William (Moderator): Report of the Committee on High School Mathematics Courses, *California Schools*, **31** (1960), 3–15.

Mosteller, Frederick: What Has Happened to Probability in the High School?, *Mathematics Teacher*, **60** (1967), 824–831.

Myers, Sheldon, and Marion G. Epstein: Mathematical Reform and the College Entrance Examination Board, *American Mathematical Monthly*, **70** (1963), 665–667.

National Council of Teachers of Mathematics: "Insights into Modern Mathematics,"*Twenty-third Yearbook* (Washington, D.C.: The Council, 1957).

———: Report of the Secondary School Curriculum Committee, *Mathematics Teacher*, **52** (1959), 389–417.

———: "The Growth of Mathematical Ideas," *Twenty-fourth Yearbook* (Washington, D.C.: The Council, 1960).

———: "The Revolution in Mathematics" (Washington, D.C.: The Council, 1961).

———: "Enrichment Mathematics for the Grades," *Twenty-seventh Yearbook* (Washington, D.C.: The Council, 1963).

———: "Enrichment Mathematics for the High School," *Twenty-eighth Yearbook* (Washington, D.C.: The Council, 1964).

National Science Foundation: "Science Course Improvement Project," 1, NSF 62–38, Courses, Written Materials, Films, Studies (Washington D.C.: The Foundation, 1962).

On the Mathematics Curriculum of the High School, *American Mathematical Monthly*, **69** (1962), 189–193.

Phillips, Jo McKeeby: The Baby and the Bath Water, *School Science and Mathematics*, **63** (1963), 291–304.

Pieters, Richard S., and E. P. Vance: The Advanced Placement Program in Mathematics, *Mathematics Teacher*, **54** (1961), 201–211.

Raphael, Brother L., F.S.C.: The Return of the Old Mathematics, *Mathematics Teacher*, **60** (1967), 14–17.

Rappaport, David: Proposed Revision and Acceleration of the High School Mathematics Program, *School Science and Mathematics*, **60** (1960), 214–221.

Report of the Cambridge Conference on School Mathematics: "Goals for School Mathematics" (Boston: Houghton Mifflin Company, 1963).

Rosenberg, Herman: Great Challenges of Mathematics Education, *Mathematics Teacher*, **55** (1962), 360–368.

Rosskopf, Myron F. (Chairman of Editorial Committee): New Developments in Secondary-school Mathematics, *Bulletin of the National Association of Secondary-School Principals* 43 (1959).

Rourke, Robert E. K.: Some Implications of Twentieth Century Mathematics for High Schools, *Mathematics Teacher*, **51** (1958), 74–86.

Sasse, Katharine J. S.: Mathematics for the Non-college-bound in Junior High School, *Mathematics Teacher*, **58** (1965), 232–240.

Schneider, Helen, and Burton W. Jones: "The New Mathematics Curricula: What and Why" (Washington, D.C.: National Council of Teachers of Mathematics, 1963). (Pamphlet.)

Stone, Marshall: The Revolution in Mathematics, *American Mathematical Monthly*, **68** (1961), 715–734.

Taylor, Angus E.: Convention and Revolt in Mathematics, *Mathematics Teacher*, **55** (1962), 2–9.

Taylor, Ross: First Course in Algebra—UICSM and SMSG: A Comparison, *Mathematics Teacher*, **55** (1962), 478–481.

Thwaites, Bryan: "On Teaching Mathematics" (New York: Pergamon Press, 1961).

Vance, E. P., and others: "Program Provisions for the Mathematically Gifted Student in the Secondary School" (Washington, D.C.: National Council of Teachers of Mathematics, 1958).

Wagner, John: The Objectives and Activities of the School Mathematics Study Group, *Mathematics Teacher*, **53** (1960), 454–459.

Weaver, J. F.: Action Research and Curriculum Development: International Clearinghouse on Science and Mathematics Curricular Developments, *Arithmetic Teacher*, **14** (1967), 228–230.

Weiss, Sol: Innovations and Research in the Teaching of Mathematics to the Terminal Student, *Mathematics Teacher*, **60** (1967), 611–618.

Willerding, Margaret F.: A Critical Look at the New Mathematics for Seventh Grade, *School Science and Mathematics*, **62** (1962), 215–220.

Wilson, Jack: What Mathematics for the Terminal Student?, *Mathematics Teacher*, **53** (1960), 518–523.

Woodby, Lauren G.: "Emerging Twelfth Grade

Mathematics Programs" (U.S. Office of Education Bulletin OE29060, 1965).

――――: "The Low Achiever in Mathematics" (U.S. Office of Education Bulletin OE29061, 1965).

Zant, James H.: Improving the Program in Mathematics in Oklahoma Schools, *Mathematics Teacher,* **54** (1961), 594–599.

――――: A Proposal for the High School Mathematics Curriculum: What Does It Mean?, *Mathematics Teacher,* **59** (1966), 331–334.

――――: Effect of New Mathematics Program in the Schools on College Mathematics Courses, *American Mathematical Monthly,* **70** (1963), 200–202.

Zoll, Edward J.: Research in Programmed Instruction in Mathematics, *Mathematics Teacher,* **62** (1969), 103–110.

five | a theory of mathematical learning

Schools exist for the primary purpose of promoting learning, and teachers of mathematics have as their primary objective the promotion of learning in mathematics. This is not a simple or routine task. The things that are to be learned and the maturity of the students vary from grade to grade, and learning has varied aspects and can take place through many avenues. The students may not all learn things in the same ways, or at the same speed, or with the same facility and completeness. Yet the teacher has the dual task of setting appropriate objectives with respect to the things to be learned and of planning kinds of learning activities which in his judgment give promise of providing his students with the kinds of experiences that can bring them to the attainment of the objectives. To this end, it is necessary that the teacher have a good understanding not only of the desirable mathematical objectives themselves, but also of the ways in which students learn mathematics. Moreover, he must remember that there are phases, or stages, in learning, as well as degrees of learning, and that initial understanding or mastery of skills can deteriorate through disuse or lack of review or application. Such considerations should impel him to consider carefully the instructional means and devices which he plans to use and to adapt them for optimum effectiveness in enabling the students to attain the desired objectives.

What are the objectives, and how can they be attained?

CONSIDERATIONS WITH RESPECT TO THE LEARNING OF MATHEMATICS

As has been said, the problem of instruction is that of promoting learning. Since the learning must be done by the student, the problem of instruction becomes that of guiding the activities of the student in such ways that proper learning will take place. This cannot be stereotyped. The teacher who gives thought to ways in which students learn mathematics will be more likely to attain effective results than the one who does not. It seems reasonable, therefore, that some important considerations with respect to how mathematics is learned should be set forth at the outset. It would be difficult to give a better statement of such considerations than the following analysis by two distinguished teachers of mathematics, although it was published nearly two decades ago.

Children do not grow and develop in mathematical knowledge in a vacuum of such knowledge. Quantitative thinking is acquired in active mental dealing with quantitative situations. The quantitative aspects of a situation can go unnoticed unless they are deliberately brought to the sphere of attention of the student. . . . The child grows and develops in a numerical and geometric environment in which he changes his behavior to ever more complex organized patterns.

But progress is not made along a straight line from the fundamentals to the generalized theorems. This is the way the final learning can be organized, and is frequently so organized in texts, but it is not the way most students grow in wisdom. Our initial learnings in algebra are not Peano's axioms, nor is our initial learning in geometry Hilbert's postulates. Rather, the initial learning is in an area in which exploration first takes place. We count, measure, draw, and make preliminary statements which are refined downward toward the foundations and upward toward more abstract, complex, and generalized relations. After a while we discard many particular theorems for one more generalized theorem, and in advanced states of learning only is the area of exploration reorganized as a straight line mathematical development.

The growth in mathematical knowledge by each individual student thus calls for direction by a skillful teacher who has a balanced emphasis on the various phases of learning. He uses the heuristic method only so far as pupils need directed questions in the quest of their learning. He has an experimental attitude that allows freedom of approach in learning to the degree that the experiment is headed toward a desired concept, or relationship, and directs the experiment back to fruitful approaches when the student is adrift. He recognizes that drill can be dangerous and boring as well as good habit formation procedure. He balances each step from concrete experience to semiconcrete representations, to words and symbols, to generalized abstract theorems through proper evaluation and by appropriate attainable challenges. He recognizes also that not all learning begins in concrete material objects, but that much new learning may start in already learned abstractions. Thus algebraic fractions are referred back to the abstractions learned in the study of arithmetic fractions and not back to parts of concrete objects. Geometry is related to geometrical drawings, trigonometry is related back to geometry and algebra.

It is just because of this sequential aspect of mathematical knowledge that proper balance becomes the all important aspect in its learning. Unless a clearly and correctly formed mathematical concept emerges from a learning situation and it is related to other phases of already learned mathematics through sufficient practice to gain skill in the use of the concept, the learning of all later mathematics dependent upon this concept is seriously (and sometimes totally) impaired. The lack of correct concepts in arithmetic may be one of the great reasons for the difficulty algebra presents to so many of our students. It is this balance that is indirectly referred to in every chapter in this text [i.e., Clark and Fehr's text]: a mathematical problem within the comprehension of the student, but still a problem as the start of learning; motivation, sufficient to send him on toward the solution; the challenge to abstract, to generalize, to form concepts; the proper use of sensory aids, of drill, of appropriate language; not doing too much nor failing to do enough; and adapting these measures to the various individual differences in learning. To gain such balance is to become a master teacher—the goal of all professionally minded educators.[1]

Learning begins with exploration

Proper teaching balance is essential to the learning of mathematics

[1] John R. Clark and Howard F. Fehr, Learning Theory and the Improvement of Instruction: A Balanced Program, *Twenty-first Yearbook* (Washington, D.C.: National Council of Teachers of Mathematics, 1953), pp. 346–348.

FOUR FUNDAMENTAL ASPECTS OF LEARNING
AND OF TEACHING MATHEMATICS

Mathematics is a cumulative and continuously unfolding subject. New concepts and relations draw upon the past for their meanings, and themselves become ingredients of future concepts and relations. Unless what has gone before has been soundly mastered and is accessible for ready retrieval for use in connection with new topics, the students may have difficulty in understanding these, and unless these, in turn, are soundly mastered, they themsevles may not be readily retrievable for use in understanding still other new topics, later on. Thus, with every new topic, the teacher has the responsibility for directing the learning activities of the students so that they will gain as nearly as possible full mastery of that topic.

Understanding new topics requires mastery of the old

Full mastery implies several things. To attain it the students must first come to understand what the new concept or relation means mathematically. After that, they need to work with it, on their own, until their understanding is deepened and they come to view the concept or relation with a feeling of confidence and familiarity, so that it becomes a part of their mathematical background. Moreover, if they are to be able to use it later on, they need to become conscious of its abstract generality, so that they can come to have a feeling for situations, mathematical or otherwise, in which it may find appropriate application, i.e., in situations other than that in which it was initially learned. Further, if the new concept or relation or skill is to be kept intact and firm in memory, most students will need to have occasion to use it from time to time even after it is no longer new to them.

Problems of learning

Thus, in connection with every new topic, the student is confronted with four fundamental problems of learning:

1　Acquiring initial understanding of the new concept, relation, or skill
2　Working with it extensively so as to deepen this understanding or skill well beyond the point of mere "threshold" understanding or mastery
3　Learning to see and to look for ways in which the new concept, relation, or skill may be transferred to, or applied in, situations other than that in which it was initially learned
4　Preventing the new concept or relation or skill from being forgotten or getting "rusty"

These are four aspects, or phases, of the total problem of learning mathematics, but their implications are essentially distinct and supplemental rather than identical. Moreover, each of these fundamental aspects of learning implies an equally fundamental instructional problem for the teacher. Accordingly, we shall devote

Problems of
teaching

the rest of this chapter to consideration of four basic problems of learning and of instruction in mathematics: (1) teaching for understanding, (2) teaching for assimilation, (3) teaching for transfer, and (4) teaching for permanence.

TEACHING FOR UNDERSTANDING

As generally conceived, the foremost problem of direct instruction in secondary school mathematics is the teaching of new material. It is this phase of instruction that makes the heaviest demand upon the skill and artistry of the teacher. The primary jobs are to explain, to make clear, to challenge, to guide to discovery, to develop understanding. To meet these responsibilities, the teacher must not only consider the logical relationships involved in the unit or topic, but also be keenly aware of the relation of the new concepts to the experiential background of the students. He must be able to anticipate probable difficulties and detect and clear up actual difficulties as they occur in the course of the development. He must be able and continually willing to view the unfolding and (to the students) unfamiliar subject matter, not merely through his own experienced eyes but from the standpoint of immature students to whom it may be all new and strange.

DEVELOPING UNDERSTANDING
OF NEW MATERIAL

In getting a class started on a new and unfamiliar topic, usually it is not enough for the teacher to give a lecture on the topic. Secondary school students are seldom able to assimilate adequately and immediately any lengthy one-sided discussion of unfamiliar subject matter by the teacher. Points of difficulty inevitably arise, and failure to get them cleared up promptly may result in blocking the understanding of subsequent parts of the lecture.

Telling can provide
explanation

This is not to say that merely "telling" is always out of place. There are times when teachers must resort to telling in order to help the students to understanding, as, for example, in clarifying the meaning of new terms or notation or basic concepts. In such cases, however, the telling should take the form of explanation or illustration, using any supplementary means or devices which are available and seem likely to be helpful. Moreover, to avoid discussion becoming one-sided, it should be interspersed with frequent questions addressed by the teacher to the class, both for the purpose of checking on understanding and of eliciting questions or contributions.

Sometimes, by well-chosen questions, the teacher may be able to direct the thinking of the students so that they will be led to sense or "discover" for themselves facts or relationships of which they have not been consciously aware before. The advantage of this is manifest. Understanding arrived at in this way not only becomes more deeply impressed in the students' minds than it would have been otherwise, but the very fact that they have gained this understanding for themselves gives students a sense of being active participants in the discussion. It casts them in the role of quasi-investigators rather than mere passive recipients of information. That they have been guided toward the discovery by the helpful questioning of the teacher need not detract from their justifiable feeling of pride in their achievement.

Asking promotes participation

Thus an element of prime importance to success in building understanding of new material is the active participation of the students. It is not always easy to get students to raise questions, because all too often the difficulties that arise are not well enough formulated or crystallized in their minds so that they can put them into words. Then, too, some students are quite sensitive about appearing slow of perception, or "dumb," in the eyes of their classmates or of the teacher, and rather than run the risk of embarrassment, they often let matters pass in silence. Such barriers to full and free discussion can be broken down only by tact and sympathetic encouragement on the part of the teacher. Students should be encouraged to raise questions at any time they fail to follow the discussion clearly.

Encouraging strengthens students' confidence

At best, however, students cannot be depended upon to bring up all points which may need special attention in the course of a discussion or explanation. The teacher must anticipate these as far as possible and be always alert to detect them as they become apparent. This can often be done by noting that the students wear puzzled expressions, even though they may not actually raise questions. Always at such times, and frequently in any case, the teacher should check the understanding of the discussion by means of questions addressed to members of the class, and at the completion of the discussion of any new topic a check test of some sort should be given before passing on to other activities. It is entirely inadequate, after finishing a discussion, to close with some such general questions as: Is that clear to all of you? Are there any questions? The silence with which such questions are generally received is absolutely no assurance that the class has followed the discussion with understanding. It may simply mean that the students have not understood the discussion well enough even to ask intelligent questions about it.

Checking for understanding prevents gaps

DEVELOPMENTAL TEACHING

Just as there is no single way in which students learn to understand new concepts and relations, so there is no single way of teaching new material which is effective in all situations. To develop understanding of new ideas successfully, the teacher must adapt his procedure to the learning situation as he finds it, and modify his procedures in the light of changing circumstances. Developmental teaching is an art. It has many faces, and it takes a variety of avenues for attaining its goal of bringing about understanding. It can be neither standardized nor stereotyped. Procedures which are used successfully by one teacher may prove to be unsuccessful when tried by another, or perhaps even by the same teacher under different circumstances. Much depends upon the personality of the teacher, upon his enthusiasm, tact, understanding of adolescents, and his ability to sense intuitively the procedures which will serve best to capitalize the psychological classroom situation of the moment or modify it in such a way that it may be made to contribute most powerfully to the objective which has been set. That teacher will be most successful in developmental work who has at his command *various* methods of procedure and who uses them so as to make them supplement each other most advantageously.

> The teacher must be able both to adapt and to modify his procedures

> The teacher must be sensitive to varieties of possibilities

One of the greatest mistakes which many teachers make is to try to cover too much ground in a given period of time or to try to cover a given amount of material in too short a period of time. This nearly always results in superficial learning or in no learning at all. Particularly in the developmental teaching of new material, the teacher should avoid forcing the process too rapidly. The development of new concepts and principles is a slow process, and it always requires a certain amount of discussion. Sometimes it will be necessary for the teacher to carry the burden of the discussion in building up and coordinating the necessary background and in giving a first presentation of the new material, but so far as possible this should be done in such a way as to avoid lecturing. When it is feasible to guide students into exploratory activities through appropriate questioning or laboratory exercises so that they may discover things for themselves, it should be done. When it is necessary for the teacher to give direct information, it should be given briefly and concisely and should be checked by pointed and searching questioning. New understandings, as they are developed, should be given permanence, clarity, and interest by means of adequate illustration and application.

> The teacher should never rush through the explanation of new concepts

Developmental work is not the job of the teacher alone. To be successful, it requires the continuous interaction of the students' best efforts with those of the teacher. The aim at all times is to develop in the students a broadening background of mathematical understanding and foster a continuing interest in the subject to the end that the students will gain added appreciation of its nature and usefulness and will acquire increasing ability to do independent thinking in the field. The teacher must plan and direct the activities of the class toward these goals. He must strive to secure the highest possible degree of cooperative effort on the part of the students. He must be tactful and sympathetic, helping when necessary, encouraging, guiding, checking, and always stimulating the students to put forth their own best efforts. Such a program of developmental teaching may be expected to yield highly satisfactory results, not only in developing mastery of the new subject matter immediately in hand, but also in building up an appreciation of mathematics and its contributions, in developing an increasing ability to do independent mathematical thinking, and in stimulating interest in the pursuit of further mathematical study.

The teacher must strive to stimulate the students' best efforts

TEACHING FOR ASSIMILATION

While acquiring clear initial understanding of new mathematical concepts and relations is an absolute prerequisite to adequate mastery of new material, the process of mastery can by no means be regarded as ending with this step. On the contrary, this is merely a beginning. Adequate mastery implies more than just a threshold understanding of a topic. It implies also a feeling of familiarity—a feeling of being comfortably at home with the material. Students, as a rule, cannot gain this feeling without a good deal of independent practice. Just as learning to translate new words or phrases or sentences in an unfamiliar language does not guarantee ease or comfort or facility in reading or using that language, so learning the meanings of new mathematical words, symbols, expressions, or principles does not guarantee comfortable facility in using them in mathematical contexts. New concepts, by and large, are not adequately mastered without being met in varied contexts, nor principles and relations without repeated application, nor processes without extensive practice, nor any of these without prolonged and sustained intellectual effort and practice. This second stage in the learning program is what we shall think of as the assimilation stage.

THE ASSIMILATION OF UNDERSTANDING

In this stage of their learning the students are mainly on their own. Their job is to go beyond the initial acquaintance with the new ideas upon which their attention was focused during the develop-

Building familiarity

mental stage. Now they will work with these ideas themselves, to fix them more firmly in mind and make them more fully their own; to gain deeper insights; to build familiarity with new technical words and notation involved; to study examples to discover the part played by the new concepts or relations; to think about new problems to see whether, and how, the new ideas are involved, and to work many problems in which they *are* involved. Thus the assimilation stage in their learning is a work period for the students, a time for independent thinking and study, to the end that the new ideas may become less new, that the unfamiliar may take on familiarity and so become firmly established in mind and well organized into the student's mathematical background.

We have spoken of this as a period, or stage, in learning. This must not be misconstrued as being one continuous period. Although it may extend over several days, it need not be an unbroken succession of class periods devoted exclusively to study of a given topic. Indeed, better results will probably be attained if this extended learning time is spread over parts of several days, interspersed with other activities. But the assimilation work should at least begin very soon after the developmental work on a particular topic or unit, so that independent study can begin while new ideas are still fresh in mind.

Spacing study over several days

In the developmental work the teacher has an active and prominent role in helping to build new understanding. From this point on, the teacher's role, although no less important than before, is less prominent. The students and their activities now occupy the center of the stage, the teacher serving as a sort of prompter and director operating from the wings. Of course, there will be need of some general discussion from time to time for purposes of stimulating motivation and to clear up points that present persistent difficulties, but this will be incidental to the main part of the work, in which independent individual study is the main activity and the students are the main participants. The teacher's role is to guide and direct their work, stimulate and encourage them, help them over stumbling blocks, evaluate their progress, and do all he can to get them to put forth their best efforts to achieve mastery of the new ideas on which they are working.

Assimilation work; the teacher as prompter

DIRECTING STUDY IN MATHEMATICS

Students often pursue wasteful and inefficient procedures in studying mathematics. They waste time. They read superficially, and they are careless about their written work. They are unsystematic. They allow their attention to be distracted by trivial things. They become impatient with matters that require long and

Sloppy study habits must be corrected

concentrated thinking. They do not take time for careful analysis and planning before starting their work. Sometimes, if they are not sure how to begin, they waste time waiting for the teacher to get them started, instead of forming the habit of depending upon themselves as far as possible.

It is not surprising to find these characteristics in young and immature students, but if they are to do effective independent study, they need to acquire mature and effective study habits. A part of the teacher's task must be to offer help in this direction.[2]

Some teachers make the mistake of rushing to the assistance of students the moment they ask for it, and of virtually doing their work for them. This is bad practice for two reasons. In the first place, it does the students little or no good. Mastery can come only through one's own effort; it is not likely to be gained by avoiding major responsibility for results and relying to an excessive degree upon help. In the second place, if the teacher allows students to impose unduly upon his willingness to help them, he is likely to find himself swamped with demands of this nature. The resulting pressure and stress can leave him physically tired and mentally and emotionally disorganized.

Developing independence in the student

It does not take a good teacher long to size up the attitudes and the potentials of his students. For some a well-directed question or perhaps the mere explanation of a word may be all that is needed to set them on their way. For others more extensive questioning and explaining may be needed. It is important to get each student to identify or pinpoint as well as he can what it is that is causing his difficulty, so that the problem can be attacked at its root and without waste of time. It is a fine art to determine just who really needs help, what and how much help is needed, and in what manner it can best be given. This can be done successfully only by a teacher who understands the attitudes and abilities of his students, who knows the difficulties to be expected, and who possesses a trained insight which will enable him to get directly at the root of the student's difficulty, even though the student himself may not realize precisely what is causing him trouble.

Get to the root of each student's problems

TEACHING FOR TRANSFER

We have referred to the gaining of initial understanding and to the assimilation or deepening of such understanding as representing essentially two *stages* in learning. That is to say, a student cannot work intelligently with a concept or relationship until he has come to have some understanding of it. After initial understanding has

[2] For suggestions see Henry Swain, "How to Study Mathematics" (Washington, D.C.: National Council of Teachers of Mathematics, 1955).

been gained, the student can proceed with independent practice, so that he may develop a deeper and fuller understanding and, finally, a feeling of comfortable familiarity with the concept or principle involved.

We now turn our attention to a third aspect of learning, the *transfer* of learning. This means learning to perceive mathematical patterns in certain situations and to transfer them to other situations. In a sense we might think of this as the highest goal in mathematical learning, because it appears to represent the one indispensable element of both generalization and intelligent application of principles. Perceiving and sensing the same pattern in several different instances may suggest the conjecture of a generalization, while recognizing the same pattern in a particular instance and in a generalization already formed may suggest that particular instance may be a special case under the general principle.

The highest goal in mathematical learning

Transfer is not essentially a stage in learning a concept or relationship. It might better be thought of as an *aspect* of learning. It can come about as soon as a student gains his first understanding of a principle, and this happens sometimes, especially with very bright students. But as a rule it is a phenomenon which occurs only after a deep and familiar understanding has been gained.

THE TRANSFER OF LEARNING

When we recognize in a set of circumstances a pervasive pattern which suggests a generalization, then transfer of learning has taken place. Again, when we recognize in some particular new situation a pattern which matches the pattern of some situation or generalization met before, then again transfer of learning has taken place. Transfer is a conscious relating of something new to something old or familiar, an interpreting of the new in terms of the familiar. It is the essential element in all generalization, classification, and application. It may be either as a new generalized pattern or as an example or application of some previously encountered pattern or generalization. Its prime requisites are perception, recognition, and association of patterns that are counterparts in a familiar situation and in a new situation. Without such recognition and association there could be no discovery of new generalizations nor any application of generalizations already made, and so no evolving or cumulative mathematical structure. When we recall the strong emphasis which contemporary mathematics places on pattern and structure, it would seem to follow that the recognition and relating of pattern—generalization, application, insight; in short, the transfer of learning—constitute the very essence and genius of mathematics as a cumula-

Transfer is deliberate relating of the new to the old

Transfer requires perception, recognition, and association

tive subject and, indeed, of all education as a cumulative and expanding process. To bring about such transfer would seem, then, to be a paramount goal of the mathematics teacher.

SIMILARITY PATTERNS

With effective transfer in mind, the pedagogical question becomes: How can the teacher arrange the learning activities for the students so that conditions will be favorable for transfer to take place? This question has been notably neglected in writings on the teaching of mathematics. Yet it is a question of major importance to classroom teachers who recognize transfer as an important objective and who seriously want some explicit help.

How to arrange for effective transfer to take place?

Teaching to promote transfer would seem to resolve itself into the problem of teaching students to do two things: (1) to learn to recognize similar patterns in new situations and in other situations with which they are familiar, and (2) to form the habit of consciously seeking out such similarities or analogies. The best approach is probably through examples in which the teacher *calls attention* to the similar patterns in the new and the old (familiar) problem or structural situations.

Students must be taught to recognize similarities and to look for them

> To secure maximum transfer, in the sense of applying "an integrated knowledge," a whole principle . . . to all tasks involving the same principle, teachers of mathematics must teach in such a way that demonstration exercises (or tasks) serve as examples of the application of that principle.[3]

The following will serve as illustrative examples.

1 After having learned and accepted the generalization that the area of any triangle is half the product of the measures of the base and the altitude, a seventh-grader is challenged to see if he can discover a general rule for determining the area of a regular polygon of any given number of sides. Suppose that, by drawing diagrams of several regular polygons (e.g., an equilateral triangle, a square, a regular hexagon, etc.), he notes that each can be inscribed in a circle, and it occurs to him that the respective distances from the center of this circle to the vertexes of the polygon are all the same, being radii of the circle. This in turn may suggest to him the further considerations that if triangles were formed by drawing such radii to all the several vertexes, then (*a*) the area of the polygon will be the same as the sum of the areas of these triangles, (*b*) the triangles are all isosceles and all alike, and so will have equal areas, and (*c*) he can find the altitude and the base of any of them by measuring, and so he can find the area of any of the

Generalization and application occur through perception and recognition

---

[3] Myron L. Rosskopf, Transfer of Training, *Twenty-first Yearbook* (Washington, D.C., National Council of Teachers of Mathematics, 1953), pp. 203–227.

triangles. He will observe, too, that the number of triangles is the same as the number of sides of the polygon.

Now here is a pattern which holds for all the cases he has studied. If he consciously recognizes this pattern, he will be likely to come up with the general rule that the area of the polygon can be found by multiplying the length of one side of the polygon (which is the base of one of the triangles, and which he can measure) by half the distance from the center of the polygon to a side (which he can measure) and then multiplying this result by the number of sides of the polygon. Even if he refines his rule no further than this, he will have arrived at a generalization (to be met later on as a theorem), and he will have done it through observing and recognizing a pattern which he has found in all the cases he has examined. This recognition and use of a pattern to lead to a generalization is surely an instance of the transfer of learning.

From the specific to the general

2   The following example describes the discovery (conjecture) of a rule or formula that was arrived at by junior high school students through observing, describing, and verifying a pattern which appeared consistently in a number of cases, and so led to the conjecture of a generalization. This example was reported by one of the students in the *Mathematics Student Journal*. We give it in her own words:[4]

> Our class was experimenting one day, and we discovered that if you have a given number, N, which can be written as a product of two prime numbers, P and Q, then the sum of the factors of N is $(1 + P) \times (1 + Q)$.
>   Example: $15 = 3 \times 5$. The factors of 15 are 1, 3, 5, 15.
>   The sum of the factors is 24. $24 = (1 + 3) \times (1 + 5)$.

The fact that no proof of the generality of the theorem was given (though the proof is simple) does not detract from the value of the conjecture for these young students. The important thing is that through their experimentation they had recognized a consistent pattern and had formulated this pattern into a generalization. This is a good example of the transfer of learning—a forward transfer, from specifics to a generalization.

Transfer through identification

3   At a somewhat less simple level, and as an example of applying facts or principles already known, suppose that a student in analytic geometry is asked to identify and discuss the locus represented by the equation $2x^2 + y^2 - 12x + 4y = 42$. If he recognizes that this equation is in the pattern of the general equation of the second degree in two variables, $Ax^2 + Bxy + Cy^2 + Dx + Ey + F = 0$, and if he recalls that every such equation represents one of the conic sections, transfer has taken place through his identification of a

[4] Martha Kirk, A Theorem on Factors, *Mathematics Student Journal*, **10** (1966), 5.

pattern in a particular case with a familiar pattern in the general case.

If, further, he recalls that when, in the general equation, $B = 0$, $A \neq 0$, $C \neq 0$, and $A \neq C$, then the conic is either an ellipse or a hyperbola with its axes parallel, respectively, to the coordinate axes, and if he notes that in his particular equation this pattern is present, and if, as a result, he identifies the locus as being either an ellipse or a hyperbola with its axes parallel to the coordinate axes, then again transfer has taken place.

If, still further, he recalls that when, in the general equation, A and C have the same sign, the locus is an ellipse, and if he recognizes this pattern in his particular equation and identifies the locus as an ellipse, then again transfer has taken place.

Suppose now that he recalls the general type of equation of an ellipse with its axes parallel to the coordinate axes:

$$\frac{(x-h)^2}{a^2} + \frac{(y-k)^2}{b^2} = 1$$

and finds that he is able to put his particular equation in this same form:

$$\frac{(x-3)^2}{(4\sqrt{2})^2} + \frac{[y-(-2)]^2}{8^2} = 1$$

and that by comparison of the elements in the two similar patterns he can make these identifications: $h = 3$, $k = -2$, $a = 4\sqrt{2}$, $b = 8$, here again transfer of learning has taken place through identification of corresponding elements in analogous patterns. If he now attaches the correct meanings to h, k, a, and b, he is in a position to discuss several of the properties of the given locus: symmetries, location of the center, directions and lengths of the major and minor axes, extent, eccentricity, etc.

The key element in this whole process has been the transfer of learning: the association, identification, and interpretation of elements of a particular pattern in a particular problem with, and in terms of, corresponding elements and properties of a known general pattern. We have noted the occurrence of such transfer at several places in the foregoing analysis. It could have been noted at still other places.

Transfer is essential to sequential learning

Without such transfer—such recognition, association, identification, and interpretation of pattern—sequential learning simply cannot take place. Since sequential development is the very essence of mathematics, it is of great importance that students should learn not only to understand such associations when pointed out to them, but to actively search for them as means to help them in their own problems and proofs. There is scarcely a problem, and never a theorem, in which arrival at a solution or a proof does not involve some association of patterns: some transfer of learning.

Some students, particularly very bright students, recognize similar patterns in different situations (and note the implications of these) more easily and more quickly than other students do, sometimes even without giving it any conscious attention. But most students need to be taught to see such pairs of patterns, to become consciously aware of their similarities or analogies, to note how the patterns are related, and to keep on the lookout for the occurrence of such similarities and correspondences and their implications for the work in hand. The best means to this end appears to be through well-chosen examples, in the discussion of which the teacher calls attention, deliberately and explicitly, to the association of the pattern pairs and to the generalizations or the applications which the association suggests.

Well-chosen examples help develop perception and recognition

TEACHING FOR PERMANENCE

The developmental and assimilative phases of instruction represent, essentially, the stages during which actual learning of new material takes place. Any subject matter, however, is likely to be forgotten, no matter how well it has been initially mastered, unless it is maintained by repeated application and practice. This is particularly true of mathematical skills and relationships. Skills need to be perfected and maintained through systematic drill, and concepts and relationships must be reviewed and applied at frequently recurring intervals. The instructional effort which is directed toward these ends may well be called *teaching for retention.* While it generally involves material that has already been learned rather than new material, its importance as a means of strengthening and maintaining learning is commensurate with the importance of the developmental and assimilative phases of instruction as means of *acquiring* new learning. Its avenues are drill, review, and application.

DRILL

The place of drill in mathematics has been a much-discussed issue. The old mathematics of the 1890s placed great emphasis on memorization and rote learning. The reaction against the excessive use of rote drill, with the increase of emphasis on concepts and meanings, which came about in the early years of this century, surely was justified and doubtless was overdue. However, it caused many educators to go to the opposite extreme and to inveigh against all drill as being futile and without value. These extremists

Excessive use of drill and the reaction against it form two extreme positions

took the position that the development of concepts and understandings is all that matters, and that drill has no place in the educative process. This point of view overlooks the important element of fixation, without which it would be manifestly impossible to carry on any process at a reasonable level of efficiency.

An enlightened present-day view of mathematical learning must reject both of these extreme positions as untenable. Drill must be recognized as an essential means of attaining some of the desired controls, just as a strong emphasis on concepts and meanings and patterns and relationships must be recognized as being essential for understanding. Both are necessary; neither alone is sufficient. Many of the operations of mathematics need to be performed not only correctly, but with considerable facility and speed, if they are to be most useful. Some of them need to be actually automatized. Facility in such operations can be attained only through systematic and repeated practice in using them, i.e., through drill.

If learning in mathematics is to be effective, however, understanding must go hand in hand with operational efficiency. Skill in a procedure is of no use unless one can recognize circumstances in which the procedure is appropriate. In general, if students are to be drilled on a procedure, they should be given as full a comprehension of it as their level of maturity will permit. In particular, they should be given an understanding of why it is important for them to become skillful in using the procedure on which they are being drilled. Without such understanding to provide motive, drill work can become pretty dreary and dull, just as long-continued repetition of finger exercises on a piano or on a typewriter or long practice on a particular football maneuver can be dull.

Students will work, and work hard, on things they consider interesting or important, but they soon become bored with things they regard as uninteresting or unimportant.

REVIEW

Review is sometimes identified with drill because both are characterized by repetition and both aim at the fixation of reactions, concepts, or relationships. As the terms are used in this book, however, a distinction is made between drill and review. Drill is aimed mainly at the automatization of relatively detailed processes and reactions. Review, on the other hand, aims not only at the fixation and retention of details, but also at the thoughtful organization of the important things in a chapter or unit into a coherent whole in order that the relationship of the various parts to each other and to the whole unit may be clearly understood.

Review should usually be concerned with more or less comprehensive units of subject matter. One of its functions is indeed to make recall more certain and more effective, but it aims to achieve this through the deliberate processes of organizing, systematizing, and relating elements to each other through giving, indeed, a "re-view," or a new look, at the unit which has been studied, rather than through reducing reactions to the plane of automatic responses. It emphasizes thought and meaning rather than habit formation. Thus, while drill and review have some things in common, they also have certain differences. Each has its proper function, and each is highly important in the study of mathematics.

Review work may be incidental in the sense that it may be integrated with the other work of the course, or it may be specialized by making it the primary feature and objective of particular assignments. Both of these types of review are necessary to the most effective teaching. Review of the incidental type is especially valuable for the gradual building up and clarification of concepts through repeated reference and through continual reapplication in those situations in which they play component parts. Concepts and principles are generalized through being met with in many situations which vary in other particulars and from which the concepts and principles are gradually dissociated and abstracted. Perhaps this process may not be recognized as review at all if it is systematically made an integral part of the regular work, but it is review in a real and important sense. One of the strong arguments for a continuous program of integrated mathematics is that this sort of incidental or integrated review would necessarily run systematically throughout the entire program, giving strength and coherence to the entire structure through continual interassociation of the components.

At the same time there is need of special review work to supplement the incidental review which has been described. The functions of the special review are to help the student organize more or less comprehensive bodies of material with reference to their logical relationships, to assist him in classifying their important ideas, and to give him a sense of the unity of the whole which might otherwise be lacking. The review lesson, which should be planned with this idea dominant, will generally follow the assimilative study of a unit. In preparing for a review lesson, the student should be expected to summarize the outstanding ideas which have been considered in the unit and to make an outline from which he can give a brief but coherent and systematic discussion of the material in the unit or division. The preparation of such an outline will make it necessary for the student to review the unit in the fullest sense of the term. Through making the necessary association of the ideas in the unit, he will be aided not only in remembering them, but in understanding them and appreciating their interrelations.

A "re-view" is really a "new look"

Incidental review

Specialized review

On the whole, most teachers do a better job of conducting drill work than they do of conducting review work of this type. This is probably due in part to their failure to recognize the main function of review as different from that of drill. Students need to be taught how to review material, just as they need to be taught how to study. They cannot review effectively without definite instructions. Yet all too commonly the only instructions they receive are something like, "Review chapters 7 and 8 for tomorrow." The task of helping students plan their review work is a responsibility which every teacher should take seriously.

Effective review requires definite instructions

MAINTENANCE

Even after mathematical learning has been well and soundly achieved, there still remains the job of keeping what has been learned fresh and readily accessible. Without subsequent application and use, concepts can become vague and fuzzy, relations and procedures can become uncertain, and skills can become rusty. To prevent this from happening it is necessary to drill on the skills and to refresh the concepts from time to time, even after primary attention has been turned to other topics.

A planned program of cumulative drill and review work is aptly designated a "maintenance" program. The learning of new material of course draws upon the already-established background as a frame of reference, and to this extent the learning of new material serves as a means of maintenance, but such maintenance is only incidental to the mastery of the new material. Adequate maintenance of skills and understandings cannot be assured by incidental contacts, but requires an instructional program specially designed to this end.

A sound maintenance program must be planned, not incidental

The fundamental requirement of a satisfactory maintenance program is that it shall operate to prevent the forgetting of facts, concepts, and relationships and forestall the disintegration of skills. To this end it must provide for systematic application of the important elements of the instructional program and for appropriate or needed practice on these elements even after current attention and emphasis have passed on to other matters. Therefore the planning of a really adequate maintenance program must be built upon the following principles:

What to include?

1   The materials to be included should be selected from the point of view of relative values. The program should not be cluttered up with trivial things. Only significant skills, concepts, relationships, principles, and problem situations should be included.

2   In accordance with established principles of drill and review, the items should be distributed throughout the program in such a way that practice on any particular element will not be too greatly concen-

trated but will recur at increasing intervals and in decreasing amounts.

3 The maintenance program should be diagnostic, preferably self-diagnostic, so that each student may be able to discover his own weaknesses. To this end some means should be provided whereby each student may systematically keep a record of and study his own achievements in detail.

4 There should be available supplementary practice material for remedial work on the various particular elements included in the maintenance program. This supplementary material can be used most effectively if it is keyed with the diagnostic record. In this way each student will be able not only to determine those things on which he most needs practice, but to carry on his own remedial work with a minimum of direction.

5 The different sets of exercises in the maintenance program should be comparable in terms of some uniform scoring or rating schedule so that each student may keep a record of his general achievement and his progress. This will be of great value in stimulating pride, effort, and genuine interest in maintaining skills and principles after the original interest due to their newness has worn off.

Drill books, workbooks, and exercise books

Numerous textbooks published in recent years recognize the need for systematic maintenance work and make provision for it through sets of drill exercises, diagnostic inventory tests, cumulative reviews, and the like, placed at strategic points in the texts. In a few cases these exercises appear to have been prepared hastily, but in most cases they are valid and suitable. These same comments are equally applicable to the multitude of drill books and workbooks and sets of practice exercises which are now commercially available to supplement textbooks. They are not all equally good, but the better ones are valuable aids to the teacher in carrying on an adequate maintenance program. Many teachers lack both the experience and the time needed to prepare thoroughly suitable materials for regular maintenance work. Prepared materials which are scientifically planned and for which standards of attainment are available serve at least three useful purposes: (1) they make for economy of time and labor, and therefore for efficiency in instruction; (2) they provide a strong motive to achievement, since they foster the students' continued study of their own performances; and (3) they provide the best possible insurance against forgetting and against the deterioration of skills and understandings.

EXERCISES

1 Make a clear, concise statement of the main objective of each of the four fundamental stages, or aspects, of learning mathematics discussed in this chapter.

2 Explain why all these aspects of learning (and of teaching) mathematics are complementary and necessary parts of the whole job of learning mathematics.

3 Point out, for each of these four aspects, the the effect on the student's learning that would result if the teacher neglected to give attention to that aspect of learning in his teaching.

4 In your opinion, which of these four aspects of learning is most neglected by teachers? Give reasons for your answer.

5 Outline for class presentation a developmental discussion of some topic in algebra or geometry, as you would for presenting it to a high school class. List the things you would want to emphasize or highlight, and select the illustrations you would use. Also try to anticipate and list what difficulties you think the students might be likely to have in understanding clearly your development of the topic.

6 Explain why directed study is important in the process of learning mathematics. Why should directed study of a topic begin soon after the developmental discussion of that topic?

7 Let $\overrightarrow{BA}$ and $\overrightarrow{BC}$ be the sides of $\angle ABC$ and let K be a point in the interior of $\angle ABC$. If $\overline{AC}$ is drawn, show that $\overrightarrow{BK}$ intersects $\overline{AC}$. Suppose you have assigned this as an exercise, and suppose one of your capable students cannot find a way to plan out the proof and get started. Outline a series of questions you might ask him that you think would help him in developing the proof.

8 Mention and discuss some dangers which teachers need to guard against while conducting directed study in mathematics.

9 What is the main function of drill in mathematics? Why is drill necessary? Defend your answer.

10 Mention some important principles of drill procedure and discuss them.

11 It has been said that one great advantage of having routine procedures thoroughly habituated is that this frees the mind to focus more completely on other matters of higher intellectual order, such as seeking for proofs. Comment on the implications and the importance of this with respect to the need for drill.

12 Give an example of some principle or procedure in algebra on which, in your opinion, students need drill for thorough habituation. Plan a drill lesson on this procedure in which thinking, as well as drill, would be involved and the interest of the students maintained.

13 In what respect are drill and review, as discussed in this chapter, alike? In what respects do they differ? Discuss.

14 Explain why review is important in learning mathematics.

15 Take some chapter or section from a high

school textbook in mathematics and prepare an outline which you would give to students for reviewing that chapter or section of the course.

16 Teachers commonly use examples and analogies to illustrate and clarify mathematical concepts, relationships, and principles. In what sense can this be considered teaching for transfer?

17 Explain why factoring of algebraic expressions is a perfect example of the transfer of learning.

18 Since every step in a proof must be justified by some definition, postulate, or fact (theorem) which has already been learned, comment on the assertion that every step in a proof involves a transfer of learning.

19 Some elements of algebra and geometry are now included in the junior high school courses, and even in the lower grades. Discuss the assertion that this spiral type of learning is a good example of the transfer of learning.

20 See if you can discover a pattern (or formula) which yields the sequence of integers 8, 9, 11, 15, 23, 39, 71, 135 as its first eight terms. Did your method of discovering it involve any transfer of learning? Discuss.

21 How would you define real mathematical insight? Can such mathematical insight into the meaning of a pattern or formula or generalization be attained without the transfer of learning? Discuss.

22 One of the important objectives of modern school mathematics is to get students to understand and appreciate the meaning of a deductive proof. When teachers strive for this, it can be said that they are teaching for transfer. Explain.

23 Discuss the proposition that instruction in mathematics can be fruitful only to the extent to which transfer takes place.

24 Explain what is meant by a maintenance program, as the term is used in this chapter. Explain how you, as a teacher, would plan and set up a maintenance program, for example, in beginning algebra.

25 Compare several recent textbooks in beginning algebra to see what provision they make for systematic maintenance work. Select the one that you feel does this best, and discuss your reasons for selecting it.

26 Examine several recent textbooks in high

school geometry and try to decide which one would be the most helpful for the kind of maintenance program in geometry you would like to use.

27 Many textbooks in school mathematics now provide cumulative reviews at ends of chapters or at other strategic places. These are intended to serve as maintenance programs. Examine several textbooks for this feature and try to judge how adequately they serve this objective.

28 Describe some mathematical concept or relationship or principle which you feel you had not really mastered well when you finished high school. Try to account for your lack of mastery, and tell what your teacher could have done to help you gain the proper mastery.

BIBLIOGRAPHY

Anderson, John D.: A Mathematics Seminar, *Mathematics Teacher*, **54** (1961), 109–110.

Archer, Allene: "How to Use Your Library in Mathematics" (Washington, D.C.: National Council of Teachers of Mathematics, 1958).

Bittinger, Marvin L.: A Review of Discovery, *Mathematics Teacher*, **61** (1968), 140–146.

Bruner, Jerome S.: On Learning Mathematics, *Mathematics Teacher*, **53** (1960), 610–619.

Charosh, Mannis: "Mathematical Challenges: Selected Problems from the *Mathematics Student Journal*" (Washington, D.C.: National Council of Teachers of Mathematics, 1965).

Dadourian, H. M.: How to Make Mathematics More Attractive, *Mathematics Teacher*, **53** (1960), 548–551.

Davis, Robert B.: The Madison Project's Approach to a Theory of Instruction, *Journal of Research in Science Teaching*, **2** (1964), 146–162.

Elder, Florence: Mathematics for the Below-average Achiever in High School, *Mathematics Teacher*, **60** (1967), 235–240.

Fehr, Howard F.: The Role of Insight in the Learning of Mathematics, *Mathematics Teacher*, **47** (1954), 393–400.

————: Reorientation in Math Education, *Mathematics Teacher*, **61** (1968), 593–601.

Keller, M. Wiles: Semantics and Mathematics, *School Science and Mathematics*, **68** (1968), 103–113.

Kluttz, Marguerite: The Mathematics Laboratory: A Meaningful Approach to Mathematics Instruction, *Mathematics Teacher*, **56** (1963), 141–145.

Lowry, William C.: Approaches to Discovery Learning in Mathematics, *High School Journal*, February, 1967, pp. 254–260.

Lund, F. W. (Editor): "New Approaches to Mathematics Teaching" (New York: St. Martin's Press, Inc., 1963).

Marks, John L., and James R. Smart: Using the Analytic Method to Encourage Discovery, *Mathematics Teacher*, **60** (1967), 241–245.

Moser, James M.: Mathematics by Analogy, *Mathematics Teacher*, **61** (1968), 374–376.

Pólya, George: On Learning, Teaching, and Learning Teaching, *American Mathematical Monthly*, **70** (1963), 605–619.

Quadling, D. A., and others: The Use of the Axiomatic Method in Secondary Schools, *Mathematics Teacher*, **60** (1967), 398–403.

Randall, Karl: Improving Study Habits in Mathematics, *Mathematics Teacher*, **55** (1962), 553–555.

Schmidt, Roland L.: Using the Library in Junior High School Mathematics Classes, *Mathematics Teacher*, **56** (1963), 40–42.

Sister Margaret Cecilia: Mathematics Projects, *Mathematics Teacher*, **54** (1961), 527–530.

Sister Mary Corona: Seminars: An Integrating Force in a Program of Concentration, *Mathematics Teacher*, **48** (1955), 209–213.

Smith, Robert E.: A Desk, Some Chairs, and a Blackboard, *American Mathematical Monthly*, **69** (1962), 658–666.

Sobel, Max A.: "Teaching General Mathematics" (Englewood Cliffs, N.J.: Prentice-Hall, Inc., 1967).

Sueltz, Ben A.: Drill-Practice-Recurring Experience, *Twenty-first Yearbook* (Washington, D.C.: National Council of Teachers of Mathematics, 1953), pp. 192–204.

Swain, Henry: "How to Study Mathematics" (Washington, D.C.: National Council of Teachers of Mathematics, 1961).

Trimble, Harold C.: The Heart of Teaching, *Mathematics Teacher*, **61** (1968), 485–488.

Van Engen, Henry: Some Psychological Principles Underlying Mathematics Instruction, *School Science and Mathematics*, **61** (1961), 242–250.

Vaughn, William D.: Some Drill Techniques for Arithmetic, *Mathematics Teacher,* **50** (1957), 436–437.

Wallen, Rev. C. J.: Stressing the Creative Aspects of Mathematics in Teaching the Gifted Child, *Mathematics Teacher,* **55** (1962), 243–248.

Weiss, Sol.: Innovations and Research in the Teaching of Mathematics to the Terminal Student, *Mathematics Teacher,* **60** (1967), 611–618.

Willerding, Margaret F.: The Uselessness of Mathematics, *School Science and Mathematics,* **68** (1968), 403–411, 495–505.

Willoughby, Stephen S.: Discovery, *Mathematics Teacher,* **56** (1963), 22–25.

Young, J. W. A.: The Teaching of Mathematics, *Mathematics Teacher,* **61** (1968), 287–295.

six | means to effective instruction in mathematics

Motivation, devices, and planning are discussed in this chapter

The variety of devices and procedures which teachers have used in the effort to make their instruction in mathematics bear fruit is so great, that unless care is taken, the discussion of these could easily become haphazard and disconnected. To prevent this, the chapter has been organized under the following three main headings: (1) stimulating and maintaining interest in mathematics, (2) special methods, devices, and media for teaching mathematics, and (3) planning for effective learning and teaching.

Each of these categories is itself pretty broad, and the three are not, of course, mutually exclusive. Planning, for example, must take account of ways of stimulating the students' interest in their work, as well as of methods and devices and equipment which the teacher may employ. It is believed, however, that arranging the discussion under these three headings will give it some measure of organization and coherence, and will bring into focus some ideas useful and important for mathematics teachers.

STIMULATING AND MAINTAINING INTEREST IN MATHEMATICS

Students work best when they are interested

It may be taken as axiomatic that students will work most diligently and most effectively at tasks in which they are genuinely interested. To create and maintain interest becomes, therefore, one of the most important tasks of the teacher of secondary school mathematics. It is also one of the most difficult problems the teacher encounters. The interest of students of secondary school age is capricious. It is easily caught by any new thing, but it is as easily distracted to other new things. Ordinarily, it cannot be depended upon to maintain itself for any great length of time unless the work has been carefully and deliberately planned to that end, and even then it usually needs occasional stimulation. Thus the motivation of the work in mathematics has two aspects, namely, creating or arousing interest and maintaining the interest after the novelty of the work in hand has worn off.

Novelty, usefulness, and stimulation of curiosity help to arouse interest

As a rule, students readily *become interested* in things which are new or exciting, or for which they can perceive practical values or applications to situations and fields of study that have already caught their interest; and in things which involve puzzle elements or elements of mystery. Other things being equal, possessing a background of related facts tends to intensify interest in new work, but this is neither a necessary condition nor a sufficient guarantee for the awakening of interest. Novelty is sometimes more compelling than familiarity. The elements of novelty, usefulness, and sheer intellectual curiosity are the primary stimuli for the awakening of interest.

Maintaining interest is important but not easy

It is easier to initiate interest than it is to maintain interest after the work has got under way and the novelty has worn off. In this connection it is worthwhile to observe that students tend to *remain interested* in those things which they can do most successfully and understand most completely. Inability to understand is likely to beget a condition of listlessness, inattention, and general loss of interest. On the other hand, the work should not be diluted and should not evade the intellectual stretching without which there can be no mathematical growth. The work should be made to present, as far as possible, a continual challenge. Consequently, it is of the greatest importance that work in mathematics be so organized and conducted as to emphasize the values and the inherent intellectual challenge of the subject and to ensure understanding and a reasonable degree of competence by keeping the subject matter and the activities at a level of difficulty appropriate to the intellectual maturity of the students. Within these conditions are to be found the motives basic to hard and effective work in mathematics. Interest in the subject can be effectively augmented by numerous special devices and activities, some of which can be used in connection with class instruction, while others, such as mathematics clubs and special programs, are essentially coordinate and supplementary activities.

MOTIVATION THROUGH THE USE OF MULTISENSORY AIDS AND DEVICES

Most people gain new impressions more vividly through sensory experiences than they do through reading or abstract reasoning. The remarkable growth and public acceptance of motion pictures, radio, and television leave no doubt of the interest-getting power of these audio-visual media. Advertisements in newspapers and magazines and on billboards and television commercials are found to be more effective when they have eye appeal than when they are confined to mere statements in words, even though the connection between the picture and the subject may be pretty farfetched. Thus a pleasant wooded lake and an attractive young lady seem to be standard adjuncts in advertising almost anything from soap, cigarettes, and beer to refrigerators, automobiles, and waterfront lots.

Teachers of mathematics have been slower than their colleagues in English, geography, science, history, and the social studies to take advantage of this eye-and-ear appeal as a means of stimulating interest. This has been partly due to the nature of the subject, which is essentially one of ideas rather than things. That, in turn, accounts in large measure for the fact that not very many really good pictorial or physical representations of mathematical topics have been commonly available. Commercially, such devices have been limited mainly to some good sound films and filmstrips and a number of not-so-good ones and to certain rather expensive models and mechanical devices for illustrating theorems in geometry. For one reason or another, these aids and devices have not been widely used, though as they are improved, it can be expected that their use will increase.

Multisensory aids, however, are not limited to motion pictures and filmstrips, and increasing attention is being given to the employment of other sensory devices both for motivation and for instruction. Evidence of this is found, for example, in the efforts to improve the effectiveness of textbooks through more and better diagrams and illustrations, the improvement of type face and format, and the liberal use of color. It is also seen in the number of suggestions in textbooks and elsewhere for stimulating interest in mathematics through projects involving the use of instruments and the construction and use of visual or mechanical devices for illustrating mathematical concepts, facts, and principles. Activities

Multisensory aids can contribute to mathematical learning

of this kind are commonly called "laboratory work in mathematics." Part of a later section in this chapter will be devoted to discussion of such work as an important avenue to learning. Its importance, however, even from the standpoint of motivation alone, is so great that it must not be overlooked in this connection.

MOTIVATION THROUGH APPLICATION
TO OTHER FIELDS OF STUDY

The relation of mathematics to other fields of study often provides an important means of stimulating interest. At all levels of secondary education from the junior high school to the junior college the contribution which mathematics has made and can make to the more adequate development and understanding of many subjects is coming to be recognized more fully than ever before, and teachers should not fail to stress its importance from this stand-point.

Application of
mathematics to
physical sciences,
biology, social
sciences, and other
fields

The dependence of physics, chemistry, and astronomy upon mathematics is so manifest that it is hardly necessary to dwell upon it here. Mathematics is, literally, indispensable in the study of these subjects, and no informed person would question its instrumental value in this connection. Up to the middle of this century biologists had not considered that mathematics was of special importance for work in their field, except perhaps for research in the upper reaches of certain specialized branches. Since then, however, this attitude has changed. New avenues have been opened up for systematizing and expanding this science and for investigating and interpreting biological phenomena through the formulation of precise mathematical expressions of the rela-tionships and changes involved. Remarkable advances have been made through the application of mathematical procedures to advanced studies in genetics, heredity, nutrition, growth and maturation, senescence, metabolism, fatigue, the effects of various stimuli on organisms, and many other special phases of biological and physiological study. Indeed, it is hardly too much to say that it is no longer possible to pursue the study of biological phe-nomena very far beyond the early descriptive stages without the aid of mathematical analysis and treatment.

The social sciences are also beginning to draw heavily upon mathematics, particularly statistical and graphic methods, for the investigation and interpretation of social phenomena. Some of the mathematics used in connection with these subjects is so simple and so enlightening that it can be incorporated easily and very appropriately even in junior high school courses which take up such topics as public health, safety campaigns, thrift, population trends, expenditure of public moneys, and others that deal in simple fashion with social and economic phenomena. Economics and sociology deal essentially with mass phenomena, and there is a widespread belief that the only mathematics used in con-nection with these subjects is statistics. It is quite true that sta-tistics, including graphics, is more extensively and more obviously used than other mathematical procedures in the elementary work in these fields, but in some of the more advanced work, especially in theoretical studies related to social and economic phenomena, there are important applications of mathematics, such as high-speed computation, stochastic processes, linear programming, and game theory, which are nonstatistical in nature.

In one way or another mathematics leaves its imprint upon the foundations of many of the school subjects. Its applications are more manifest in some than in others, but seldom, indeed if ever, are they lacking altogether. We have seen that they are not limited to the physical sciences, but have important bearings upon the biological and social sciences as well. The industrial arts require mathematics. Psychology is finding more uses for it all the time. Even English, the foreign languages, and the fine arts are enriched by an understanding of the mathematical principles of form and number, of symmetry and order, upon which they are based. By continually impressing upon students the relationships and applications of mathematics to other school subjects, teachers can stimulate interest in the study of mathematics and can at the same time give the students a more comprehensive and complete idea of the nature of the other subjects.

MATHEMATICS IN BUSINESS, INDUSTRY, AND THE PROFESSIONS

Another means of stimulating interest in mathematics is by pointing out its applications in fields of work in which people gain their livelihood. All boys and many girls must face the practical problem of selecting an occupation and earning a living, and they are often concerned to learn something about opportunities and requirements in different fields. Most people do not realize that mathematics has come to have an important place in many vocational fields, and that one who has a good mathematical background has a valuable asset. Many articles and books have been published which discuss applications of mathematics in specialized branches of industry.

We have mentioned the usefulness of mathematics in the biological and social sciences. It is obvious that students desiring to go into teaching or advanced study in these fields will be seriously handicapped without a sound mathematics background. The same can be said for the specialized fields of anatomy, physiology, psychology, and medicine.

Students scarcely need to be told that mathematics, along with the physical sciences, form the very foundation of engineering. Calculating devices can now be made to handle much of the engineer's routine work, but they cannot do his thinking for him, and this is mostly in terms of mathematics and physics.

Up to about 1960 the fields of business and commerce had not placed much emphasis on mathematical training beyond simple arithmetic, and this is still true as regards the low-level jobs. But the explosive impact of the electronic computer has revolutionized many business practices involving data processing. It has also opened up a whole new category of remunerative related occupa-

Computer science offers career opportunities

tions which require, for the most part, extensive mathematical preparation. It now appears that the demand for personnel equipped and trained to handle these jobs is destined to exceed the supply for years to come.

MOTIVATION THROUGH INTEREST
IN MATHEMATICS AS A CAREER

Until near the middle of this century the opportunities for careers in mathematics were far fewer, more circumscribed, and financially less attractive than they are today. The professional mathematician found little demand for his services outside the field of teaching, and even in teaching good jobs were not always easy to find.

Now, however, the situation is different. Whereas before 1940 there were almost no business or industrial job opportunities for professional mathematicians as such, today there are literally thousands, and the number is still growing, both in volume and diversity. The demand for professionally trained mathematicians in business and industry is greater than the supply, and the demand is increasing faster than the supply. The capable young man or woman who wishes to make a career in the field of mathematics and who is willing to take the time and make the effort needed to secure the necessary professional training will find a variety of opportunities open to him. He will not need to worry about whether or not he can get a job when he has finished his training. Moreover, because of the scholarships and subsidies which are available at most universities for promising young mathematicians, he may find the financial burden of securing an advanced degree considerably less than he might have expected.

A variety of rewarding careers are available in mathematics

These changed conditions have come about as a result of the explosive growth of mathematics itself and of the applications of mathematical ideas to problems in many fields. Whole new segments or branches of mathematics have come into being. New ideas are being applied to both new and old problems. Old ideas are being applied to new problems and to old problems in new ways. New practical problems stimulate new research in pure mathematics, and new discoveries in mathematics suggest new theoretical developments and new practical applications.

The remarkable developments in mathematical statistics and high-speed computing and data processing, and the great variety of striking applications of these developments, have made these branches of mathematics more widely known and appreciated than some of the others. The fact is, however, that the whole range of mathematics offers career opportunities to young men and women with professional training in the subject. Among such opportunities are professional careers in teaching, in computer theory and techniques, and in applying mathematical theory to the solution of a wide variety of problems arising in business and industry. Many doors are open to the high school student who shows capability and interest in mathematics and who wishes to make it his profession.

MOTIVATION THROUGH MATHEMATICAL RECREATIONS AND CLUBS

In the minds of a good many people the concept of motivation has become identified with, and in some cases limited to, the idea of games, puzzles, plays, anecdotes, and other interesting, but sometimes more or less trivial and unrelated, matters, often referred to under the generic title of "mathematical recreations." It is unfortunate that this should be the case, because motivation implies a much broader and more significant connotation than this and takes place through various avenues. At the same time such mathematical recreations and peripheral activities, if kept within *Mathematical* proper perspective, can be valuable and legitimate in relieving the *recreations can help* tedium of necessary routine work and in presenting an aspect of *relieve tedium* mathematics the existence of which is at times not even suspected. It is a rare person, especially child, who is not interested in games or in things which are unusual or unsuspected and which contain elements of surprise or mystery. While mathematical puzzles, contests, and games cannot be permitted to pre-empt too much of the time allotted to regular classwork, there is abundant evidence that the moderate and appropriate employment of such devices does add much of interest and zest to the courses.[1]

Mathematical recreations take a great variety of forms: puzzles, cryptograms, unusual problems involving special equations, mosaics and tesselations, dissections and other special geometric patterns and problems, problems of paper folding, mazes, problems of number theory, number curiosities and puzzles, and hundreds of other forms. Among published sources a few magazines and numerous books have been devoted wholly to mathematical recreations, and new ones are continually appearing. The *Scientific American* has long carried a special department devoted to mathematical puzzles and diversions, and *School Science and Mathematics* and the *Mathematics Student Journal* each has a problem department as a regular feature.

Mathematics clubs Mathematics clubs provide another good milieu for stimulating *stimulate interest* student interest. Such clubs have been formed and used for this

[1] Louis Grant Brandes, Why We Use Recreational Mathematics in Our Secondary School Mathematics Classes, *School Science and Mathematics*, **54** (1954), 289–293.

purpose for many years with students at various stages of mathematical maturity, from the junior high school to the college. Programs and activities can be adapted to special interests of the students, and for students at various levels of sophistication.

MOTIVATION THROUGH INTELLECTUAL CURIOSITY

Undoubtedly, the most powerful and enduring source of motivation resides in the intellectual curiosity of the student. Curiosity impels him to try to discover answers to questions that are, as yet, for him, unanswered: why things happen as they do; why things work as they do; whether or not this particular problem involves a relation that is a special case under this or that more general principle or whether observed similarities in several special cases suggest the conjecture of a generalization; whether theorem B could be invoked to justify step 5 in the proof of theorem A. A great deal has been said, and rightly so, about the importance of discovery[2] in school mathematics. The impulse to discover mathematical relations, principles, and facts springs wholly from intellectual curiosity about them. Discovery and curiosity are interactive; each is the best stimulant to the other. The student whose curiosity about a problem or a theorem keeps him working on it until he discovers a solution or a proof not only gets satisfaction from making his discovery, but the fact that he has succeeded almost invariably increases his self-confidence and stimulates his curiosity about other problems and an interest in seeking their solutions.

Curiosity stimulates discovery

Discovery, in turn, arouses further curiosity

Teachers and textbook writers have not always recognized and taken advantage of the power of sheer intellectual curiosity as the motive *par excellence* for profitable work in school mathematics. As a consequence they have sometimes failed to organize and present the work in a manner designed to stimulate the student's interest through a challenge to his curiosity. A notable instance of this is to be found in the fact that practically all theorems of demonstrative geometry are set up as exercises in establishing certain prestated conclusions rather than as exercises for free exploration and investigation of the consequences of certain hypotheses. Thus the element of discovery of the central fact or relationship in each theorem is removed at the outset, whereas this element of discovery could in many cases be retained and used to quicken the interest of the students. For example, the statement, "Prove that an inscribed angle is measured by half of its intercepted arc," sets forth a task to be performed, while the

Teachers should strive to create challenge

[2] For a good discussion of teaching for discovery see Donovan A. Johnson and Gerald R. Rising, "Guidelines for Teaching Mathematics" (Belmont, Calif.: Wadsworth Publishing Company, Inc., 1967), pp. 58–66.

question, "What relation, if any, exists between the measure of an inscribed angle and the measure of its intercepted arc?" is designed to whet the curiosity of the student instead of satisfying it at the outset.

Of course, "the discovery method" has limitations; not all mathematics can be taught in this way. Certainly, not every relation and theorem can be formulated by every student (nor some of them by any student) through original discovery. There just is not enough time,[3] and students differ a great deal in their ability to generalize. But when teachers can see or make opportunities for stimulating curiosity, through discovery or otherwise, these opportunities should not be neglected, but should be made to bear fruit.

As a rule secondary school students are not lazy. That they may often appear to be is largely because their work is so generally set up for them as tasks rather than as challenges. In mathematics, challenges would be problems or theorems in which they match their wits against the inexorable logic of the situation to see if they can come up with a solution or a proof. If the problem or theorem is stated in such a way that the challenge is not emphasized, the students will often become bored and indifferent. Most students in the secondary school are persistently curious individuals, and they will work, and work hard, at things that interest them. They do not hate mathematics, as some seem to think; they hate only drudgery and boredom and frustration. Teachers need to remind themselves continuously that to bring out the best in their students they must appeal to interest motives, and that intellectual curiosity is one of the strongest, as well as the most desirable, of these motives. The range of the potential intellectual interests of these students is practically unlimited. The writers of modern detective fiction have recognized this and have capitalized on it. The enormous popular response which has brought this type of fiction to the front rank in sales and library circulation can be attributed only to the general reader's insatiate interest in the development and denouement of a problem situation.

Evidence that mathematics is not devoid of strong appeal to the curiosity and interest of people can be found in the appearance and widespread sale, over the past few years, of a large number of books on mathematical recreations and popular mathematics for the general reader. Even the more serious among these books are attaining sales records far beyond expectation.

Further evidence of the power of intellectual curiosity as a motive is found in the success which has accompanied the intro-

The challenge should be "see if you can . . ."

---

[3] One teacher reported to the authors that in extolling the virtues of the discovery method he quoted an old Chinese proverb to the effect that "One discovery is worth a thousand tellings," whereupon an iconoclast in the class responded, "Yes, and they take about the same amount of time."

duction of some of the concepts, notation, and terminology of "modern" mathematics into the mathematics courses of the junior high school. The testimony of teachers who have used such material in the ninth grade, and even in the earlier grades, is that its challenge to the sheer intellectual curiosity of the students almost invariably provides a powerful stimulant and motive to their study of mathematics.

Mathematical situations lack, of course, the lurid human interest of the ordinary mystery novel, but they do not lack the essential curiosity-provoking possibilities. "Think-of-a-number" games are popular at parties, even among people who anticipate or recall the study of algebra with dread; yet the games are nothing but algebra, somewhat obscured, perhaps, by a screen of mysticism which only serves to stimulate curiosity. People are interested in seeing how numbers behave, and algebra is essentially the science of the behavior of numbers. Puzzle problems in mathematics have often been criticized as being unreal or having no genuine application to life situations. A little experience in teaching algebra, however, will soon convince the most skeptical critic that problems which purport to represent "real" situations may not be interesting to students, and that problems may be quite interesting to them without being "real." As a matter of fact, it is quite possible that the presence of the puzzle element in problems is often a greater stimulus to *interest* than those elements of so-called reality which authors of textbooks try so hard to incorporate in problems.

Obviously, there must be system and organization in mathematics. Arithmetic and algebra cannot and should not consist entirely of number games and puzzles, nor demonstrative geometry of incidental and undirected investigations. These are sequential subjects and must be developed in sequential form. Haphazard or piecemeal work will achieve nothing of value. But within the framework of the systematic organization of a course in mathematics at any level of secondary instruction there are many opportunities for motivating the work by deliberate stimulation of the curiosity of the students along the lines indicated. The greater the extent to which this is done, the greater will be the interest, understanding, and assiduity with which the students will work, and the more meaningful and worthwhile will the work become to them.

Problems need not be "real" to be interesting

A FINAL WORD ON MOTIVATION THROUGH STIMULATING INTEREST

The means and devices which have been discussed in the foregoing pages will be found helpful in stimulating and maintaining interest in mathematics. In themselves, however, they cannot be

The best means to motivation is a competent and inspiring teacher

regarded as panaceas or guarantees. In the last analysis the greatest factor in creating interest is a sympathetic, well-informed competent, and inspiring teacher. No devices can yield the fruit of a continuing and enthusiastic student interest if they are grafted upon the dead stump of incompetent instruction. The truly inspiring teacher must first of all be thoroughly grounded in the subject matter of mathematics, well beyond the level of any material which he is expected to teach, in order that he may inspire the confidence and respect of his students. He must have a sympathetic understanding of student difficulties and must be always ready and willing to offer proper guidance and stimulation. Finally, he must have an enthusiastic interest in his subject and in teaching it. He must believe in its values and its contribution to the educational well-being of the students. Enthusiasm is contagious, and sane enthusiasm backed by sympathetic and enlightened competence is the only real guarantee of the effective maintenance of student interest. Devices are helpful, but they are not sufficient unto the task. The inspiring teacher is the real *sine qua non.*

AIDS TO INSTRUCTION: MEDIA AND METHODS

In comparison with the biological and physical sciences, mathematics instruction has suffered in the past from a notable lack of special physical facilities and special instructional devices for giving meaning to various concepts and relations, providing motivation for the students, and increasing the effectiveness of the instruction. This is due in part to a lack of imagination and aggressiveness on the part of teachers, but it is due also to the fact that until rather recent years not much experimental work had been done in mathematics with new media or with nontraditional methods of instruction. In the past decade, however, a good deal of progress has been made. Special equipment has been invented

The teacher should watch for good innovations

or vastly improved, and some innovations in teaching method have been tried, with promising results. These steps suggest new and perhaps better approaches to some of the problems which face the mathematics teacher.

SOME INNOVATIONS IN EQUIPMENT AND METHOD

Traditionally, the equipment available to the mathematics teacher has been limited pretty much to the textbook and the chalkboard, with perhaps a few models for use in solid geometry and some rulers and protractors for linear and angular measurement and some supplementary textbooks and workbooks. These teaching aids were far from negligible, as anyone who has tried to teach mathematics in a room without a chalkboard can attest, but with a chalkboard alone it is often hard even for a good teacher to accomplish all that he envisions. Today the situation is quite different. Now many kinds of direct and indirect teaching aids are available, subject only to the limitations of financial resources. Some are in the form of audio-visual equipment such as animated films, filmstrips, improved projection equipment, and the overhead projector, with its adaptability for use in large classes and with its large variety of sets of commercially available transparencies and overlays prepared and adapted for different courses; timesaving desk calculators (now available in either hand-operated, electric, or miniature electronic computer form); supplementary books for the mathematics library; models; measuring instruments of various kinds and other physical equipment for laboratory work in mathematics; bulletin boards; a variety of prepared materials for programmed instruction; and many special devices too numerous to mention. In passing, we should note that while its use is not limited to mathematics teachers, the ordinary duplicating machine is one of the best teaching aids in mathematics. In addition to the kinds of things mentioned above, helpful teachers' manuals and commentaries are available for most textbooks. In some schools team teaching is being tried with apparent success, and in a few places which have access to a large electronic computer, computer-oriented courses and computer-assisted courses are being tried. Some schools have experimented with teaching mathematics courses by film loop and closed-circuit television.

> *Direct and indirect teaching aids*

> *Team teaching and computers suggest new approaches*

It is impossible to discuss all these means at length here, but we shall give some attention to a few which seem to be of special importance to teachers or which represent significant innovations.

AUDIO-VISUAL DEVICES

The use of audio-visual devices in the teaching of mathematics is not new, but it is increasing rapidly. One reason is that more teachers have come to see the usefulness of films, filmstrips, and transparencies than ever before, and have learned how to use projection equipment successfully. Another is that the projection equipment and facilities for its use have been greatly improved. A third is that the number and accessibility of films, filmstrips, and transparencies have increased enormously, and their quality has also improved. Sets of films for mathematics instruction have already been produced under the auspices of such agencies as SMSG, UICSM, CUPM, and NCTM, and other sets are sure to

> *Audio-visual devices are improved and more accessible*

follow. In 1968 the National Council of Teachers of Mathematics announced the forthcoming production of a new second series of forty-two sound-and-color instruction films for elementary school teachers and students. Still another reason for the rapid increase in the use of audio-visual and other aids in the classroom is the availability of funds from the U.S. Office of Education for the purchase of such equipment.

What we see has greater impact on us than what we hear

Most people tend to be visual-minded. Visual representation of geometrical objects and graphical or diagrammatic representation of concepts and relations seem to have a stronger and more enduring impact than mere verbal description or explanation. The very fact that teachers have always used the chalkboard extensively for such representations is proof of this. But it is not always easy to make *good* representative drawings, and sometimes too much time is required. Many of these materials can be had, professionally drawn, on filmstrips, and can be projected with no delay on a screen or a wall, or even directly on the chalkboard itself. Representations of polar or rectangular charts are cases in point. Opaque projectors can be used to project charts or printed materials and drawings. A better technique, which has more versatility made possible by recent developments in copying equipment, is to copy the drawing or printed material on a transparency and then project it with the overhead projector. One reason for its versatility is that it uses transmitted light, and the image can be clearly visible without darkening the room. The overhead projector is limited to the use of transparencies, either prepared ahead of time as overlays or built up by the teacher during the discussion, but in some ways it is the most adaptable of teaching aids. The teacher can use it for either large or small classes, just as he would use the chalkboard, and there is the further advantage that he can face the class all the while and can write on the transparency without getting between what he is writing and the students.

The availability of these various visual and audio-visual teaching aids has had considerable influence on teaching procedures in school mathematics, and their influence is sure to increase. Both commercial companies and organizations concerned with the teaching of mathematics are producing more and better films, filmstrips, and transparencies at an increasing rate. Projection equipment, already good, will become even better.

LABORATORY WORK IN MATHEMATICS

The use of multisensory aids, when well coordinated with the other classroom learning activities, can serve a double purpose, namely, to stimulate interest and provide a most effective means of clarifying many mathematical concepts and relations through the experience of associating them directly with physical things. Thus it serves as a highly important avenue for organic learning, as well as for motivation. Such practice is often referred to as "laboratory work in mathematics," for the activities which do, or could, take place in the mathematics laboratory bear much the same relation to the mathematics courses as their counterpart activities in the physics or biology laboratory bear to those courses. It is true that the idea of the mathematics laboratory has not yet received the same general acceptance as the science laboratory has, but this may well be because mathematics teachers have not themselves recognized and insisted upon its importance as the science teachers have. Actually, most mathematics teachers have been too passive in this respect. Teachers of science, art, music, home economics, and other subjects do not hesitate to ask for space and equipment for this type of work, and they get it. But most mathematics teachers do not even ask for it, though to do so would be both reasonable and proper. Fortunately, this situation is changing rapidly. Laboratory work in mathematics is now receiving increasing attention. New classrooms are being designed with this as one of the primary considerations. Textbooks, teachers' manuals, and professional journals for teachers are giving more suggestions for such work than they ever have before. Special courses are being given to equip teachers and prospective teachers for such work, and the mathematics laboratory has become almost a standard adjunct of institutes and professional meetings for mathematics teachers. Its importance in the learning of mathematics may be compared with the importance of laboratory work in the learning of physics, chemistry, and biology and that of field work in biology and geography. In view of the significant contribution which it can make and the fact that teachers have only begun to exploit its possibilities, it must be given more than passing mention here.

New emphasis is given to the importance of laboratory work

As the name implies, the underlying idea of the mathematics laboratory is that students will develop new concepts and understandings particularly well through experimental activities dealing with concrete situations such as measuring and drawing; counting, weighing, averaging, and estimating; taking readings from instruments; recording, comparing, analyzing, classifying, seeking patterns, and checking data; and that interest will be stimulated and understanding will be clarified through obtaining original data or impressions from concrete physical situations and working with such data. Most work of this nature will involve the use of various kinds of physical equipment and will entail such activities

Learning through activities

as those listed here. Some of this work can be done in the class-room that is suitably arranged and equipped; some can take the form of elementary field work, such as determination of angles and distances and the mapping of small areas. Most students find such work highly interesting, and it is doubtless true that through it they can develop many mathematical concepts and insights with an interest and a clarity often not attained through a strictly intellectual approach. It is also likely that these concepts and prin-ciples become more enduring and more functional and mean-ingful when they are seen in relation to actual applications.

There is, of course, some danger that, unless proper precautions are taken, laboratory work in mathematics may degenerate into more or less aimless playing with instruments, models, and gadg-ets. Activities which are mere busywork and which contribute nothing toward understanding are worthless. To be productive of learning, the activities must be carefully planned, closely super-vised, and guided toward definite ends. Responsibility for the effectiveness of whatever laboratory-type work is done rests squarely with the teacher, and the discharge of that responsibility depends upon adequate planning and supervision of the activities.

Laboratory work needs careful planning

The activities involved in laboratory-type work in mathematics fall broadly into two classes which, though not mutually exclusive, may be called, respectively, "demonstrations" and "experimental activities." By the term "demonstration" we have in mind the illustration and explanation to the teacher or to the class of some mathematical concept or relation by a method in which some physical equipment or device is used to illustrate and help clarify the explanation. Thus the term is used here in the sense in which it is commonly used in connection with classes in physics or chemistry. For example, various physical devices have been used for the following purposes: to illustrate operations with positive and negative numbers, or the manner in which the trigonometric functions vary; to confirm the identification of the center of gravity of a flat triangular solid with the geometrical centroid of a triangle of the same shape and size; and to verify the geometric description of the locus of the vertex of an angle whose sides pass through two fixed points. Demonstration activities therefore are associated with the "giving out," or transmitting to others, of information and ideas already acquired by the demonstrator. The demonstrator may be either the teacher or a student; or perhaps a small group of students may cooperate in giving a demonstration. Any demonstration which is well planned and effectively carried out involves a real learning experience. Although it is ostensibly aimed at the receiving audience, every experienced teacher knows that the students giving the demonstration will probably learn

Demonstration activities

even more through the deeper and clearer insight engendered by the activity itself.[4]

Experimental
activities

In speaking of *experimental activities* we shall have in mind any kind of activity which (1) is carried on individually or by small groups working together and (2) is aimed primarily at helping the experimenters themselves to clearer understandings. This sort of activity can take many forms. A student who has obtained timed temperature readings in a physics class in an experiment on the cooling rate of a liquid may, by working with these data in tabular and graphic forms, be helped to a clear understanding of the law of cooling and its mathematical representation. Checking the solutions of simultaneous equations by accurately made large-scale graphs can serve to clarify and deepen the interpretation of graphs as well as make the algebraic solutions seem concrete and realistic. By estimating and then measuring distances or angles, students clarify their concepts of a yard, a rod, 100 feet, or an angle of elevation of 15° or 45°. Real appreciation of how many things make 1,000 will be sharpened by outlining on a piece of cross-section paper a rectangle containing 1,000 squares and then drawing a little ring in each one. The axioms for solving linear equations can be given point and meaning by the use of a pair of balances. A model cut from a large potato can be used to illustrate that the volume of a triangular pyramid is one-third that of the prism in which it is inscribed. Indeed, the illustration of many theorems of plane and solid geometry by means of physical devices adds a satisfying tangibility to the formal proofs. In the junior high school the properties of geometric figures and concepts of distances, angles, weights, areas, volumes, and loci can be given a more vivid impact through work of this experimental nature than through any other means.[5]

Space limitations make it impossible in this book to extend the discussion of laboratory work in mathematics, though there is a great deal more to be said about it. Fortunately, a number of excellent references dealing with many aspects of this subject in detail are now available.

PROGRAMMED INSTRUCTION

Programmed instruction is no longer a novelty. It is an outgrowth of the "teaching machine" movement which dates back to the early 1950s and came to prominence in that decade. For various

[4] For specific suggestions on conducting such activities, see the article by Emil J. Berger, Principles Guiding the Use of Teacher- and Pupil-made Learning Aids, *Twenty-second Yearbook* (Washington, D.C.: National Council of Teachers of Mathematics, 1954), pp. 160–163.
[5] *Ibid.*

reasons the excitement over mechanical teaching machines faded after a few years (as might have been expected), but programmed instruction in the form of specially designed books has continued to be regarded as a potentially valuable contributer to instruction in mathematics.

Pros and cons of programmed instruction (PI)

The relative benefits of programmed instruction (PI) in mathematics, as contrasted with the usual class instruction by teacher and conventional textbook, have been and still are a controversial question. Advocates of the use of programmed instruction claim a number of advantages for it, among which are the following:

1 It encourages and helps students to discover concepts and relationships for themselves by providing them with sound sequences of developmental exercises.
2 It permits each student to proceed at his own optimum pace. It can be used in situations where the number of students desiring to take a subject is too large to be handled effectively in regular classes by the available staff.
3 It can be used in small schools, where the number of students desiring to take a subject is too small to justify the organization of a class in that subject.
4 It can be used to advantage as a supplementary instructional device in classes organized along conventional lines.

On the other hand, there are some who feel that such potential advantages of programmed instruction are partially or wholly offset by other considerations. Among these adverse criticisms the following have been mentioned:

1 Once a course is programmed, it is inflexible. It cannot be modified either in content or emphasis without making a new program for it.
2 Some courses in mathematics which have been programmed have been too traditional in content and organization and do not reflect the spirit of modern mathematical thought.
3 Among the important values claimed for the usual teacher-class instructional pattern are the ability to communicate understanding to others and the feedback and interaction between teacher and students and between students and students. Teaching machines and programmed instruction make no provision for these valuable interactions and make little demand upon the ability to communicate ideas.

Unquestionably, students can and do learn some things through programmed instruction. Most of the studies that have been carried on have been centered on the question of whether they learn these things better through programmed instruction or through the usual textbook-teacher form of instruction. What experimental evidence is now available on the question of which is better is inconclusive and sometimes conflicting.

The more penetrating question of whether the things that can be learned through programmed instruction include all the essential things which mathematics teachers believe students *should* learn (such as increasing independence from guided step-by-step direction) is another matter. Many teachers believe that programmed instruction per se falls short in this respect. They believe that the narrowly fragmented objectives upon which PI is built, and toward which it is oriented, do not imply proper attention to some of the more general, and perhaps more subjective, values which they want their students to derive from the study of mathematics.

Programmed instruction has too often been viewed by its advocates as a panacea. Instruction that depends wholly on programmed material is suspect. But programmed material viewed as a teaching aid, on a par with workbooks, filmstrips, and so on, has undoubtedly large potential for use in special situations.

Perhaps the advocates of programmed instruction have claimed too much for it, and perhaps the critics have been too harsh. Perhaps the "either-or" position for comparing programmed instruction and the usual textbook-teacher instruction is not the best position from which to judge them. Perhaps for some purposes or in some situations one has more advantages than the other. Perhaps ways may be found to make the two patterns of instruction supplement and reinforce each other.

Experimentation and inquiry into the usefulness of programmed instruction in the teaching of mathematics will go on. Its potential in this direction continues to be the subject of serious study, not only by individual investigators, but in large-scale studies under the auspices of responsible groups, such as SMSG and UICSM. On the whole there appears to be reason for hope that programmed instruction will find a useful place as a supplementary medium of instruction.

THE COMPUTER AND SCHOOL MATHEMATICS

The digital computer and its role in the program of school mathematics is a matter to which some schools are already giving attention, and which is undoubtedly assuming the proportions of a major issue. The tremendous impact of the computer on procedures in business and industry has brought about a new "computer revolution" comparable in its effect on society with the industrial revolution, and has opened up new vistas for the future, some yet only dimly seen. Through the part it plays in automation, data processing, and information retrieval it has revolutionized a variety of practices as diverse as the preparation of bank statements and the guidance of ballistic missiles, or as the prediction of outcomes of elections and the processing of ice cream. With an impact perhaps comparable with that of the automobile, the telephone, and the radio, the computer is certain to affect education and to demand attention in the program of the schools, and particularly in the program of school mathematics.

What direction this recognition will take, however, is not yet well established. The purchase, installation, and maintenance of computer hardware are still very expensive. Moreover, the number of teachers who understand computers well enough to be qualified to teach courses with or about computers is still small. Issues such as the following arise:

Some issues about computer-oriented instruction

1   What should be taught about computers? Should it be merely information about purposes for which computers are used, or should it be technical information about the physics and the circuitry of the hardware, or should it be the programming of problems?
2   Should the emphasis on computers affect the existing courses in school mathematics? If so, how?
3   Should new special courses in "computer mathematics" be introduced?
4   Should special courses in computer programming per se be introduced?
5   What, if anything, could or should be done in the way of computer-assisted instruction in mathematics itself?

These and other issues will have to be examined, debated, and experimented with, and judgments are not likely to be unanimous.

Experiments with computer-oriented instruction

A number of high schools have already instituted courses in programming and data processing, and some experimentation has been done in using computers for supplementing or assisting in the work of other courses. Much more may be expected along this line. Among other things being tried is a variant of programmed instruction (PI) known as computer-assisted instruction (CAI), in which a whole programmed course is stored in the memory of a computer, much as such a course is stored in printed form in a PI book, and is made accessible to students through auditory and visual terminals of the computer. Other adaptations are certain to be explored.

As computer facilities become less expensive and more accessible, it seems certain that the number and variety of computer-oriented courses will increase markedly. With the advent of the computer, and in view of its adaptability to such a multitude of uses and of its increasing accessibility, a whole new industry has opened up—an industry which already employs many thousands

Career opportunities

of people and will require increasing numbers and which offers a broad range of interesting and remunerative occupations to those who qualify themselves to enter it. It has been estimated that many years will pass before the manpower needs of the computer-science industry will be met.[6]

---

[6] Donald D. Spencer, Computers: Their Past, Present, and Future, *Mathematics Teacher,* **61** (1968), 65–75.

TEAM TEACHING

*What team
teaching is*

An innovation which has attracted considerable attention since about 1960 is team teaching. In one plan of team teaching two normal-sized sections in a course are scheduled to meet at the same time and are assigned to a "team" of two or more teachers who work cooperatively with the whole group. The whole group meet together as one large class for at least the part of their work which involves mainly discussion and developmental work by the teacher. This of course requires a large room. For such activities as directed study, testing, and working with individual students, the large group may be redivided into the two sections which meet separately, preferably in smaller classrooms if these are available. If the smaller rooms are not available, the teachers must arrange some plan for working together with the whole group in the one large room.

*Advantages and
problems of team
teaching*

Theoretically, such a plan has much to commend it and should have some distinct advantages to both students and teachers. Teachers who have actually engaged in this type of team teaching in mathematics for substantial periods of time seem to agree unanimously that the advantages are real and substantial. Certain problems are involved however. Some of them are probably not serious, but some could, indeed, be critical. Teachers should consider these problems with care before embarking on a program of team teaching. A fair picture of team teaching in mathematics and of some of the methods employed, problems encountered, and advantages claimed is given in the following brief account of one such program which has been carried on with apparent success since 1965, as reported by the two members of the teaching team involved.[7]

Teaching Procedures

When the entire class meets together (usually about four times a week), one of the instructors starts the actual teaching while the other checks attendance and takes care of other routine matters. After his task is done, the second teacher may help with the presentation or may work on plans for future lessons or on tests. Since the overhead projector is extensively used in the presentations, transparencies for numerous diagrams and overlays must be prepared ahead of time.

When the presentation is finished, the class is redivided into smaller groups (either at random or according to some plan) for study. Both teachers now work with the smaller groups, checking

---

[7] The summary is based on a discussion presented before the Michigan Council of Teachers of Mathematics May 3, 1968, by Norman Dunham and Ronald Lott, Everett High School, Lansing, Mich.

on students' work and giving help to those who need it. Homework is assigned every day. A part-time assistant is employed to help with checking homework, duplicating tests, etc.

Some Problems

One potentially serious problem, especially in small schools, is the feasibility of scheduling multiple sections of the same course at the same times and the availability of rooms suitable for team teaching and of pairs of teachers to make up the teams. Still another, though less serious, problem develops at times of semester change, when some students are necessarily rescheduled from regular sections into team-teaching sections for the first time, while others who have been in team-teaching sections are rescheduled back into regular sections.

Team teaching requires a high degree of coordination and planning by the members of the team so that they will not present students with conflicting ideas or points of view. Team teachers must be willing to compromise on teaching methods and approaches and must be able to accept criticism.

Some Advantages Claimed

Better planning   In team teaching the daily lessons and assignments are better prepared, since the two teachers work them out together and each can contribute from past experience ideas and approaches which he has found successful, and can call attention to trouble spots to be anticipated.

Better testing   Tests and quizzes are better prepared because, again, their construction is always based on the pooled ideas of both members of the team. More time is available for analyzing test results for diagnostic purposes and of doing item analysis for the purpose of improving future tests. Also, the teacher who is not involved in presenting the lesson can check tests, analyze results, and return papers to the students sooner than would be the case if each teacher had to do all the presentations. This is an advantage to the students, because any reteaching of troubling questions revealed by the test can be done with minimum delay. Also the one-teacher presentations to the large group allows some extra time for restudying course structure and methods, doing follow-up studies, and working on other things related to the improvement of the course.

Better presentations   With two teachers involved, the students get a variety of presentations and explanations. No two teachers present a topic in exactly the same way, and a student who has been confused by one teacher's explanation may be able to understand the principle or problem better as explained by the other teacher. Also, since the students can go to either of the teachers for special help when they need it, personality conflicts can be avoided and some students will be more willing to seek help.

Increased efficiency   The team-teaching approach has led to greater efficiency in clerical and routine matters. The combined thinking of the two members of the team has resulted in several procedures designed to save time and minimize labor.

Administrative assistance   Because team teaching is a relatively new, different, and still experimental method of instruction, it may often be possible to get ready approval of requests for equipment and facilities (special rooms, audio-visual equipment, teachers' assistant, etc.), whereas approval of such requests for regular one-teacher classes may be denied or delayed.

Conclusions

The team members who reported on the program summarized above found team teaching to be more helpful to both the students and the teachers than the usual one-teacher arrangement. They expressed the desire to see the program expanded in their high school so that facilities for team teaching would be improved, and they hoped to persuade other members in the mathematics department to become involved in the team-teaching program.

PLANNING FOR EFFECTIVE LEARNING AND TEACHING

As in any other undertaking, instruction in mathematics aims at certain outcomes or objectives, and the likelihood of attaining these objectives will depend in large measure on how well the enterprise has been planned. If the objectives of the course as a whole are to be realized, then long-range planning in terms of these must be done. On the other hand, courses are made up of component parts (units or large topics, chapters in a textbook), each focused upon some broad general topic, and each of these comprehensive units is made up, in turn, of smaller units which form the foci of the daily lessons.

We accept the premise that desirable behavioral objectives as the result of a course, a unit, or a daily assignment must find their

Basic premises   attainment in terms of attitudes toward, and of competence in, mathematics. We further believe that desirable attitudes toward mathematics are not likely to result in the absence of at least a degree of capability, and that the best motivation a student can have is the attainment of competence. Therefore, in discussing the planning of courses, units, or daily assignments, we shall consider them mainly from the standpoint of planning for developing insight and mastery in the mathematics to be studied.

Teachers should, and usually do, at least have a hand in the long-range planning of the courses they are to teach. For the intermediate-range planning of units or chapters and for the detailed planning of daily lessons, the responsibility must be theirs alone. Here, subject only to supervisory help and approval, they are on their own. The actual instruction takes place day by day in individual classrooms, and this requires careful day-by-day planning, since each teacher is responsible for what goes on in his classroom.

PLANNING A SCHEDULE FOR A COURSE

Some considerations for planning a course

It has been suggested that the layout plan for a course may best begin with a days-and-pages schedule. The main use of such a device is that it does provide a schedule which, if followed, will ensure that no principal part of the proposed coverage will be omitted from the course. In making such a schedule, the course, as represented in the textbook, should first be laid out into the main chapters or units that are to be included. Opposite this will be set the total number of days that are available for the course. Then these two layouts must be fitted or matched to each other so that, at least on paper, all the work to be included in the course can also be included in the number of days available. After the days-and-pages schedule is blocked out for the major units or chapters, it can be refined into a contents schedule by weeks, and even by days if desired. Usually, this will require some adjustment of preliminary estimates, and perhaps the curtailment of certain units or the omission of certain topics. If this is necessary, the adjustment is much better made at the outset than corrected after the course is started.

In laying out a time schedule for a course there is always the likelihood that a few days will be lost, as far as instruction is concerned, during the semester or the year. Actually, this likelihood must be anticipated in many schools. Unscheduled interruptions and delays are almost certain to occur. Football games, illness, special meetings, unexpected holidays, and other things may call for dismissal of classes. When this occurs, the reduction of available days entails a corresponding reduction in the amount of work that can be accomplished. Then, too, even experienced teachers, operating under well-planned schedules, are likely to encounter some necessary slowdowns during the course. These considerations imply and emphasize the importance of leaving a few buffer days or catch-up days in the time schedule. They imply also the importance of weighing the different units and the different parts of each unit on the scales of relative importance. If some units or parts of units must be omitted from the course, they should be topics of lesser importance. Only by careful study and preplanning can the principle of relative values be systematically applied to the different parts and worked into the plan, and only by leaving some leeway in the form of buffer days can there be much assurance of having enough time even for all the topics of prime importance in the course.

UNIT PLANNING

In making a plan for a chapter or a unit of a course, first consideration must be given to the objectives one hopes to accomplish through the study of that chapter or unit. These objectives, as regards the new work, will be centered upon the main topic or focal concept of the unit. Objectives have been classified in various ways, and every author and every teacher has his own preferred way of listing them. One method of classification that has, at least, the advantage of being simple and explicit is to list the objectives as (1) things to know and understand and (2) things to be able to do. For the most part these are interrelated. The separation is mainly for emphasis. Part 1 can include such things as important new technical symbolism and terminology, concepts, facts, and relationships. Part 2 will include, essentially, ability to explain, use correctly, and apply the things listed under part 1. A unit plan might take the form indicated in the following illustrative sample.

GEOMETRY. UNIT ON PARALLEL LINES IN A PLANE

I. *Things to know and understand*

A. The meanings of the following words and expressions:

1. Parallel lines	11. The parallel postulate
2. Transversal	12. Converse
3. Alternate-interior angles	13. Angle bisector
4. Intersect	14. Quadrilateral
5. Intercept	15. Convex quadrilateral
6. Corresponding angles	16. Diagonal
7. Congruent angles	17. Consecutive vertices
8. Congruent line segments	18. Parallelogram
9. Coplanar	19. Rhombus
10. Exterior angle of a triangle	20. Distance between two lines

21. Trapezoid

22. Isosceles trapezoid

23. Median to a side of a triangle

24. Determine

25. Perpendicular lines

26. Degree measure

27. Right triangle

28. Acute angle

29. Complementary angles

30. Supplementary angles

31. Interior angles

32. Bisect

Learning relevant facts

B. The basic facts related to parallel lines in a plane

1. Two parallel lines lie in one and only one plane.

2. If two lines in a plane are both parallel or both perpendicular to the same line, then they are parallel.

3. One and only one line can be parallel to a given line through a given external point.

4. If two parallel lines are cut by a transversal, each pair of alternate-interior angles are congruent, and each pair of corresponding angles are congruent.

5. If two lines in a plane are cut by a transversal so that a pair of alternate-interior angles are congruent, or so that a pair of corresponding angles are congruent, then the lines are parallel.

6. If two parallel lines are cut by a transversal, then the interior angles on the same side of the transversal are supplementary.

7. If a line lies in the plane of two parallel lines and is perpendicular to one of them, then it is perpendicular to the other also.

8. The sum of the degree measures of the angles of any triangle is 180.

9. The acute angles of any right triangle are complementary.

10. The measure of any exterior angle of a triangle is the sum of the measures of the opposite interior angles.

11. The segment joining the mid-points of two sides of a triangle is parallel to the third side and is half as long.

12. The diagonals of a parallelogram bisect each other.

13. The diagonals of a rhombus are perpendicular to each other.

14. The median to the hypotenuse of a right triangle is half as long as the hypotenuse.

15. In a 30-60-90 triangle the hypotenuse is twice as long as the shorter leg.

16. If three or more parallel lines intercept congruent segments on one transversal, then they intercept congruent segments on any other transversal.

Doing and knowing are interactive

II. *Things to be able to do*

A. Illustrate and explain the meanings of each of the words or expressions listed under I*A* above.

B. Explain and illustrate the statements of the basic facts given under I*B*.

C. Classify as definitions, postulates, or theorems the statements given under I*B*, and be prepared to prove those which are theorems.

The advantages accruing to such intermediate-range planning are perhaps not always obvious, but they are very real. In the first place, the planning of a unit forces the teacher to think through the unit carefully, ahead of time. It enables him to note the things he wants to highlight, to compare relative values of topics, and to estimate appropriate time allotments so as to use the time available for that unit to best advantage. Also, it provides the best possible insurance against overlooking some important item that should be included in the study of the unit. Moreover, the comparison of relative values of topics to be included provides a sound basis for setting up a time schedule in terms of relative values of topics for the daily lessons covering the unit. Finally, the pre-study of the unit gives the teacher the best possible preparation for presenting his class with a sort of preview of the highlights of the unit at the outset. It is always a good thing to do this. Students who can see where they are going and why things are relevant will work with better insight, stronger motivation, and usually with better success than students who are just given day-by-day assignments, with no picture of unity or coherence to help them see the details as parts of a whole.

Good planning ensures better preparation

Unit planning, of course, requires time, but it is not wasted time. An hour, or perhaps even a half hour, spent in planning a unit will usually return good dividends in terms of efficiency in planning the daily lessons, of motivation and effectiveness of the students' work, and in satisfaction for both the students and the teacher.

PLANNING FOR DAILY LESSONS

Learning is an active process. It is achieved not in any single way, but through a variety of activities, and is approached through a variety of avenues: reading, listening, asking questions, working with material objects, writing, drawing, comparing, analyzing, interpreting, computing, etc. The one thing that is common to all these activities is thinking. These activities need to be so planned that they will lead the learner along the path toward understanding and mastery of the subject at his level of advancement. Each activity is important, and each should contribute to the attainment of some aspect of mastery.

Effective instruction cannot be guaranteed by any single simple formula. It goes without saying that if instruction is to be really effective, the subject matter must be selected and organized in such a way as to make it appropriate and suited to the age and intellectual development of the students. Further, it must be presented in an understandable and interesting way, and there must be provision for ample practice. Skills and concepts once developed must be maintained through reapplication, and not allowed to deteriorate through disuse. Since students do not learn with equal facility or at an equal rate, there must be provision for individual differences. If the instruction is to attain a maximum of usefulness, it must be carried on with the deliberate purpose of securing a maximum of transfer and in such a way that the relation of mathematics to other fields of learning and activity is made manifest. These considerations involve careful planning and adequate testing of outcome.

The day-to-day planning of the details and sequence of each day's work must fall to the lot of each individual teacher. It is a continuing responsibility, and it is of the greatest importance, because the daily lesson plan for a class determines just what learning activities will go on in that class during that period. Any teacher who faces a class without having well in mind an orderly plan for the things he expects to do or to have the students do during the period is running a grave risk of wasting time and dissipating effort. Experienced teachers may not need actually to write out a detailed plan for each lesson, though many do so anyway, but young and inexperienced teachers will find it a great help to do so. Indeed, the very act of writing out the plan forces a crystallization of the plan in the teacher's mind. This in itself is an important step toward a successful consummation of what is planned. Although daily lesson plans often do need to be modified to take advantage of unforeseen circumstances or to adapt the work to unavoidable delays, the teacher who can make such needed modifications against the backdrop of a well-ordered plan will be in a much stronger position than one who does not bother to plan each day's work with care.

Planning lessons makes for effective teaching

Lessons have sometimes been classified according to the aims or the types of activities to be carried on: the developmental lesson, the drill lesson, the review lesson, the testing lesson, etc. Such classifications can be helpful by bringing into focus the main objective of the day's work and the kinds of activity which seem most likely to attain the objective.

There still remains, however, the need to decide upon the details of the period's work and the ordering of these details. Apart from such routine matters as taking the roll, the number of kinds of activity which may be included in the learning-teaching situation is not great. Most of them would be included in the following list:

1 Testing for any of several purposes
2 Explaining or discussing new concepts or procedures
3 Drilling or reviewing
4 Directing the work of students at chalkboard or at seats (directed study or directed learning; may include laboratory activities)
5 Assigning work to be done by the students

Each of these kinds of activity requires detailed planning if it is to serve its purpose. A test designed for diagnostic purposes will probably differ from a quiz set up for a drill exercise, not only in the use to which it is to be put, but also in the time required. Explaining or discussing new concepts in a developmental lesson requires that the teacher clarify in his own mind, and ahead of time, the precise things upon which he wants to focus the discussion. It also requires that he consider well just how the explanation can best be made, what illustrations will best serve his purpose, and how he can secure participation in the discussion by the members of the class. The intelligent assignment of work to be done by the students demands consideration of its aim and of its suitability for the students in respect to amount and difficulty.

Not all the activities listed above will be required in each day's work. Some periods will be devoted entirely to testing or to developmental discussion. On other days, during the assimilation stage, supervised study may well occupy most of the period. A brief discussion for purposes of motivation can often be helpful in such cases. Drill work, review, the making of assignments, and short quizzes should be scheduled in the period's activities at times when it is judged that they will yield the greatest advantage, and this may vary from day to day.

Substance and order are both important

The essence of a good daily lesson plan lies in two things: (1) the careful estimation and selection of those activities which give the most promise of good dividends in terms of the immediate objectives and (2) the arrangement of these activities into a properly ordered schedule, with approximate time allotments, so that the period may be used to best advantage. A short checklist of fundamental activities such as that given above can serve as a guide in lesson planning. Such lesson plans are simple and easy to make. They can ensure that the important activities for a given period are carried on in the best order and that within the limitations of the period appropriate time allowances are made for each.

Making a lesson plan

Before making out a daily lesson plan, the teacher should carefully think through the main things he wants to do and the things he wants the students to do during the class period for which the plan is to be made. These should be set down precisely in the order in which he wants them to occur, with estimated time allowances. The lesson plan should be neither perfunctory nor stereotyped, but should be adapted to taking full advantage of the educational possibilities of the class situation. Obviously, different activities will receive special emphasis on different days. On some days most of the time will be spent on developmental work, while on the other days the main activity will be directed study, and still other days will be given over largely to testing. The wise variation of the class-period activities is a major factor in stimulating interest

PLANE GEOMETRY
Topic: Proportion

Order of activities	Minutes
Check quiz on review assignment	10
Discussion of proportion and of meaning of theorems 1–6, with illustrations	25
Drill work	None
Directed study	None
Assignment for tomorrow (see back of card)	10

ALGEBRA
Topic: Fractional Equations

Order of activities	Minutes
Test	None
Review briefly principles of solving linear equations	5
Discussion and explanation of fractional equations and how they may be solved. Work out four illustrative cases with the class (see back of card)	20
Send class to chalkboard to work on exercises 1–6, page 144	15
Assignment for tomorrow (see back of card)	5

SEVENTH-GRADE MATHEMATICS
Topic: Percents

Order of activities	Minutes
Review of terms used: base, rate, percentage; meanings; examples	5
Discussion: meaning of 100% of a number; 1%, 50%, 25%, 10%, 3%, 38%; 217%; etc. How to find n% of a base if n is a given number. Try to get a rule formulated; a formula.	20
Assignment for tomorrow (see back of card)	5
Directed study: class working at seats on tomorrow's assignment.	15

Figure 6-1
Sample lesson-plan outlines.

and preventing boredom and disciplinary difficulties. It is possible, however, to use a general outline form, such as the ones in Fig. 6-1, which will be objective enough to serve as a useful guide in planning and, at the same time, sufficiently flexible to permit adaptation of the lesson plan to any class situation.

A PRACTICAL HINT ON PLANNING

Many a young teacher in beginning his first job is obsessed with the fear that he will run out of anything to say before the class period is over and thus leave himself and the class at loose ends. If he is at all competent, a little experience will convince him that the contrary is true: there usually is not enough time for all he wants to do. Well-planned discussions which elicit participation by the class will consume time at an unexpected rate, so that the real danger lies in having to leave untouched some of the work that the teacher has planned to get done during the period. Yet the tendency to overestimate what can be done during the period is very persistent. Sometimes the shortages can be made up in the next period or two by careful replanning and perhaps curtailing the work of succeeding days. If, on the other hand, these shortages are not compensated in some such way and are allowed to accumulate, they can only result, eventually, in some major hiatus in the course. Unfortunately, this often does occur. Indeed, it is likely to occur unless the teacher adheres pretty closely to a pre-established days-and-pages time schedule. Some people will object that such a schedule is too mechanical and may compel the class to leave some topics before they are fully mastered. But the alternative is to leave some part of the course, and perhaps some major part, wholly untouched.

To make the daily lesson plans fit a long-range schedule, the teacher will need to give careful attention each day to the relative importance of the ideas presented in the portion of the textbook assigned for that day. In planning each day's lesson it is important to highlight only the key concepts or relations and save most of the time for them. Only in this way can the full benefit of the textbook and the teacher's enriching discussion be realized, and only in this way can there be any real assurance of ordered and orderly progress through the course.

Focus on the most important things

With respect to unit or block planning, much the same considerations hold and much the same things may be said. The major difference is in degree, and not in kind. It lies in the larger scope of the unit and the fact that it usually covers several days instead of a single day. The same principle of relative importance should govern selection of the elements of the unit to be emphasized, and the danger of overestimating what can be accomplished is just as real here as in planning the daily lesson. Judgment in these matters can mature quickly, and experience can be a great help. But even with experienced teachers, hope sometimes overrides judgment, and beginning teachers must face this problem without the benefit of experience to guide them. It is hoped that

Planning provides
a safeguard

observance of the cautions noted above may contribute toward wise planning of units and lessons, and thus toward the avoidance of frustration and disappointment.

IN CONCLUSION

Nearly everything that a teacher does in connection with his work requires some kind and degree of planning. Even the details of his lesson plans must be thought through, appraised, and decided upon. If he is to give a test, he ought to decide what particular things he wants to test for, and then he ought to plan the test so that it will reveal, in terms of the objectives, the particular information he wants. To conserve his own time, he ought to try to arrange the test so that the papers can be checked without excessive labor, and this takes careful planning. If he is to present new material in the form of discussion with the class, he should identify ahead of time the main things he wants to bring out, and he should so plan his discussion that it will highlight and emphasize them. Illustrative examples should be selected with care, and ahead of time, instead of trusting to the inspiration of the moment to provide suitable ones. If the work is to include a field trip or a laboratory type of exercise, there are many things that need to be carefully planned ahead of time, because it is hard to adapt or change such work after it is started. The things to be done must be decided upon in advance and with definiteness, equipment and supplies made ready, and careful instructions given to the students. Forgetting to provide some important instruction or some piece of needed equipment can nullify the exercise and result in loss of time and disruption of morale. Drill and review tasks need to be very carefully planned lest they be aimless and ineffective, and the same thing may be said of chalkboard work by the students.

Providing suitable learning experiences for students of superior ability cannot be done incidentally. Directed study can be effective only to the extent to which a proper background has been established and the learning experiences are planned expressly to consolidate and extend this background. Assignments for homework can bear proper fruit only if they are well designed to produce certain predetermined results and are reasonable in their demands upon the student's ability, understanding, and time. In short, assuming academic and professional competence on the part of the teacher, intelligent planning at all levels provides the key to efficient instruction and effective learning. The key may fit imperfectly or stick a bit at first, but experience and faithful use will smooth and ease its operation. It is a *sine qua non* and must not be neglected.

A plan should be the teacher's servant, not his master

A final word of caution should be given with reference to the use of lesson plans. In planning the work of a class period the teacher must of necessity work on the assumption that the activities of the period will follow a definite course without interruption or diversion. All experienced teachers know, however, that this assumption is often wrong. Circumstances which cannot be foreseen inevitably arise at times, and often such circumstances make it advisable for the teacher to depart from his prepared plan. If by doing so it is possible to capitalize on some unexpected situation and thereby stimulate the interest of the students in their work or repair some unsuspected weakness, the teacher should not hesitate to divert the activities of the period from their charted course. Normally, of course, the best results will be obtained by following the prepared plans, but the teacher should not feel obligated to follow them with a slavish fidelity which would forbid him to take advantage of unforeseen opportunities. Frequently, the most effective teaching may be accomplished through spontaneous teacher reaction to unexpected student problems and unpredicted teaching situations.

EXERCISES

1 Comment on the proposition that insight and curiosity are the most powerful and enduring sources of motivation for the study of mathematics.

2 It has been truly said that most children enter school with attitudes favorable toward mathematics but that by the time they reach high school many of them have acquired a negative attitude toward the subject. How do you account for this change?

3 Drill work in arithmetic and algebra is necessary, but it often seems dull and uninteresting to students. Can you find or devise a way of conducting such drill work so that it will be more interesting to the students? Describe your plan.

4 Interest in some simple algebraic identities, and insight into their meanings and applications, can be strengthened by numerical and geometric illustrations. Devise numerical and geometric illustrations for these identities: $a^2 - b^2 = (a - b)(a + b)$; $(a-b)^2 = a^2 - 2ab + b^2$; $(a+b)^2 = a^2 + 2ab + b^2$.

5 Find or devise at least two recreations in the form of mathematical fallacies and present them to the class. Such recreations are always interesting to students, stimulating curiosity and careful thinking.

6 Most high school students are interested in simple probability and the laws of chance. Devise some simple experiments in drawing numbers from prearranged sets so that the calculated probabilities can be tested experimentally by the students. Try out these experiments on your class.

7 Make a list of suggestions which you think would be helpful in organizing or sponsoring a mathematics club in the junior or senior high school.

8 The converse of the Pythagorean theorem is often assumed without proof, but the challenge to prove it can provide strong motivation for good students in geometry. By way of being prepared yourself, devise or find two proofs of the Pythagorean converse.

9 Show how the concurrent study of functions, equations, and inequalities in high school algebra can be of added interest and can increase insight into the properties of all three.

10 Explain in what ways the study of a finite geometry of, say, seven points can help to give insight into ordinary high school geometry, and thereby make for increased interest in the subject.

11 Obtain from the National Council of Teachers of Mathematics its most recent pamphlet, "Reviews of Films." From this list select a few that you think you would especially like to use.

12 If you can obtain the use of an overhead projector, work with it until you are proficient in its use. Then prepare a demonstration in which you explain and illustrate some of the ways in which it can be used to advantage in teaching mathematics.

13 Prepare several transparencies for use with the overhead projector in some course in high school mathematics. Exhibit and discuss these before your class.

14 Discuss the main contributions which laboratory or field work can make to the learning of mathematics. Give examples to illustrate your points.

15 At what levels or in what courses in mathematics do you think laboratory and field work can contribute most to learning?

16 Discuss at some length the need for careful planning of laboratory or field work in mathematics to prevent it from becoming desultory and aimless.

17 Summarize and discuss the principal arguments advanced in support of programmed instruction in mathematics.

18 Summarize and discuss the main criticisms of programmed instruction in mathematics.

19 Discuss the potential advantages of team teaching, where it is feasible.

20 Comment on some of the problems and limitations associated with team teaching in mathematics.

21 Do you think that team teaching would result in better planning than is usually done by individual teachers? Discuss.

22 Select a standard textbook for a year's course in high school algebra or geometry and assume that you are to use it next year. Then make a time schedule to serve as an approximate guide for the year's work. Assume that you will have thirty-six weeks of instructional time, including tests and examinations. For each topic or unit you will include in the course, estimate the time in weeks which you can safely allot to that topic or unit. Such a schedule can be valuable to you in many ways. Make it with care, and report it to the class for discussion and criticism.

23 It is probable that during any semester various circumstances may cause cancellation of classes for a few days. Many teachers feel that it is well to take this into account in making the overall time schedule for the course. About how many buffer days per semester would you allow in your time schedule to absorb these lost class periods? Enumerate several possible circumstances that might cause such loss of time.

24 Select some unit, chapter, or section in a standard textbook in high school algebra or geometry and make an overall plan for teaching the unit. Include a detailed list of objectives in terms of "things to know" and "things to be able to do." Indicate the concepts or relations that would receive special emphasis, and estimate the number of class periods that would be required. Present your outline to the class for discussion and criticism.

25 Based on the unit plan called for in exercise 24, select a section that you estimate would require about three class periods to cover. Decide what principal things you would aim at on each of the three days, and what particular things you would do or have done in order to attain your objectives most effectively. Then make out a daily lesson plan for each of the three days, using a pattern somewhat like that of the examples shown in this chapter. Present these lesson plans to the class for discussion and criticism.

26 *Consider the topic "quadratic functions, equations, and inequalities." Assuming that you are going to teach this topic, do the following things by way of planning:*
   a. Under the two headings "things to know" and "things to be able to do," list the detailed objectives you would want your students to attain through their study of this topic.
   b. Tell what particular things you would highlight under this topic.

27 In connection with the topic of exercise 26, discuss the following questions:
   a. Do textbooks and teachers usually present this topic in such a way as to arouse the interest and curiosity of the students? How important is this?
   b. What difficulties can you expect students to have with this topic, and what mistakes can you anticipate in their work? Why do students have these difficulties, and why do they make these mistakes?
   c. How can you, as a teacher, help them to

overcome these difficulties and to avoid these mistakes? Be as specific as you can.

28 Suggest some suitable provision that could be made in connection with the topic of exercise 26 for students of exceptionally high ability.

29 Comment critically on the treatment of the topic of exercise 26 in three representative high school textbooks. For each of the three books tell what you liked best and what you liked least about its treatment of this topic.

BIBLIOGRAPHY

Aids for Evaluation of Mathematics Textbooks, *Mathematics Teacher,* **58** (1965), 467–473.

Allen, Frank B.: Building a Mathematics Program: An Adventure in Cooperative Planning, *Mathematics Teacher,* **49** (1956), 226–234.

Auclair, Jerome A., and Thomas P. Hillman: A Topological Problem for the Ninth Grade Mathematics Laboratory, *Mathematics Teacher,* **61** (1968), 503–507.

Barnett, I. A.: Reflections of a Teacher, *American Mathematical Montly,* **75** (1968), 893–895.

Bittinger, Marvin L.: A Review of Discovery, *Mathematics Teacher,* **61** (1968), 140–146.

Boeckmann, Hermann: Elementary Field Survey: An Enrichment Course for High School Students, *School Science and Mathematics,* **67** (1967), 132–134.

"Computopics" (Washington, D.C.: Association for Computing Machinery, March, 1967.) (Special issue: extensive annotated bibliography on computers and career opportunities.)

Davidson, Patricia S.: An Annotated Bibliography of Suggested Manipulative Devices, *Arithmetic Teacher,* **15** (1958), 509–524.

Davis, Robert B.: Madison Project Activities for 1965–1966: Report on Unfinished Business, *American Mathematical Monthly,* **73** (March, 1966), 301–304.

Devine, Donald F.: Student Attitudes and Achievement: A Comparison between the Effects of Programmed Instruction and Conventional Classroom Approach in Teaching Algebra, I, *Mathematics Teacher,* **61** (1968), 296–301.

Ellis, Glenn: Rx for Inertia, *Mathematics Teacher,* **59** (1966), 126–128.

Frame, J. S.: Facilities for Secondary School Mathematics, *Mathematics Teacher,* **57** (1964), 379–391.

Garfunkel, J.: A Project in Mathematics, *Mathematics Teacher,* **61** (1968), 253–258.

Geometry Class (Wheaton, Ill.): Tricky, Troublesome Triangles, *School Science and Mathematics,* **69** (1969), 31–33.

Granito, Dolores: What to Do in a Mathematics Club, *Mathematics Teacher,* **57** (1964), 35–40.

Greenholz, Sarah: Successful Practices in Teaching Mathematics to Low Achievers in Senior High School, *Mathematics Teacher,* **60** (1967), 329–335.

Gurau, Peter K.: Individualizing Mathematics Instruction, *School Science and Mathematics,* **67** (1967), 11–26.

Hansen, Viggo P.: High Achiever Math-lab Concept Becomes Project to Assist the Low Achievers, *Educational Equipment and Materials,* **3** (1967), 3–5.

Henderson, George L.: Mathematics by Radio in Wisconsin, *Mathematics Teacher,* **61** (1968), 56–62.

Hillman, Thomas P.: A Current Listing of Mathematics Laboratory Materials, *School Science and Mathematics,* **68** (1968), 488–490. (Good annotated bibliography.)

Hirschi, L. Edwin: Encouraging Creativity in the Mathematics Classroom, *Mathematics Teacher,* **56** (1963), 79–83.

Hoffman, Walter, and others: Computers for School Mathematics, *Mathematics Teacher,* **58** (1965), 393–401.

Johnson, Donovan A., and Gerald R. Rising: "Guidelines for Teaching Mathematics" (Belmont, Calif.: Wadsworth Publishing Company, 1967).

Kenna, L. A.: "Understanding Mathematics with Visual Aids" (Paterson, N.J.: Littlefield, Adams, & Company, 1962).

Klinkerman, Ginger, and Faith Bridges: Team Teaching in Geometry, *Mathematics Teacher,* **60** (1967), 488–492.

La Frenz, Dale E., and Thomas E. Kieren: Computers for All Students: A New Philosophy of Computer Use, *School Science and Mathematics,* **69** (1969), 39–41.

Larsson, Robert D.: Mathematics Enrichment Program for High School Students, *American Mathematical Monthly,* **70** (1963), 205–206.

Marks, John L., and James R. Smart: Using the Analytic Method to Encourage Discovery, *Mathematics Teacher,* **60** (1967), 241–245.

Marx, Robert: Mathematics Can Be Fun, *School Science and Mathematics,* **68** (1968), 123–129.

Mattson, Robert J.: Mathematics Leagues: Stimulating Interest through Competition, *Mathematics Teacher,* **60** (1967), 259–261.

May, Kenneth O.: Programming and Automation, *Mathematics Teacher,* **59** (1966), 444–454.

Montgomery, James: The Use of Closed Circuit Television in Teaching Junior High School Mathematics, *School Science and Mathematics,* **68** (1968), 747–749.

Moskowitz, Shiela: The Crossnumber Puzzle Solves a Teaching Problem, *Mathematics Teacher,* **62** (1969), 200–203.

NCTM: The following publications are available from the National Council of Teachers of Mathematics, 1201 Sixteenth St., Washington, D.C., 20036:

Computer Facilities for Mathematics Instruction (1967)

Computer Oriented Mathematics (1963)

"Enrichment Mathematics for High School" (*Twenty-eighth Yearbook,* 1963)

A Guide to the Use and Procurement of Teaching Aids for Mathematics (1959)

The High School Mathematics Library (3d ed., 1967)

How to Use Films and Filmstrips in Mathematics Classes (1960)

How to Use the Overhead Projector in Mathematics (1966)

Mathematics Clubs in High Schools (1958)

Puzzles and Graphs (1966)

Recreational Mathematics (1963) (bibliography)

Reviews of Films (1963)

School Mathematics Contests (1968)

Yearbook on Instructional Aids (1969)

Osborne, Alan R.: Using the Overhead Projector in an Algebra Class, *Mathematics Teacher,* **55** (1962), 135–139.

Paarlberg, Teunis J.: The Mathematics League, *Mathematics Teacher,* **60** (1967), 38–40.

Paige, Donald D.: A Comparison of Team versus Traditional Teaching of Junior High School Mathematics, *School Science and Mathematics,* **67** (1967), 365–367.

Pethtel, Richard D.: Closed-circuit Television Instruction in College Mathematics, *Mathematics Teacher,* **61** (1968), 517–521.

Ransom, William R.: "Thirty Projects for Mathematical Clubs and Exhibitions" (Portland, Me.: J. Weston Walch, Publisher, 1961).

Salkind, Charles T.: "The MAA Problem Book, II" (Syracuse, N.Y. The L. W. Singer Company, 1966).

Scheid, Francis: A Mathematics Film Series, *American Mathematical Monthly,* **73** (1966), 659–662.

Shuster, Carl, and Fred A. Bedford: "Field Work in Mathematics" (East Palestine, Ohio; Yoder Instruments, distributor).

Sister Mary Victor Korb, R.S.M.: Positive and Negative Factors in Team Teaching, *Mathematics Teacher,* **61** (1968), 50–53.

Sobel, Max A.: "Teaching General Mathematics" (Englewood Cliffs, N.J.: Prentice-Hall, Inc., 1967).

Spencer, Donald D.: Computers: Their Past and Future, *Mathematics Teacher,* **61** (1968), 65–75.

Sweet, Raymond: Organizing a Mathematics Laboratory, *Mathematics Teacher,* **60** (1967), 117–120.

Szabo, Steven: Some Remarks on Discovery, *Mathematics Teacher,* **60** (1967), 839–842.

Unkrich, Harmon: Using the Overhead Projector in Teaching Geometry, *Mathematics Teacher,* **55** (1962), 502–505.

Whitman, Nancy C., and Linda Oda: Developing Spatial Perception via the Experimental Technique, *Mathematics Teacher,* **59** (1966), 631–633.

Willoughby, Stephen S.: "Contemporary Teaching of Secondary School Mathematics" (New York: John Wiley & Sons, Inc., 1967), pp. 59–90.

Zoll, Edward J.: Research in Programmed Instruction in Mathematics, *Mathematics Teacher,* **62** (1969), 103–110.

seven | evaluation of instruction

Evaluation of instruction must concern itself both with the progress of individual students and with the quality of instruction. The teacher is expected to concern himself not only with how his students are progressing, but equally, with how he is performing as a teacher. Such evaluation cannot be an after-the-fact appraisal; it must be a continuous process, an integral part of the learning and teaching interaction between student and teacher. It does not occur in a vacuum; it is an appraisal of the extent of progress toward predetermined goals. There is probably no more accurate test of the fundamental philosophy of any curriculum than a careful analysis of its evaluation program; the techniques used; the aims, objectives, and functions implied; and the interpretation and use of obtained results.

The scope of an evaluation program

NATURE AND PURPOSES OF EVALUATION

In its most primitive form evaluation was little more than a series of tests and examinations used to determine students' grades. Measurement of a student's progress remains a central aspect of evaluation, but the uses to which the results are put are many and varied. Standards of achievement have been more clearly defined, more carefully differentiated, and better adapted to different kinds of capability and individual levels of attainment. Furthermore, the program of evaluation has been extended beyond the mere measurement of proficiency of performance with basic skills; it incorporates efforts to measure the development of interests and appreciations and to discriminate between varying degrees of aptitude in a given subject field. Also, the techniques of evaluation include not only the giving of tests, whether standard or teacher-made, but also interviews, informal observations, anecdotal records, student projects, aptitude and inventory tests, and other methods of obtaining evidence relating to the student's development.

Broadened conception of measurement

The aims of evaluation of instruction also encompass appraisal of the relative effectiveness of various teaching methods and the adequacy of textbooks and the comparative value of other teaching aids, such as films, filmstrips, models, and programmed material.

Other aims

Although evaluation should be placed on as objective a basis as possible, some value judgments must be subjective. A significant part of evaluation is a mental attitude on the part of the teacher that manifests itself in a continuing concern over such questions as: Does this method work? Are the pupils progressing? Is the showing of this film the best way to spend the time required?

Subjective judgment has a place

Thus evaluation can perform a very important function in the educative process. It should no longer be considered merely as a separate procedure to be used at convenient intervals for the purpose of determining marks; rather, it should be thought of as a continual process closely related to each aspect of the total program of the student's development. The major responsibilities of a truly effective evaluation program may thus be considered to be the following:

Responsibilities of an evaluation program

1 To provide a basis for more intelligent guidance of teaching and learning through appraisal of aptitudes and diagnosis of errors
2 To evaluate instructional procedures
3 To evaluate learning aids
4 To measure the attainment of instructional objectives and provide an adequate basis for reporting students' progress
5 To provide guides for the development of more effective educative experiences
6 To take inventory of students' readiness
7 To secure information for use as an aid in seeking intelligent and effective parent and community cooperation

The teacher of mathematics has the responsibility of determining the contribution that mathematics can make to the educational development of the individual and then designing a program of evaluation sufficiently comprehensive to measure progress toward maximum benefit from all phases of that contribution. Those goals for which quantitative measures have not been devised must be evaluated by using judgments based on observation of students' attitudes and reactions. Absence of objective measuring techniques should in no way diminish the comprehensiveness of the program of evaluation. It is also important that the testing techniques be characterized by balance of emphasis between factual

The program should include goals that cannot be measured objectively.

and functional objectives, between tangible and intangible outcomes, between the how and the why, between mere recall and integrated thinking, and between measurement as a check on the completed process and as an aid to more effective instruction.

A satisfactory evaluation program should be further characterized by *continuity*. For efficient guidance there must be a continual check on the student's progress, not only from the standpoint of immediate accomplishment, but also from the standpoint of retention. Furthermore, the use of this check for prognostic and diagnostic purposes should be emphasized fully as much as its use as a measure of achievement.

Evaluation is a continuous process

If the evaluation program is to be thoroughly comprehensive

and balanced, it must neglect no significant aspect of the subject matter covered and it must take into account all the important objectives which have been set up. Since it can command but a limited part of the school time, it must obviously consist of only a sampling of subject matter and problem situations. Thus the real task of such a program is to use data of varied types collected through several different media to shape a composite appraisal picture of each pupil as an individual and as a member of his group. Care must thus be exercised to ensure that the sampling is truly representative of all the important aspects of the total program.

Evaluation should be based on wide sampling

The formulation of a sound philosophy of evaluation is but a necessary prerequisite to the construction of a satisfactory program of evaluation. With the above characteristics as guiding criteria, the teacher or administrator can proceed more safely with the technical details incident to the selection or construction of valid and reliable instruments of measurement for use in any particular instructional situation. There are at least five steps to be followed in setting up efficient testing techniques:

1   Determination of those significant aims and objectives which are to be the goals of instruction
2   Provision of pertinent behavior situations to guarantee a valid measure of students' reactions
3   Securing a reliable record of students' reactions
4   Accurate and systematic tabulation of the record as an aid in the deduction of implied results
5   Intelligent interpretation of the results in terms of students' needs and as an aid to more effective instruction

Steps to effective testing techniques

Evaluation has a very definite function in the learning process which takes place in secondary mathematics; the program of evaluation should be designed in terms of the functional aims as well as the factual aims of mathematical instruction. Is the instructional program such that functional learning and factual learning supplement each other? Are the students learning the why as well as the how? Are they building up integrated funds of information rather than stores of segregated bits of factual knowledge? Is the program of instruction such that it will provide the student with the techniques of critical thinking? Will it develop the ability (1) to distinguish between essential and unessential data; (2) to determine the reliability of facts and the reasonableness of results and conclusions; (3) to generalize circumspectly from known facts to unknown situations and new problems; (4) to evaluate arguments, ideas, and conclusions critically? Carefully selected techniques of evaluation should be used in determining to what extent these aims have been realized by students, both as individuals and as groups. Furthermore, it should be constantly

Functional aims

emphasized that the most significant functions of effective evaluation include not merely use as an aid in determining students' marks, but use as an aid to the improvement of instruction as well.

THE TECHNIQUES OF EVALUATION

The determination and perfection of techniques to be used in the evaluation of mathematical instruction are a definite responsibility of teachers of mathematics. These techniques, in the main, consist of teacher judgments and teacher-made or commercially produced tests. Teachers should be extremely conscientious in their efforts **Teachers'** to evaluate students' efforts, and in those situations which do not **responsibility** submit themselves very well to measurement scales, appraisals should be based on discriminative and impartial judgments arrived at after careful deliberation. Such judgments may be made through the medium of oral recitations in class, comparative class observations, the personal interview, the anecdotal record, and the prolonged case study.

If prepared tests are to be used, the teacher will at times have to consider the comparative advantages and disadvantages of standardized[1] and teacher-made tests. Each has certain advantages over the other. Some standardized tests possess norms which provide for more equitable comparisons between groups than can **Standardized tests** be made by teacher-made tests. They are usually constructed by **versus** individuals of wide experience and preparation in both subject **teacher-made tests** matter and the techniques of testing. This increases the likelihood of greater reliability and validity. Furthermore, such tests usually are subject to a greater degree of objectivity in administering and in scoring.

On the other hand, it is probable that standard tests which are used year after year may exert some "backward influence" which might partially nullify their validity for the content of the work of a particular class. There is also the danger of ignoring local conditions that could make standard norms inappropriate.

A distinct administrative advantage of the standardized test is that it reduces the time which the teacher needs to devote to the details of a testing program. This, however, in the minds of some, is a questionable advantage, the agrument being that thoughtful effort on the part of the teacher in the details of test construction

[1] See the following yearbooks prepared by C. K. Buros: *The Third Mental Measurements Yearbook* (1949), pp. 399–442; *The Fourth Mental Measurements Yearbook* (1953), pp. 483–527; *The Fifth Mental Measurements Yearbook* (1959), pp. 561–615; *The Sixth Mental Measurements Yearbook* (1965), pp. 884–921. Also see Sheldon S. Myers, Annotated Bibliography of Mathematics Tests, *Twenty-sixth Yearbook* (Washington, D.C.: National Council of Teachers of Mathematics, 1961), pp. 181–216.

might be a distinct contribution in the direction of improved instruction. The teacher should always "take" his own test. This is a necessary ingredient of test construction, to eliminate ambiguities and check on the level of difficulty. The process often reveals sources of difficulty for students.

A test should be restricted to the purpose for which it is designed

The use of such extramural tests as those prepared by the College Entrance Examination Board and the Board of Regents of the University of the State of New York, as well as other tests designed primarily as final examinations, should be definitely restricted to the purposes for which they were designed and the situations to which they are related. Interpretation of test results should not be based on the assumption that the published norms are appropriate for the particular group being tested.

One of the major advantages of the test made by the teacher over the standard or extramural test is its flexibility and adaptability to local situations and to repeated evaluations. Tests of subject-matter

Advantages of teacher-made tests

mastery should include the material which the class has studied, and no other material. They should emphasize those things that have been emphasized in the class, and no item should have much place in a test for a particular class unless that class, in its study,

Test items should reflect the things emphasized in class

has given some attention to that item. Students are quick to sense the situation if what is emphasized in class as being important does not agree with what is stressed in the test questions. When this occurs they are likely to become conditioned to overlooking much of what is emphasized in class, and adopt the pattern of test emphasis to guide them in their preparation for tests.

It must be recognized that individual differences exist among classes and teachers, just as they exist among individual students. Extramural tests can take some account of different levels of difficulty, but they cannot take account of differences in details of subject matter or emphasis or differences in the methods of presentation and the points of view of different teachers. Only the teachers themselves can make tests which will do so. Other advantages of teacher-made tests over standardized tests lie in their relative inexpensiveness and their inexhaustible availability.

When the tests to be used are to be constructed by the individual teacher or by groups of teachers, there are two major problems to be considered, namely, (1) what is to be tested, and (2) what is the

Problems to be considered in test construction

most effective method of testing it? The answers to these two questions are to be found in the answers to certain supplementary questions. What are the instructional objectives to be measured? Is the test to be designed primarily for the purpose of measuring the attainment of standards, or is it to serve as a medium of instruction or as an aid in the educational guidance of the individual student? What are the distinguishing characteristics of prognostic, diagnostic, and achievement tests? Such questions as these must be settled by the teacher before he can construct an entirely satisfactory test.

Another question of special importance in this connection is whether a problem-type test or a short-answer test is better suited to the particular situation. If the teacher wishes to sample the student's ability to organize and integrate information, then the problem type is the better medium. Certain types of mathematical **Problem tests versus** subject matter are much better adapted to the problem-type test, **short-answer tests** e.g., solving verbal problems, solving geometrical originals, proving theorems, and constructing geometric figures. On the other hand, the short-answer test makes it possible to cover a much wider range of material, and it virtually eliminates subjectivity in determining scores. The interpretation of scores is subject to the teacher's subjective judgment; but the interpretation can be applied with complete impartiality. The wider range of sampling that is possible with a short-answer test gives it an advantage over the problem type in the matter of diagnosis and prognosis. The relative ease in scoring short-answer tests is more than offset by the time and effort required for their construction. Aside from the fact that they are generally not good tests of organizing ability, their chief disadvantage lies in the fact that the construction of really good short-answer tests requires much time, considerable experience, and great care. A good short-answer test is neither superfluously easy nor obscurely difficult. It should require more than mere recall.

Tests are made in various forms, and the determination of which of these forms is most suitable for a particular situation is sometimes a real problem. One must know and weigh the functions, advantages, and limitations of the different forms, such as true–false, direct recall, multiple-response, completion, and matching, and decide which one will lend itself most advantageously to the case in hand.

Whether problem-type or short-answer tests are being constructed, the following criteria should be observed;

1 A test should be as highly objective as possible. The element of personal interpretation should be minimized in the determination of the correctness or incorrectness of the student's reactions to behavior situations.

2 A test should be reliable. The reliability of a test is determined by the consistency with which it measures what it sets out to measure. There are many sources of unreliability, not all of which are attributes of the test itself. The behavior of the examiner, the mental and physical condition of the student, and the conditions under which the test is given have a great deal of influence upon the reliability of the results obtained from any test. Certain other causes of unreliability are inherent

within the test itself, e.g., ambiguity in the instructions for taking the test, lack of clearness in statement of problems and questions, inadequate sampling of the items of information to be tested, inefficient methods of scoring, and erroneous interpretations of test results.

3   A test should be valid. A test can be valid only insofar as it accomplishes for a selected group of pupils the specific purpose for which it was designed. Two significant attributes of validity are reliability and objectivity, although they do not alone guarantee the validity of a test. To be valid the test must be further characterized by that comprehensiveness and discriminative power most pertinent to the particular function for which it is designed. These criteria imply that the teacher must not only be thoroughly familiar with the objectives of instruction for the material to be tested, but must also be well versed in the techniques of apt and precise phraseology and efficacious organization.

Criteria for test construction

4   A test should be economical of the teacher's time. The amount of time required for the construction, administration, and interpretation of a test should not be excessive. The time element, however, is a function of the expected returns from the test.

5   A test should be "student-conscious." The elements of the test should be couched in nonambiguous language, and reasonable tasks should be set for reasonable periods of time. In test items designed to measure understanding of a principle or ability to apply a principle, computation should be minimized.

6   A test should motivate the best efforts of the students. The questions should be so worded and presented that they will discourage guessing and bluffing.

7   A test designed to discriminate between students' abilities must provide for measurement of the entire range of abilities. If anything like accurate discrimination between students' abilities is to be approximated, there must be questions easy enough so that all students can answer them and questions so difficult that perfect scores will be highly improbable, if not impossible. Some questions should be so designed that the student will have the responsibility of distinguishing between essential and nonessential data.

Tests can be put to many uses, such as prognosis of success, guidance during the learning process, diagnosis of difficulties, and measurement of achievement. The type of test to use will depend largely upon the objective to be measured. An open-book test is ideal for determining ability to find, organize, and apply information. But the typical short-answer test is more adapted to measuring ability to recognize or recall a wide range of information. However, the form of the test is not necessarily a clue to its purpose; this is more a function of the use to which the results are put. One significant key in judging the effectiveness of a program of instruction is knowing what use is made of test results.

Use of tests should agree with their purpose

PROGNOSIS AND GUIDANCE

As an aid to more effective guidance of students, tests may be used to analyze present status of mastery and to predict possible future achievement. Such tests should be provided not only to measure mechanical ability and functional information, but also to make inquiry into students' interests, aptitudes, work habits, and study skills.

Uses of inventory tests

The inventory test is used for the purpose of "taking stock" of mathematical information and ability. It should show what a student knows about a certain topic. Under the modern philosophy of mathematical education the student has many opportunities to learn something of elementary algebra and a good deal of intuitive geometry by the time he enters the secondary school. As he proceeds up the instructional ladder, seasonal inventory tests, carefully placed and skillfully used, will prevent a great deal of unnecessary repetition of experience on his part and waste of effort on the part of the teacher. They will also serve somewhat as insurance against the monotony of learning which might result from students' familiarity with material selected by the teacher. Such tests may also be used effectively to bring to light the background which the students have for the study of new units and thus aid in the guidance program. The construction of an inventory test on a unit of instruction is not essentially different from the construction of a final achievement test on the same unit. The use of two such comparable tests, one before and the other after the teaching of the unit, will serve as a good indicator of the learning

Inventory and achievement are comparable tests

that takes place during the unit. Such a test on exponents and radicals is given here with its tabulation chart. There is also a tabulation chart for a similar test, identical in form, which was given at the end of the unit. A comparative study of Tables 7-1 and 7-2 will give information concerning each student and the class as a whole on the learning situations recorded in the test.

TEST: EXPONENTS AND RADICALS

1. How many square roots does a number have? _____.
2. 5 is a square root of _____ because _____ times _____ is _____.
3. If $x = \sqrt{y}$, then _____ = y.
4. The hypotenuse of this triangle (Fig. 7-1) is _____ feet long.

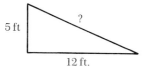

5 ft

12 ft.

Figure 7-1

5. Construct geometrically a line segment $\sqrt{3}$ inches long.
6. (a) $\sqrt{2} =$ _____; (b) $\sqrt{3} =$ _____; (c) $\sqrt{5} =$ _____.

7. (a) $\sqrt{\dfrac{a^2}{b^2}} =$ _____; (b) $\left(\dfrac{4}{7}\right)^2 =$ _____.

8. The simplest way to express $\sqrt{x^2 y}$ is _____.

9. In the expression $\sqrt[3]{x^2}$ the index is (a) _____ and the exponent is (b) _____. The sign $\sqrt{\ }$ is called a (c) _____ sign.

10. $x^{3/2}$ means the (a) _____ root of the (b) _____ power of (c) _____.

11. (a) $\dfrac{x^5}{x^3} =$ _____; (b) $x^{3/4} \div x^{1/2} =$ _____; (c) $a^{3/2} \cdot a^{1/4} =$ _____.

12. (a) $x^5 \div x^5 = x^{(\quad)}$ (Supply the exponent in the answer.) (b) To what *number* is the above answer equal? _____.

13. (a) $a^5 \div a^7 =$ _____. (b) Does a^{-3} equal $\dfrac{1}{a^3}$? _____.

14. $\sqrt{73}$ is between _____ and _____. (Fill blanks with two consecutive whole numbers.)

An examination of Table 7-1 reveals the fact that, as a whole, this unit constituted new material for the entire class. The meaning of square root, item 2 of the test, was generally understood; so no time had to be spent on its development. Furthermore, the teacher was able to determine those students, B, E, F, and H, who would probably need special attention.

Analysis of test results (margin)

TABLE 7-1
Students' responses before studying the unit

Questions:	1	2	3	4	5	6a	6b	6c	7a	7b	8	9a	9b	9c	10a	10b	10c	11a	11b	11c	12a	12b	13a	13b	14	Student's standing
Student:																										
A	x	x					x					x	x		x	x	x									8
B																										0
C		x				x	x					x	x					x					x	x		8
D		x										x	x		x									x		5
E	x	x																								2
F		x										x			x											3
G		x							x								x		x	x						5
H		x											x													2
Class standing	2	7	0	0	0	1	2	0	0	1	0	4	4	0	3	1	1	2	0	0	1	0	1	1	2	
Familiar material	x																									

Table 7-2 gives the record of responses after the period of instruction on the unit. It reveals that pupils A, E, F, and G needed further individual attention on certain specific items and that, from the point of view of the entire class, items 3, 8, 11b, 11c, 13a, and 14 should be retaught.

In the prediction of mathematical achievement some of the most

TABLE 7-2
Students' responses after studying the unit

Questions:	1	2	3	4	5	6			7		8	9			10			11			12		13		14	Student's standing
						a	b	c	a	b		a	b	c	a	b	c	a	b	c	a	b	a	b		
Student:																										
A	x	x	x	x	x	x	x	x	x	x		x	x	x	x		x	x						x		17
B	x	x		x	x	x	x	x	x	x		x	x	x	x	x	x	x			x	x		x	x	20
C	x	x		x		x	x	x	x	x	x	x	x	x	x	x	x	x	x	x	x	x		x		21
D	x	x		x	x	x	x	x	x	x	x	x	x	x	x	x	x	x	x	x	x		x	x		22
E	x	x		x	x	x	x	x	x	x		x	x	x	x		x	x				x			x	17
F	x	x		x		x	x	x	x			x	x	x	x	x					x		x		x	15
G	x	x		x	x	x	x	x	x	x		x	x	x	x		x	x	x			x	x	x		19
H		x		x	x	x	x	x	x	x	x	x	x	x	x	x	x	x			x	x	x	x	x	21
Class standing	7	8	1	8	6	8	8	8	8	7	3	8	8	8	8	5	7	7	3	2	5	5	4	6	4	
Need to reteach			x								x								x	x			x		x	

important factors seem to be comprehension of general mathematical techniques, classroom attentiveness, originality, habits of study, and general intelligence. The most efficient prediction seems to be accomplished through a combined use of prognostic tests, intelligence tests, and teachers' marks.

As a corollary to their use as an aid in prediction of achievement, prognostic tests can be used to reduce the number of failures either by eliminating those who are unprepared, or unable for any cause, to proceed further with mathematical study or by providing a basis for the construction of a differentiated mathematical curriculum. Such tests should also serve as an aid in the vocational and educational guidance of students and in the better classification of students. The discovery of superior ability and unusual aptitude in mathematics is just as important a function of prognosis as is the discovery of the inferior or average.[2]

Vocational guidance

For the construction of efficient prognostic tests in mathematics the teacher should be familiar with those abilities and interests essential to further progress. Mathematical tests which are to be used as an aid in vocational guidance should be based on a knowledge of those mathematical skills, concepts, and principles incident to success in any chosen vocation. The general characteristics of comprehensiveness, discriminative power, reliability, validity, balance, and flexibility must then be carefully observed in the framing and organization of the test items.

The knowledge necessary for constructing prognosis tests

[2] An important program of this type is the Advanced Placement Program of the College Entrance Examination Board.

DIAGNOSIS AND REMEDIAL TEACHING

Probably one of the most significant steps toward improved instruction that has been taken in recent years is that of incorporating into the instructional program plans for discovering learning difficulties and detecting needs for remedial teaching. Such plans call for the intelligent use of inventory and diagnostic tests, along with personal interviews to discover and analyze students' difficulties with a view to setting up specific remedial measures to correct errors and remove difficulties.

Use of tests in remedial instruction

Such a program should be keyed to bring to light distinct weaknesses in learning which call for specifically planned remedial action. An important by-product of any diagnostic program which is carefully constructed will be the discovery of latent interests and abilities that need to be challenged. A second important by-product of the diagnostic program can be the evaluation of instructional procedures. Have they been relatively effective or ineffective? Answers to such questions must be sought in a carefully structured composite picture of individual or group reaction to a specific diagnostic testing pattern. This is particularly true if the tests have been designed for diagnosis of basic understanding, insight into problem solving, and intelligent interpretation of results, as well as proficiency in fundamental skills.

The intelligent use of such a program of diagnosis is an important aspect of effective teaching. Its real value, however, definitely will be dependent upon a carefully planned follow-up remedial program and a careful check on, and interpretation of, attained results.

TESTS AS LEARNING AIDS

One of the basic aims of evaluation is to bring about improved learning. Properly motivated, tests can be used as effective learning aids. Students can learn from tests before, during, and after their administration. Students should be taught how to prepare for a test. Preparation should be an exercise in reviewing, memorizing, relating, generalizing, and organizing. It should not be an all-night cram session, with a mass of material memorized for twenty-four-hour retention. The best way to discourage this kind of preparation is to construct the test so that such preparation proves inadequate. One good way to discourage cramming is to give an open-book test frequently enough for it to have an impact. The open-book test does not measure memorization of facts, but the ability to organize and use them.

How tests can improve learning

Discourage "cramming"

The act of taking the test is, for some students, an excellent learning experience. The well-motivated test sometimes leads to problem solving and deductive, rational thinking beyond the student's normal capability.

Perhaps some of the best learning comes from review of the completed test after it has been graded. If the tests are promptly returned and discussed with the students, this can be an excellent setting for meaningful discussion, sharpening of hazy ideas, and correction of misconceptions.

Practice tests play a very important role in the assimilation period of instruction. They can aid the student in self-diagnosis, but they should never be used by the teacher in any other capacity than to help the student discover for himself information concerning his status of achievement in intelligent understanding of subject matter, the speed and accuracy with which he can perform the prescribed operations, and his relative progress as a member of his class group. Such tests must be shaped to reflect individual efficiency in the perspective of group activity.

Advantages of oral tests

Oral tests may be used with material that calls for responses which can be readily obtained and simply stated. They may be administered through pointed questions promiscuously, yet evenly, distributed over the entire class or through the medium of team contests. The two principal keynotes of successful oral practice are speed and accuracy of response.

Written tests may be used for both the simple-response and the difficult-response type of practice. As in the case of the oral tests, written tests may be shaped to emphasize speed and accuracy. It should be re-emphasized at this point, however, that understanding is a major responsibility of instruction in secondary mathematics, and some of the practice tests should be designed to that end.

Precautions to be observed in using timed tests

Timed tests frequently serve to stimulate interest and attention through competition with other students or competition with one's own previous time record or similar material. Precautions which the teacher must observe are as follows: (1) Do not overemphasize speed at the expense of accuracy; (2) provide for check-up and practice on understanding as well as on speed and accuracy; (3) vary the type of practice material to prevent monotony of effort; and (4) do not continue practice to the point of fatigue.

ACHIEVEMENT

In the measure of achievement the teacher is not merely interested in testing mechanical proficiency in certain fundamental processes and factual information. He is also interested in the measure of reasoned understanding of concepts, techniques, and principles.[3] Such a testing program should be so designed that it will compare and discriminate between relative abilities, as well as measure retention and understanding of learning. The selection of test items must be in terms of an authoritative list of ultimate objectives, which in turn have been carefully analyzed into immediate aims of instruction in the light of the significant implications and limitations of the local situation. Although comprehensiveness is one of the important characteristics of an efficient achievement test, it is quite obvious that no such test can be sufficiently comprehensive as to include all items of specific information into which an instructional unit may be analyzed. The test is thus a function of the different items used. They must therefore represent an adequate sampling of the entire unit, and each item must make a significant contribution to the composite power of the test to discriminate between pupils of high and low levels of general achievement. The validity of any achievement test is largely a function of the success with which each individual test item performs the function for which it was designed.

Just as in the case of prognosis and diagnosis, several different evaluation procedures can be used for measuring achievement: the standardized tests, the informal teacher-made tests, observations, interviews, anecdotal records, and student reports and projects. While standardized tests are available for many different purposes, there are cautions that should be observed in their use. The content of such a test may not conform closely enough to the local program of instruction, and it can vary widely, from author to author, in tests designed, theoretically, for the same general purpose. A comparison of local scores with published norms can thus be inaccurate and misleading. Furthermore, such tests are valid only in the context of the objectives for which they were designed. Interpretations of results should keep these limitations in mind.

Teacher-made tests have the advantage of being constructed entirely in the context of the local teaching situation. The objectivity of such tests, however, usually is not so well defined as in the case of standardized tests. Also, the question structure of teacher-made tests frequently fails to reflect as high a level of expertness as does that of the standardized tests. In the construction of an achievement test for a specific instructional unit and for a given group of pupils the teacher should use the following criteria as guides in selecting the content and shaping the questions:

Margin notes:
Broad objectives in achievement testing

Selection of items

Evaluation procedures

Selection of the content of teacher-made tests

[3] For a basic philosophy of such testing and for representative test items see Maurice L. Hartung and Harold P. Fawcett, The Measurement of Understanding in Secondary Mathematics, *The Forty-fifth Yearbook of the National Society for the Study of Education* (Chicago: University of Chicago Press, 1946), part I, pp. 157–174. Also see *Twenty-second Yearbook* (1954), pp. 339–409, and *Twenty-sixth Yearbook* (1961) (Washington, D.C.: National Council of Teachers of Mathematics).

1 The different levels of achievement potential within the group should be recognized.
2 For each level the test should provide an approximately equal number of items.
3 The items should hold the students responsible for concepts, principles, and understandings, as well as for basic skills.
4 The items should be selected and worded in the context of reasonable expectations of individual and group performance for the specific instructional unit.
5 The items should be so constructed that they discriminate between different levels of ability.
6 The items should be such that they lend themselves to reliability in scoring.

Other evaluation techniques

Both standardized tests and tests made by teachers have their advantages and limitations. Each type of test can make significant contributions toward effective evaluation of achievement. But whether the two types of test are used separately or combined to secure the benefits of both, there remain gaps to be filled in before the true picture of either individual or group achievement can be composed. The observation of performance, the personal interview, the analysis of anecdotal records, and the studious appraisal of projects and reports, each and all can make significant contributions to the intelligent evaluation of students' progress.

INTERPRETATION AND USE OF RESULTS

Purposes of evaluation

If evaluation were its own end, it would be a colossal waste of time and thought. The immediate purpose of evaluation is to provide a basis for action. The ultimate end is a changed situation brought on through action. The significance of any program of evaluation is very definitely dependent upon the interpretation and use of the results obtained. It is highly important that the results of a given test be interpreted and used in the context of the function for which the test was constructed and administered. For example, the results from a test designed solely for diagnostic purposes should never be used for the purpose of measuring achievement and then assigning grades. There are sometimes fundamental differences in the construction of such tests, to say nothing of the moral obligation of the teacher to play fair with the student.

Essential statistical procedures

In many cases it is necessary that the teacher be familiar with certain simple but fundamental statistical procedures in order to derive maximum benefit from a testing program. The techniques of classifying and tabulating data; grouping into significant class intervals; determining range of distribution; computing measures of central tendency, variability, and relationship; and ranking scores: these are the more important statistical measures with which the teacher should be familiar in order to summarize efficiently the results of a testing program.

Interpretation of
results

Not only must the teacher have a certain amount of mechanical proficiency in the techniques of tabulating and analyzing test data, but he must also be able to make logical inferences from such findings. He must know the appropriateness of various measures and the extent and limitations of their implications. The conclusions drawn must be consistent with the fundamental assumptions underlying the tests and the statistical measures used.

Scores versus
grades

In the measure of achievement the teacher must know the difference between a test score and a grade. Furthermore, he must know when test scores should be translated into grades, and be familiar with the recommended techniques for careful conversion. He must know how to detect a typical class error from a diagnosis test, and he must be able to determine whether particular detected errors imply the need for group or individual remedial measures.

Teachers should be familiar with the various purposes and limitations of each aspect of a functional testing program. For maximum value the results should be used within the domain they are designed to serve, in the effort to construct from all sources of relevant information a composite, yet comprehensive, picture of the individual student.

EXERCISES

1   Distinguish among diagnostic, prognostic, and achievement tests as to characteristics and function.

2   Name different ways in which each type of test may be used in the improvement of instruction in mathematics.

3   What are some of the recommended measures for improvement of essay-type examinations?

4   Contrast the relative effectiveness of different kinds of short-answer tests (true–false, multiple-choice, completion, etc.).

5   Discuss the relative merits of factual and functional testing in secondary mathematics.

6   What are some recommended procedures for measuring mathematical aptitude?

7   What is validity in a test?

8   What is reliability in a test?

9   Give examples of material from secondary mathematics which you consider not well adapted to objective tests.

10   Suggest ways to evaluate this material.

11   In test construction how much importance should be given to "range of difficulty" and "distribution of item difficulty"?

12   Briefly evaluate the advantages and disadvantages of standardized tests with national norms.

13   What are some of the common errors in secondary mathematics that call for remedial work?

14   What are some of the more important techniques for discovering students' errors?

15   What are some of the recommended techniques for determining the degree of difficulty of test items?

16   What are some of the recommended procedures for transforming test scores into grades?

17   Compare the relative merits of the percent and ranking techniques of determining grades.

18   What basic assumptions underlie the practice of "grading on the curve"?

19   What are some of the recommended techniques for testing appreciation and understanding in secondary mathematics?

20   Take some topic in algebra, and enumerate five specific objectives which you would hope to have your students attain through their study of this topic.

21 Make five test items, each designed to test for one of the specific objectives of exercise 20. Make a marking key to be used in grading the test papers.

22 Make an analysis sheet for tabulating the responses of each student for each of the five test items of exercise 21.

23 Explain what uses you would make of the analysis sheet of exercise 22.

24 Take some topic in geometry and list specific objectives that are best measured by open-book tests.

25 Make open-book test items to measure the specific objectives of exercise 24.

BIBLIOGRAPHY

Angel, James L.: National, State, and Other External Testing Programs, *Review of Educational Research*, **38** (1968), 85–91.

Balch, John: The Influence of the Evaluating Instrument on Students' Learning, *American Educational Research Journal*, **1** (1964), 169–177.

Barnes, Ward E., and John W. Asher: Predicting Students' Success in First-year Algebra, *Mathematics Teacher*, **55** (1962), 651–657.

Becker, J. P.: Geometry Achievement Tests in NLSMA, *American Mathematical Monthly*, **75** (1968), 532–538.

Bowers, N. D.: Meaningful Learning and Retention, *Educational Research*, **31** (1961), 527.

Braverman, B.: Right Answer, Wrong Solution, *Mathematics Teacher*, **50** (1957), 340–342.

Callicutt, W.: Problems of Predicting Success in Algebra, *Bulletin of the National Association of Secondary-School Principals*, **45** (1961), 107–111.

Celinski, Olgierd: Announced Repetitive Tests as a Basis for Self-directed Study and Evaluation, *Journal of Experimental Education*, **36** (1968), 17–26.

Cliffe, Marion C.: The Place of Evaluation in the Secondary School Program, *Mathematics Teacher*, **49** (1956), 270–273.

———: Mathematics Evaluation in a Large City, *Bulletin of the National Association of Secondary School Principals*, **43** (1959), 161–165.

Clifford, Paul I.: Testing the Educational and Psychological Development of Adolescents, *Review of Educational Research*, **38** (1968), 29–39.

Coffman, William E.: Developing Tests for the Culturally Different, *School and Society*, **93** (1965), 430, 433.

Coken, Leonard: An Interim Report on the National Longitudinal Study of Mathematical Abilities, *Mathematics Teacher*, **58** (1965), 522–526.

Elder, Florence: Using Take-home Tests, *Mathematics Teacher*, **50** (1957), 526–528.

Ennis, R. H.: Concept of Critical Thinking, *Harvard Educational Review*, **32** (1962), 81–111.

Gordon, I. J.: Testing and Evaluation, *Educational Leadership*, **20** (1962), 73–76.

Gurau, P. K.: Time for Testing, *Mathematics Teacher*, **60** (1967), 133–136.

Habel, E. A.: Implications Arising out of Students' Errors, *Journal of Higher Education*, **29** (1958), 81–88.

Harsh, Richard: Place of Testing and Evaluation in Learning, *California Journal of Secondary Education*, **35** (1960), 40–65.

Hawthorne, Frank S.: Evaluation in a Large State: The New York Regents Examinations, *Bulletin of the National Association of Secondary School Principals*, **43** (1959), 165–168.

Johnson, Donovan A.: What Can the Classroom Teacher Do about Evaluation?, *Bulletin of the National Association of Secondary School Principals*, **43** (1959), 154–161.

——— and Gerald R. Rising: "Guidelines for Teaching Mathematics" (Belmont, Calif.: Wadsworth Publishing Company, 1967), pp. 363–375.

Kinsella, John J.: Evaluation of Student Learning in Secondary School, *Bulletin of the National Association of Secondary School Principals*, **43** (1959), 125–128.

Koenker, R. H.: Measuring the Meanings in Arithmetic, *Arithmetic Teacher*, **7** (1960), 93–96.

Lehnoff, A. K.: Self-evaluation: One Approach, *Educational Leadership*, **20** (1962), 34–37.

Lowry, W. C.: Course Requirements and Grading, *Mathematics Teacher*, **52** (1959), 633–635.

Mayo, Samuel T.: What Experts Think Teachers Ought to Know about Educational Measurement, *Journal of Educational Measurement*, **1** (1964), 79–86.

Mervin, Jack C., and Martin J. Higgins: Assessing the Progress of Education in Mathematics, *Mathematics Teacher*, **61** (1968), 130–135.

Morgan, H. G.: What Is Effective Evaluation?, *Journal of the National Education Association*, **48** (1959), 15–17.

Myers, Sheldon S.: "Mathematics Tests Available in the United States" (Washington, D.C.: National Council of Teachers of Mathematics, 1959). (Pamphlet.)

———: A New Approach of Evaluation of Competence, *Bulletin of the National Association of Secondary-School Principals,* **43** (1959), 150–154.

———: Cooperative Mathematics Tests: A Progress Report, *American Mathematical Monthly,* **69** (1962), 223–225, 917.

———: The College Board and Mathematics Reform, *Mathematics Teacher,* **56** (1963), 147.

——— and Marian G. Epstein: Mathematical Reform and the College Board Mathematics Examinations, *American Mathematical Monthly,* **70** (1963), 665–667.

National Council of Teachers of Mathematics: The Evaluation of Mathematical Learning, *Twenty-second Yearbook* (Washington, D.C.: The Council, 1954), pp. 339–409, 432–434.

———: Evaluation in Mathematics, *Twenty-sixth Yearbook* (Washington, D.C.: The Council, 1962).

Payne, Joseph N.: Giving the Student a Part in His Evaluation, *Mathematics Teacher,* **50** (1957), 77–78.

Place of Testing and Evaluation in Learning, *California Journal of Secondary Education,* **35** (1960), 40–65.

Romberg, Thomas A., and James W. Wilson: The Development of Mathematics Achievement Tests for the National Longitudinal Study of Mathematical Abilities, *Mathematics Teacher,* **61** (1968), 489–495.

Sampson, Tom: Tests in Algebra, *Mathematics Teacher,* **55** (1962), 117–119.

Shimberg, Benjamin: New Cooperative Mathematics Tests, *American Mathematical Monthly,* **67** (1960), 1027.

Smith, Fred, and Sam Adams: "Educational Measurement for the Classroom Teacher" (New York: Harper & Row, Publishers, Incorporated, 1966).

Weir, E. C.: Some Thoughts on Evaluation, *Bulletin of the National Association of Secondary-School Principals,* **41** (1962), 23–29.

Wernick, William: A List of Standard Corrections, *Mathematics Teacher,* **57** (1964), 107.

Wilson, V. W.: Techniques of Evaluating Pupil Progress, *School and Community,* **48** (1961), 18.

Wood, R.: The Place and Value of Item Banking, *Educational Research,* **10** (1968), 114–125.

Wrightstone, J. W.: Teacher-made Tests and Techniques, *Educational Leadership,* **19** (1961), 170–172.

——— and J. I. Krugman: A Guide to the Use of Anecdotal Records, *Educational Research Bulletin* 11 (New York: Board of Education of the City of New York, 1949).

2

the teaching
of
selected topics
in
secondary
mathematics

INTRODUCTION

The teacher of mathematics, like all other teachers in the secondary school, is a person of whom many things are expected. His obligations are not confined to the classroom, but extend along many avenues to the promotion of the effective functioning of the school and the maintenance of harmonious relations and constructive understanding between the school and the community. The sponsoring of extracurricular activities, cooperation in maintaining a smoothly operating physical organization, participation in counseling and guidance, keeping careful records, making necessary reports promptly, and participation in worthy community interests are but illustrative of the range of demands upon the teacher. It must not be forgotten, however, that his first and foremost obligation is to teach effectively.

Demands on the teacher

Teaching mathematics in the secondary schools is a task which, if seriously undertaken, will challenge the best efforts of the best teachers. It requires more than a thorough knowledge of the subject matter to be taught, though that, of course, is a *sine qua non*. It requires more, even, than a broad perspective of the field of mathematics itself and an understanding of the place and importance of mathematics in any valid scheme of general education. It demands skill in the techniques of teaching each particular topic or aspect of the subject; in developing generalized concepts; in coordinating generalizations with applications; in discriminating between essential and unessential matters within the subject; in knowing where to place emphasis and where to anticipate difficulties, in detecting difficulties when they do occur, in sensing their precise nature, and in knowing how to help the students avoid or overcome them.

The first task of the teacher in connection with the teaching of any division, unit, topic, or aspect of mathematical subject matter is to decide just what the immediate and definite objectives are, i.e., which concepts or items of information the students are to gain from their study of that topic, which skills are to be mastered, and which techniques and materials will be most effective in producing the desired results. Economy and clarity of learning will come only insofar as the multitude of details related to the unit are subordinated to the main issues and are organized and integrated around the few really major concepts and skills, so that these will stand out in bold relief against the background of contributory detail. Having decided what important things are to be emphasized in a particular unit, the teacher is in a position to view the whole problem in its proper perspective and to organize and present the material of the unit in a more effective manner.

The teacher of mathematics must remain alert at all times to the

Planning the
instructional
program

major objectives of mathematical instruction. If these are to be attained in an effective and economical manner, the teacher must plan his work with at least five things in mind:

1 He must decide what exercises and activities will contribute most effectively to produce the desired understandings and skills. This teaching material should be selected with great care.
2 He must analyze these teaching materials carefully to anticipate the specific difficulties which the students are likely to encounter in attaining the objectives of the unit.
3 In order to help the students avoid or overcome these difficulties, the teacher must become expert in sensing the procedures and devices that promise to be specifically helpful and must learn to be adept in adjusting his procedure to the requirements of each immediate situation. Explanations and developmental discussion should be pointedly and skillfully organized. Devices and illustrations should be selected with great care.
4 A careful selection and arrangement of motivating materials must be made. The teacher must keep in mind that it is his responsibility to create, stimulate, and maintain interest in mathematics, as well as strive for proficiency in skills and the amassing of information.
5 He must give careful thought to evaluation techniques and remedial procedures.

Analysis of
instructional
problems

No teacher can do a thoroughly good job of teaching mathematics unless he is willing to make a careful analysis of his job and be guided by that analysis in making his preparations and in conducting the work of the class. The analysis of the instructional problems involved in the teaching of any topic in secondary mathematics seems to divide itself, rather logically, into six considerations, as follows:

1 What background of experience and understanding may the student be expected to have when he begins the study of the topic?
2 What are the particular understandings or abilities which the student should acquire or strengthen through the study of the topic?
3 What activities or procedures on the part of the teacher and student will enable the student to gain the desired understandings and abilities most effectively?
4 What specific difficulties may the student be expected to encounter in his effort to acquire the desired understandings and abilities?
5 What specific suggestions, devices, and procedures will most effectively help the student to avoid or overcome the specific difficulties of point 4?
6 What materials and procedures related to the particular topic will best stimulate and maintain the student's interest?

It is the purpose of Part Two to consider some of the more important instructional units of secondary mathematics in the perspective of these questions.

eight | the teaching of arithmetic

The new program in mathematics at both the elementary and the secondary levels of instruction continues to place emphasis on the fundamental structure of mathematical systems, the understanding of notational patterns, the clarification of definitions, the removal of tacit assumptions, the refinement of basic terminology, and the characteristics of a knowledgeable approach to problem solving. To meet the demands of such a program, all teachers of arithmetic must keep themselves alert to the threefold nature of their responsibility: They must place due emphasis upon the meanings, relationships, and properties which cement the fundamental structure of the number systems of arithmetic. They must orient their instruction in a program designed to maintain and strengthen facility in the basic skills. And finally, no teacher of arithmetic has met his full responsibility to his students until he has provided them with a sound basis for careful analyses of problem situations which they may encounter.

Threefold responsibility

THE RESPONSIBILITY IN ARITHMETIC OF THE SECONDARY SCHOOL

It is the responsibility of the elementary school to lay the fundamental groundwork of basic concepts, principles, and skills upon which the arithmetical structure must be built. In constructing its curriculum and formulating its instructional program, the secondary school is justified in assuming that the elementary school has met this educational obligation. But even if this assumption is valid, the secondary school still has a responsibility for continuing the enrichment of this background and preventing its atrophy through disuse. The broader mathematical obligations of the junior and senior high schools, however, are to strengthen and increase the working vocabulary of arithmetical terms; to effect a clearer understanding of basic concepts, relationships, and principles; to develop further facility in the fundamental skills; to shape a more mature concept of the basic structure of the number system of arithmetic; and to emphasize the abstraction of arithmetical processes to problem situations.

Obligations of mathematics instruction

One of the major responsibilities of the junior high school is that of careful, though elementary, consideration of the evolution of the field of real numbers as the significant number system of arithmetic. Careful attention should be given to the fact that a need for greater computational freedom and a desire for a closed number system combine to project the pattern of development from the basic structure of the natural-number system through the domain of integers and the field of rational numbers to the field of real numbers. This should be accomplished in the framework of the accompanying modifications of the basic postulates of the natural-number system into the field postulates of the real-number system. As each new number system is created to accommodate each newly defined operation, the teacher has the definite responsibility of acquainting the students with what new computational patterns are possible.

These extensions call for definitions of new operations as well as modifications of previously defined operations. The set N of natural (counting) numbers is closed only under the operations of addition and multiplication, where addition is the process for finding the cardinal number of the union of two disjoint nonempty sets, and multiplication is the process for finding the cardinal number of the cartesian product of any two nonempty sets. The extension to the set J of integers makes it possible to define subtraction as the inverse of addition, but does not call for any significant modification of the basic operations of addition and multiplication.

When the extension is made to the set Q of rational numbers, several troublesome problems arise. Not only is it necessary to modify the definitions of addition, subtraction, and multiplication, as well as define the new operation of division, but the concept of equality changes. No longer does it necessarily symbolize the identity relation of "is the same as." Rather, depending on the context, it may carry the connotation not only of the identity relation, but also of the equivalence relation of "have the same value as." Actually, as will be seen later, this fact serves to introduce a means of classification rather than to create a troublesome ambiguity. As these new definitions are framed, it must be kept in mind that none of the properties by which the operations have previously been characterized are to be lost. Problems must be handled with great care to prevent inconsistencies in the process of development. The extension from the set Q to the set R of real numbers is even more troublesome than is that from J to Q. The definition of irrational numbers is the source of the trouble. The real-number line and the expression of rational numbers as finite decimals or infinite repeating decimals can be helpful in overcoming this difficulty. This technique provides for the definition

A major responsibility of the junior high school

Extension from natural numbers . . .

. . . to integers

. . . to rational numbers

. . . to real numbers

. . . to complex
numbers

of irrational numbers as those numbers which can be expressed as infinite nonrepeating decimals. When this is done, the set R of real numbers can be defined as the set of all numbers which can be expressed in decimal form, either finite or infinite. The four basic operations can then be related to previous definitions. The new operation made possible by the extension to R is what might be called "limited extraction of roots." The word "limited" is necessary, since the extraction of even roots of negative real numbers is still impossible. This operation becomes possible only when the extension is made to the set C of complex numbers. To complete this extension new definitions of the four basic operations again become necessary. However, this presents no serious complication. When this has been accomplished, the new system is closed not only under addition, subtraction, multiplication, and division, but also under the process of the extraction of roots. The necessity for this last extension to the set C of complex numbers, normally, will not arise until later in the algebraic study of the solution sets of quadratic equations. However, only after this has been accomplished has the number field of elementary mathematics been structured within the framework of the diagram of Fig. 8-1.

The measurement problems of geometry and trigonometry offer still further opportunities for emphasis on the fundamental skills and basic understandings of arithmetic. The field of real numbers is sufficient to take care of all the computational needs, and no new extensions of the number system are needed. However, certain new adaptations and guides for computation and interpretation become necessary. This is due to the approximate nature of measurement and the controls that are necessary to guarantee justified results when computing with approximate data. Basic and informed instruction in the exercise of such controls of computation and interpretation is a definite responsibility of all teachers of secondary mathematics.

Although the instructional material of the junior and senior high schools offers a greater abundance of situations which are more nearly numerical in nature, the responsibility for increasing accuracy and facility in numerical computation does not end here. This responsibility extends even into the junior college, as does the building up of a progressive increase in the student's understanding of the basic structure of arithmetic and appreciation for the power and significance of applications of arithmetical techniques to environmental problem situations.

THE FIELD OF RATIONAL NUMBERS

A number system consists of a set of elements, at least one well-defined operation upon these elements, a set of postulated properties, and all the theorems which are derivable as consequences

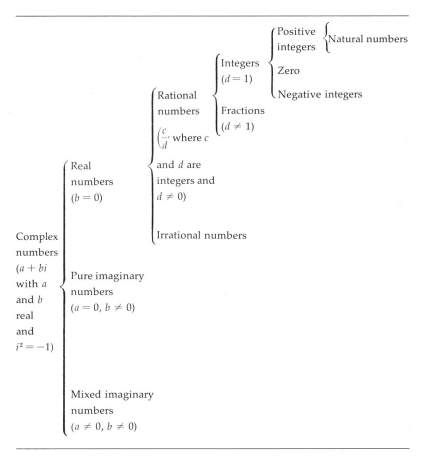

Figure 8-1
The number system of elementary mathematics.

of the implications of the basic set of postulates. The first such
system with which the study of arithmetic brings us into contact
is the natural-number system, whose postulates ($N1$ to $N11$) are
listed on page 60. The set of elements is the set of natural numbers $N = \{1,2,3,4, \ldots\}$, and there are two well-defined binary
operations of addition and multiplication. The statement that each
operation is well-defined means that when any two elements are
combined by either operation, there is no ambiguity in determining what the result is.

In the statement of postulates $N1$ to $N11$, the relation of equality
was used. Such a relationship between two or more natural numbers is characterized by the following five basic properties.

**The natural
number system**

**Addition and
multiplication are
well-defined
operations**

**Properties of
equality**

$E1$. *Reflexive property.* If a is in N, then $a = a$.
$E2$. *Symmetric property.* If a, b are in N and $a = b$, then $b = a$.
$E3$. *Transitive property.* If a, b, c are in N such that $a = b$ and $b = c$, then
   $a = c$.

E4. *Addition property.* If a, b, c are in N and $a = b$, then $c + a = c + b$.

E5. *Multiplication property.* If a, b, c are in N and $a = b$, then $ca = cb$.

These five properties are stated here as characterizing the relationship of equality between natural numbers. They also hold for equality between all numbers. The first three properties (reflexive, symmetric, and transitive) are the properties which characterize the more general *equivalence* relation. They hold for such relations as similarity and congruence of geometric figures; equality of areas, perimeters, and volumes; equality of the measures of line segments and angles; and many other types of relations, both mathematical and nonmathematical.

The equivalence relation

Under the closure property for the system we are assured that there exist natural numbers which are the respective sums or products for any such combinations of natural numbers. In spite of this fact, there are certain restrictions of operation incident to the closure property which become the motivation for desirable extensions of the number system to the domain of integers and the field of rational numbers. If a, b, and c are natural numbers such that $a + b = d$ and $a \times c = e$, then we know that d and e are also natural numbers. But if a, d, and e are natural numbers, does it follow that there exist natural numbers b and c such that the equalities are satisfied? It is a simple matter to supply examples which show that the answer to this question may be either yes or no. For example, if $a = 3$, $d = 7$, and $e = 15$, then $b = 4$ and $c = 5$ are natural numbers such that $a + b = d$ and $a \times c = e$. If, on the other hand, $a = 16$, $d = 7$, and $e = 5$, then there exist no natural numbers b and c such that the equalities are satisfied.

The need to extend number system

The restrictions on addition, illustrated in the foregoing paragraph, lead to the extension of the number system to include zero and the negative integers. In this extension the new operation of *subtraction* is defined as the inverse operation to addition in the sense that $a - b = c$ when a, b, and c are natural numbers, if and only if $b + c = a$. Zero is introduced as the *additive identity*, namely, the element 0, such that $a + 0 = 0 + a = a$ for every element a in the new system.

Subtraction and additive identity

The integer $-a$ (called the *additive inverse* of a) is assumed to exist such that $a + (-a) = (-a) + a = 0$. This new number system is the *domain of integers* in which the set of elements is $J = \{\ldots, -3, -2, -1, 0, +1, +2, +3, \ldots\}$, where the integer a is said to be positive if it is greater than zero ($a > 0$) or negative if it is less than zero ($a < 0$). The definitions of addition and multiplication in the new system are such that the closure, commutative, associative, and distributive properties are retained and the subset of positive integers is *isomorphic* with the set of natural numbers in the sense of this definition: If a one-to-one correspondence exists between the elements of set $S = \{a, b, \ldots\}$ and set $S' = \{a', b', \ldots\}$ such

The domain of integers

Isomorphism

that, if $a \leftrightarrow a'$ and $b \leftrightarrow b'$, then $a + b \leftrightarrow a' + b'$ and $a \times b \leftrightarrow a' \times b'$, then the two sets are said to be *isomorphic* with respect to addition and multiplication.

The cancellation law for addition still holds, but now becomes a provable theorem rather than a stated hypothesis. On the other hand, the law of cancellation for multiplication remains among the postulates, but in the modified form: For $a, b, c \in J$ and $c \neq 0$, if $c \times a = c \times b$, then $a = b$. The principle of trichotomy holds for the integers as stated for natural numbers. However, the introduction of 0 as the additive identity provides for these equivalent statements of the property:

Trichotomy

1   For $a, b \in J$, one and only one of the following relations holds: $a = b$, or there exists a positive integer c such that $a = b + c$ ($a > b$), or there exists a positive integer d such that $a + d = b$ ($a < b$).
2   For $a, b \in J$, one and only one of the following relations holds: $a - b = 0$, $a - b > 0$, or $a - b < 0$.
3   For $a \in J$, one and only one of the following relations holds: $a = 0$, $a > 0$, or $a < 0$.
4   For $a \in J$, one and only one of the following relations holds: $a = 0$, $a > 0$, or $-a > 0$.

The principle of finite induction does not hold for zero and the negative integers, but it does hold for the set of positive integers, due to the isomorphism which exists between this set and the set of natural numbers. In fact, the principle probably is stated more often in the phraseology of positive integers than of natural numbers.

In the context of the extensions of the operations of addition and multiplication to the set J, the only questions which arise are concerned with how these operations apply to zero and the negative integers. The answers to these questions are to be found in the following theorems, which are derivable as implied consequences of the basic postulates of the system. In the statements of these theorems, a and b are to be considered as representing any integers.

Theorem 1. $a \times 0 = 0 \times a = 0$.

Theorem 2. $a + (-b) = a - b$ if $a > b$. (This is in accordance with the definition of subtraction and the concept that $a > b$ if and only if there exists a positive integer c such that $a = b + c$.)

Theorem 3. If $b > a$, then $a + (-b) = -(b - a)$, the additive inverse of $b - a$.

Theorems 2 and 3 make it possible to extend the definition of subtraction to apply to a, b, and c as integers. Also, in the light of these two theorems, further significance can be given to the inverse relation existing between the operations of addition and subtraction. It is not difficult to prove:

Theorem 4. $(a + b) - b = (a - b) + b = a$. (Thus each of the operations, addition and subtraction, is seen to destroy, or cancel, the effect of the other.)

Theorem 5. $a \times (-b) = -(a \times b)$, the additive inverse of $a \times b$.

Theorem 6. $(-a) \times (-b) = a \times b$.

The restrictions on multiplication, illustrated previously for natural numbers, can be shown to prevail in the domain of integers. These restrictions lead to another extension of the number system of arithmetic, this time to include numbers of the form a/b, where a and b are integers and b is different from zero. Such numbers are called "rational numbers," or on occasion, "fractions." In this extension the new operation of *division* is defined as the inverse operation to multiplication in the sense that $a \div b = c$, when a, b, and c are integers, if and only if $b \times c = a$. Division by zero is of course excluded, since by definition $a \div 0 = c$ if and only if $c \times 0 = a$. Since c is an integer, theorem 1 (above) states that a must be zero; then the equality holds for any integer c, whence the quotient of $a \div 0$ is seen to be undefined. An accepted equivalent form of the symbol for division is a/b. Thus the definition of a rational number may be more formally stated: *A rational number is a number which may be expressed as the quotient of two integers.*

The set of elements of this new system is the set Q of all rational numbers, and the definitions of equality, addition, and multiplication are

Equality: $\dfrac{a}{b} = \dfrac{c}{d}$ if and only if $ad = bc$

Addition: $\dfrac{a}{b} + \dfrac{c}{d} = \dfrac{ad + bc}{bd}$

Multiplication: $\dfrac{a}{b} \times \dfrac{c}{d} = \dfrac{ac}{bd}$

With these definitions the operations of addition and multiplication retain the closure, commutative, associative, and distributive properties. The subset of rational numbers $a/1$, where a is any integer, and the set J of all integers can be shown to be isomorphic with respect to addition and multiplication. The number 1 serves as the *multiplicative identity* in the sense that $1 \times r = r \times 1 = r$ for any rational number r, and the reciprocal of any nonzero rational number r serves as the *multiplication inverse* of r in the sense that $r \times 1/r = 1/r \times r = 1$.

The set Q, with the operations of addition and multiplication, forms an *ordered number field* for which the basic postulates are as follows:

For a, b, c rational numbers

F1. *Closure.* If $a + b = r$ and $a \times b = s$, then r and s are rational numbers.
F2. *Commutative.* $a + b = b + a$ and $a \times b = b \times a$.

Division

Rational number

Field of rational numbers

F3. *Associative.* $(a + b) + c = a + (b + c)$ and $(a \times b) \times c = a \times (b \times c)$.

F4. *Distributive.* $a \times (b + c) = (a \times b) + (a \times c)$.

F5. *Additive identity.* The rational number 0 is such that $a + 0 = 0 + a = a$ for every rational number a.

F6. *Additive inverse.* For each rational number a there exists a rational number $-a$, called the *additive inverse* of a, such that $a + (-a) = (-a) + a = 0$.

F7. *Multiplicative identity.* The rational number 1 is such that $a \times 1 = 1 \times a = a$ for every rational number a.

F8. *Multiplicative inverse.* For each nonzero rational number a there exists a rational number $1/a$, called the *multiplicative inverse* of a, such that $a \times 1/a = 1/a \times a = 1$. (The symbol a^{-1} is also used to represent the multiplicative inverse of a.)

F9. There exists a proper subset P of Q such that for each nonzero element a of Q one and only one of a or $-a$ is in P.

F10. If a and b are elements of the subset P, then $a + b$ and $a \times b$ are also in P.

Actually, the preceding paragraphs oversimplify the extension from the domain of integers to the new system whose set of elements is the set Q of all rational numbers. From the properties of multiplication it follows that the product 3×4 is the unique integer 12. So when we write $3 \times 4 = 12$, this relation of equality is to be interpreted as meaning "the integer 3 multiplied by 4 *is the same as* the integer 12." From what is known about fractions, or rational numbers, we know that this uniqueness does not exist for the quotient of $3 \div 4$. Not only is $4 \times \frac{3}{4} = 3$, but also $4 \times -6/-8 = 3$, $4 \times \frac{9}{12} = 3$, $4 \times \frac{75}{100} = 3$, and so $4 \times r/s = 3$ for any rational number r/s, provided $r \times 4 = s \times 3$. These fractions are all equal in value. Thus, when we write $r/s = \frac{3}{4}$ if and only if $r \times 4 = s \times 3$, as required by the definition of "equality in rational numbers," the symbol $=$ is used with two distinct meanings. In fact, the complete statement of the "equality" $r/s = \frac{3}{4}$ should read: "For $r, s \in J$ and $s \neq 0$, the fraction r/s is *equivalent to* the fraction $\frac{3}{4}$ if and only if the integer $r \times 4$ *is the same as* the integer $s \times 3$." The symbol $\frac{3}{4}$ thus represents an infinite set of fractions, each equivalent to $\frac{3}{4}$ in the sense of the definition. For this reason, $\frac{3}{4}$, or any other fraction of the set, may be used as a symbol to identify the set, called an *Equivalence class* *equivalence class.* Thus we may define the rational number $\frac{3}{4}$ as the equivalence class

$$\frac{3}{4} = \left\{ \frac{r}{s} \,\middle|\, r, s \in J, s \neq 0, r \times 4 = s \times 3 \right\}$$

It is in this sense that the symbols a/b and c/d are used in the definitions of the rational operations. If we wish to find the sum $\frac{3}{4} + \frac{5}{12}$, the definition states that this is the rational number *Rational numbers* *as equivalence* *classes* $(3 \times 12 + 4 \times 5)/(4 \times 12) = \frac{56}{48} = \frac{7}{6}$. Here the symbol $=$ has been used for the purpose of stating that $(3 \times 12 + 4 \times 5)/(4 \times 12)$, $\frac{56}{48}$, and $\frac{7}{6}$ are symbols for the same equivalence class. In this context the symbol $=$ carries the meaning "is the same as." For example,

$^{56}/_{48} = {}^{7}/_{6}$ is to be interpreted as meaning that the equivalence class represented by $^{56}/_{48}$ *is the same as* the equivalence class represented by $^{7}/_{6}$, just as $8 + 5 = 13$ means that the integer represented by $8 + 5$ *is the same as* the integer represented by 13. Similarly, in multiplication we have, for example, that $\frac{3}{4} \times {}^{10}/_{9} = {}^{30}/_{36} = {}^{5}/_{6}$.

Since both addition and multiplication, as defined, can be proved to be independent of the representatives of the respective classes, the operations are said to be "well defined" in the sense that the class of the sum or of the product is uniquely determined.

Among the theorems which are derivable as implied consequences from these field postulates for rational numbers, there are two which clearly define the inverse relation that exists between multiplication and division. They are:

Theorem 7. If a and b are rational numbers and $b \neq 0$, then $a \times 1/b = a \div b$.

Theorem 8. If a and b are rational numbers and $b \neq 0$, then $(a \times b) \div b = (a \div b) \times b = a$.

Theorem 7 should be recognized as a formalized statement of the rule frequently stated as follows: In division you can invert the divisor and multiply. This theorem, while stated here for rational numbers, can be shown to apply both to real numbers and to complex numbers. Likewise, theorem 2, on page 197, which relates addition and subtraction of integers, can be shown to hold for rational numbers, real numbers, or complex numbers. Furthermore, theorems 4 and 8 also can be shown to apply to the extended systems, thus pairing addition with subtraction and multiplication with division as inversely related field operations.

In this more general context theorems 2 and 7 lend authority to **Field operations** what might be regarded as a fundamental property of field operations, namely: Any computation involving any one or all of the four field operations may be transformed into an equivalent computation involving the respective inverse operations. For example, theorem 7 states not only that division can be accomplished by inverting the divisor and multiplying, but also that multiplication can be accomplished by inverting one of the factors and dividing. Similarly, theorem 2 states that addition may be accomplished by inverting one of the addends and subtracting, or that subtraction can be accomplished by inverting the subtrahend and adding.

COMMON FRACTIONS

Before his junior high school experience, the student has had little, if any, opportunity to associate a symbol such as a/b with the concept of rational number. His use of this symbol has been either as representing a *ratio* expressing a relation between two numbers, and not used in situations involving computation, or as representing a number, called a *common fraction*, and subject to specified computational patterns. The fundamental operations with such numbers have the dubious distinction of being considered as among the more troublesome parts of arithmetic.

Difficulties in dealing with common fractions

The very real and serious difficulties which many students encounter in working with common fractions may stem from any one or more of several causes. One of them is failure to have a clear concept of what a fraction represents numerically. Another is an apparent reluctance to concede that in operations with fractions the numerators and denominators must be given attention separately; that frequently it is not sufficient to think of fractions merely as single numbers as one would think of integers, but rather as the expressed quotients of two numbers. This is tantamount to nonrecognition of the real meaning of the numerator and denominator and of the role each has in expressing the value of the fraction. Such recognition requires reflective thought, and thinking is hard, and often slow, work. A third source of difficulty lies in the characteristic impatience of youth—the desire to be done with a problem quickly, and preferably in a single step. This, coupled with fuzzy concepts, uncertain thinking, disregard of definitions, and a tendency to speed things up by uncritical use of analogy, can and often does produce in students a state of mind altogether unfavorable to clear thinking. Such a state of mind leads to a willingness to use any device that will produce a quick answer.

Teachers, of course, cannot disregard these things. Failing to get acceptable progress through the necessarily slow process of insisting on clear thinking about fractions and faced with limited time, teachers often have recourse to the only apparent alternative, that of providing the students with ready-made rules. Students usually like to have them, because the rules provide them with patterns that are easy to follow and which do enable them to get quick results. Rules per se are not bad; indeed, they are very necessary for generalizing and crystallizing procedures and for economizing time and effort. But such rules without accompanying insight are merely arithmetical tools. They may promote computational proficiency, but they do not represent genuine mathematical understanding, which alone can lead to intelligent use of any acquired mathematical tools.

Dangers in the use of rules

While this is recognized by practically all teachers, there are two extreme schools of thought about rules in mathematics. One holds that students should *never* be taught a process until it has been rationalized. The other holds that rationalization will always be easier to understand if students are first given the rule and shown how it works and that the use of the rule or procedure should *always* precede the justification. It is almost certain that neither of these extreme positions is tenable. But without rationalization, whether first or last, genuine growth in mathematical insight cannot take place. The danger in the "rule first, rationalization later" theory is that of time pressure. Inevitably, and perhaps before getting around to the rationalization, comes the need to move on to other things, and to teachers under this pressure the temptation to compromise on reasonable mechanical proficiency in the use of the rules can become very strong.

Too frequently the technique of simplifying fractions, or "reducing fractions to lower terms," is taught as a mechanical process of cancellation. Such a procedure leads to a confused concept of the significance of cancellation and very often reduces it to a mere crossing out of numbers. Such a performance as

$$\frac{\cancel{4}+2}{\cancel{4}+9}=\frac{2}{9} \quad \text{or} \quad \frac{\cancel{7}+3}{\cancel{7}\times 3}=\frac{3}{3}=1$$

then may, and not infrequently does, result. In instruction which leads to this sort of performance, no basic understanding of the interrelationship among the fundamental operations or of the structure of fractions is developed. It needs to be pointed out to students that the horizontal bar of a fraction indicates a division; that, for example,

$$\frac{8}{18}$$

indicates the division of 8 by 18. Stress should also be laid upon the principle that division and multiplication are inverse processes, just as addition and subtraction are inverse processes. Thus, in the multiplication and division of any number by the same number (other than zero), one operation nullifies, destroys, or cancels the effect of the other. This means, simply, that the net effect is multiplication, or division, of the given number by 1. Thus

$$\frac{8}{18}=\frac{2\times 4}{2\times 9}=\frac{2}{2}\times\frac{4}{9}=1\times\frac{4}{9}=\frac{4}{9}$$

We simplify all this detail by using the convenient device of cancellation:

$$\frac{8}{18}=\frac{\cancel{2}^1\times 4}{\cancel{2}_1\times 9}=\frac{1\times 4}{1\times 9}=\frac{4}{9}$$

The small 1's should be written in to give emphasis to what has actually taken place. Similarly, the net effect of adding the same number to and subtracting it from a given number is equivalent to the addition, or subtraction, of zero. Thus $7+2-2=7+0$ (or $7-0)=7$. Cancellation can be used to indicate what has taken place here. There would be no division, however, but merely a neutralizing, which can be indicated by simply crossing out the numbers which neutralize each other: $7 + \cancel{2} - \cancel{2} = 7$. In the fraction

$$\frac{4 + 2}{4 + 9}$$

the student should be taught that he must think of the operations involved as if the division were expressed in the form $(4 + 2) \div (4 + 9)$. In such situations he can recognize that the additions must be performed before the division and that, since addition and division are not inverse processes, no cancellation is possible.

The principles of the preceding paragraph are recognized as based on the inverse properties of the field of rational numbers ($F6$ and $F8$, page 199). Furthermore, the principles of cancellation are simply those of theorem 4 (page 197) and theorem 8 (page 200). If the instructional program in arithmetic has given the correct emphasis to the basic structure of the number systems of arithmetic, the bases for answers to many of the "why questions" of the type indicated here will have been constructed before the questions arise. If the student cannot ferret out his own answers to such questions, the teacher can direct the student to this informational background as an aid in his search for the desired answers.

Multiplication of rational numbers

Multiplication of fractions usually presents little difficulty. In the first place, the definition is rather simple: $a/b \times c/d = ac/bd$. Second, it can be made to seem reasonable by giving various concrete illustrations and by identifying such notation as $1/3 \times 6/7$ with the corresponding verbal expression "one-third of six-sevenths." Graphic or geometric illustrations are effective and are easy to devise. Although the procedure actually represents a definition of the product, it is well to present illustrations to show that the results which it gives are in accord with actual experience and common sense. Another scheme for rationalizing the definition of the product of two rational numbers can be developed in the following manner. If we let r represent the quotient of $3 \div 4$ and s the quotient $5 \div 2$, then we may write

$$r = \frac{3}{4} \quad \text{and} \quad s = \frac{5}{2}$$

or from the definition of division, $4 \times r = 3$ and $2 \times s = 5$. From the multiplicative property of equality it now follows that $(4 \times r) \times (2 \times s) = 3 \times 5$. Using the associative and commutative properties for multiplication, this may be written in the form $(4 \times 2) \times (r \times s) = 3 \times 5$. Thus $r \times s$ is the quotient of $(3 \times 5) \div (4 \times 2)$, or

$$r \times s = \frac{3 \times 5}{4 \times 2}$$

Now by substitution we have

$$\frac{3}{4} \times \frac{5}{2} = \frac{3 \times 5}{4 \times 2}$$

Products of fractions can often be simplified by cancellation. As a precautionary measure against mistakes it is well to have students form the habit of expressing the product as a single fraction before doing the cancellation. For example, instead of writing

$$\frac{1}{{}^1\!3} \times \frac{{}^2\!6}{7}$$

it is better for them to write

$$\frac{1}{3} \times \frac{6}{7} = \frac{1 \times {}^1\!3 \times 2}{{}^1\!3 \times 7} = \frac{1 \times 1 \times 2}{1 \times 7} = \frac{2}{7}$$

because it systematizes the form and may prevent mistakes due to careless writing. Of course, after a student thoroughly understands the full significance of what is taking place, he no longer needs to bother with so much minuteness of detail.

The procedure for dividing by a fraction is familiar to most students who know how to multiply fractions, for the reason that, after a single simple adjustment, the division problem actually becomes a problem in multiplication. Few, however, of those who know *how* to divide by a fraction understand *why* the inversion of the fractional divisor and the consequent multiplication actually give the required value. Here again is a case of a rather familiar process which for the most part is used quite empirically. Where used correctly, it gives correct results. Unfortunately, however, the word "invert" seems to stand out as the only important thing in the minds of the students, with the result that sometimes they invert the dividend instead of the divisor and then wonder why the result they get is incorrect or perhaps even ridiculous. The only sure safeguard against such a situation is to get the students to understand the rationale of the procedure. This need not be a long or tedious matter, for a few rather simple illustrations will usually suffice.

While there are several elementary avenues to satisfactory rationalization, it must be kept in mind that the foundation upon which any approach must be based consists in the facts that (*a*) multiplication and division are inverse processes and (*b*) 1 is the identity element for multiplication and division. Thus it follows, for example, that

$$16 \div 4 = \frac{16}{4} = \frac{16 \times \frac{1}{4}}{4 \times \frac{1}{4}} = \frac{16 \times \frac{1}{4}}{1} = 16 \times \frac{1}{4}$$

Division of
rational numbers

and that

$$9 \div \frac{1}{3} = (9 \times 3) \div \left(\frac{1}{3} \times 3\right) = (9 \times 3) \div 1 = 9 \times 3$$

Unless some effective measures are taken to have the students understand what is actually taking place and see why the process must give the required result, there will always be some danger of mistakes occurring, and at best the students will have attained only a mechanical proficiency without corresponding mathematical insight. The best teachers will never be content with this.

Addition and subtraction of rational numbers

The greatest source of trouble in this area, however, is the addition and subtraction of fractions, particularly when the fractions have different denominators. The difficulty stems from the sources that have already been mentioned: the desire of the students for short cuts and quick answers; the time pressure on the teachers and the consequent tendency to give inadequate attention to rationalizing the procedure; the excessive dependence on the mechanical use of rules; and the failure to check results for reasonableness. There is the additional fact that the procedure here is, characteristically, a bit more involved than is that in the operations discussed previously. This of course intensifies the pressure on the teacher and tends to diminish any disposition to insist on rationalization and checking, although they are made even more important by the circumstances.

Unitary analysis

One of the most effective ways of giving meaning to the addition of fractions is the method of unitary analysis. Under this method as applied, say, to the fraction $3/7$, it would be emphasized that the fraction is made up of 3 "unit fractions," each of which is $1/7$, or

$$\frac{3}{7} = \frac{1}{7} + \frac{1}{7} + \frac{1}{7} = 3 \times \frac{1}{7} = \frac{1}{7} \times 3$$

This decomposition both establishes an identity as shown and suggests the usefulness of identifying the form $3/7$ with the form $3 \times 1/7$. But it does more. Through this latter identification (which curiously is seldom used and often not even recognized by students, even though teachers always assume that it is so obvious as to require no comment), a reversal of the decomposition suggests the fundamental concept of the combination of fractions with like denominators, out of which the formal rule grows. That is to say,

$$\frac{1}{7} + \frac{1}{7} + \frac{1}{7} = \frac{1}{7} \times 3 = \frac{1}{7} \times (1 + 1 + 1) = \frac{1 + 1 + 1}{7} = \frac{3}{7}$$

This illustrates what goes on in the combination of fractions whose denominators are alike. The effect of such an illustration, however, will usually be negligible unless two things are explicitly and *separately* emphasized about the single fraction which makes up the sum, namely, (1) how its denominator is determined and (2) how its numerator is determined, and preferably in the order mentioned. This may seem a trivial insistence, but it is not. It is justified by both psychological considerations and practical experience. The matter should not be hurried; it should be soundly established in the minds of the students by both discussion and practice before taking them on to the more troublesome case of combining fractions whose denominators are not alike. Once it has been established that the fraction a/b can always be written in the form $a \times 1/b$, the distributive property can be used to provide the rule for finding the sum of any two fractions with a common denominator.

Fractions with common denominators

$$\frac{a}{b} + \frac{c}{b} = \left(a \times \frac{1}{b}\right) + \left(c \times \frac{1}{b}\right) = (a + c) \times \frac{1}{b} = \frac{a + c}{b}$$

Once the handling of fractions with like denominators is thoroughly understood by the students, the way is open for proceeding to the general case of fractions whose denominators are not necessarily alike. Recalling that for any given fraction an equivalent fraction having any nonzero denominator we like can be written, let us then say to the students, "If the denominators are not alike, make them alike. Then we shall know how to combine them." First this idea should be used as the basis for rationalizing the definition of addition for rational numbers. The use of a few sums such as $\frac{3}{4} + \frac{5}{7}$ and $\frac{2}{3} + \frac{7}{2}$, where the denominators have no common factor, can provide background for the general case, which is presented here in abbreviated form and with all supporting authority to be supplied.

The general case

$$\frac{a}{b} + \frac{c}{d} = \left(\frac{a}{b} \times \frac{d}{d}\right) + \left(\frac{b}{b} \times \frac{c}{d}\right)$$

$$= \frac{ad}{bd} + \frac{bc}{bd}$$

$$= \left(ad \times \frac{1}{bd}\right) + \left(bc \times \frac{1}{bd}\right)$$

$$= (ad + bc) \times \frac{1}{bd}$$

$$= \frac{ad + bc}{bd}$$

In each illustrative example, as well as in the general case, care should be taken to relate the definition to the familiar technique of finding the common denominator. Once the rationalization has been accomplished, the way is clear for introducing the use of the least common denominator (lcd) to simplify the procedure. This, of course, will require determination of the least common denominator, the building up of all denominators to this form by writing in the needed factors, and corresponding adjustment of numerators. This is best understood if all the denominators are first written in full factored form and the lcd is also written in factored form and if all these factored expressions are written out separately for reference. For example, consider the sum of the fractions $5/42 + 7/12 + 1/2$. Now

$$42 = (2)(3)(7) \qquad 12 = (2)(3)(2) \qquad \text{lcd} = (2)(3)(2)(7)$$

$$\frac{5}{42} + \frac{7}{12} + \frac{1}{2} = \frac{5}{(2)(3)(7)} + \frac{7}{(2)(3)(2)} + \frac{1}{2}$$

$$= \frac{5(2)}{(2)(3)(2)(7)} + \frac{7(7)}{(2)(3)(2)(7)} + \frac{1(3)(2)(7)}{(2)(3)(2)(7)}$$

$$= \frac{10}{84} + \frac{49}{84} + \frac{42}{84}$$

$$= \frac{10 + 49 + 42}{84} = \frac{101}{84}$$

In such cases it is simpler and probably better to use parentheses, as shown, to indicate multiplication. The meaning of this notation will have to be explained to students who have not had any experience with algebra, but this should take little time and cause no difficulty.

At the outset, of course, much simper cases would be used—examples in which the identification of the lcd can be very easily made at sight—and perhaps the work in the seventh grade should be largely limited to such cases. It is believed, however, that even here the routine illustrated above will do much to build fundamental understanding of the rationale underlying the process and thus remove it from the realm of mere mechanical tools. Even in the seventh grade the generality of the procedure can be enhanced by giving some illustrations of cases in which the lcd is not immediately discernible as a single whole number. The advantage of this will become more and more apparent as the students go on to subsequent work in arithmetic and in algebra.

Furthermore, even in its simplest form this procedure tends to rationalize the rote process used in the elementary grades for finding the lcd in such situations. It is possible that there may be some students at the seventh-grade level who are not yet sufficiently mature to be able to comprehend such rationalization, even in its simplest form. For such students the rote method of successive multiplications of the largest denominator by the integers 2, 3, 4, etc., will have to continue to suffice.

Everything which has been said in this section applies with

equal validity and in all details to both proper and improper fractions. Indeed, since mixed numbers and integers can be written as improper fractions, it can be said to apply to them as well, after they are written in fraction form. Sometimes multiplication, and always division, by mixed numbers can be accomplished most easily by reducing these numbers to improper fractions and proceeding accordingly. It is well to give students some experience in this, both for the understanding of the specific applications and for strengthening the sense of the generality of the methods.

DECIMAL FRACTIONS

Unfortunately, it is frequently true that students, even upon graduation from high school, either have failed to take advantage of the opportunity or have not had the opportunity to learn the full significance of place value in the structure of our numeral system. It not only binds together the thought processes which constitute the rationale of the fundamental operations, but also simplifies the mechanics of the several algorisms. It is the keystone of our numeral system, and thus should receive emphasis throughout the elementary and secondary schools. Indeed, since the junior high school is the grade level at which the concepts and skills of arithmetic should be treated with a fair degree of maturity, these are the grades in which special emphasis should be given to place value and its significance to basic understanding in the effective use of numbers. In these grades pupils are expected to strengthen the skills and understandings of arithmetic and extend them to include less mechanical computation techniques with decimal fractions and common fractions. These extensions involve certain difficulties. It is important that teachers be aware of them so that steps can be taken to anticipate them and prevent them from becoming serious impediments to the students' genuine mastery of the subject.

There has been, and continues to be, debate as to whether the better approach to the study of fractions is to have the first serious use of fractions be with decimal or common fractions. Regardless of the merits of either side of the argument, it is true that any decimal fraction, with a finite number of places, can be written as a common fraction with some power of 10 as the denominator. Therefore it follows that the four fundamental operations for rational numbers provide the necessary guides for any desired computation with decimal fractions. However, the student who has really mastered the fundamental operations with whole numbers should have little difficulty in extending them to numbers

Special cases of common fractions

involving decimal fractions. The procedures themselves are identical in the two cases. There is one new element, however, in cases where decimal fractions are involved, and that is the proper placement of the decimal point in the answer. This usually causes no difficulty in finding sums or differences, because when the numbers are written carefully columnwise, the decimal point in the sum or difference falls naturally into place in line with the others.

Addition and subtraction

Mistakes are more likely to occur in placing the decimal point in products or quotients than in sums or differences. As a rule such mistakes are due to haste and carelessness, because the decimal point is too often placed by rote rule alone and without any checking to see whether the result is reasonable or not. It is also true that a good many students seem not to be impressed by the seriousness of the error which is introduced by a misplaced decimal point. The comment "But it's all right except the decimal point" is neither uncommon nor insincere on the part of the students; yet it implies unawareness of how serious the error is. Students need to be made and kept sensitive to the fact that even if an answer is numerically correct so far as the sequence of digits is concerned, misplacement of the decimal point represents one of the most serious mistakes that could be made, because such a mistake can make the answer unreasonably large or small. As students learn arithmetic they need to be kept aware that the formal procedures are not divorced from common sense and that the results they get by using these procedures will not be right unless they can be confirmed by common sense.

Multiplication and division

This suggests a quick, easy, powerful, and in most cases a foolproof method of checking on the placement of the decimal point in a product or a quotient, namely, checking by mental estimate. Consider the product 27.43 × 12.08, which upon multiplication yields the digits 3313544 and requires that the decimal point be properly placed to give the true value of the product. Since 27.43 is a little less than 30 and 12.08 is a little more than 10, the required product *must* be in the neighborhood of 30 × 10, which is immediately seen to be 300. Hence the product *must* be somewhere near 300, and this requires that the decimal point be placed after the third digit; that is, the product must be 331.3544. This is readily confirmed by the usual rule, but more significantly, it is confirmed by the student's common sense. From such considerations even young students can readily learn to detect and correct careless misplacement of the decimal point and verify the correct position.

Placement of the decimal point in quotients can be determined and checked through similar considerations. For example, when 87.01646 is divided by 1.06, the sequence of digits 82091 appears in the quotient. The question of placing the decimal point can be resolved immediately by considering that, since the dividend is a little less than 90 and the divisor is just a little greater than 1, the quotient *must* be somewhere in the neighborhood of 90 and must also be less than 90; so it will probably be between 80 and 90. Hence, in order to yield such a quotient, the decimal point *must* be placed after the second digit. That is, the quotient must be 82.091.

Another effective method for placing the decimal point in the quotient is the following one. It is easily observed that $10 \times 1.06 = 10.6$, which is smaller than the dividend, and that $100 \times 1.06 = 106$, which is larger than the dividend. It follows, therefore, that the integral part of the quotient must be a two-digit number, since it lies between 10 and 100. The decimal point is thus to be placed immediately following the second quotient figure. Continued trial of successive powers of 10 is not a difficult procedure for establishing limits between which the quotient must lie. Practice will improve the estimate and reduce the number of trials necessary. Here again confirmation is easily made by applying the customary rule, but it is equally important to have the rule confirmed by the estimate. Indeed, the student's feeling of power and assurance is enhanced by encouraging him to make his preliminary estimate of the answer even before performing the computation. To this end such exercises as the following can be used to great advantage. They can be constructed easily and are unlimited in scope and variety.

Exercise: In the following products or quotients the digits are correct and in the right order. Place the decimal point where it should go, putting zeros if necessary before or after the digits given, and read the correct answer.

$38.501 \times 6.93 = 26681193$		$202.9372 \div 28.03 = 724$
$81.072 \times 39.6 = 32104512$		$129.10072 \div 19.88 = 6494$
$512.47 \times 2.53 = 12965491$		$4693.4705 \div 0.965 = 48637$
$70.386 \times 0.945 = 66514770$		$4.654728 \div 89.514 = 52$

Checking is important

The importance of inculcating in students the habit of checking their work by such estimates can hardly be overemphasized. Of course, it does not provide any check on the numerical work, but it does provide a powerful and easy and almost certain way of avoiding blunders through misplacement of the decimal point, and it injects a rationale into the work with decimal fractions which can hardly be attained in any other way. Actually, students almost always enjoy it, and the assurance and confidence which can result may often be of extreme importance with respect not only to the correctness of the work itself, but also to the student's attitude toward it.

Of course, when dealing with decimal fractions, the point should always be made that these numbers are fractions. All the principles and techniques used with fractions still apply. The only differences at all are due to a possible simplification in notation due to the fact that the fractions to be used are now restricted to those whose denominators are powers of 10, the base of our number system. In particular, the rules for finding the product and quotient of two fractions still apply. For example, the product 27.43×12.08 can be found as the product of the two common fractions $2,743/100 \times 1,208/100 = 3,313,544/10,000$, which may, in turn, be written as the decimal fraction 331.3544. Such procedure illustrates the reason why there are as many digits in the fraction part of the product of two decimal fractions as there are in the sum of the digits in the multiplier and the multiplicand. Similarly, the quotient $87.01646 \div 1.06$ can be found as

$$\frac{8,701,646}{100,000} \div \frac{106}{100} = \frac{8,701,646}{100,000} \times \frac{100}{106} = \frac{82,091}{1,000}$$

which can be written as the decimal fraction 82.091.

Such demonstration provides the rationale of the inverse rule used to find the number of digits in the fraction part of a quotient. Incidentally, once the rule for multiplication is established, the inverse relationship of division to multiplication could be used to obtain the corresponding rule for division.

Probably the most immediately direct and systematic physical application used to explain and illustrate decimals in arithmetic is the money system of the United States. Built as it is, directly on the decimal system of notation, it forms a practically perfect physical illustration of that system, and it has the advantage of being familiar to everyone. However, it offers but a single means of illustration. Another, intrinsically just as good, though less familiar to most people, is found in the metric system of weights and measures, which of course is an important element of the mathematics program in its own right. But because it is not the system of weights and measures in most common use in this country, few people learn anything about it through informal everyday experience in the way they learn about money. As a rule, if it is learned at all, it is learned in school as a part of the work in mathematics, and its introduction generally occurs after the study of decimal fractions is begun. This, of course, imposes a drastic limitation on its use in *developing* the concept of decimal fractions, but does not impair its later usefulness as a means of illustrating and strengthening this concept. Indeed, if the simple elements of the metric system could be taught concurrently with the subject of decimal notation and decimal fractions, it would seem to afford an excellent opportunity for strengthening and enriching the understanding of both.

PERCENTAGE

In the preceding section we were concerned only with that set of fractions whose denominators can be expressed in the form 10^n, where n is a positive integer. Since this set is a proper subset of the set of all fractions of the form a/b, where $a, b \in J$ and $b \neq 0$, no new definitions of the fundamental operations were necessary. In fact, all computational patterns were subject to considerable simplification as a result of the conveniences of our decimal numeral system with its place-value characteristics. In this section we shall further restrict the fractions in which we are interested to only those which have the common denominator 100. The literal translation of the two Latin words *per centum* is "by the hundred." Thus any rate percent is always expressible as the ratio of some number to 100. True, any such rate may be converted either to a decimal-fraction equivalent or to a common-fraction equivalent[1] for computational purposes, but then it is no longer a rate percent. Since this set of fractions is a proper subset of the set of all decimal fractions, the basic patterns of computation are the same. The only new areas of difficulty are those concerned with interpretation and application associated with this concept of the ratio of two numbers. It is of interest to speculate as to why the number 100 is always used as the base of this ratio (the denominator of the fraction), which is of such great importance in business, industry, and everyday affairs. For convenience in making comparisons it is desirable that there be a common base, and the fact that our system of numeration is decimal more or less dictates that this base be some power of 10. The first power does not offer much latitude for making comparisons, and the third power (1,000) provides much more than is commonly needed. A natural compromise, therefore, has been the second power, or 100.

Of all the special topics or centers of attention in arithmetic, none has more widespread utility and direct application than the subject of percentage. It is involved in the numerical record and analysis of all kinds of activities, from the very simple to the very complex, and to those who understand its language it provides a concise and efficient means of interpreting, comparing, and communicating many kinds of quantitative information. Since it is so closely allied to the subject of decimal notation and fractions, one might conclude that its application would involve no difficulties that are not involved in the study or application of decimals as such. Unfortunately, however, experience indicates that this is not the case. Percentage has been and continues to be one of the

Percents as fractions with denominator 100

Percentage has many important applications

---

[1] For example, 87½ percent may be expressed in decimal fraction form as .87½ or .875. In common-fraction form it can be written as $875/_{1,000}$, $175/_{200}$, or ⅞.

most troublesome parts of arithmetic. In spite of its importance as an instrument for analysis and a vehicle for communication, many students fail to attain an assured mastery of it.

Various studies have been made from time to time to determine why students have so much difficulty with percentage, and these have usually taken the form of listing mistakes which students have made on percentage problems. But teachers ought to be concerned not only with what mistakes are made but with why they are made. To point out merely that students do not understand the principle of percentage does not provide much indication of just why they do not understand, or of what could be done to help them understand better. The computational skills involved in the mechanics of percentage are merely those involved in computing with decimal fractions, but they do not suffice for the interpretation and analysis of percentage problems stated in words or drawn from original situations. The latter require an exact understanding of the technical vocabulary and symbolism which have come to be associated with percentage, the ability to interchange different but equivalent forms with assurance, and the habit of meticulously careful analytical reading. The student who thoroughly understands a problem in percentage and who understands the related language and symbolism usually will have little difficulty in solving it.

Several things seem to contribute to the confusion that is so prevalent with respect to percentage. The terminology that has come to be universally employed is itself confusing and unfortunate. In the identification of "percent" with "hundredths," the base number often is not mentioned, though neither of these concepts has meaning except as referred to some base. The further representation of, say, "37 percent," or "37%," by the decimal fraction "0.37" fails to emphasize the clarifying idea that 0.37 itself means 37×0.01 and that the % symbol merely stands for the decimal fraction 0.01. These alternative representations of the same thing thus tend to add to the student's confusion, especially when such expressions as "0.37%" are encountered. Experienced teachers will verify that students often fail to make any distinction in their minds between "37%" and "0.37%." When the subject is taught by "cases," three explicit rules can indeed be developed for the three explicit relations among the three elements involved, but these tend to become confused in the students' minds, and students often have trouble determining "which case this is." Even the single overall rule or formula $base \times rate = percentage$ (or $b \times r = p$) requires that the rate must be represented by the decimal or common fraction only, not by use of the % symbol; yet even this is seldom emphasized in the textbooks.

Difficulties with percentage are more of understanding than of computation

Characteristic difficulties

What, then, can be done to make the teaching of percentage more productive of worthwhile results? The terminology and symbolism associated with percentage without doubt present certain ambiguities and difficulties. It seems reasonable, however, to believe that more can be done than usually has been done to make percentage intelligible to students and enable them to think about it with clarity.

Importance of the basic formula

Nearly all textbooks that treat the subject of percentage stress the solution of problems by use of the rule or formula, base × rate = percentage. This gives the fundamental relationship of the three elements and provides a pattern for explicit determination of percentage when the base and rate are known. Many textbooks go further and give explicit formulas for each of the three "cases."

Dangers in the "three-case" rule

This may, of course, give quicker results when the students have the three formulas before them and the cases of all their problems identified. But, by the same token, it obviates the need for thinking about the problem and in effect avoids, rather than promotes, training in problem analysis. Moreover, students often get the formulas confused with each other unless they have them all written out before them. Failure to identify correctly the given data is a further major source of mistakes. Also, students frequently fail to check their results by first making rough estimates. Thus they are at times led through mechanical reaction to a rule to accept results which common-sense estimates would show to be ridiculous.

The only apparent reason for teaching percentage by cases with their accompanying three formulas is the belief that with typed problems this method will produce answers more quickly than other methods. But actually, even if that is true, the advantage is more apparent than real, because the same results can be attained about as quickly and with less chance of confusion if all three cases are fed into the one basic formula or rule and the resulting equation solved, when necessary, by a single step which students can learn to use easily and with understanding. As an example, consider this problem: At a school-district election, 1,400 people voted. If this was 35 percent of all the eligible voters, how many eligible voters were there in all? Steps in the solution would be as follows:

$$\text{Base} \times \text{rate} = \text{percentage}$$
$$\text{Base} \times (0.35) = (1,400)$$
$$\frac{\text{Base} \times (0.35)}{(0.35)} = \frac{1,400}{(0.35)}$$

Since the *base* (total number of eligible voters) is to be determined, it can be done immediately by dividing each member of the equation by the coefficient 0.35, giving the result indicated in the third line of the solution. If the objection is raised that this requires a little bit of algebra, one must reflect that the special formula for this case is itself derived by precisely this method.

The fundamental relationship

Furthermore, this difficulty, if difficulty it is, can be greatly reduced by the realization that such emphasis on this fundamental relationship in percentage problems points out that there are always three numbers involved, and that one of them (*percentage*) is the product of the other two (*base* and *rate*). If the product number (percentage) is not known, then the operation called for is multiplication; if it is known, then the operation called for is division.

As in the multiplication of any two numbers, so in percentage there are three associated relations: $p = b \times r$, $b = p \div r$, and $r = p \div b$. Furthermore, the rate, if it is a known number, usually is labeled with the percent sign. This means that in percentage the problem situation is reduced to being able to distinguish between the number upon which all computation is based (the base) and the number which is derived through multiplication (the percentage).

In this connection it can be very helpful to dwell on the important fact that, since a rate percent is a ratio, the basic formula can be written in the form of the proportion $p/b = r/100$. The important implication to be derived from this proportion is that any problem dealing with percents can be so expressed. Once this conversion of the problem situation has been accomplished, the remainder of the process of finding the solution involves no more

Importance of the base

than one operation, either that of finding a product or that of finding a quotient. The proportion also helps to underscore an important consideration which is entailed in any problem involving percents. Whatever the operations might be, the freedoms of operation and interpretation are always related directly to the base. Abstractly, 30 percent is larger than 20 percent, but 30 percent of 50 is much smaller than 20 percent of 500. Although all rate percents have the same denominator, finding the sum or difference of two or more percents can be completely without meaning, as can the finding of the average of several percents. It is only when such problems are considered within the context of the base or bases of reference that proper operations can be performed or correct interpretations made.

The 1-percent method

As either an alternative or a supplementary device the "one percent method," or "method of unitary analysis," can be used, often to great advantage in clarifying students' thinking. In this method primary attention is focused at the outset on the concept of one single percent of the base as an entity—a whole "little" number or quantity in itself. If this is done, then such an expression as "63 percent of the distance" comes to be thought of not just as some part of the required distance, but actually as 63 parts, all equal and each being 1 hundredth of the required distance. This obviates the need for translating from percents to decimal equivalents, and so avoids the mistakes which so often accompany attempts to make this translation. Now 63 percent becomes not 0.63 (a decimal fraction of the whole) but 63 "little wholes." It brings the thinking from the realm of fractions into the realm of whole numbers; from a field of possible uncertainty or confusion into a realm of familiarity. Then, if one of these percents can be found, any number of them can be found by a turn of the hand. It requires only the kind of reasoning one uses in determining the cost of 4½ gallons of gasoline at 35 cents a gallon or the cost of 115 postage stamps at 6 cents each. And no matter which case a percentage problem represents, 1 percent of the base can always be found. As an example, consider again the problem about the voters, discussed above. Here our problem is clearly to determine the base number, which is the total number of eligible voters. It is given that 35 percent of this total is 1,400 people. Think of this as 35 little groups of people, each group containing 1 percent of the total number of eligible voters, with the total number of people in the 35 groups being 1,400. Now that is exactly equivalent, arithmetically, to such a question as this: If 35 notebooks cost $14.00 or 1,400 cents, how much does each cost. Very few students will not know how to find the cost of one notebook under these conditions; so it is not very hard to lead them to see how to determine the number representing 1 percent of the required base. Then, having determined that 1 percent of the total number of eligible voters is 40 (that is, ¹/₃₅ of 1,400), it follows that the total number must be 100 times as much, or 4,000.

Now it is easy also to answer at once such questions as the following ones: If 47½ percent of the eligible voters are men, how many men are eligible to vote? If 3.7 percent of the eligible voters are at least 80 years old, how many of the voters are not yet 80 years of age? If the number of eligible voters increases by 18 percent in the next 5 years, how many will there be then?

Limitations of this method   There are, of course, some drawbacks to this method of analysis. It certainly requires careful and exact reading and interpretation of the problems, and the students will learn to handle the method only through honest, painstaking, and protracted effort on their part and on the part of their teachers. Some old mental associations and fixed habits will probably have to be broken down in order that the primary concept of a single percent of the base number may come to occupy the focus of attention. This method requires superior teaching, and usually it will not produce answers as quickly as the use of the formula will. For these, and perhaps other, reasons it has not come into widespread use either in textbooks or by teachers. But it does aim at the fundamental objectives of clear thinking about percentage relationships, and if it is systematically and persistently used with good teaching and adequate supervision, it can do much to help students clarify their thoughts on this important aspect of arithmetic.

There are other considerations which teachers should take into account as means of clarifying and highlighting the main concepts associated with percents and for providing conditions favorable to effective mastery of this subject. Space limitations preclude detailed discussion of them here, but one or two should at least be mentioned.

Use of graphs

The concepts of *base, rate,* and *percentage* and the relations among them can be clarified and made vivid by the extensive use of graphs, and teachers should capitalize on this means of strengthening and enriching the concepts. Most textbooks do employ this device to a limited extent, but they need to be supplemented. Fortunately, it is easy to find many examples of graphic illustrations of situations that involve percentage. Newspapers, magazines, financial reports, business articles, brochures, and advertising material are rich sources of such examples. Bar, circle, and line graphs lend themselves readily to use in such illustrations. A great variety of good illustrations is readily available for study, and it can be supplemented at will by having the students make graphic illustrations of their own problems. The systematic use of graphs to illustrate problems and principles of percentage can do much to clarify and fix the concepts and principles involved.

Two trouble spots

Teachers need to be sensitive to the fact that problems which involve more than 100 percent of the base number are especially troublesome to many students. The trouble may often be traced to failure to read carefully or to interpret relations or notation correctly. This, in turn, may result from the habit of expecting the percentage to be less than the base, since this is almost always the case in the early problems used to introduce the subject. Similarly, students often have trouble in cases that involve numbers less than 1 percent of the base. The trouble in this case usually arises from failure either to interpret correctly or to write correctly the notation representing the fraction of a percent. These two trouble spots are serious enough to merit the teacher's special attention in planning the work in percentage. In both of these cases the use of graphs can be very helpful for illustrating such problems, and the use of the 1 percent method described above can make a real contribution to the analysis of such problems.

The need for good problem material

As a final suggestion, teachers should be warned that poorly graded sets of problems can be a major source of difficulty and frustration to students. In general, the authors of textbooks make sincere efforts to provide well-ordered lists of exercises leading gradually from very simple ones to more difficult or complicated ones, but sometimes they do not succeed very well. Yet nothing is more frustrating to students than to be expected to solve problems for which they have not had adequate preparation. A hard problem placed inappropriately early in a list when the students are not ready for it is not only nonproductive, but actually destructive of confidence and morale. In planning assignments for classwork or homework the teacher will be well advised to go through in detail any lists of problems that are to be assigned, to be sure that this situation does not arise. Problem lists should always be regarded as self-administering exercises designed to lead the student step by step to increased mastery and insight and self-reliance. Exercises which are out of place in a problem list do not contribute to this objective and should be either eliminated or properly relocated in the list.

RATIONAL NUMBERS AS DECIMAL FRACTIONS

Attention has already been called to the fact that, when one is using decimal fractions, it is sometimes desirable to express a fraction in common-fraction form. This can be done simply by writing as a common fraction what one reads. For example, .35 is read 35 hundredths, which, written in common fraction form, becomes $35/100$, and $.16^2/_3 = 16^2/_3/100 = 50/300$. Furthermore, it is not difficult to prove that any rational number can be expressed either as a finite (terminating) decimal fraction or as a repeating infinite decimal fraction. There are three basic patterns in such conversions:

Three basic patterns for converting a rational number to the decimal form

1. A rational number in its lowest terms and of the form $a/(2^m5^n)$ will convert into a finite decimal fraction of either m or n decimal places, depending on which is the larger number.
2. A rational number in its lowest terms and of the form a/b, where b has neither 2 nor 5 as a factor, will convert into an infinite repeating decimal with no more than $b - 1$ digits in the repetend.
3. A rational number in its lowest terms and of the form $a/(2^m5^nb)$, where b has neither a 2 nor a 5 as a factor, will convert into an infinite repeating decimal with no more than $b - 1$ digits in the repetend. There will be m or n (whichever is larger) digits in the decimal fraction before the first digit of the repetend occurs.

Rational numbers as decimal fractions

When these facts have been established, the basis has been provided for another version of the definition of a rational number: *A rational number is a number which can be expressed uniquely either as a finite decimal or as an infinite repeating decimal.* In fact, the argument can be presented to support the statement that any finite decimal can be expressed uniquely as an infinite repeating decimal. If this is done, the definition can be revised still further to read: *A rational number is a number which can be expressed as an infinite repeating decimal.* In either form this definition of a rational number provides a sound basis for the extension of the number system from the field Q of rational numbers to the field R of real numbers.

THE FIELD OF REAL NUMBERS

If, in any expressed product, the factors are all equal, the process used to find the product is called *involution,* or the process of raising to indicated powers. The inversely related operation is *evolution,* or the process of extracting indicated roots. For example, $(a^{1/2})^2 = (a^2)^{1/2} = |a|$. Just as the inverse relations of subtraction and division made it necessary to extend the number system to accommodate the demands of closure, so does evolution call for extensions. One extension is to the set R of real numbers. This is accomplished by the definition of *irrational numbers,* numbers such as $\sqrt{2}$, π, and e, which cannot be expressed as the quotient of two integers. A second extension is to the set C of complex numbers in which the elements are of the form $a + bi$, where a and b are real numbers and $i^2 = -1$.

Irrational numbers as decimal fractions

The definition of a rational number as a number which can be expressed as a finite decimal or an infinite repeating decimal provides the basis for defining an irrational number as a number which can be expressed as an infinite nonrepeating decimal. It is fairly simple to prove that numbers like $\sqrt{2}$ and $\sqrt[3]{5}$ cannot be expressed in the form a/b where $a, b \in J$ and $b \neq 0$, thus proving them to be irrational numbers. To prove that π or e is irrational is a much more involved problem. The set Q and the set of irrational numbers are disjoint sets, and the set of all real numbers is defined to be the set $R = Q \cup \{x|x \text{ is an irrational number}\}$. Thus we have a real number is a number which may be expressed uniquely as a finite decimal, an infinite repeating decimal, or an infinite nonrepeating decimal. An equivalent definition is: *A real number is a number which can be expressed as a finite decimal or as an infinite decimal.*

Real numbers as decimal fractions

Addition and multiplication as defined for rational numbers, supplemented by the laws of exponents, need no further definition to accommodate to the set R. Subtraction, division, and evolution thus become the related inverse operations. The set R, with addition and multiplication, forms an ordered field, since the operations satisfy the ten field postulates $F1$ to $F10$.

An important property which should be postulated for use at this point of development is: *There exists a one-to-one correspon-*

The real-number
line

dence between the set of all real numbers and the set of points on a line. This line is called the *real-number line*. With the introduction of the number line it becomes possible to introduce still a fifth equivalent statement of the Principle of Trichotomy, namely: *For* $a, b \in R$, *one and only one of the following relations holds: (1) They represent the same point* ($a = b$); *(2) the point represented by a is to the left of the point represented by b* ($a < b$); *(3) The point represented by a is to the right of the point represented by b* ($a > b$). Moreover, the property of *denseness* of the rational numbers within the dense

Order property

Denseness of
rationals and reals

set of the real numbers can be illustrated without too great difficulty or abstraction. First, it can be shown that if $a, b \in Q$, then $(a + b)/2 \in Q$ and lies between a and b. This process can be repeated to find a rational number between a and $(a + b)/2$ or between $(a + b)/2$ and b. The repetition of the process can be continued to find infinitely many rational numbers between any two rational numbers, no matter how close together the points which represent them are situated on the number line. The points a and b should be so selected that the sequence of points obtained could be marked clearly on the line. The same process can be used for a sequence of irrational points between any two selected points. For example, $(\sqrt{2} + \sqrt{3})/2$ is irrational, and the point which represents it lies between the points that represent $\sqrt{2}$ and $\sqrt{3}$, respectively.

With the extension to the field of real numbers, the number system of arithmetic, with one exception, is complete from the point of view of meeting the computational demands that our environment is likely to create. The one exception is the ability to extract even roots of negative numbers. To meet this demand it becomes necessary to make one further extension to the set of com-

Complex numbers

plex numbers which is the basic set of the field C of complex numbers. There are different equivalent patterns for the definition of the elements of C. Possibly the simplest is to define a complex number as a number of the form $a + bi$, where a and b are real numbers and $i^2 = -1$. It now becomes necessary to define equality and the operations of addition and multiplication.

$a + bi = c + di$ if and only if $a = c$ and $b = d$
$(a + bi) + (c + di) = (a + c) + (b + d)i$
$(a + bi) \times (c + di) = (ac - bd) + (ad + bc)i$

The field of
complex numbers

With these definitions it is possible to show that the set C satisfies all the field properties (page 198–199) except F9 and F10. The field C is not an ordered field. Also, it is possible to establish an isomorphic relation, with respect to addition and multiplication, between the set of complex numbers of the form $a + 0i$ and the set R.

The set Q is a proper subset of R, which in turn is a proper subset of C. (See Fig. 8-1.) From this fact it follows that the field of rational numbers is a *subfield* of the field of real numbers, which in turn is a subfield of the field of complex numbers.

The complete formalization of the concept of field is possibly beyond normal instructional responsibility at the level of the junior high school. However, students should emerge from this program with a clear understanding of the basic properties of each significant number system and how they control and give authority for the computational procedures used. The groundwork must be laid for later formalization in the senior high school of the field postulates and informed orientation in the language and procedures of the field of complex numbers, the number field of elementary mathematics.

Because the four operations of addition, subtraction, multiplication, and division satisfy the field properties, independently of whether the set of elements is Q, R, or C, they are frequently called the "four field operations." Since the field of rational numbers is a subfield of both the field of real numbers and the field of complex numbers, the four field operations are also, at times, referred to as the "four rational operations."

Four field operations

THE DECIMAL NUMERAL SYSTEM

Concomitant with the need for clear comprehension of the basic structure of each of the number systems of arithmetic there is the essential necessity for informed understanding of our decimal system of numerals. The concept of place value is possibly the greatest single simplification and efficiency device in our notational system. It would be difficult to overemphasize its nature and importance. Other numeral systems have been decimal in nature, and some of them have used place value, but in a rather restricted form. For example, in the Roman system of numeration, which is decimal, a symbol for a small number preceding a symbol for a larger number indicates a subtraction of values, and a symbol for a small number following a symbol for a larger number indicates an addition of values. Thus, IX means $10 - 1$, or 9, and XI means $10 + 1$, or 11.

Place value

Our more efficient use of place value makes it possible to use only ten individual symbols in the construction of number symbols, no matter how large or how small the value of the number to be represented. Thus each digital symbol (0, 1, 2, 3, 4, 5, 6, 7, 8, 9) in the symbol for a number might be said to have ascribed to it two values, a *place value* and a *digit value*. In the symbol 1302 the digital symbols have certain values because of the position they have in the symbol: the 1 indicates the number of thousands, the 3 indicates the number of hundreds, the 0 indicates the number of tens,

Two values for each digit in a numeral

and the 2 indicates the number of ones. The concept of one-to-one correspondence enables us to determine the digit value of each of these symbols, i.e., to tell *how many* each symbol represents. For example, compare the number symbol 1302 with the word "seeded." There are just as many thousands in the number symbol as there are letters *s* in the word; we call it "one" and use the symbol 1 to indicate the number. There are the same number of hundreds as there are letters *e*; we call it "three" and write it 3 There are just as many tens as there are letters *b*; we call it "zero" and write it 0. There are just as many ones as there are letters *d*; we call it "two" and write it 2. Thus, in such numbers, each digital symbol performs two functions; it is both a numeral and a place holder. In any numeral, each digital symbol performs two functions: (1) It serves as a place holder, since it holds a place, or position, in the numeral, and by virtue of this function it acquires place, or positional, value; (2) it serves as a cardinal number, since it tells the count of the units of a specific positional value present in a given number.

Significance of 0

Convention has made of 0, the symbol for zero, a much more flexible symbol than any of the nonzero numerals. As indicated in the previous paragraph and in the field properties, it has the full stature of cardinal number, integer, rational number, real number, or even complex number. But convention decrees that it is proper to use this symbol in the capacity of a mere place holder. For example, the distance from the earth to the sun is 93 million miles. This is a satisfactory measure stated in terms of a large unit, 1 million miles. There are occasions when it is desirable to write this as a numeral. Since convention has decreed that it is not necessary to use a decimal point in writing a numeral unless it is necessary to indicate the ones position, some scheme for distinguishing the ones position becomes necessary when writing symbols for such numbers as 93 million. By common agreement and use the symbol has become 93,000,000, rather than some such symbol as 93,xxx,xxx. The same situation holds for small numbers. For example, to write 4 thousandths as a decimal, three places are required to the right of the decimal. Since 4 occupies only one place, some symbol must be used to fill the other two. While .xx4 is quite satisfactory as far as filling the basic need is concerned, convention has established .004 as the proper symbol.

In spite of the great notational and computational convenience intrinsic to the conventional flexibility ascribed to the symbol for zero, there are some situations in which it is absolutely incorrect to use the symbol in the sense of a mere place holder. For example, consider this box score of a baseball game played in Chicago between New York and Chicago.

New York: 000   100   002   3
Chicago: 001   000   04x   5

The 1, 2, 4, and each 0 are numerals which tell *how many* runs were scored during each team's respective efforts to score. The x in the position of the last half of the ninth inning is a mere place holder which convention has established as a proper method for filling out the box score when the home team has already won the game and makes no effort to score any more runs. The symbol 0 would be entirely incorrect in this position because it has numerical significance in such a box score and therefore cannot be used in the capacity of a mere place holder.

Proper instructional emphasis on place value can remove computation from the status of rote performance. For example, in finding the sum of 54 and 28, the addends are aligned according to the positional value of the digits:

$$\begin{array}{r} 54 \\ +28 \\ \hline 82 \end{array} \qquad \begin{array}{r} 54 \\ -28 \\ \hline 26 \end{array}$$

$4 + 8 = 12$, with the 2 recorded in the ones column and the 1 ten added with the other tens to secure a total of 8 tens. Similarly, in finding the differences, the digits are properly aligned according to place value. In subtraction, one of the 5 tens must be converted to 10 ones and combined with the 4 ones; then 14 ones less 8 ones is 6 ones, and 4 tens less 2 tens is 2 tens. Notice that nothing is said about "carry" or "borrow." They are merely convenient words which can be used *if the process is understood, but not until then.* In multiplication, place value is the key to the proper placement of the partial products in order that they may be added correctly, and in division, it can be used with ease and effectiveness as an aid in estimating and placing trial quotients, as well as in the attendant multiplication and subtraction.

BASES OTHER THAN TEN

Different bases as teaching aids

A study of systems of numeration using bases other than ten can be a distinct aid to the teacher and to the students in attaining a clearer understanding of the significance of place value in number symbolism. In the examples of this section we shall agree to use the concept of place value along with addition in the structure of any numeral. For example, in base ten, 2345 is to be interpreted as meaning $2(1000) + 3(100) + 4(10) + 5(1)$, or in either of two equivalent forms, $2(10^3) + 3(10^2) + 4(10^1) + 5(10^0)$ or $2(10^3) + 3(10^2) +$

4(10) + 5(1). In this example 10 is used to represent ten. In other words, in base ten the numeral 10 represents *one of the base*. Similarly, this symbol can be used to represent the base in any numeral system which employs the concept of place value. As a result of this fact, in this section, where we are discussing numeral systems with different bases, we can neither interpret nor read 10 as "ten." We shall interpret it *only* as meaning "one of the base," whatever the base might be, and read it as "one-oh."

A numeral system, with base b and using the concept of place value along with the principle of addition, requires a symbol for zero as well as $b - 1$ nonzero symbols. In this section we shall use the familiar symbols 0, 1, 2, 3, 4, 5, 6, 7, 8, 9 of the decimal system insofar as we can. In the duodecimal system (base twelve) it becomes necessary to introduce two new symbols, one for ten (t) and one for eleven (e). Since we are not inventing number names, we shall adopt the policy of reading each number digit by digit. Thus 1743 will be read "one-seven-four-three," whatever the base might be, realizing that only in base ten does it carry the specific meaning of "one thousand seven hundred forty-three." With such a convention the symbols t and e will be read by using their customary letter names. Table 8-1 shows the base symbols in each of four different bases with their equivalent numerals in the remaining three bases. Also, the numerals equivalent to 995-ten are shown in the other three bases.

There are two basic techniques, multiplication and division, which may be used in converting from a given numeral in one base to an equivalent numeral in another base. This of course implies the necessity for computing in the context of the respective bases. A good exercise here is the construction of the tables of basic computation facts in each of several different bases.

TABLE 8-1
Comparing numeral systems using different bases

	Base two (binary)	Base eight (octal)	Base ten (decimal)	Base twelve (duodecimal)
Digital symbols	0, 1	0, 1, 2, 3, 4, 5, 6, 7	0, 1, 2, 3, 4, 5, 6, 7, 8, 9	0, 1, 2, 3, 4, 5, 6, 7, 8, 9, t, e
Base symbols and their equivalents	10	2	2	2
	1000	10	8	8
	1010	12	10	t
	1100	14	12	10
Equivalent numerals	1, 111, 100, 011	1743	995	$6te$

TABLE 8-2
Basic computation facts for base eight

Addition

+	0	1	2	3	4	5	6	7
0	0	1	2	3	4	5	6	7
1	1	2	3	4	5	6	7	10
2	2	3	4	5	6	7	10	11
3	3	4	5	6	7	10	11	12
4	4	5	6	7	10	11	12	13
5	5	6	7	10	11	12	13	14
6	6	7	10	11	12	13	14	15
7	7	10	11	12	13	14	15	16

Multiplication

×	0	1	2	3	4	5	6	7
0	0	0	0	0	0	0	0	0
1	0	1	2	3	4	5	6	7
2	0	2	4	6	10	12	14	16
3	0	3	6	11	14	17	22	25
4	0	4	10	14	20	24	30	34
5	0	5	12	17	24	31	36	43
6	0	6	14	22	30	36	44	52
7	0	7	16	25	34	43	52	61

Table 8-2 shows such tables for base eight. In the addition table the sum of $5 + 7$ may be found by looking for the number which is at the intersection of the row headed by 5 on the left and the column headed by 7 above. Here the sum is found to be 14 ($5 + 7 = 14$ in base eight). Of course, this same sum is to be found in the row headed by 7 and the column headed by 5 ($7 + 5 = 5 + 7$). Furthermore, it should be obvious that this table also serves as a subtraction table, since the differences $14 - 7 = 5$ and $14 - 5 = 7$ can be found. Similarly, the multiplication table shows $6 \times 5 = 5 \times 6 = 36$-eight, since 36 is found either in the space at the intersection of the row headed by 6 and the column headed by 5 or in the row headed by 5 and the column headed by 6. Just as the addition table can be used to render the inversely related subtraction facts, so can the multiplication table be used to render the inversely related division facts. It must be kept in mind in this connection, however, that division by 0 is undefined.

The techniques for converting from a given numeral in one base to equivalent numerals in other bases will be illustrated by using the equivalent numerals of the last line of Table 8-1.

Example 1: Consider the numeral 1743-eight.

  (*a*) Use multiplication to convert to an equivalent numeral in base two.

  (*b*) Use division to convert to an equivalent numeral in base two.

(*a*) The numeral 1743 means $1(10^3) + 7(10^2) + 4(10) + 3(1)$, where each 10 carries the meaning of eight. From Table 8-1 we find 10-eight $\rightarrow$ 1000-two. (The arrow $\rightarrow$ will be used to mean "converts into.")

Also 4-eight $(= 2 + 2) \rightarrow 10 + 10 = 100$-two
  3-eight $(= 2 + 1) \rightarrow 10 + 1 = 11$-two
  7-eight $(= 4 + 2 + 1) \rightarrow 100 + 10 + 1 = 111$-two
We thus have

Base eight	*Base two*
$1743 = 1(10^3) + 7(10^2) + 4(10) + 3(1)$	$1(1000^{11}) + 111(1000^{10}) + 100(1000) + 11(1)$
	$11(1) =$ 11
	$100(1000) =$ 100000
	$*111(1000^{10}) =$ 111000000
	$*1(1000^{11}) =$ 1000000000
1743 ——————————————————	$\longrightarrow$ 1111100011
	$*1000^{10} = 1000 \times 1000$
	$1000^{11} = 1000 \times 1000 \times 1000$

(*b*) Since division is essentially a technique for finding how many groups of a smaller number are contained in a larger number, it may be used as a means for converting from one base to another. The problem of finding the numeral in base twelve which is equivalent to 1743-eight is merely that of regrouping in terms of twelve rather than eight. Since 14 is the numeral for twelve in base eight, the problem of conversion becomes one of dividing, in the context of eight as a base, 1743-eight by 14-eight and recording the remainders as they would be written as numerals in base twelve. The remainder from the first division will be the digit in the ones position; the remainder from the second division will be the digit in the base (10) position; that from the third division will be the digit in the base-squared (10^2) position; and so on until the final quotient is zero.

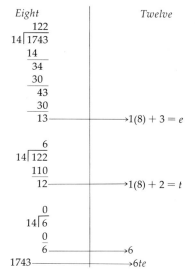

TABLE 8-3
Basic numeral equivalents, bases eight and two

Eight	Two	Eight	Two
1	1	6	110
2	10	7	111
3	11	10	1000
4	100	10^2	1000^{10}
5	101	10^3	1000^{11}

The reader might check these conversions by converting 1,111,100,011-two and 6*te*-twelve to base ten. Use multiplication for one conversion and division for the other. The results from each conversion should be the same. According to the table it should be 995-ten.

The conversion from base eight to base two in example 1*b* provides the basis for an interesting deduction which leads to an effective simple technique for conversion between these two bases. Table 8-3 shows a basic list of equivalent numeral relations which exist between the two systems. Note that each period of three in base two can be converted into an equivalent digital numeral in base eight. Each period in the numeral 1,111,100,011-two converts, respectively, into the digital symbols 1-eight, 7-eight, 4-eight, and 3-eight. These are seen to be the digital symbols in the equivalent numeral 1743-eight. Conversely, in converting from base eight to base two, all that is required is to transform each digital numeral in base eight into its equivalent numeral in base two, and then write the numeral in base two with these numerals in their respective period positions to accord with the given numeral in base eight.

Example 2: (*a*) Convert 11,101,001,111-two to base eight.
(*b*) Convert 62041-eight to base two.

(*a*) 11-two → 3-eight; 101-two → 5-eight; 1-two → 1-eight; and 111-two → 7-eight. Therefore, 11,101,001,111-two → 3517-eight.

(*b*) 6-eight → 110-two; 2-eight → 10-two; 0-eight → 0-two; 4-eight → 100-two; and 1-eight → 1-two. Therefore 62041-eight → 110,010,000,100,001-two.

These relations are used effectively in various forms of electronic computers. Since the computations are accomplished by means of electric circuits and a connection is either made (symbol is 1) or not made (symbol is 0), numbers must be programmed in base two for the machines. The ready transformation to base eight provides simpler notation than base two for recording the results as they are taken from the machines.

VERBAL PROBLEMS

Importance of
problem solving

To be able to apply correct computation to the solution of genuine problems can be regarded for most people as the end product of the study of arithmetic, for it is here that arithmetic finds its practical usefulness. It is also, for most people, the most difficult aspect of arithmetic. The reason for this is not hard to find. Computation per se resolves itself through rationalization into patterns of procedure to which the student eventually becomes habituated, using them in much the same way as correct habits of speaking. Furthermore, when a computation is presented, the student faces not the question of what he is to do, but only the requirement of doing it.

Problem situations, on the other hand, require not only that the student be able to do the things that need to be done, but also that he decide what things need to be done and in what order. In other words, the first difficulty confronting him, even at the arithmetic level, is one of comprehension.[2] A student must be able to read carefully and critically to deal intelligently with problem situations presented verbally. In whatever form a problem may be presented, one must be able to interpret correctly the various situations involved before he can make any effective analysis. At this level of teaching the major *structure* difficulties will be those of recognizing the basic characteristics of each of the four rational operations. For example, when a problem situation calls for combining of two or more groups of objects into a single group, the student must be able to recognize that either addition or multiplication will accomplish the desired result, and that a careful analysis will tell him which of the two to use. Subtraction is used to answer such questions as: What is the difference? What is left? How many are gone? How much larger? How much smaller? How many fewer? What is the gain? What is the loss? Division may be used to answer such questions as: How many small groups of the same size are there in a larger group? How many elements are there in each small group when a large group of elements is separated into a given number of smaller groups of the same size? In brief, subtraction and division are the operations to be used when a comparison is being made between two or more sets of elements.

The amount of *operational* difficulty a student will have will depend almost entirely upon the computational facility acquired in the elementary school. The difficulties of *judgment* and appraisal of results are of the type which persist at all levels of instruction, and are subject to increasing maturity of treatment with advancing years of study.

---

[2] Refer to Fig. 3-2, the flow chart for problem solving. Reread the accompanying discussion.

Sources of
students' difficulties   A good many studies have been made in the attempt to identify
the causes of students' difficulty with verbal problems. Examina-
tion of published material on problem solving in arithmetic indicates that much of the difficulty can be attributed to one or more of
the following causes:[3]

1 Computation
2 Lack of reasoning ability
3 Poor procedure or complete absence of systematic attack
4 Difficulty in selecting the processes to be used
5 Failure to comprehend the meaning of the problem
6 Inefficient reading habits
7 Vocabulary difficulties
8 Short attention span
9 Inability to select essential data
10 Carelessness in transcribing
11 Poor eyesight and other physical defects
12 Lack of interest
13 Guessing for the sake of a quick answer

Such a list can be of some help to teachers in trying to identify
causes of difficulty with verbal problems experienced by individuals, and perhaps to some extent by classes, but it does not
provide specific remedies. The causes listed above are not in
themselves simple or specific, but are individually highly complex.
Furthermore, they will seldom, if ever, occur singly. For the most
part they are not mutually exclusive but are interwoven and interdependent. For example, difficulty in selecting the processes to be
used might be due to failure to comprehend the meaning of the
problem, lack of reasoning ability, absence of systematic attack, or
inefficient reading habits. Inefficient reading habits in turn may
result from lack of interest, poor eyesight, vocabulary difficulties,
or short attention span.

The truth is that the solution of verbal problems requires intellectual activity of a higher order and more complex nature than
that involved in sheer computation. It requires conceptual understanding, insight, originality, independence of thought, and self-
reliance. Some students are more richly endowed with these characteristics than are others. The characteristics are not specifics but
complexes, and they usually can be developed only slowly, with
painstaking, patient, and unremitting effort.

Efforts have been made and experiments have been carried out
to try to determine a best method for teaching problem solving

Suggestions for
teaching   and reducing it to a system. Some of them have been more or less
well defined and even given names:

1 The *restatement method,* in which the students are asked to restate each
problem in their own words as a means of clarifying the problem.

[3] The order of listing here does not imply relative importance.

2 The *analysis method,* in which effort is made to have the student systematically analyze the problem by requiring him to go through the following sequence of steps: (*a*) What is required? (*b*) What is given? (*c*) What operations are to be used? With what numbers? In what order? (*d*) Estimate the answer. (*e*) Solve the problem. (*f*) Check the answer by an estimate.

3 The *method of analogies,* in which the student is given a simple oral problem similar to, but shorter than, the more difficult written problem.

4 The *method of dependencies,* in which the student is taught to recognize and focus on fundamental dependence relations existing among elements in the problem under consideration. This is, in fact, the central core of the analysis method mentioned above.

5 The *graphic method,* in which the student is taught to use some graphic or diagrammatic scheme to help him identify the elements of the problem and formulate an explicit statement of their relations to each other. This method is rather specially helpful because it exhibits the problems visually and thus makes the relations easier to detect and formulate.

Because of space limitation, it is not feasible to illustrate all these methods here, but one illustration of the graphic method will be given because of its special helpfulness. Consider the following problem (the diagram of Fig. 8-2 may be helpful).

Example: A shipment of coats was received, and all but one of the coats were sold before Christmas. On the following January 2 the marked price on this coat was reduced by 20 percent, and the next day the coat was sold at its reduced price of $60.00. At this price it still yielded a profit which was equivalent to 25 percent of the cost of the coat. What did it cost and what was the pre-Christmas marked price?

$$SP = cost + profit$$
$$= cost + 25 \text{ percent of cost}$$
$$= 125 \text{ percent of cost}$$
$$= \$60.00$$

from which cost can easily be determined as $48.

$$SP = \text{marked price} - \text{reduction}$$
$$= \text{marked price} - 20 \text{ percent of marked price}$$
$$= 80 \text{ percent of marked price}$$
$$= \$60.00$$

from which the marked price is easily determined to be $75.00.

No single method stands out as the one best method of teaching verbal problems. Each of those mentioned above has given fair results. Teachers ought to become familiar with all the methods suggested above and make use of those which seem best suited to the requirements of each immediate situation, adapting them as needed and perhaps devising other ways of helping students learn to clarify the elements and relations involved in verbal problems.

At the risk of some repetition it may be worthwhile to list a few statements which can serve both as prerequisites to effective

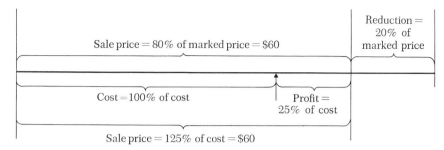

Figure 8-2
The graphic method of problem solution.

problem solving and as suggested ways in which the teacher can help students improve their abilities in this direction.

Aids to problem solving

1   Since the problems are written problems, the students must be able to read.
2   The students must be able to use the fundamental processes of arithmetic.
3   The students must understand the fundamental characteristics of each of the fundamental operations. They must be able to recognize these characteristics in a problem situation.
4   The students must be able to distinguish between essential and unessential data; hence some definite instructional program may be necessary to aid them in acquiring this ability.
5   The students must be able to distinguish the known from the unknown. Some specific instruction in this may be needed.
6   The students must be able to sense such relationships as may exist among given data and the required information.
7   The students must be able to translate verbal expressions into mathematical symbols. This is one of the most important of all techniques necessary for an intelligent approach to the solving of verbal problems. The teacher should place a great deal of emphasis upon the translation of the English statements of problem situations into their symbolic statements. Attention should be called to the simplification of operations which results from the use of significant symbolism and diagrams.
8   Independence and confidence are great aids in problem solving. Students should know how to estimate and how to check answers.

EXERCISES

1   What is meant by a well-defined operation upon the numbers of a given number system?
2   State the postulates for the natural-number system.
3   State the definition of an integral domain.
4   State the definition of a number field.
5   When are two sets of numbers said to be isomorphic with respect to addition and multiplication?

6   Show that the set of complex numbers whose elements are of the form $a + 0i$ and the set R of real numbers are isomorphic with respect to addition and multiplication.

Prove each of the following theorems for the real numbers a and b.

7   $a \times 0 = 0 \times a = 0$.
8   $a + (-b) = a - b$.
9   $(a + b) - b = a = (a - b) + b$.

10 $a \times (-b) = -(a \times b)$.

11 $(-a) \times (-b) = a \times b$.

12 If $b \neq 0$, then $a \times 1/b = a \div b$.

13 If $b \neq 0$, then $(a \times b) \div b = a = (a \div b) \times b$.

14 Show that addition and multiplication, as defined for rational numbers on page 198, are both associative and commutative and that multiplication is distributive over addition.

15 Show that the erroneous definition $a/b + c/d = (a + c)/(b + d)$ for the sum of two rational numbers cannot hold, since the definition would not be well defined. Recall that a/b and c/d represent equivalence classes and that their sum should represent a unique equivalence class.

16 Given that a and $b \in R$ and that the operation # is defined by the relation $a \# b = a + (a \times b)$, where $+$ and $\times$ are ordinary addition and multiplication, respectively. Is the system closed under the operation #? Is the set commutative under the operation #? Is the set associative under the operation #?

17 Given the set Q of rational numbers with the ordinary operations of subtraction $(-)$ and division $(\div)$. Prove the following:

 a. The system is closed under each operation.

 b. The set Q is associative under neither operation.

 c. The set Q is commutative under neither operation.

 d. Division is distributive over subtraction in the sense that $(a - b) \div c = (a \div c) - (b \div c)$.

18 Given the set of positive integers and the two binary operations # and * defined by $a \# b = a + 3b$ and $a * b = 3ab$, where $+$ and $\times$ are ordinary addition and multiplication, respectively.

 a. Is the set closed under each operation?

 b. Is the set associative under each operation?

 c. Is the set commutative under each operation?

 d. Is * distributive in either order over #?

19 Explain as you would to a class the details of performing the division $295.6 \div 4.73$. Justify each step, including placement of the decimal point by the customary rule, and then show that a rough estimate confirms this placement of the decimal point.

20 Without performing any pencil-and-paper computations, make rough mental esti-

mates of the approximate values of the following products and quotients: 38.47×6.24; 253.19×19.41; 85.72×12.15; 26.06×0.486; 0.0945×51.54; $281.6 \div 71.12$; $165.3 \div 85.10$; $47.364 \div 24.336$; $19.528 \div 0.493$; $0.7238 \div 0.0352$.

21 Give a report to the class in which you explain and illustrate the use in physics and chemistry of the metric system and its counterpart of numbers written in decimal notation.

22 Solve and explain the following problems by using the 1 percent method and illustrating each with a diagram:

 a. 29% of ____ is 145.

 b. 72 is ____% of 180.

 c. 88 is ____% of 28.

 d. 13% of 485 is ____.

 e. 0.3% of 220 is ____.

 f. 41% of ____ is 1,476.

 g. 52 is ____% of 260.

 h. 126% of 77 is ____.

 i. ____ is 15% more than 80.

 j. 44% less than 350 is ____.

23 Solve and explain each of the foregoing problems by direct substitution of given values in the basic formula, base $\times$ rate $=$ percentage, with solution of the resulting equations.

24 Explain why the quotient $\frac{7}{8} \div \frac{3}{5}$ is correctly given by taking the product $\frac{7}{8} \times \frac{5}{3}$.

25 In teaching the addition or subtraction of mixed numbers, some teachers instruct the students to add or subtract the integer parts and the fractional parts of the numbers separately and combine the results. Others have the students change all the mixed numbers to improper fractions, find the sum of these, and then convert this back to a mixed number. Give examples in which you think the first of these methods would be preferable and explain why. Do the same for the second method.

26 Consider the following statement:
$5\frac{2}{7} \times 3\frac{3}{4} = 5 \times 3 + 5 \times \frac{3}{4} + \frac{2}{7} \times 3 + \frac{2}{7} \times \frac{3}{4}$

 a. If the statement is wrong, criticize it.

 b. If the statement is correct, justify it.

 c. Present an alternative method of performing the multiplication. Which method do you prefer? Why?

27 Consider the numeral $1{,}451 \equiv 1(10)^3 + 4(10)^2 + 5(10)^1 + 1$ and (*a*) interpret it in base eight and write its equivalent in base ten; (*b*) interpret it in base twelve and write its equivalent in base ten; and (*c*) interpret it in base ten and write its equivalent in base two, in base eight, and in base twelve.

28 Give illustrations to show the significance of place value in addition, subtraction, multiplication, and division.

29 Consider a symbol a/b as a common fraction with its numerator and denominator written in base ten and reduced to lowest terms. Use the fact that $10 = 2 \times 5$ to explain the following three statements:

a. If b is of the form 2^n, 5^n, or $2^m \times 5^n$ ($m < n$), then a/b will convert into a terminating decimal fraction of n decimal places.

b. If b is a prime number other than 2 or 5, then a/b will convert into a repeating decimal and the repetend will contain no more than $b - 1$ digits. (For example, $2/7 = .\overline{285714}$.)

c. If b is of the form $2^n \times c$, $5^n \times c$, or $2^m \times 5^n \times c$, where $m < n$ and c does not contain either 2 or 5 as a factor, then a/b will convert into a repeating decimal. There will be n decimal places preceding

the first digit of the repetend. For example.

$$\frac{1}{28} = \frac{1}{2^2 \times 7} = 0.03\overline{571428}$$

30 Use only inspection to answer questions (a) to (d) about the following common fractions: (1) $5/32$, (2) $7/28$, (3) $8/72$, (4) $3/28$, (5) $9/200$, (6) $7/375$.

a. Which fractions will convert into terminating decimals and which into repeating decimals?

b. In each terminating decimal how many decimal places will be required before it terminates?

c. In each repeating decimal how many decimal places will be required before the first digit of the repetend appears?

d. In each repeating decimal what is the maximum number of possible digits in the repetend?

31 Formulate ten verbal problems involving percentage which you consider suitable for eleventh- or twelfth-grade students.

BIBLIOGRAPHY

Adler, Irving: "Magic House of Numbers" (New York: The John Day Company, Inc., 1960).

———— and Ruth Adler: "Numbers, Old, and New" (New York: The John Day Company, Inc., 1960).

Allen, Harold Don: Understanding through Number Systems, *Mathematics Teacher*, **55** (1962), 184–188.

Bakst, Aaron: "Arithmetic for the Modern Age" (Princeton, N.J.: D. Van Nostrand Company, Inc., 1960).

Banks, J. Houston: "Elements of Mathematics," 2d ed. (Englewood Cliffs, N.J.: Allyn and Bacon, Inc., 1961).

Bates, Thomas: The Road to Inverse and Multiply, *Arithmetic Teacher*, **15** (1968), 347–354.

Bechtel, Robert D., and Lyle J Dixon: Multiplication: Repeated Addition?, *Arithmetic Teacher*, **14** (1967), 373–376.

Boyer, Carl B.: Viete's Use of Decimal Fractions, *Mathematics Teacher*, **55** (1962), 123–127.

Braumfeld, Peter, Clyde Dilley, and Walter Rucker: A New UICSM Approach to Fractions for the Junior High School, *Mathematics Teacher*, **60** (1967), 215–221.

Brumfiel, Charles F., Robert E. Eicholz, and Merril E. Shanks: "Fundamental Concepts of Elementary Mathematics" (Reading, Mass.:

Addison-Wesley Publishing Company, Inc., 1962).

Cohen, Louis S., and David C. Johnson: Some Thoughts about Problem Solving, *Arithmetic Teacher*, **14** (1967), 261–271.

Dantzig, Tobias: "Number, the Language of Science," 3d ed. (New York: The Macmillan Company, 1945).

Dwight, Leslie A.: "Modern Mathematics for the Elementary Teacher" (New York: Holt, Rinehart, and Winston, Inc., 1966).

Fehr, Howard F., and Thomas J. Hill: "Contemporary Mathematics for Elementary Teachers" (Boston: D. C. Heath and Company, 1966).

Fukuda, Donald, Edwin Mookini, and James K. M. Siu: A Straight Line Model for Multiplication, *Mathematics Teacher*, **59** (1966), 342–347.

Grossnickle, Foster E.: Verbal Problem Solving, *Arithmetic Teacher*, **11** (1964), 12–17.

Hamilton, E. W.: Number Systems: Fad or Foundation, *Arithmetic Teacher*, **8** (1961), 242–245.

Hamilton, Norman T., and Joseph Landin: "Set Theory: the Structure of Arithmetic" (Englewood Cliffs, N.J.: Allyn and Bacon, Inc., 1961).

Hannon, Herbert: A Time to Appraise the New and Reevaluate the Old in Upper Grades and Junior High School Mathematics, *School*

Science and Mathematics, **63** (1963), 171–177.

————: Concept Determines Process: A Look at the Fraction Symbol, *Arithmetic Teacher,* **13** (1966), 298–302.

Hohn, Franz E.: Teaching Creativity in Mathematics, *Arithmetic Teacher,* **8** (1961), 102–106.

Hudson, Charles: Some Remarks on Teaching Different Bases, *School Science and Mathematics,* **63** (1963), 649–652.

Johnson, Harry C.: Division with Fractions, *Arithmetic Teacher,* **12** (1965), 362–368.

Jones, Burton W.: "Elementary Concepts of Mathematics" (New York: The Macmillan Company, 1963).

Kinney, Lucien B.: Teaching Percentage for Understanding and Use, *Mathematics Teacher,* **51** (1958), 38–41.

Lay, L. Clark: "Arithmetic: An Introduction to Mathematics" (New York: The Macmillan Company, 1961).

Layton, W. I.: "College Arithmetic" (New York: John Wiley & Sons, Inc., 1959).

Marks, John L., James R. Smart, and C. Richard Purdy: "Other Bases in Arithmetic" (Boston: Ginn and Company, 1963).

McDougall, Ronald V.: Don't Sell Short the Distributive Property, *Arithmetic Teacher,* **14** (1967), 570–572.

Moise, Edwin E.: "The Number Systems of Elementary Mathematics" (Reading, Mass.: Addison-Wesley Publishing Company, Inc., 1966).

Morton, R. L.: Decimal and Duodecimal Reciprocals, *Mathematics Teacher,* **56** (1963), 333–339.

Mueller, Francis J.: On the Fraction as a Numeral, *Arithmetic Teacher,* **8** (1961), 234–238.

National Council of Teachers of Mathematics: *Twenty-first Yearbook* (Washington, D.C.: The Council, 1953).

————: *Twenty-second Yearbook* (Washington, D.C.: The Council, 1954).

————: *Twenty-fourth Yearbook* (Washington, D.C.: The Council, 1959).

————: *Twenty-seventh Yearbook* (Washington, D.C.: The Council, 1962).

————: *Twenty-eighth Yearbook* (Washington, D.C.: The Council, 1963).

————: *Thirtieth Yearbook* (Washington, D.C.: The Council, 1969).

Newman, Claire M.: The Importance of Definition in Mathematics: Zero, *Arithmetic Teacher,* **14** (1967), 379–382.

Niven, Ivan: "Numbers, Rational and Irrational" (New York: Random House, Inc., 1961).

Osborn, Roger M., and others: "Extending Mathematics Understanding" (Columbus, Ohio: Charles E. Merrill Books, Inc., 1963).

Peterson, John A., and Joseph Hashisaki: "Theory of Arithmetic," 2d ed. (New York: John Wiley & Sons, Inc., 1967).

Rappaport, David: The Meanings of Fractions, *School Science and Mathematics,* **62** (1962), 241–244.

Ringenberg, Lawrence A.: "A Portrait of 2" (Washington, D.C.: National Council of Teachers of Mathematics, 1960).

————: Infinite Decimals, *Mathematics Teacher,* **55** (1962), 10–19.

Rudnick, Jesse A.: Numeration Systems and Their Classroom Roles, *Arithmetic Teacher,* **15** (1968), 138–147.

Scott, Lloyd: Numeration, Notation, and System: Considerations of Nomenclature, *School Science and Mathematics,* **62** (1962), 551–555.

Seabloom, Edward: Rapid Repeating Decimal Fraction Interchange, *Mathematics Teacher,* **60** (1967), 42–44.

Smart, James R.: "New Understanding in Arithmetic" (Englewood Cliffs, N.J.: Allyn and Bacon, Inc., 1963).

Smith, Joe K.: A Method for Converting from One Nondecimal Base to Another, *Arithmetic Teacher,* **15** (1968), 344–346.

Sweet, Raymond, and Peter Dunn-Rankin: An Experiment in Team Teaching Seventh Grade Arithmetic, *School Science and Mathematics,* **62** (1962), 341–344.

UICSM Project Staff: Arithmetic with Frames, *Arithmetic Teacher,* **4** (1957), 119–124.

Van Engen, Henry: Rate Pairs, Fractions, and Rational Numbers, *Arithmetic Teacher,* **7** (1960), 389–399.

————: The Reform Movement in Arithmetic and the Verbal Problem, *Arithmetic Teacher,* **10** (1963), 3–6.

Wendt, Arnold: Per Cent without Cases, *Arithmetic Teacher,* **6** (1959), 209–214.

Wheeler, Ruric E.: "Modern Mathematics: An Elementary Approach" (Belmont, Calif.: Brooks/Cole Publishing Company, 1968).

Willerding, Margaret F.: Other Number Systems: Aids to Understanding, *Arithmetic Teacher*, **8** (1961), 350–356.

———: A Critical Look at the New Mathematics for the Seventh Grade, *School Science and Mathematics*, **62** (1962), 215–220.

Willoughby, Stephen S.: "Contemporary Teaching of Secondary School Mathematics" (New York: John Wiley & Sons, Inc., 1967).

Wren, F. Lynwood: "Basic Mathematical Concepts" (New York: McGraw-Hill Book Company, 1965).

the teaching of arithmetic (continued)

INEQUALITY

The arithmetic responsibility in the work with inequalities is primarily concerned with such relationships between numbers, only incidental attention being paid to situations in which variables are involved. It is important that students be made completely familiar with the basic definition and the implications of each of the five equivalent statements of the Principle of Trichotomy (see pages 197 and 220). The inequality relations of "less than" and "greater than" are not equality relations since they do not have either the reflexive or the symmetric property. However, as a consequence of their definitions, it is possible to prove that they do have, in common with the equality relation, the transitive, the additive, and, with a critical modification, the multiplicative properties.

The differences between the inequality and equality relations in the three indicated basic properties make it necessary that we be very careful in the use of inequalities. One of the important new emphases in the teaching of mathematics focuses attention upon the fact that an understanding of the principles and uses of inequalities is of tremendous significance in mathematics. Because of this fact, early introduction to these principles and continued informed use of them are considered of paramount importance. Some of the more fundamental of these properties are of such a nature that they can be dealt with, at least through concrete examples, in the arithmetic program of the junior high school. Later, more abstract patterns can be introduced at the algebra level. These properties are stated here as the following theorems.

Properties of inequality

For a, b, c, and d real numbers:

Theorem 1. If $a < b$ and $b < c$, then $a < c$. The inequality relation "is less than" is transitive.

Theorem 2. If $a < b$, then $a + c < b + c$.

Theorem 3. If $a < b$ and $c < d$, then $a + c < b + d$.

Theorem 4. If $a = b$ and $c < d$, then $a - c > b - d$.

Theorem 5. If $a < b$ and $c > 0$, then $ac < bc$.

Theorem 6. If $a < b$ and $c > 0$, then $a/c < b/c$.

Theorem 7. If $a < b$ and $c < 0$, then $ac > bc$.

Theorem 8. If $a < b$ and $c < 0$, then $a/c > b/c$.

It should be immediately evident that the corresponding theorems hold for the relation "is greater than $(>)$."

Attention has already been called to the fact that the real-number line affords a ready and effective method for ordering the real numbers. This is accomplished by establishing on a line of indefinite length a reference point, or zero point, and giving it the label O, then selecting a line segment to be used as the unit of length. In this context the real number a corresponds to the point on the line whose distance from O is $|a|$. This symbol is read "the

Absolute value absolute value of a," or "the numerical value of a," and is to be interpreted in this sense: $|a| = a$ if $a \geq 0$, or $|a| = -a$ if $a < 0$.

It is this concept which enables us to compare two real numbers in terms of their relative positions on the number line. Also, as previously indicated, the real-number line provides an effective teaching medium for laying the foundation for an understanding

Betweenness of the concept of "betweenness." In Fig. 9-1 the point B corresponds to 2, C to 5, and D to 7. The length of the line segment $\overline{BC}$ is $5 - 2 = 3$, the length of $\overline{CD}$ is $7 - 5 = 2$, and the length of $\overline{BD}$ is $7 - 2 = 5$. Since $3 + 2 = 5$, it follows that $BC + CD = BD$. When this condition holds, we say that C is between B and D. What is the corresponding argument to establish that the reference point O is between points P and B?

A basic comprehension of the concept of betweenness provides the necessary background for an understanding, and intelligent

Strict inequality use, of the important techniques for indicating intervals on the number line. From the definition of absolute value it follows that the *strict inequality* $|a| < 4$, to be read "the absolute value of a is less than 4," means that the real number a has a numerical value which is larger than -4 but smaller than 4. This is exactly what is meant when it is stated that the real number a is between -4 and 4.

Two interval symbols are used to carry the meaning of these last two statements. They are $-4 < a < 4$ or $(-4,4)$. From this it follows that the three symbols $|a| < 4$, $-4 < a < 4$, and $(-4,4)$ are equivalent and may be used interchangeably to indicate that a may be

Mixed inequality replaced by any real number larger than -4 but less than 4. Similarly, the *mixed inequality* $|a| \leq 4$ is read "the absolute value of a is less than or equal to 4." It carries the same meaning as the two *closed-interval* symbols $-4 \leq a \leq 4$ and $[-4,4]$. Each symbol indicates that a may be replaced by any real number greater than, or possibly equal to, -4 but less than, or possibly equal to, 4.

There are two other frequently occurring interval symbols,

Types of intervals neither of which can be expressed in an equivalent form using the absolute-value symbol. They are $-4 < a \leq 4$, or equivalently, $(-4,4]$, which is open at the lower end but closed at the upper end,

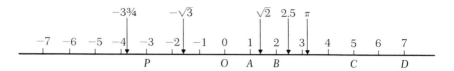

Figure 9-1
The real-number line.

and the corresponding symbol $-4 \leq a < 4$, or equivalently, $[-4,4)$, indicating an interval closed at the lower end but open at the upper end. The number line affords the basis for exercises in drawing graphs of all such interval situations. Also, excellent exercises for testing the comprehension level of the basic properties of inequalities, as stated in the previously mentioned theorems, can be found in conversions from absolute-value form to interval form of such expressions as $|a - 3| < 2$, or from interval form to absolute-value form of such expressions as $-1 \leq a \leq 5$.

It is of importance to call attention to the fact that the language, as well as the symbolism, of inequalities provides for equivalent expressions, one negative and one positive, for making the same statement. These equivalences are indicated in Table 9-1. Which form is used in a particular situation usually is a matter of personal preference or of clarity of concept.

The very basic concepts of "less than" ($<$) and "greater than" ($>$) not only call for clear identification with the concept of "not

TABLE 9-1
Equivalent symbols

Negative form	Positive form
$a \neq b$ a is not equal to b	$a \gtrless b$ a is either greater than or less than b
$a \not< b$ a is not less than b	$a \geq b$ a is either greater than or equal to b
$a \not> b$ a is not greater than b	$a \leq b$ a is either less than or equal to b
$a \nleq b$ a is neither less than nor equal to b	$a > b$ a is greater than b
$a \ngeq b$ a is neither greater than nor equal to b	$a < b$ a is less than b
$a \nlessgtr b$ a is neither less than nor greater than b	$a = b$ a is equal to b

equal to" ($\neq$), but also demand careful development as important relations, with intrinsic characteristics of their own, which exist between numbers and certain measurable quantities. The responsibility of instruction at the junior high level in building this significant structure of mathematical understanding is to help shape the foundation through the early introduction and continued pertinent discussion of the more elementary, yet fundamental, aspects of the two relations.

AVERAGES

Averages have such widespread use in everyday affairs and are so much a part of the common experience of everyone that attention should be given to their computation and interpretation in arithmetic. Standings of baseball teams, seasonal temperatures, airplane speeds, weight and height charts, mortality tables, and tax rates are but a few of the many applications of averages with

Arithmetic mean

which people are concerned. While the *arithmetic mean* of a set of measures is usually what is meant by the word "average," there are several different types of averages. The junior high school is not the place to attempt to understand the technicalities of computation of averages in complex situations. However, simple illustrations can be used to clarify basic distinctions.

Mode

The *mode* is a measure of concentration. In its simplest form it is merely that measure for which there is the greatest frequency. The

Median

median is the middle score of a distribution, and the *arithmetic mean* is the sum of all the scores divided by the total frequency. The example in Table 9-2 representing lengths of standing broad jumps made in a grade school track meet can be used to illustrate these kinds of averages. The *mode* is 5.2 feet, which means that more boys jumped this distance than any other. The *median* jump is 5 feet, which means that, when the lengths of the jumps are

TABLE 9-2

Length of jump, in feet	Number of boys making each jump
4.0	3
4.2	1
4.5	3
4.8	5
5.0	5
5.2	10
5.5	1
5.8	1

listed in order from shortest to longest with the number making each jump, the fifteenth boy, counting from either end, made a jump of 5 feet. Since half of the remaining 28 is 14, there were 14 boys who jumped a distance of 5 feet or less, and there were 14 boys who jumped a distance of 5 feet or more. The average jump, or the arithmetic mean of all the jumps, is 4.9 feet. Although no jump of this length was made, the figure does give a good picture of the lengths of all the jumps. The arithmetic mean can be computed from the measures without making a frequency distribution; the mode and the median cannot.

One of the big disadvantages of the arithmetic mean is that it can be affected very greatly by extreme values. Also, although this measure is usually thought of somewhat vaguely as a sort of middle, or "typical," value, it may not be at all typical. The set of numbers 17, 48, 106, 91, and 3 has the same mean, or "average," value as the set 53, 53, 52, 55, and 52. The average value does typify the second set very well, but the five numbers of the first set are so diverse that they simply do not run to type at all.

The mean is merely one characteristic of a set of values, and it takes no account of diversity or homogeneity. Therefore it should not be regarded as giving anything like a complete description of the set. On the other hand, it is very useful to be able to make comparisons of even a single characteristic of sets of values, and the arithmetic mean, or common average, provides probably the most simple, convenient, and useful instrument for doing so. It is a group measure which is easily understood, easily computed, simple to use, and in some sense representative of the set of values from which it is derived, even though it may not actually typify the values very well.

Weighted average

The *weighted average* is seldom mentioned except in textbooks on statistics. Actually, the name refers more to a method of computing the arithmetic mean than to a difference in the nature of the average used. As a practical tool the method employed in its computation is probably not very important except when large masses of data are involved, something which is not often true of the problems one finds in school arithmetic. But large masses of data are frequently involved in the practical experience of a good many adults, and the classification of the data and the use of the weighted mean can materially reduce the labor involved in computing the average. Stripped of the formalism in which it is sometimes clothed, neither the concept nor the method of computation involves any difficulty beyond the ability of an intelligent seventh-grader. The fact that such examples as the cost-of-living index appear continually in newspapers and periodicals makes it clear that most adults are at least concerned with averages arrived at in this way, even though they may not have occasion actually to compute them. It would seem desirable that the study of averages, at least in the senior high school, should include some attention to situations in which weighted averages can be used to advantage and to the way in which they actually are determined and used.

In their treatment of averages, textbooks on arithmetic are prone to stress the method of computing averages, but do not, on the whole, give very much attention to discussing the usefulness and the limitations of this measure. Yet these aspects are important, and teachers should not overlook this opportunity to deepen the students' insights and enrich their appreciation. This is important even in the seventh and eighth grades, but it is even more important when averages are studied or used in the later years of the senior high school. Even adults who are accustomed to the use of the term often attach to it a specific significance which is not wholly justified. Weight charts for persons at various ages are frequently looked upon with a sort of awe, as if the figures had been divinely ordained instead of being merely averages taken from large groups of people, and as if any departure from them should be regarded as cause for serious alarm. Persons who worry because they are 5 pounds "overweight" seldom reflect that the standardizing group itself undoubtedly contained many people whose weights were below the average, as well as many whose weights were above the average, and who perhaps were all equally healthy.

It is for such reasons as these that a rather strong case is being made these days for the incorporation into the high school program of some of the fundamental techniques and concepts of elementary statistics. The argument is strengthened by the increasing need which, in the normal course of everyday events, the lay public has for informed ways and means of analyzing and interpreting the vast amount of propagandizing, advertising, or even informing data with which it is constantly confronted. Whether or not one agrees that this is a valid argument for the incorporation of statistics into the high school program, the fact remains that we cannot avoid the need for a clear understanding of the concept of averages. It must certainly follow, then, that when averages are studied in the secondary school, the work should not be confined solely to their computation. The concept of dispersion could and should be brought in simply and informally along with the study of averages. In this way emphasis could be given to the limitations as well as the advantages of the average as a working tool.

Dangers in averaging percents

Attention has already been called to the fact that a major source of misinterpretation and faulty use of averages occurs in the treatment of percentage. One should never average the percents (rates) unless they are related to the same base or equal bases. For ex-

TABLE 9-3

	School A				School B		
Grade	Enroll-ment	Attend-ance	Percent	Day	Enroll-ment	Attend-ance	Percent
7	40	36	90	Monday	80	72	90
8	70	28	40	Tuesday	80	32	40
9	100	70	70	Wednesday	80	56	70
10	90	90	100	Thursday	80	80	100
11	20	10	50	Friday	80	40	50
Total	320	234		Total	400	280	

ample, let us consider two average daily attendance situations. In school A, Table 9-3, we shall ask for the average percent of attendance in five different grades on a given school day. In school B we shall ask for the average percent of attendance in a given grade for a 5-day school week. To get the average percent of attendance, we shall average the percents. We shall then analyze the appropriateness of the results thus obtained. Note that the individual percents are the same in the two cases, thus producing the same average percent, 70 percent, for each school. If this were a correct representation of the facts in both cases, then 70 percent could be used to get the attendance for each grade (school A) or for each day (school B). The totals of these numbers should then give the figure obtained in each case above as the total attendance. As should be expected, and as is shown in Table 9-4, this is the case for school B, where the base is constant. But it is not the case for school A, where the base varies from grade to grade. There is a difference of ten students. True, the enrollment figures, particularly for school A, have been exaggerated. This was done deliberately in order to give stronger emphasis to the point being made. The only way to get the correct figure for school A is to divide the total attendance,

TABLE 9-4

	School A				School B		
Grade	Enroll-ment	Percent	Attend-ance	Day	Enroll-ment	Percent	Attend-ance
7	40	70	28	Monday	80	70	56
8	70	70	49	Tuesday	80	70	56
9	100	70	70	Wednesday	80	70	56
10	90	70	63	Thursday	80	70	56
11	20	70	14	Friday	80	70	56
Total	320		224	Total	400		280

234, by the total enrollment, 320. To the nearest whole percent this is 73 percent. The grade attendance figures given by this rate percent check, as they should.

Of course, another situation in which percents can be averaged is the trivial one in which all rates are the same. This is also illustrated by Table 9-4, where in either case the average rate is 70 percent.

MODULAR ARITHMETIC

Casting out nines

The procedure commonly known as "casting out nines" is often used in business as a quick, practical way of checking arithmetical operations, especially multiplication and division. The procedure is easily learned, but many people who use it do so empirically, without understanding why it works the way it does. Actually, its validity is established through the algebra of residue classes, but without going into that it is possible to convince students of its plausibility and reasonableness by analysis of suitable examples.

The principle rests on a theorem which asserts that for any non-negative integer, the excess of nines (the remainder left after division by nine) is equal to the excess of nines in the sum of the digits. This would say, for example, that the excess of nines in the number 5,728 is the same as the excess of nines in the sum $(5 + 7 + 2 + 8)$, or 4. This can be verified immediately by direct division, but that alone would carry little conviction that the same principle would apply to other numbers. On the other hand, an analysis such as that given below may well convince students of the generality of the principle.

Let it first be observed that for any integral power of 10 the excess of nines is 1 and that for any single digit 1, 2, 3, 4, 5, 6, 7, or 8 the excess of nines is given by the digit itself. Now consider that

$$
\begin{aligned}
5{,}728 &= 5{,}000 & + 700 & & + 20 & & + 8 \\
&= 5(1{,}000) & + 7(100) & & + 2(10) & & + 8 \\
&= 5(999 + 1) & + 7(99 + 1) & & + 2(9 + 1) & & + 8 \\
&= 5(999) + 5(1) & + 7(99) + 7(1) & & + 2(9) + 2(1) & & + 8 \\
&= 5(111)(9) + 5 & + 7(11)(9) + 7 & & + 2(1)(9) + 2 & & + 8 \\
&= 555 \text{ nines} + 5 & + 77 \text{ nines} + 7 & & + 2 \text{ nines} + 2 & & + 8 \\
&= (555 + 77 + 2) \text{ nines} & + (5 + 7 + 2 + 8) & & &
\end{aligned}
$$

Therefore the excess of nines in the right member of this equation must equal the excess in 22, since that would be the residue if all the nines were cast out from each of the numbers in the sum $(5{,}000 + 700 + 20 + 8)$. The residue from 5,000 is 5; that from 700 is 7; that from 20 is 2; and that from 8 is 8 itself. But since $5{,}000 + 700 + 20 + 8 = 5{,}728$, it follows that the residue, after dividing 5,728 by 9, must also be $5 + 7 + 2 + 8$, or 22. Put another way, 5,728 and 22 have the same remainder when each is divided by nine. Furthermore, since the theorem may now be applied again to the number 22, the excess of nines in 22 must be equal to the excess of nines in the sum $(2 + 2)$ of its digits, which is 4. Thus the excess of nines for the number 5,728 can be found without performing any division at all. It is this characteristic of the process which makes it such a quick and easy checking device.

Modular arithmetic affords a more elegant method of presenting the discussion of the preceding paragraph. Such a procedure can be used with supplementary exercises as enrichment material for many students in grades 7 and 8.

Congruence relation

If a, b, m, and n are integers such that $n = am + b$, then n is said to be *congruent to b modulo m* [$n \equiv b \pmod{m}$]. Of course, if $b = 0$, then n is exactly divisible by m, or $n \equiv 0 \pmod{m}$. The remainder b is called the *residue of n modulo m,* and it may be positive, negative, or zero. For example, $98 = 14 \times 7$, $96 = 13 \times 7 + 5$, or $96 = 14 \times 7 - 2$; that is, $98 \equiv 0 \pmod 7$, $96 \equiv 5 \pmod 7$, or $96 \equiv -2 \pmod 7$. In modular arithmetic the residue of the smaller numerical value is the one generally used. If

$$n_1 = a_1 m + b_1 \quad \text{and} \quad n_2 = a_2 m + b_2$$

then
$$n_1 + n_2 = (a_1 + a_2)m + (b_1 + b_2)$$
and
$$n_1 n_2 = a_1 a_2 m^2 + (a_1 b_2 + a_2 b_1)m + b_1 b_2$$

This theorem therefore follows:

Theorem. If $n_1 \equiv b_1$ and $n_2 \equiv b_2 \pmod m$

then
$$n_1 + n_2 \equiv b_1 + b_2 \pmod m \tag{1}$$
and
$$n_1 n_2 \equiv b_1 b_2 \pmod m \tag{2}$$

The number 5,728, which may be written $5(10^3) + 7(10^2) + 2(10) + 8$, is thus seen to be congruent to $5 + 7 + 2 + 8 \pmod 9$. This sum is 22, and $22 \equiv 4 \pmod 9$.

Checking sums and products

Equation (1) of the above theorem provides a method for checking sums, and equation (2) for checking products by casting out nines. Furthermore, since subtraction and division are inverse processes to addition and multiplication, respectively, the theorem implies checks for these two operations. For example:

Sum	Excess of Nines
45,653	5
24,976	1
70,629 (excess of nines is 6)	6 = sum of the excesses

Difference

Note in the above sum that just as $70,629 - 24,976$ must give 45,653, so $6 - 1$ must give 5.

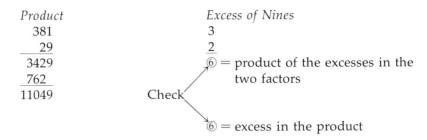

Product	Excess of Nines
381	3
29	2
3429	⑥ = product of the excesses in the
762	two factors
11049	Check
	⑥ = excess in the product

Checking differences and quotients

In checking division by this method it is desirable to express the result as an integral quotient with a remainder (possibly zero). Next, subtract this remainder from the dividend. Then the product of the excesses for the divisor and the quotient will equal the excess for the modified dividend. Thus

$2{,}578 \div 23 = 112$ with a remainder of 2
$2{,}578 - 2 = 2{,}576$, which is the modified dividend

Excess of nines for the divisor $= 2 + 3 = 5$.
Excess of nines for the quotient $= 1 + 1 + 2 = 4$.
Product of these excesses $= 5 \times 4 = 20$.
Excess of nines in this product $= 2 + 0 = ②$.
Excess of nines in the modified dividend $=$
　　excess of nines in $(2 + 5 + 7 + 6) =$
　　excess of nines in $20 = 2 + 0 = ②$.

Check

Tests for divisibility

Another important application of modular arithmetic is in the development of tests for divisibility. For example, since $10 \equiv 0$ (mod 2), it follows that $10^n \equiv 0$ (mod 2). This fact implies the test for divisibility of any number by 2 is that the digit in the ones place be divisible by 2. Similarly, the same test applies for 5. What is a test for divisibility by 4 ($=2^2$) and 25 ($=5^2$)? By 8 ($=2^3$) and 125 ($=5^3$)?

Since any composite number can be broken down into relatively prime factors, the tests for divisibility can be extended to take care of composite numbers. For example, since $6 = 2 \times 3$, the test for divisibility by 6 is the combination of the tests for divisibility by 2 and 3. Such factors must be relatively prime. For example, $18 = 2 \times 9 = 3 \times 6$. The test for divisibility by 18 is a combination of the tests for 2 and 9, *not* a combination of the tests for 3 and 6. This should be evident, for a number which is divisible by 6 is also divisible by 3.

In concluding this discussion, one thing that is not always made clear should be emphasized. The check which this method affords is not an absolutely certain one. In particular, the check for casting out nines will not detect mistakes in which the error is any multiple of 9 nor mistakes resulting from transposition of digits. For example, $381 \times 29 = 11{,}049$, and the check would indicate that this is correct. But if the product should be erroneously written as 11,409, this method of checking would not detect the error. Hence it should be used with some caution, since there is a possibility that it might fail to reveal mistakes that had been made. On the other hand, if the check numbers (excesses obtained in using this method) do not agree, then it is certain that some mistake has been made in the work.

"Clock arithmetic"

Another interesting topic to explore in this connection is that sometimes called "clock arithmetic." To work with hours, minutes, and seconds, the modulus is 60; for days and hours, it is 24; for weeks and days, it is 7; and for years and months, it is 12. In these areas of activity there are many and varied problem situations within the domain of familiarity to students of all ability levels. The newness of the computational procedures provides what might be called a built-in source of motivation. The information and the skills acquired are not to be considered as concepts and techniques associated merely with temporary games. They are of permanent value in the further study of mathematics.

SQUARE ROOT

The objectives for the study of square root are two: a clear understanding and appreciation of the meaning of the square root of a number and the knowledge of how to determine its exact or approximate numerical value. Students are usually introduced to square roots in the seventh or eighth grade in connection with the inverse process of squaring numbers. Through explanation with relatively small numbers which are perfect squares, the concept can be, and usually is, developed without difficulty. High school students may have trouble giving a precise definition of the square root of a number, but they generally understand what the term means.

On the other hand, few of the students see any clear connection between the meaning of a square root and the traditional method by which they have been taught to compute the value. Nor could they be expected to do so. The classic method, still found in some textbooks, is a notable example of an algorism which to the beginner appears to be completely empirical and arbitrary. The fact that it gives correct results will seem to him to justify it, but until he has had opportunity to discover through algebra the algorism for the square of the sum of two numbers, he will have no basis for discovering or reconstructing it for himself. He can use it only as an apparently arbitrary routine, and the only way he can learn it is simply to memorize it. But this is precisely the kind of formalism

The traditional method for finding square root

upon which so much criticism of mathematical instruction has been justly focused in the past. Present-day thinking insists that skill should go hand in hand with understanding. Therefore an alternative method of computing square roots will be advocated here, a method which derives directly from the definition of a square root, which involves only the familiar procedures of division and averaging, which encourages reasonable estimates, and in which the student can understand at every step what he must do next, and why.

Definition of square root

Let us first define square root of a number as one of two equal factors whose product is the number. For example, $\sqrt{73} \times \sqrt{73} = 73$. Let us next recall that in the process of division the divisor and the quotient are two factors whose product is the dividend.[1] If the divisor and the quotient are equal, each is a square root of the dividend. If they are not equal, the required square root must lie between them. Therefore, if a divisor which is a good approximation to the square root can be estimated, the quotient also will be a good approximation, and the average of the two will be a better approximation than either. If a still closer approximation is required, the process can be repeated with this average, or something near it, as the new divisor.

Square root by division

For example, let it be required to find a good approximation to $\sqrt{73}$. Upon reflecting that $\sqrt{64} = 8$ and $\sqrt{81} = 9$ and that 73 is about halfway between 64 and 81, we may reasonably try 8.5 as a divisor and proceed as indicated above.

$73.00000 \div 8.5 = 8.5882$, correct to four decimal places

The average of 8.5 and 8.5882 is 8.5441, which by trial is seen to be too small to be satisfactory. We therefore repeat the procedure with, say, 8.54 as a divisor.

$73.00000 \div 8.54 = 8.548$, correct to three decimal places

The average of 8.54 and 8.548 is 8.544. By trial, we find

$(8.544)^2 = 72.999936$

or almost exactly 73. Hence $\sqrt{73}$ correct to three decimal places is found to be 8.544. Actually, $\sqrt{73}$ correct to four decimal places is 8.5440.

By successive repetitions the square root can be found to any desired degree of precision, but often not more than one repetition is needed, and sometimes not any. The approximations converge toward the true value amazingly fast with successive repetitions.

This method is now used in the manuals for computing machines, and it is used in programming square-root problems for

---

[1] With suitable approximations or remainders, of course, in cases where the division is not exact.

electronic computers. Moreover, it is beginning to find its way into some arithmetic textbooks. Its advantages are obvious, since it involves only familiar processes, and students can see at every step not only what they are doing but why they are doing it. It forces students to estimate carefully and to review mentally the simple perfect squares without the usual drill procedure, and it gives results as accurate as desired. In comparison with the traditional rule-of-thumb method, this alternative method has much to recommend it.[2]

Since economy of time in the actual use of square roots is important, students should become familiar with the use of tables of squares and square roots and with interpolation in the tables. When possible, they should be made acquainted with the use of the slide rule for obtaining squares and square roots, and advanced students may well be introduced to the use of logarithms for the purpose. Also, students should be made aware that time and labor may sometimes be saved in finding square roots of fractions or of factorable numbers in which one factor is a perfect square. The principle that for a and b positive real numbers

Use of tables

$$\sqrt{ab} = \sqrt{a}\ \sqrt{b}, \text{ or } \sqrt{28} = \sqrt{4}\ \sqrt{7} = 2\sqrt{7}$$

is probably more important in algebra than in arithmetic, but there are cases when it can be a time saver even in arithmetic. In attempting to find the square root of a fraction such as $\sqrt{3/7}$ many students, even in college, work out separate, long approximations to $\sqrt{3}$ and $\sqrt{7}$ and then perform the long division $1.7321 \div 2.6458$, instead of rationalizing the denominator and transforming the expression into the equivalent $\sqrt{21/49} = \sqrt{21}/7 = 4.5826/7$, in which the division is less tedious.

MEASUREMENT AND DENOMINATE NUMBERS

People seldom realize the extent to which everybody depends on measurement of one kind or another. We go to work by a clock, which measures time. We buy gasoline by the gallon, which is a measure of capacity, and meat by the pound, which is a measure of weight. Thermometers measure temperature for us; rulers and tapes measure distance; the speedometers on our cars measure speed; pollsters, the popularity of a radio program; and engineers, the tensile strength of materials. In view of these considerations, systematic instruction in measurement should form an important part of the program in arithmetic. The facts of measurement are

[2] For an excellent discussion of the use of this method in connection with a slide rule, see Carl N. Shuster, Approximate Square Roots, *Mathematics Teacher*, **45** (1952), 17–18.

exhibited, and their various combinations and recombinations are made and recorded, through the medium of number.

Among the important concepts which should be, but not always are, made clear to students, the following should be given special emphasis:

Important concepts
of measurement

1 What a measurement means
2 The arbitrary nature of units of measure
3 The necessity of having standardized units
4 Clear concepts of the most common units of measure
5 Specific relations among some of the common units
6 The approximate nature of a measurement

These things will require considerable discussion, demonstration, and illustration by the teacher. Many excellent articles, books, and brochures provide most interesting and dramatic accounts of the evolution of our units and systems of measurement. The teacher who familiarizes himself with the fascinating story of measurement will be able to present it to his classes in such a way as to stimulate their interest, clarify their concepts, and enlist their enthusiasm in attaining the objectives mentioned above.

Of special interest in this connection is the metric system of measure. While it is not the commonly used system in the English-speaking countries, it is used over much of the world, and it is universally used in scientific circles. Its interesting history, foundation, and structure, and the fact that its units, direct and derived, are based on our common decimal-numeral system, emphasize the importance of having students become familiar with it. Study of the metric system should be directed particularly toward giving the students clear physical concepts of the common units, such as meter, centimeter, millimeter, kilometer, square centimeter, cubic centimeter, gram, and kilogram; proper knowledge and use of the nomenclature; and the ability to make correct interconversions both among units of the metric system itself and between these and units in the English system of weights and measures.

The metric system

The numbers used to express measurements have labels attached to them, such as miles, degrees, pounds, minutes. Thus a measurement will be expressed as 8 miles, 74 degrees, 5 pounds, 18 minutes, etc. The label tells the kind of unit in terms of which the measurement has been made, and the number tells how many of these units the given magnitude was found to contain. Such numbers are called *denominate*, or *dimensional*, numbers. Everybody is so familiar with them that nobody stops to think about them. About the only difficulty which can arise in their use is that which might occur in computing with compound denominate numbers, such as 3 weeks 4 days and 2 hours 18 minutes 5 seconds. For such computations students need to know the common units and subunits of various kinds of magnitudes and they need to be able to make interconversions of minutes and hours; miles, yards,

Denominate
numbers

feet, and inches; pounds and ounces; and the like. Such computations need not be troublesome if the students are taught to look upon them with common sense and not try to clothe them with formalism. Formal rules are unnecessary, and probably are actually detrimental, to ease of understanding in such cases. The student who multiplies 2 yards 2 feet 10 inches by 8 and gives his result as 16 yards 16 feet 80 inches should not be penalized, for he has correctly done what was required. It should simply be pointed out to him that it is usually preferable to express final results in the largest units possible and that this can now be done easily as follows: The 80 inches make 6 feet 8 inches. The 6 feet can be combined with the 16 feet to give 22 feet, which can be expressed as 7 yards 1 foot. Finally, the 7 yards can be combined with the 16 yards to make 23 yards. Hence the original answer of 16 yards 16 feet 80 inches can be expressed as 23 yards 1 foot 8 inches. It should be emphasized that this is no more correct than the original answer but is simply a more convenient form for expressing the same thing.

Common sense should predominate in the treatment of denominate numbers. Only a few common scales of measurement are national in extent, and even in these some units are generally used only by specialists. But some measures of distance, angular magnitude, weight, area, volume, and time are needed by everybody, and the importance and interrelationships of the common units in these systems should be emphasized. Everybody should know that there are 12 inches in a foot, 5,280 feet in a mile, 60 minutes in an hour, and 90 degrees in a right angle. It is doubtful that everyone needs to know that there are 16½ feet in a rod, but everybody should know what a square foot means and why there are 144 square inches in a square foot. Many details about denominate numbers may well be omitted from the arithmetic of the secondary school, but those parts which are commonly used by many people should not be neglected, and the things that are taught should be taught thoroughly.

Measurement numbers are obtained by counting, estimating, or measuring

Of equal, if not greater, importance in the study of measurement is the development of a basic understanding of just what a measure is and how a measure is determined. Measurement numbers may be arrived at by three different methods: counting, estimating, or measuring.

Counting

A *counting* number provides the answer to such questions as: How many students are enrolled in the arithmetic class? This is an exact number which serves as a measure of the size of the class. The unit associated with the measure would be "student." On the other hand, the 1960 population count of the number of people in the United States was announced by the Bureau of the Census as being 179,323,175. This number, while having all the appearance of being exact, even to the extent of being arrived at by a counting process, is approximate.

Estimating

Other measures are arrived at through *estimates*. Some of these are the results of scientific techniques, such as those that yield the information that the distance from the earth to the moon is 239,000 miles. Still others, such as "there were 1,500,000 people who saw the parade," result from procedures which, though much less scientific, are just as authentic for the purposes for which they were designed.

Measuring

A third technique, for determining a number which indicates a measurement, is known as *measuring,* and is a combination of counting and estimating. When measuring the length of a room, the size of an angle, or the capacity of a container, we are dealing with objects characterized by continuity, rather than discreteness, of composition. To make such measurements we must use a measuring instrument which has been graduated carefully into units and fractional parts of a unit. The process then consists in counting the number of units (usually the smallest provided by the graduation) and estimating that fractional part of a unit which seems to combine best with the counted units to give the desired measure.

Measurement numbers are approximate in nature

Such a measurement, once obtained, is not subject to the same type of verification as would be the count of the number of students in a specific class. Thus any measurement obtained as the result of an act of measuring is, by its very nature, an approximation rather than being exact.

THE NATURE OF APPROXIMATE NUMBERS[3]

The foregoing discussion of the techniques of measuring and the measures they yield leads naturally to consideration of approximate numbers. From what sources do they come? How are they to be used? What special considerations must be taken into account in computing with approximate numbers? Until comparatively recent times such concepts and questions have received no attention in school mathematics except occasional arbitrary instructions for rounding off numbers when so directed. Since about 1930, attempts have been made to get more systematic attention given to approximate numbers in textbooks on arithmetic and general mathematics. This movement, which at first consisted mainly in

---

[3] The term "approximate number," as used in this discussion, is to be interpreted to mean a number which is an approximation either to a measure obtained or to the result of a computation which is not exact. For example, to say that a certain length is 6.73 inches means that, by methods used, the number 6.73 is the best obtainable approximation to the exact measure m, which cannot be known but which lies in the closed interval $6.725 < m \leq 6.735$. Also, since $1.41415 < \sqrt{2} < 1.41425$, the number 1.4142 is the best obtainable approximation to $\sqrt{2}$ which is correct only to four decimal places.

the efforts of a few dedicated individuals, received support in the second report of the Committee on Post-War Plans and has now begun to bear fruit.

Exact numbers

Exact numbers result from counting and from applying the fundamental processes to counted quantities. When we say that there are 35 children in the sixth grade, that Jane receives $2 each week as her allowance, or that six eggs make ½ dozen eggs, we mean *exactly* what we say. The counting process sets up a one-to-one correspondence that establishes this exactness. On the other hand, numbers which are estimated results—even though they are based on counting, as in the case of the census—or which record the data resulting from measurement are *approximate* numbers. This is true whether we are measuring distance, direction, temperature, or what not. If we say that Jack is 5 feet 6 inches tall, we

Approximate numbers

can only mean that, if given correct to the nearest inch, his height is nearer to this measurement than it is to any other. No measurement can be more precise than the precision of the measuring instrument or more accurate than the relative accuracy of the observation made.

Approximate numbers also may arise from certain mathematical processes that require infinitely many steps of which only a finite number can be performed, or a finite number of steps not all of which are pertinent to the interpretation of the data being studied. Examples are the extraction of certain roots, such as $\sqrt{2}$ and $\sqrt[3]{6}$; the expansion in decimal form of certain nonterminating fractions, such as $2/3 = 0.\overline{6}$ and $1/7 = 0.\overline{142857}$; the evaluation of transcendental numbers, such as $\pi = 3.14159 \ldots$ and $e = 2.71828 \ldots$; and the expression of a fraction, such as $5/32$, correct to three decimal places. It should not be inferred from the above remarks that irrational numbers or fractions are necessarily approximate. Whether rational numbers or irrational numbers are exact or approximate depends upon the interpretation of the data involved. If we have a square whose side is exactly 1 unit in length, then $\sqrt{2}$ is the exact length of its diagonal. The actual measurement of these lengths would of course be only approximate.

It should also be stated that exact numbers may be fractional even though the approximation is integral; for example, if lemons are selling at 79 cents a dozen, the 40 cents one pays for ½ dozen is an approximation to the 39½ cents which is the exact price. The context in which any given number is used will frequently play an important part in determining whether it is to be regarded as an exact or an approximate number. An individual who states that he purchased 2 pounds of butter is using the number 2 in an exact sense if he means two 1-pound cartons, whereas the actual weight of the butter only approximates 2 pounds. Furthermore, the use of formulas in practical computations frequently gives rise to approximate numbers either because of the approximate nature of the formula itself (as in the case of the formula $A = 3.14r^2$, or $A = \frac{22}{7}\ r^2$, for the area of a circle and formulas resulting from scientific experimentation) or the use of approximate data in an exact formula (as would result in substituting measurements in the formula $A = lw$ for the area of a rectangle).

Although facility and accuracy in computation with exact numbers are both a desirable and a necessary goal of arithmetical instruction in the elementary school, the secondary school should stress the "exercise of common sense and judgment in computing from approximate data, familiarity with the effect of small errors in measurements, the determination of the number of figures to be used in computing and to be retained in the result, and the like."[4] There is no justification whatsoever, for example, in stating that the circumference of a circle whose radius is given as 3 inches is $2(3.1416)(3) = 18.8496$ inches. The measurement of the circumference can be no more precise or accurate than the measurement of the radius used in finding the circumference. It is, then, very important that the teacher and student understand certain fundamental criteria for judging approximativeness[5] and rules for computation with approximate data.

The need for judgment in the use of approximate numbers

CRITERIA FOR JUDGING APPROXIMATIVENESS

The three principal criteria for judging approximativeness are the position of the decimal point, the number of significant digits, and precision and accuracy.

Decimal point

The position of the decimal point. A number may be said to be correct to within a certain unit (e.g., to units, tenths, hundredths, etc.). The distance from the earth to the sun is usually given as 93,000,000 miles. Here the unit of measurement is 1,000,000 miles, and the measurement is considered correct to this nearest unit. The world record for the 100-yard dash is 9.1 seconds. Here either a second or one-tenth second may be taken as the unit of measurement. The observation is said to be correct to tenths of a second. In such cases as these the number of decimal places in the observation proves to be a criterion for judging approximativeness.

Significant digits

The number of significant digits. Our decimal system of numeration is definitely characterized by the fact that the significance of any particular digit in a number is determined by the position it

---

[4] National Committee on Mathematical Requirements, "Reorganization of Mathematics in Secondary Education" (Boston: Houghton Mifflin Company, 1923), p. 7.

[5] By "approximativeness" is meant the closeness with which the approximate number approaches the exact number.

occupies. In the number 333.3 each 3 denotes a value one-tenth as large as the one on its left and ten times as large as the one on its right. Thus the number 333.3 is given to four significant digits, since each 3 has a specific relative significance in the make-up of the number. If we consider the numbers 303, 3.03, and 33, it is evident that the presence or absence of the zero affects the relative magnitudes of the 3s. In the first two numbers the 3 on the extreme left is of a magnitude 100 times as great as that of the 3 on the extreme right, while in the third number the 3 on the left is only 10 times as great in magnitude as the 3 on the right. Now consider the numbers 33, 3.3, 0.033, and 330. It is just as evident that the presence or absence of the zero does not affect the relative magnitude of the 3s. In each case the magnitude of the 3 on the left is 10 times that of the 3 on the right. In the number 330, as in 0.033, the zero serves merely as an aid in placing the decimal point to distinguish 330 from 33, 3.3, 0.033, 33,000, etc., in which case it is not considered a significant digit. Each of the numbers 303 and 3.03 is given to three significant digits, while each of the numbers 33, 3.3, 0.033, and 330, where zero merely helps to place the decimal point, is given to two significant digits. Similarly, both 93,000,000 and 9.1 are given to two significant digits.

The value of π to seven significant digits is $\pi = 3.141593$.

This value is very frequently stated as $\pi = 3.1416$.

Rounding off numbers

In the second of the preceding sentences, the value of π given in the first sentence has been *rounded off*. The rules usually given for rounding off numbers may be stated as follows:

1 If a whole number, given to a certain number of significant digits, is to be rounded off to a stated number of significant digits, the digits that are to be dropped should be replaced by zeros. When the digits that are to be dropped are located to the right of the decimal point, the use of the zeros is not correct.

2 If the first digit on the left of those that are to be dropped is 5, 6, 7, 8, or 9, then the first digit on the extreme right of the digits which are to be retained should be increased by unity. This process is known as "forcing the digit." If the first digit on the left of those that are to be dropped is 0, 1, 2, 3, or 4, then no change is made in the digits retained.

A supplementary rule to number 2 that is frequently used, particularly in more mature circles, is as follows:

2a If the portion of the number to be dropped consists only of a 5 in the first left-hand position, either alone or followed by zeros, then the first digit on the extreme right of the digits to be retained is rounded to the nearest even number.

3 If, after the forcing, the significant digit on the extreme right is 5, a bar should be placed over it in order to indicate that, if there should be a necessity to drop this 5, the next digit on its left should remain unchanged. For example, 3,464,832 is rounded off to 3,46$\bar{5}$,000. If it should then become necessary to round off the second number, it would be rounded off to 3,460,000.

If we apply the above rules to round off the numbers 296 and 303 to two significant digits, we obtain in each case 3_0_0. The zero on the left thus becomes a significant digit and is underscored to indicate that fact. Whether the zeros to the right of all nonzero digits of an approximate number are significant or not must be determined from an analysis of the situation which produced the number. In the case of a measurement, the significance of such zeros can be determined if the precision of the measurement or the unit of measurement is known. In the case of rounded numbers, it can be determined only by reference to the numbers from which the rounded numbers were obtained. If only a number, such as 39,000, is given and nothing is known about what it represents or how it was obtained, then there is no way of deciding whether any of the zeros are significant or not. However, all zeros would be significant in 390.00 meters because the two zeros to the right of the decimal point would be used not as an aid in placing the decimal point, but to signify that in the application of the specified unit of measurement no other quantities were found to occupy the two places to the right of the decimal point. Similarly, the zeros in $390 and $390.50 would be significant, except in the case when the amounts were given as mere estimates. Zero is significant whenever it is used other than as a mere place holder to assist in the proper placement of the decimal point. All nonzero digits are significant.

To illustrate, the following numbers are all correct to five significant digits: 3.2674, 30207, 3126_0_, 312.67, 3126.0, 0.031267, 0.000031267, 0.00030067, 2400.0, 3000_0_.

Precision and Accuracy

Although precision and accuracy are distinctly different as criteria for the measure of approximativeness, they can be most effectively discussed when contrasted with each other. Measures may be precise to within certain specified units, such as 1,000,000 miles, 1 mile, 1 second, and $1/10$ of 1 second. Similarly, numbers may be precise to units, tenths, hundredths, etc. On the other hand, a measure or a number may be accurate within a certain percent of error or a certain number of significant digits.

The most effective measures of both precision and accuracy are in terms of the errors involved. The maximum apparent error (positive or negative) that could be involved in a measurement is defined as follows: "If an approximate number is given as correct to k significant digits, then its error is at the most equal to ±0.5 of a unit in the kth place, counting from the left to the right."[6]

---

[6] Aaron Bakst, Approximate Computation, *Twelfth Yearbook* (Washington, D.C.: National Council of Teachers of Mathematics, 1937), p. 124.

The *upper* and *lower limits* of the true value of any approximation are obtained by adding this maximum error to, and subtracting it from, the approximate number. The maximum *apparent error* (or *absolute error*) involved in any approximation made to k significant digits is thus seen to be 0.5 of a unit whose magnitude is determined by the kth place of the approximation. For example, the upper and lower limits of the true value of the distance from the earth to the sun are 93,500,000 and 92,500,000 miles, respectively; so the limit of the apparent error is 500,000 miles.

Apparent error

In the measure of time for the foot race the upper and lower limits are, respectively, 9.15 and 9.05 seconds, and the limit of the apparent error is seen to be 0.05 second. *The precision of a measure or a computation is evaluated in terms of the apparent (or absolute) error.*

Precision

The two measures 93,000,000 miles and 9.1 seconds are both correct to two significant digits. The percent of accuracy of a measure or a computation is determined by the *relative error* involved, i.e., the ratio of the apparent error to the approximate number. The relative errors, to two significant digits, for the two approximate numbers given above are, respectively,

Relative error

$$\frac{500,000 \text{ miles}}{93,000,000 \text{ miles}} = \frac{0.5}{93} = 0.0054 \qquad \text{and} \qquad \frac{0.05 \text{ second}}{9.1 \text{ seconds}} = 0.0055$$

The percent of error is thus seen to be approximately the same in the two cases, about ½ of 1 percent. One approximation might be far less precise than another and yet be much more accurate. For example, suppose we have the two measurements 0.000341 inch and 1,256 feet. The first measure is much more precise because its maximum apparent error is 0.5 of a millionth of an inch, while that of the second measure is 0.5 of a foot. The first measure is correct to three significant digits, and the second to four; the relative errors are, respectively,

$$\frac{0.0000005}{0.000341} = \frac{0.5}{341} = 0.0015 \qquad \text{and} \qquad \frac{0.5}{1,256} = 0.0004$$

Thus the percent of error is 0.15 percent in the first measurement and 0.04 percent in the second; in other words, the second measure, although far less precise than the first, is about four times as accurate. *The accuracy of a measure or a computation is evaluated in terms of the relative error or percent of error made.*

Accuracy

When a common fraction is used in giving approximate data, the denominator of the fraction states the unit of precision used in making the measurement, while the numerator indicates the number of significant digits to which it is read. The unit of precision in each of the following measurements is ¼ inch: ¾ inch, 6¼ inches, and 34¾ inches. The number of significant digits in each is ¾ inch, one; 6¼ inches = $^{25}/_4$ inches, two; and 34¾ inches =

139/4 inches, three. While 6¼ inches has the same numerical value as 6⁴/₁₆ inches, there is a great deal of difference in the precision of the two measures. Similarly, there is definite significance to be attached to a measure of 5⁰/₈ inches as contrasted to one of 5 inches. The maximum apparent error in 5⁰/₈ inches is ¹/₁₆ inch, while in 5 inches it is ½ inch.

COMPUTATION WITH APPROXIMATE DATA

In any computation involving approximate data, the result can never be any more precise or accurate than the least precise or the least accurate of the data used. While the rules for such computation may be stated in several different forms, probably the two most satisfactory rules are:

1 In the addition or subtraction of approximate numbers of the same degree of *precision,* perform the operation and retain the result to the same degree of precision. If one approximate number is of a greater degree of precision than the other, first round the more precise number to within one degree of precision of that of the less precise number. Perform the operation and then round the result to the same degree of precision as that of the less precise number.

Addition and subtraction

2 In the multiplication or division of approximate numbers of the same number of *significant digits,* perform the operation and then round the result to the same number of significant digits. If one approximate number has more significant digits than the other, first round the more accurate number so that it has only one more significant digit than the less accurate number. Perform the operation and then round the result so that it contains the same number of significant digits as the less accurate number.

Multiplication and division

With some sacrifice in economy of effort but no essential difference in significance of results, some writers prefer, for very elementary work with approximate numbers, to simplify these rules to read: In any computation with approximate numbers first perform the required operation with the given numbers just as if they were exact numbers, then round the results (1) in addition or subtraction, to the same unit of precision as the least precise number used, and (2) in multiplication or division, to the smallest number of significant digits that occur in any number used.

The rule for multiplication may, of course, be extended to control the results obtained in raising an approximate number to any given power, and the rule for division extended similarly to the extraction of indicated roots.

The intelligent use of these rules combined with care in the statement of original data will produce results that can be justified as the best possible results to be obtained from the given data.

If instruction in computation with approximate numbers is

kept at a level appropriate to the maturity of the students, it need not be confusing to them, and if properly taught and well motivated, it can add interest to the course. In Shuster's opinion,

> It is not at all difficult to teach the simple rules for computing with approximate data in the seventh, eighth, and ninth grades. In fact, it is far easier to teach all the student needs to know about the topic in these grades than it is to change the computational habits of graduate students who have always used "exact" computation.[7]

This is not the place to undertake a detailed exposition of the theory of computing with approximate data. Numerous excellent discussions of the subject that are now available[8] deal adequately with both its mathematical and pedagogical aspects and do so in much greater detail than would be possible here. On the other hand, it may be desirable to enumerate the central concepts and principles upon which attention would have to be focused in a systematic study of the subject. The order in which these are listed below represents the order in which they would probably appear in the logical development of the theory of approximations. They are as follows:

Central concepts of approximate numbers

1 What a unit of measurement is
2 Why we can be certain that no measurement is exact
3 The approximate nature of the number that is used to record the measurement
4 The apparent (or absolute) error that is always associated with the approximate number and the consequent range of values, any of which might be properly represented by the approximate number as written
5 The tolerance (or permissible error) used in industry
6 Estimates as approximate numbers; other ways in which approximate numbers may arise
7 The approximate number as a multiple of the smallest unit in terms of which it is expressed
8 The concept of precision of a measurement or of an approximate number and the consequent implication with respect to the size of the apparent error
9 The inconsistency involved in the use of "ragged decimals" to represent approximate numbers in sums or differences
10 The accepted principle and the rule for rounding off answers in the addition and subtraction of approximate numbers
11 Significant digits
12 The concept of the relative error of an approximate number and the meaning of accuracy
13 The relation of accuracy to the number of significant digits used in expressing the approximate number
14 Why high precision of an approximate number does not necessarily imply a high degree of accuracy, and conversely
15 Why the accuracy of a product or quotient involving approximate

---

[7] Carl Shuster, Working with Approximate Data, *Twenty-second Yearbook* (Washington, D.C.: National Council of Teachers of Mathematics, 1954), p. 310.
[8] See Bibliography at the end of this chapter.

numbers depends on the number of significant digits in each of the factors rather than upon their precision.

16 The accepted principle and the rule for rounding off answers in the multiplication and division of approximate numbers

This is an imposing array, and it is true that some serious study is required in order to attain clear mastery of these concepts and principles. Such mastery ought to be a part of the equipment of every teacher of arithmetic in the secondary school. On the other hand, it is by no means suggested that all these things be taught in a single sequence or even in a single year. Rather, the instruction should be spread over all the grades from 7 to 12, and the concepts and principles introduced in any grade should be only those which students in that grade can be expected to master satisfactorily.

USING NUMBERS EXPRESSED
IN SCIENTIFIC (STANDARD) NOTATION

An effective method of indicating significant digits, particularly when using very large or very small numbers, is the scientific (or standard) form of notation. A number is said to be written in the scientific, or standard, form of notation when it is written as the product of a number between 1 and 10 and an integral power of 10. Any significant zeros would be excluded from the power of 10. For example, the volume of the sun is 1,300,000 times the volume of the earth, while Mars is only 0.150 times as large as the earth. If we use S, M, and E to represent the volumes of the sun, Mars, and the earth, respectively, the above statement may be written in scientific notation as

$$S = 1.3 \times 10^6 E \qquad \text{and} \qquad M = 1.50 \times 10^{-1} E$$

The advantages of expressing numbers in standard, or scientific, notation are not as apparent in the work of the junior high school as they are in grades 11 and 12. It would be perfectly feasible to introduce this notation even in the seventh grade as an alternative way of expressing numbers which are positive integral powers of 10, and to extend it by the end of the ninth grade to include representation of decimal fractions in this form. However, it is not seriously needed as a tool until the eleventh or twelfth grades, when it can be very helpful to students in physics, chemistry, trigonometry, shop mathematics, or any course in which use is made of logarithms or the slide rule or in which extensive evaluation of formulas is required. The main advantage of its earlier introduction is that a good many junior high school students who do not take physics or mathematics in the senior high school might still get some acquaintance with this notation and the way in which it is used.

Importance of
scientific notation
The particular usefulness of this notation lies in the fact that it provides a means for writing very large or very small numbers in a convenient compact form that is easy to read and work with and that lends itself well to quick mental estimates and approximations. Consequently, the objectives to be sought are simply clear understanding of the notation and facility in using it to find products, quotients, or square roots of numbers. It is also useful in checking such operations, particularly the position of the decimal point. The only requirements are an understanding of positive and negative exponents and well-supervised practice to such a point that the students can work with the notation with confidence and facility and interpret their results with assurance.

Most operations with the slide rule consist in finding products, quotients, or some combination of the two, and a major source of trouble is the proper location of the decimal point in the answer. Of course, the ordinary rules for placing the decimal point can apply, but they are inconvenient when several factors are involved or when factors are very large or very small. Mistakes can easily be made in such cases, and it is desirable to have an independent method of checking, because misplacing the decimal point is one of the worst mistakes that can be made. The use of scientific notation provides such a check, and it is a check based on common sense. Consider such a case as $(73,200,000 \times 0.0000211)/0.0045$. Direct computation yields a number with the sequence of digits 34323 but provides no easy way for setting the decimal point. But if these numbers are written in scientific notation, the problem becomes $(7.32 \times 10^7 \times 2.11 \times 10^{-5})/(4.5 \times 10^{-3})$, which can be rewritten

$$\frac{7.32 \times 2.11}{4.5} \times \frac{10^2}{10^{-3}} \quad \text{or} \quad \frac{7.32 \times 2.11}{4.5} \times 10^5$$

Now $(7.32 \times 2.11)/4.5$ is shown by even a quick rough estimate to have a value somewhere near 3, and this is to be multiplied by 10^5. Thus, when the sequence of digits has been determined as shown above, it is clear that the required answer must be 3.4323×10^5, or $343,230$. If the original numbers are approximate numbers, the result should be rounded off accordingly. In this case it would be given as $340,000$.

In taking square roots of numbers, a slight modification is sometimes needed, because the standard form must now contain a factor of the form 10^n, where n is an *even* integer. Such modifications are easily made. For example, $\sqrt{169,000}$ is written as $\sqrt{16.9 \times 10^4}$ instead of $\sqrt{1.69 \times 10^5}$, in order that the result will contain a factor which is an even integral power of 10. Thus

$$\sqrt{169{,}000} = \sqrt{16.9 \times 10^4} = \sqrt{16.9} \times \sqrt{10^4} \approx 4.11 \times 10^2 \approx 411$$

which is correct to three significant digits as given by the slide rule.

Three demands on
the student made
by scientific
notation

As stated above, the use of scientific notation makes only three demands on the student: an understanding of exponents, knowledge of how to multiply and divide mentally by powers of 10 by moving the decimal point, and the ability to make quick mental estimates of products or quotients of numbers between 1 and 10. The simplicity of the process and the incentive which it could provide probably would justify its introduction on a limited scale in the junior high school. Its usefulness in connection with the slide rule, logarithms, and the evaluation of formulas is undoubted. Students in chemistry, physics, solid geometry, trigonometry, or shop mathematics will find the ability to use this notation an important asset.

ESTIMATING

In view of its importance there is probably no phase of arithmetic which is more neglected than estimating. Everybody gets so involved with the formal processes of computing and with the rationale of analyzing problems that estimation gets overlooked. Yet it is important, and it should not be neglected. Indeed, the systematic practice of estimating can be a valuable ally to the student both in the analysis of problems and in checking the reasonableness of solutions. It is indispensable in operating a business or planning any sort of project. Budgets, tax rates, construction bids, merchandising, manufacturing, and a host of other intensely practical things are based on estimates; without intelligent estimates they could not be planned or operated. If students could be kept aware of this, it would help to enrich their arithmetical experience, deepen their insight, and simplify their thinking.

Estimating can be tremendously helpful, too, in checking the results of computations. It has been mentioned before that students often experience uncertainty over the proper placement of the decimal point in products, quotients, or square roots of numbers that involve decimal fractions. This is a serious matter because misplacement of a decimal point is a bad mistake indeed— much worse than many students seem to realize. But if they become accustomed to making rough estimates of their answers, they are not likely to make this mistake. The estimates do not even have to be very good ones, and they can generally be made mentally with radically rounded-off numbers. For example, 0.327×49.2 yields a product consisting of the sequence of digits 160884, in

Importance of
estimating

which the decimal point must be properly placed. If the student reflects that 0.327 is close to ³/₁₀ and that 49.2 is about 50, it will be clear to him immediately that the product must be somewhere near 15, which is three-tenths of 50. Therefore the only place where the decimal point can make sense in the answer is after the 6. That is, the answer *must* be 16.0884, since 160.084 is more than ten times as large as the estimated answer, while 1.60884 is only about one-tenth as great as we know the answer must be. If students would consistently use this kind of estimate as a check, or even as a *method,* for placing the decimal point, there would hardly be any need for the formal rules. What is here advocated, however, is not the abandonment of the formal rules for placing the decimal point, but the use of estimates of this kind as a supplementary check—a double insurance against a very bad kind of mistake that occurs far too often.

OTHER TOPICS IN ARITHMETIC

But for limitations of space it would be easy to extend the scope of this chapter to include discussion of numerous other topics. Any extensive survey of courses in arithmetic or courses in which arithmetic has a prominent role would reveal a wide variety of objectives, content, and emphasis. It is doubtful that all the additional topics that could be mentioned would be found in any single course. The orientation of each course will determine at least in part the topics that will receive emphasis in the course, and the degree of such emphasis.

While detailed discussion of these further topics cannot be given here, it may be worthwhile to list some of them. Among those which represent significant parts or aspects of arithmetic at the secondary school level are the following:

Simplified or abridged computation	Arithmetic of the shop
Evaluation of formulas	Consumer arithmetic
Ratio and proportion	Various social applications of
The slide rule	arithmetic
Teaching arithmetic with calculating	Simple descriptive statistics
machines	

Before undertaking the teaching of one of these topics or aspects of arithmetic, the teacher will do well to subject it to a deliberate analysis to try to determine the particular objectives toward which the study is to be pointed, what specific difficulties the students may be expected to encounter, and what methods can best be employed. Only in this way can the work be best organized, presented, and studied to minimize the difficulties, highlight the important concepts or skills, and in general bring about the attainment of the objectives so far as this can reasonably be done.

A FALSE DICHOTOMY

More than half a century ago a reaction against excessive use of formalized drill in arithmetical instruction had begun to make itself manifest. As time went on, this reaction took on an extreme form, with the insistence in some quarters that understanding *rather than* computational proficiency should be the aim, and some people went so far as to insist that understanding should be, in effect, the sole aim in teaching arithmetic. Such catch phrases as "meaning versus drill" have formed the captions of many articles and discussions on objectives, subject matter, and methods.

Nobody will deny that there was good reason for this reaction, for it had become evident that exclusive reliance on drill had not automatically produced adequate understanding either of the processes themselves or of their application to problem situations.

Competence is based on both understanding and skill

On the other hand, it should have been clear, as it has now become clear, that proficiency in computation could not automatically develop as an incidental by-product of understanding any more than understanding could emerge as an incidental by-product of drill. The "meaning versus drill" type of phrase, which has by no means disappeared even yet, implies an "either one or the other but not both" situation which is completely unrealistic and unjustified. Competence in arithmetic does not consist *only* in understanding any more than it consists *only* in skill in computing. The two are complementary parts, and for satisfactory mastery of the subject neither is sufficient without the other. The question of which is the more important is something like asking whether one's right leg or left leg is the more important in walking. The answer is that the question is nonsensical; each leg is as essential as the other, and both are necessary.

Arithmetic must be taught and studied with *both* understanding and computational proficiency as primary objectives, and each of these objectives must be approached through methods appropriate to it. Both are necessary; neither alone is sufficient. To think of the one versus the other is to set up a false and vicious dichotomy which is based on superficial thinking and which is completely unrealistic. Instruction based on such a dichotomy and oriented exclusively toward either of these objectives would inevitably lead at best to one-sided learning having little basis for either present application or further extension.

PROVISION FOR THE SUPERIOR STUDENT IN ARITHMETIC

Most of the topics discussed in these chapters are included in textbooks and syllabuses with the hope that all the students will attain some degree of mastery of them. This being the case, the regular content of the courses is necessarily geared to what most of the students can reasonably be expected to accomplish, and often even this modest coverage is cut down to accommodate slow students. But in all classes there will be some students who could easily handle work beyond the normal assignments, and sometimes even students who are exceptionally talented in mathematics. Although it is not always realized, these have commonly been the most neglected students of all. Teachers are not slow to recognize students of outstanding ability, and because they can do the assigned work without help and often in a small fraction of the time required by other students, they are left pretty much on their own. In the absence of really challenging requirements they often become bored and negligent about doing even the work expected of the class as a whole. Yet these superior students, and especially the really talented ones, are the potential from which the future professional scientists and mathematicians must come. Their talent should not be wasted, but conserved and cultivated with special care.

Various suggestions have been made for ways of making suitable provision for gifted students. In large school systems the superior students are sometimes assigned to special sections where they can progress faster and farther than in other sections. In both large and small schools differentiated assignments within the sections have been used with some success. Other suggestions include assignment of supplementary problems, group or individual projects of various kinds, mathematics clubs, and mathematics contests.

The gifted student needs areas for special study

Such administrative and instructional devices have been adequately discussed elsewhere, and the discussion need not be elaborated here. They can provide fairly well for the "better" students, but the highly talented student who is capable of original and independent study can be developed to his fullest capacity only by special individual work.

One suggestion that seems promising is that this can perhaps best be done through a *problems course,* in which the individual student will select, with the approval of the teacher, an area of work in which he is interested and on which he will do independent study and eventually make a formal report to the teacher or the class. This area may, but need not, parallel the regular classwork, and the special work should be done in addition to the regular classwork, not instead of it. It should not be just an interesting but trivial "recreation," but should represent a serious, extended, and sequential study of the chosen area. Successful implementation of such a program would of course imply a highly competent and interested teacher and appropriate library facilities.

At first thought it might appear that such areas for special study would be associated only with the senior high school or with college courses. Upon reflection, however, one can readily identify many topics associated even with arithmetic which could provide avenues for stimulating and worthwhile investigation by highly talented students. The following are examples of such topics:

Some suggested
areas for special
study

The history of arithmetic	The slide rule
The metric system	Modular arithmetic
Square root	Arithmetic in scales of notation other
Tables and interpolation	than ten
Magic squares	Calculating machines
Computing with approximate	Cross number puzzles
numbers	

Significant independent investigation of any of these topics would require high intelligence, sound knowledge, insight, intuition, persistence, virtuosity, and insatiable curiosity on the part of the student. These are characteristic of students highly endowed with mathematical talent. Less ambitious projects which might be undertaken by superior but less talented students might include fairly extensive independent work on such things as graphical methods, short cuts in arithmetic, applications of arithmetic in such various areas as banking, insurance, taxation, and sports, and making up lists of original verbal problems. The *Mathematics Student Journal* often publishes interesting problems for investigation.[9]

PROVISION FOR THE LOW ACHIEVER

The instructional problems associated with the low achiever are quite different from those created by the superior student. They are more likely to be caused by absence of the desire to achieve than by failure to provide a challenge. This is not entirely the case, however, since there are students who are below average in academic ability, some because of low learning potential and others because of certain physical or psychological deficiencies. Inability to interpret definitions, recognize basic relations, generalize procedures, and analyze problem situations will hinder the progress of those of low mental ability. Poor eyesight, poor hearing, and other physical handicaps, along with short attention span, limited reading ability, and inefficient study habits, can be just as severe deterrents to normal progress in arithmetic. Cultural limitations and environmental conditions also make their contributions to the problem of the low achiever in our schools. Needless to say, such a variety of causes producing poor achievement creates a

The low achiever
needs
encouragement

Causes of low
achievement

[9] Howard F. Fehr, Mathematics for the Talented, *Bulletin of the National Association of Secondary-School Principals*, **38** (1954), pp. 103–110. See also Donovan A. Johnson and Gerald R. Rising, "Guidelines for Teaching Mathematics" (Belmont, Calif.: Wadsworth Publishing Company, 1967), pp 199–209.

variety of curriculum and instructional problems. While remedial materials and instruction will be needed, just to repeat "more of the same" will not be sufficient. The use of programmed materials designed to meet individual needs and allow progress at individually distinct rates, of simple computer-oriented exercises, and of other new and interesting devices can be helpful in offsetting boredom from the necessary repetition. Also, repetition can be disguised by such devices as construction of addition and multiplication tables and their use in the discovery of the inverse relations, subtraction to addition and division to multiplication; construction of operational tables for simple modular arithmetic; using the number line to locate points corresponding to integral and simple fractional values; and the comparisons of numbers by means of their relative positions on the number line. Exercises such as the following provide such disguised remedial practice in the different basic operations:

Means of helping the low achiever

1   Find an integer which is an exact divisor of each of these numbers: 119, 51, 255, 136, and 816.
2   See if you can discover a method for finding the sum of the positive integers from 1 through 50 which is faster and easier than actually adding them.
3   Think of a whole number. Multiply it by 3 and then add 5. Subtract twice the original number, and multiply the result by 2. Now if you subtract 10, the result should be twice your original number. Why is this so?
4   There are five men in a room and each man shakes hands with each of the other men in the room. How many different handshakes are there?
5   Use the numbers 1, 2, 6, 8, 9, 12, 13, 15, 16 to fill in the blanks in the magic square in Fig. 9-2. The sum of the four numbers along each row, column, and diagonal is to be 34. No number is to be used more than once.

14			11
	5	4	10
			7
3			

Figure 9-2
Exercise 5: magic square.

6   It will cost $1 to cut a log into four equal sections. At this same rate, how much would it cost to cut the same log into eight equal sections?

The collection of environmental data for the construction of simple statistical tables, with their accompanying bar, line, or circle graphs, and the computation of simple averages offer a variety of interesting and challenging projects. Also, there are many opportunities for significant instruction in the area of measurement. Such laboratory techniques as the use of measuring sticks, tapes, and protractors, as well as the counting of the squares enclosed in a polygonal or circular region, drawn on graph paper, can lead to an understanding of the nature of measurement and of how to use the results obtained from any act of measuring. These are but a few of the procedures that can be used to advantage in efforts to help the low achiever attain his potential in arithmetic.[10]

The need for laboratory materials

The selection and arrangement of topics must be appropriate to the needs of the students involved. The units, in general, should be short enough so that a weak attention span will not be too severely taxed. There should be available a sufficient supply of laboratory materials. Such materials do not need to be of the expensive type; frequently, materials made by students can be just as effective, if not more so, as those purchased at a costly price. Where funds are available there should be on hand a supply of the current pertinent literature providing suggestions and aids for the improvement of instruction. Each student should be given daily opportunities to perform under supervision. While library material, laboratory equipment, and a carefully planned curriculum are all necessary for an effective program for the low achiever, they will be to no avail without a well-prepared and sympathetically interested teacher.

[10] Lauren G. Woodby (Editor), "The Low Achiever in Mathematics" (Washington, D.C.: Government Printing Office, 1965); see also Johnson and Rising, *op. cit.*, pp. 187–198.

EXERCISES

1 (*a*) to (*h*) Prove each of the theorems 1 to 8 on pages 236–237.

2 For each of these theorems 1 to 8 write the corresponding theorem for the relation "is greater than" (>).

3 What modifications in the proofs for theorems 1 to 8 are necessary to structure the proofs for the new theorems of exercise 2?

4 For each of the theorems 1 to 8 write the corresponding theorem for the relation "is less than or equal to" (≤).

5 Restate the theorems of exercise 2 for the relation "is greater than or equal to" (≥).

6 What modifications will be necessary in the proofs of the previous theorems in order to develop the arguments for the new theorems of exercises 4 and 5?

7 Construct an illustration to show that the arithmetic mean of a set of scores is affected by extreme scores but that the median and mode are not.

8 Consider the following two sets of integers: $A = \{78,72,62,33,20\}$ and $B = \{56,55,54,51, 49\}$. (*a*) Find the average (mean) of each set. (*b*) For each set find the sum of the absolute deviations of the individual numbers in each set from the average of that set. Then for each set find the average of these deviations. (*c*) Compare the averages (means) of the two sets. (*d*) Compare the average deviations in the two cases. (*e*) Discuss the implications of this exercise. Explain why the use of the averages alone to typify the two sets would be misleading and how one can arrive at a more adequate comparison of the two sets by using their average deviations as well as their means.

TABLE 9-5

Item	A	B	C	D	E
Price	$0.60	$4.85	$0.15	$1.40	$0.90
Number of items	20	65	100	35	10

9 Five kinds of items in a store are priced as shown in Table 9-5, and the number of items of each kind in stock is given. (a) Compute the average of the five prices. (b) Compute the weighted average price for all the items. (c) Explain why the weighted average gives a better index of the average price of all the items in stock than the mere average of the five prices themselves.

10 Perform the operations indicated in parts a to c, and check the result in each case by casting out nines. Be prepared to explain your work (a) 5,793 + 8,610 + 2,944 + 877 + 5,555 =   ; (b) 2,184 × 362 =   ; (c) 64,833 ÷ 147 =   .

11 The casting out of what number in base twelve is equivalent to casting out nines in base ten? What number in base five? In base $b >$ two?

12 Devise tests for divisibility by 4, 5, 7, 8, 9, and 11. [*Hint:* When the positive residue is greater than one-half the modulus, use the equivalent negative residue. For example, $27 \equiv -1 \pmod 7$ rather than 6 (mod 7).]

13 Which of the following numbers are divisible by 12, 15, 18, or 66? (a) 280,764; (b) 113,445; (c) 3,012,180.

14 Devise tests for divisibility by 2, 3, 4, and 5 in a number system in base six.

15 Obtain an approximation to $\sqrt{486}$, correct to one decimal place, by each of the following methods, and be prepared to explain your work to the class as you would to a class of high school students: (a) the traditional method; (b) the method of estimating, dividing, and averaging; (c) the slide rule; (d) logarithms; (e) a computer.

16 Explain as you would to a class (a) why "stepping off a distance" is properly regarded as an example of measurement, (b) why someone else stepping off the same distance might get a different numerical result, and (c) why it is important to have standardized units of measure that are known and accepted by everybody as a basis of common understanding.

17 What error is there in saying that $^5/_{15} = 0.33$?

18 If cans of a certain kind of food are priced at three for 35 cents, what is the exact price and what is the approximate price of one can?

19 Which of the fractions $^1/_8$, $^1/_7$, and $^5/_6$ necessarily give rise to approximate numbers when expanded in finite decimal form?

20 Give the number of significant digits in each of the following approximate numbers: 2.5; 2.05; 2.50; 0.25; 250; 2,500; 250.0; 0.0025; 0.2500; 205,000; 205,000.0; and 0.00002050.

21 Which is the more precise measurement and which is the more accurate in each of the following cases: 2.56 inches or 3,216 feet; 52.3 seconds or 15 seconds.

22 The following approximate numbers represent measurements with the same basic unit: 47.2; 5.7; 1,238; 0.05; 265. (a) Which is the most precise? (b) Which of the numbers is the most accurate? (c) Write each in the form (the approximate number) ± (its apparent error). (d) Give correctly the sum: 47.2 + 1,238. (e) Give correctly the product: 0.05 × 265.

23 Determine the maximum apparent error, the relative error, and the percent of error in each of the following measurements; (a) 6.5 feet; (b) 0.000020 inch; (c) 5 inches; (d) $5^0/_4$ inches; (e) 0.005 centimeter; (f) 117.200 miles per hour; (g) $2^{14}/_{16}$ inches.

24 Determine the relative error and the percent error in each of the following measurements: 418.0 feet, 4,180 feet, 46.3 seconds, 4 minutes 46.3 seconds, 25,000 miles. Which of these measurements is the most accurate?

25 Find the perimeter of each of these quadrilaterals: (a) $6^7/_8$ inches, $5^3/_8$ inches, $12^2/_8$ inches, $8^0/_8$ inches; (b) 56.246 inches, 40.300 inches, 35.20 inches, 27.18 inches.

26 What is the area of the rectangle whose length is measured as 16.72 inches and whose width is measured as 8.46 inches?

27 Give several instances in which approximations or rounded numbers are more directly useful than the original numbers and explain why.

28 Express the following numbers in scientific notation: 3,865; 2,604,000; 79.60; 0.154; 0.000,553; 512.6; cos 5°23′.

29 Express the following numbers in ordinary notation: 2.65×10^5, 5.34×10^{-2}, 7.953×10^{-11}, 4.49×10^{12}, 6.308×10^0.

30 Express the following numbers in standard notation and, without any actual computation, give rough mental estimates of the answers: (a) $(237 \times 5150)/16$; (b) $(729 \times 0.035)/9.8$; (c) $(6980 \times 0.047)/0.518$; and

(d) $(44600 \times 0.00923 \times 1.016)/(0.815 \times 254)$.

31 The star Arcturus is about 223,700,000,000,-000 miles from the earth. Find this distance in light-years if one light-year is approximately 5,870,000,000,000 miles. Express the numbers in scientific notation and explain the process you followed to get your answer.

BIBLIOGRAPHY

Arnold, C. J.: An Answer to "Arguments against Universal Adoption of the Metric System," *School Science and Mathematics,* **51** (1951), 310–315.

Bakst, Aaron: Approximate Computation, *Twelfth Yearbook* (Washington, D.C.: National Council of Teachers of Mathematics, 1937).

Banks, J. Houston: "Learning and Teaching Arithmetic," 2d ed. (Englewood Cliffs, N.J.: Allyn Bacon, Inc., 1963).

Beckenbach, Edwin F.: Geometric Proofs of the Irrationality of $\sqrt{2}$, *Arithmetic Teacher,* **15** (1968), 244–250.

Bergamini, David: "Mathematics," Life Science Library (New York: Time Inc., 1963).

Bernstein, Allen: A Study of Remedial Arithmetic Conducted with Ninth Grade Students, *School Science and Mathematics,* **56** (1956), 25–31, 429–437.

Boley, Daniel L.: A Simple Criterion of Divisibility, *Mathematics Teacher,* **61** (1968), 501–502.

Botts, Truman: Linear Measurement and Imagination, *Arithmetic Teacher,* **9** (1962), 376–382.

Bowman, M. E.: "Romance in Arithmetic: Currency, Weights, and Measures" (London: London University Press, 1950).

Callanan, Cecilia: Scientific Notation, *Mathematics Teacher,* **60** (1967), 252–256.

Cohen, Louis S.: A Rationale in Working with Signed Numbers, *Arithmetic Teacher,* **12** (1965), 563–567.

———: A Rationale in Working with Signed Numbers—Revisited, *Arithmetic Teacher,* **13** (1966), 564–567.

Dubisch, Roy: Applications of Finite Arithmetic, *Mathematics Teacher,* **53** (1960), 322–324, 430–432; **55** (1962), 162–164.

Evenson, A. B.: "Modern Mathematics" (Glenville, Ill.: Scott, Foresman and Company, 1962).

Fehr, Howard F.: Fractions as Operators, *Arithmetic Teacher,* **15** (1968), 228–232.

——— and Thomas J. Hill: "Contemporary Mathematics for Elementary Teachers" (Boston: D. C. Heath and Company, 1966).

Feldman, Leonard: A Multiple View of the Euclidean Algorism, *Arithmetic Teacher,* **12** (1965), 556–559.

Foster, B. L.: Euclid's Algorithm Revisited, *Mathematics Teacher,* **60** (1967), 358.

Frege, G.: "The Foundations of Arithmetic" (Oxford: Basil Blackwell & Mott, Ltd., 1950).

Fremont, Herbert: Pipe Cleaners and Loop: Discovering How to Add and Subtract Directed Numbers, *Arithmetic Teacher,* **13** (1966), 568–572.

Giffel, William J.: Primes and Things, *School Science and Mathematics,* **62** (1962), 684–687.

Griffin, Harriet: Discovering Properties of the Natural Numbers, *Arithmetic Teacher,* **12** (1965), 627–632.

Haines, Margaret: Modular Arithmetic, *Arithmetic Teacher,* **9** (1962), 127–129.

Hamilton, W. W.: Field Work Modifies Our Program in Arithmetic, *School Science and Mathematics,* **51** (1951), 527–531.

Hursh, Ronald E.: The Number Line in the Junior High School, *Arithmetic Teacher,* **13** (1966), 553–555.

Ingham, Carolyn, and Joseph M. Payne: An Eighth-grade Unit on Number Systems, *Mathematics Teacher,* **51** (1958), 392–395.

Johnson, Donovan A.: A Unit on Our Number System, *School Science and Mathematics,* **52** (1952), 556–561.

——— and William H. Glenn: Exploring Mathematics on Your Own (New York: McGraw-Hill Book Company, 1961). (Series of eighteen pamphlets.)

——— and Gerald Rising: "Guidelines for Teaching Mathematics" (Belmont, Calif.: Wadsworth Publishing Company, 1967).

Jones, Burton W.: Miniature Number Systems, *Mathematics Teacher,* **51** (1958), 226–231.

Martin, J. Gregory, Jr.: Discovering the Mathematics of a Slide Rule, *Arithmetic Teacher,* **15** (1968), 23–25.

Moise, Edwin E.: "The Number Systems of Elementary Mathematics" (Reading, Mass.: Addison-Wesley Publishing Company, Inc., 1966).

Morton, R. L.: Divisibility by 7, 11, 13, and Greater Primes, *Mathematics Teacher*, **61** (1968), 370–373.

National Council of Teachers of Mathematics: "Computer Oriented Mathematics" (Washington, D.C.: The Council, 1963).

———: "Report of the Conference on Computer Oriented Mathematics and the Secondary School" (Washington, D.C.: The Council, 1963).

———: "Measurement," Topics in Mathematics for Elementary Teachers, Booklet 15 (Washington, D.C.: National Council of Teachers of Mathematics, 1968).

Paige, Donald D.: Primes and Factoring, *Arithmetic Teacher*, **9** (1962), 449–452.

Parsons, Kenneth B., and Stanley P. Franklin: Divisibility by Two, *Mathematics Teacher*, **53** (1960), 639.

Pierson, Elliott: Junior High Math and the Computer, *Mathematics Teacher*, **56** (1963), 298–301.

Rassweiler, Merrill, and J. Merle Harris: "Mathematics and Measurement" (New York: Harper & Row, Publishers, Incorporated, 1955).

Read, Cecil B.: Arguments against Universal Adoption of the Metric System, *School Science and Mathematics*, **50** (1950), 297–306.

———: Comments on Computation with Approximate Numbers, *Mathematics Teacher*, **46** (1953), 479–483.

Rudnick, Jesse A.: Numeration Systems and Their Classroom Roles, *Arithmetic Teacher*, **15** (1968), 138–147.

Scheid, Francis: Clock Arithmetic and Nuclear Energy, *Mathematics Teacher*, **52** (1959), 604–607.

Schiff, Herbert J.: Let Them Measure, *School Science and Mathematics*, **57** (1957), 291–292.

Seymour, Kenneth A.: A General Test for Divisibility, *Mathematics Teacher*, **56** (1963), 151–154.

Shuster, Carl N.: Teaching Computation with Approximate Data, *Mathematics Teacher*, **42** (1949), 123–132.

———: Approximate Square Roots, *Mathematics Teacher*, **45** (1952), 17–18.

Sister M. Barbara Stastny, O.S.F.: A Test for Divisibility, *Mathematics Teacher*, **53** (1960), 627–631.

Smart, James R., and John L. Marks: Mathematics of Measurement, *Arithmetic Teacher*, **13** (1966), 283–287.

Smith, Joe K.: A Method for Converting from One Nondecimal Base to Another, *Arithmetic Teacher*, **15** (1968), 344–346.

Stein, Sherman K.: "Mathematics, the Manmade Universe" (San Francisco: W. H. Freeman and Company, 1963).

Stenzel, Jane G.: Math for the Low, Slow, and Fidgety, *Arithmetic Teacher*, **15** (1968), 30–34.

Sweet, Roy: High School Computer Programming in the Junior High School, *Mathematics Teacher*, **56** (1963), 535–537.

Ward, Morgan, and Clarence Ethel Hardgrove: "Modern Elementary Mathematics" (Reading, Mass.: Addison-Wesley Publishing Company, Inc., 1964).

Willerding, Margaret F.: A Teaching Unit in Modular Arithmetic, *School Science and Mathematics*, **60** (1960), 511–518.

———: "Elementary Mathematics: Its Structure and Concepts" (New York: John Wiley & Sons, Inc., 1966).

Williams, Wendell M.: A Complete Set of Elementary Rules for Testing Divisibility, *Mathematics Teacher*, **56** (1963), 437–442.

Willoughby, Stephen S.: "Contemporary Teaching of Secondary School Mathematics" (New York: John Wiley & Sons, Inc., 1967).

Wren, F. Lynwood: "Basic Mathematical Concepts" (New York: McGraw-Hill Book Company, 1965).

Youse, Bevan K: "Arithmetic: A Modern Approach" (Englewood Cliffs, N.J.: Prentice-Hall, Inc., 1963).

ten the teaching
of algebra
in the
junior
high school

A large share of the difficulties students experience in their study of algebra may be traced to the fact that it presents a radically new and different approach to the study of quantitative relationships, characterized by a new symbolism, new concepts, a new language, a much higher degree of generalization and abstraction than they have encountered previously, and an essential dissociation of many of its parts from intuition and concrete experience. Also, in contrast to arithmetic, algebra is more concerned with the conscious examination and study of processes and basic structure than with particular answers to particular problems.

Algebra presents new difficulties to students

These various difficulties are not insuperable, although teachers often have been too preoccupied, negligent, or uninformed to take proper account of them. On the contrary, experience has shown that through careful analysis, thoughtful planning, and skillful teaching a great deal can be done to obviate or minimize them. No single topic is free from them. It is the job of the teacher to analyze each topic, to learn to anticipate the particular difficulties that are likely to occur in connection with it, and to plan to teach it in such a way that the difficulties may be avoided or forestalled as far as possible. Such a practice will go far toward enabling the teacher to explain away those difficulties which cannot be avoided altogether.

These difficulties can be overcome

THE FIRST COURSE IN ALGEBRA

In general, the content of the first course in algebra should not be very extensive in depth, nor should it be formalized to the extent that the work of later courses will be. Its main objective should be to introduce the students to the meaning and use of certain basic algebraic concepts, such as literal symbols, signed numbers, formulas, polynomial functions, graphs, equations, and inequalities. It is not intended that the algebraic work of the junior high school shall lead to any large degree of technical skill in algebraic operations, nor is it intended that this work shall be thought of solely in terms of its preparatory values. Rather it is conceived as

Content and goals

serving the double purpose of extending the conceptual background of the student as a sound transitional basis for later work and of providing mathematical experiences interesting in themselves and more general than those encountered in the earlier arithmetic.

For more effective work in such a beginning course in the formal attention to algebra there must be a minimum list of prerequisite expectations of algebraic experience. The Commission on Mathematics gives the following list of such prerequisites for its proposed first course in algebra:

Prerequisites

> Graphs and Formulas: Use of line segments and areas to represent numbers. Reading and construction of bar graphs, line graphs, pictograms, circle graphs, and continuous line graphs. Meaning of scale. Formulas for perimeters, areas, volumes, and percents—introduced as generalizations as these concepts are studied. Use of symbols in formulas as placeholders for numerals arising in measurement. Simple expressions and sentences involving "variables."[1]

Algebra in earlier grades

Such algebraic work as may be attempted in the earlier grades to meet prerequisites should be informal, and it should be interesting. The main idea should be to give the students an understanding of the meaning of the language and symbolism of algebra as expressed in the formula and the simple equation, and an understanding of the simplicity, power, generality, and importance of these mathematical tools.

Most of the work in algebra in these earlier grades should be focused upon the interpretation of graphs and associated concepts, making clear the meaning of literal symbols, their use in setting up formulas and simple equations, and the evaluation of such formulas and the solution of such equations.[2] Many commonplace relationships already familiar to the pupil give rise to formulas. Such relationships may be used to advantage by having the pupils translate their verbal expressions into symbolic language. Many familiar arithmetical problems can be used to derive equations from verbal rules. Some examples are given in the following list, which could easily be extended.

Use of simple equations

In any uniform or average-rate motion, distance equals rate times time. . . . . $d = r \times t$

Simple interest equals principal times rate times time . . . . $i = p \times r \times t$

Circumference of a circle equals pi times length of diameter . . . . $C = \pi \times D$

Perimeter of a rectangle equals 2 times the sum of the length and the width. . . . . $p = 2(l + w)$

The annual rent on a home equals 12 times the monthly rent. . . . $R = 12 \times r$

Percentage equals base times rate. $p = b \times r$

Margin equals selling price minus cost. . . . . $m = s - c$

---

[1] Report of the Commission on Mathematics, "Program for College Preparatory Mathematics" (New York: College Entrance Examination Board, 1959), pp. 19–20.

[2] *Ibid.*, pp. 18–19.

Area of a rectangle equals length of base times height. . . . . $A = b \times h$

The score in a basketball game is the number of free throws plus

   twice the number of field goals made good . . . . $S = f + 2g$

The diagonal of a square is equal to the length of one side times

   the positive square root of 2. . . . . $d = s \times \sqrt{2}$

The volume of a rectangular solid is equal to the product of the

   length, width, and height . . . . $V = l \times w \times h$

The length of the hypotenuse of a right triangle is equal to the

   positive square root of the sum of the squares of the legs . . . . $h = \sqrt{a^2 + b^2}$

The number of ounces is equal to 16 times the number of pounds. $n = 16 \times p$

The number of gallons in a tank is (about) equal to 7½ times the

   number of cubic feet . . . . $g = 7\tfrac{1}{2} \times f$

The number of centimeters is (about) 2.54 times the number of

   inches. . . . . $c = 2.54 \times i$

The equations used should be so simple that the student will intuitively know how to solve them. So far as possible they should grow out of familiar problem situations, although there can be no objection to setting up short lists of empirical equations for practice. Consider this problem, for example: If John earned $17.60 for 16 hours work, what was his average wage per hour? This gives rise to the equation $16 \times w = \$17.60$, and the student's task is to solve for w. Intuition furnishes a sufficient guide for this.

Of equal usefulness is this problem: Fred and Joe picked 60 quarts of cherries one day, but Joe picked 8 quarts more than Fred did. How many quarts did each pick? This suggests the equation $F + (F + 8) = 60$, or $2F + 8 = 60$. By subtracting 8 from each side, the equation becomes $2F = 52$, for which, again, the solution is reached intuitively.

Simple equations provide an easy transition to formal methods

Equations of this type provide an easy and natural approach to the more formal methods to be used later. They need not and should not be made difficult. Speed of solution is not a consideration here. The main considerations at this stage should be to ensure understanding of the derivation of the equation, to ensure understanding of the solution, and to develop the habit of using such equations in solving problems.

Such a treatment of formulas and equations, supplemented by frequent use of graphs for visual presentation of information, can provide a strong foundation upon which to build the structure of algebra. It should serve effectively in preparing the way for the student as he enters his first formal course in algebra.

No significant discussion of the subject-matter content of the first course in algebra can fail to call attention to the new emphases on precision and clarity of expression in both definitions and exposition. Probably the most pervasive single concept used in the efforts to accomplish these desirable goals of instruction is the notion of *sets*. The concepts of set and subset are simple. A set is

Concepts of sets and subsets

defined by some consideration whereby one can determine whether a particular object does or does not belong to the set. Innumerable examples can be given: the set of persons in a given algebra class, the set of chairs in a room, the set of all automobile licenses issued in Michigan in a given year, the set of numbers in a telephone directory, the set of points on a line, the set of positive integers less than 13. Indeed, the idea of sets of objects is one of the earliest concepts which children form. They use sets of objects in learning the names of numbers and in learning to count. Even in such simple matters as distinguishing between different kinds of objects, they are implicitly using notions of sets of things having different characteristics.

In view of these considerations one may reasonably ask why students should have any difficulties in studying about sets in connection with algebra. The truth is that there need be very little difficulty at all. In fact, the consideration of sets that is appropriate in connection with the first course in algebra should be largely intuitive and informal, and it should be concerned more with establishing foundations of ideas, terminology, and symbolism than with formal proofs of theorems about sets. At the same time, unless this work is carefully presented and unless enough practice

Sources of difficulty is given both in translating the set symbolism into words and in translating verbal statements into appropriate set symbolism, some difficulties may arise. These would seem to stem mainly from three sources. First, in their early experiences with sets, the attention of the students will usually have been focused either on the individual objects of the set or upon some characteristic that is common to these objects, rather than upon the set itself. Second, the usual operations with sets (union, intersection, complementation) are different from the operations of arithmetic and school algebra to which the students have been accustomed.

Venn diagrams are very useful in helping students clarify the notions of union, intersection, and complementation. They are

Terminology and concepts of sets— not algebra of sets —should be introduced in the first course also helpful in illustrations employing finite sets having small numbers of objects. It should be repeated that no extensive formal study of the algebra of sets is advocated for the first course. At the same time, an introduction to the concept of sets, explanation of the meanings attached to the terminology and symbolism employed, some simple illustrations, and perhaps some simple exercises involving union and intersection of sets can bring several advantages. Most important among these advantages is the fact that students will be learning the language, acquiring a familiarity with the concepts, and building a proficiency in the techniques used so effectively in the study of mathematics. Also, through these avenues students can be made aware that mathematics is not a subject on which the last word has been written, but a live and growing field, and that there are branches of mathematics other than the traditional algebra and geometry which are new and interesting and of growing importance. They can be given a glimpse into one of these branches and can become acquainted with some of its technical words and symbols. Few high school students realize that there are algebras other than the conventional school algebra that they study. Some acquaintance with the other algebras can do much to broaden the students' mathematical horizons and give added interest to the work of the regular course in which they are enrolled.[3]

SYMBOLS AND FORMULAS

Role of formulas in making the transition to formal work

The formula, a symbolic statement of relationship between two or more variables, provides an ideal medium for the transition from the earlier work to the more formal and systematic aspects of algebra and a theme about which a great deal of the work of the first course can be organized. It involves, or is closely associated with, a great many of the concepts of elementary algebra; the symbolic language of constants and variables; the concept of dependence and function; graphic representation of relationships; substitution and evaluation; and operations with signed numbers, literal symbols, parentheses, exponents, fractions, radicals, etc. Thus it forms a core which has points of contact not only with the previous experiences of the students, but with many of the topics which will be considered subsequently.

The student's background with formulas

The beginning algebra student is not entirely unacquainted with formulas. In his previous work in arithmetic and informal geometry he will doubtless have had some contact with such formulas as those for simple interest and for the mensuration of the simplest and most common geometric forms. If he has had a thoroughly good course in the earlier grades, he should have attained some understanding of the significance and generality of the formula as

---

[3] For illustrations of various types of suggested adaptations to elementary algebra see:

Robert R. Christian, "Introduction to Logic and Sets" (Boston: Ginn & Company, 1958).

Report of the Commission on Mathematics, "Appendices" (New York: College Entrance Examination Board, 1959).

James F. Gray, "Sets, Relations; and Functions" (New York: Holt, Rinehart and Winston, Inc., 1962).

Myra McFadden, J. William Moore, and Wendell I. Smith, "Sets, Relations, and Functions" (New York: McGraw-Hill Book Company, 1963).

Bruce E. Meserve and Max A. Sobel, "Mathematics for Secondary School Teachers" (Englewood Cliffs, N.J.: Prentice-Hall, Inc., 1962), pp. 77–176.

National Council of Teachers of Mathematics, "Enrichment Mathematics for the Grades," *Twenty-seventh Yearbook* (Washington, D.C.: The Council, 1963); "Enrichment Mathematics for High School," *Twenty-eighth Yearbook* (Washington, D.C.: The Council, 1963); "The Growth of Mathematical Ideas, Grades K–12," *Twenty-fourth Yearbook* (Washington, D.C.: The Council, 1959).

F. Lynwood Wren and John W. Lindsay, "Basic Algebraic Concepts" (New York: McGraw-Hill Book Company, 1969).

a shorthand statement of relationships between quantities and as a rule for operation. He will have had some experience in evaluating simple formulas, and perhaps will have constructed a few simple formulas from quantitative situations within his experience. He thus brings to his first course in algebra enough background to enable him to use the formula as a point of departure in his work, and his further study of the formula in turn serves to familiarize him with, and give him experience in, the progressive mastery of the new language, concepts, symbolism, and operations of algebra.

The main things the student should get from his more formal study of formulas are:

1 An understanding and appreciation of the nature and significance of the symbolism of algebra
2 An appreciation of the fact that a formula is merely the translation of an English sentence into symbolic form

Goals in studying
formulas

3 A clear concept of the meaning of a constant and a variable and the distinction between the two
4 A clear concept and appreciation of dependence and the meaning and relationship of independent and dependent variables
5 The ability to set up simple formulas expressing relationships existing in situations within the student's experience
6 Facility and accuracy in substitution in and evaluation of formulas
7 The ability to represent graphically the relationships indicated by formulas involving two variables
8 The ability to solve formulas, i.e., to transform an implicit relationship into an explicit relationship through application of the laws of algebraic operation

One of the first of the fundamental tasks the student faces in the study of formulas and algebra in general is to acquire a good understanding of the real meaning of symbolism. It is customary to introduce students to the notational significance of algebraic symbolism by having them (1) consider common situations in which the relationships between two or more elements are known, (2) state these relationships in words, and (3) abbreviate the verbal statements by substituting letters and symbols of operation and equality for the words. For example, the student may be asked to tell how to find the distance which an automobile traveling at a uniform speed will cover in a given time. His statement will probably be to the effect that the distance is equal to the rate of speed (in miles per hour) multiplied by the time (expressed in hours). He can easily be led to see that, by using letters to represent the verbal expressions, he can write this same relationship more briefly and conveniently as $d = r \times t$. That is, in this simple case he has little difficulty in associating the letter d with distance, r with rate of speed, and t with time. He thus gains almost at once the important idea that a letter may stand for a meaning which can be expressed more elaborately in words.

Meaning of
symbolism

This, however, is not the whole story. Unless the student is made keenly aware not only that the letter is to be associated with a verbal expression (e.g., *r* for rate) but that it must be identified in any particular instance *with a number*, he is likely to come to the erroneous and meaningless conclusion that "miles per hour times hours equals miles" or that "feet times feet equals square feet." Such statements are not at all uncommon, but they exhibit a lack of clarity with respect to the meaningful use of symbolism. A concept fundamental to the clear and precise use of symbols is that the student be made to understand that they primarily and essentially represent numbers, although they may refer to the enumeration or numerical measurement of some particular kinds of objects or magnitudes. The intelligent use of symbols probably can be developed most effectively through numerous illustrations of the use of letters to represent such things as lengths of line segments, weights, sizes of angles, or unknown quantities in simple verbal problems or equations. Such illustrations should be closely associated with repeated and carefully supervised practice in the actual evaluation of formulas by the direct substitution of specified numbers and the performance of the indicated operations after the substitutions have been made. The teacher should employ illustrations of these procedures freely, because the immature mind responds much more readily to illustration than it does to definition or verbal direction. During this period of development and early practice in the employment of symbols, the work of the student should be under the close supervision of the teacher in order that any misconceptions and mistakes may be detected and corrected at the outset and so prevented from becoming fixed habits.

The student must associate algebraic letters with numbers

CONSTANTS, VARIABLES, AND FUNCTIONS

Letter symbols are frequently used as variables, but they are also used as constants. A variable is a symbol that may represent any element from a specified set called its *domain,* or *replacement set.* Within limits, the domain of a variable can be whatever one wishes. The letter *r* is frequently used to represent the measure of the radius of a circle. The domain of *r* could be the set *R* of all positive real numbers, or of any desired subset of *R*. On the other hand, the domain of *r* cannot include negative numbers, because a circle does not have a negative number as measure of its radius.

Domain of a variable is arbitrary

A *constant* is a symbol used to represent a single number. There are *absolute constants.* The symbol "5" is an absolute constant; it always represents the number 5. There are also *arbitrary constants,* or *parameters.* The equation $y = mx + 5$ is the equation for all lines through (0,5). "5" is an absolute constant, but m is an arbitrary constant. Each choice of m determines a different line. If the value of m can be any real number, why is it not a variable? This can be a source of confusion for students. There is no way to look at a letter and tell whether it is a variable or a constant. One must be told or infer from context. If $y = mx + 5$ described y as a function of the two variables m and x, it could not be called the equation for a straight line. The letter m is an unspecified constant. When a particular value is specified, a specific line is identified.

The ordinary experiences of students furnish innumerable illustrations of both variables and constants. The fact that many students come through one or more years of work in algebra without any clear understanding of what is meant by either of the terms "variable" and "variation" can mean only that teachers do not take the trouble to present a sufficient number or variety of these illustrations. Changes in age, height, or weight of individuals, the distance of a moving body from a fixed point, and changes in temperature are but a few examples of many familiar situations which could be used to make the meanings of variation, variable, and constant clear. If these illustrations are to yield the desired results, however, the teacher must see to it that the attention of the students is focused upon the respective characteristics of each concept, and this emphasis must be made repeatedly and specifically.

Just as the concept of variable has suffered through the years because of the inclination of many to restrict it to considerations of variation, so the concept of function has suffered because of similar restrictions to considerations of dependence and dependent variation. Mathematicians[4] are inclined to emphasize two basic concepts of "function," namely:

1 A *function* is a set of ordered pairs of elements (a,b) so related that, when the value of a is determined in its set of admissible values, the value of b is determined uniquely in its set. The two sets are not necessarily distinct.

Thus the ordered pairs (a,a^2), $(a,\sqrt{a})$, $(a,\sin a)$ are possible functions. If the set of values for both variables is specified as the set of all positive real numbers, each set of ordered pairs is a function. To any value of the first variable corresponds a unique value of the second variable. This is illustrated in Table 10-1 for a few values of a. If the set of values for a is specified as the set of all negative real numbers and the set of values for the second variable is specified to be the set of all real numbers, then (a,a^2) and $(a,\sin a)$ are functions, but $(a,\sqrt{a})$ is not. For example, if $a = -4$, then (a,a^2)

---

[4] For interesting and helpful discussions of constant, variable, and function, see chaps. 3, 8, and 13 of "Insights into Modern Mathematics," *Twenty-third Yearbook* (Washington, D.C.: National Council of Teachers of Mathematics, 1957).

TABLE 10-1

a	a^2	$\sqrt{a}$	$\sin a$
1	1	1	$\sin 1$
2	4	$\sqrt{2}$	$\sin 2$
$\frac{1}{4}$	$\frac{1}{16}$	$\frac{1}{2}$	$\sin \frac{1}{4}$

becomes $(-4,16)$, $(a,\sin a)$ becomes $[-4, \sin (-4)]$, and 16 and sin (-4) are real numbers. On the other hand, $(a,\sqrt{a})$ becomes $(-4,\sqrt{-4})$, and $\sqrt{-4}$ is not a real number.

A function as a mapping

2 A *function* is a rule, expression, or table which defines a specific relationship between two sets (not necessarily distinct) of elements, such that when an element from one set is given, an element from the other set is uniquely determined. The first set is called the *domain* of the function, and the second set is called its *range.*

A function is not well defined unless its domain is given. The domain can be selected arbitrarily, except that each element must have an image in the range. In the function $y = (x + 5)/\sqrt{x - 3}$, if the range is selected from the set of real numbers, the domain cannot contain any value of $x \leqslant 3$.

To define a function, its domain must be known

When the rule is a formula, there are other restrictions on the domain that must be observed. For example, the formula for the area of a circle, $A = \pi r^2$, is the rule for the function (r,A). Although any real-number replacement for r will have a real image, if $r = -3$, then $A = \pi(-3)^2 = 9$, and no circle can have a radius -3. Thus, if the function F is the above set of ordered pairs (r,A), it is incorrect to say that $F(-3) = 9\pi$. McShane[5] refers to such incorrect usage as this as using a formula "beyond its domain of validity," and emphasizes that it "can lead to absurdities, not only in mathematics but in any science."

Restrictions on the domain are inherent in some formulas

The *domain* of a function F is the set of all objects x for which $F(x)$ has meaning; in other words, an object x is in the domain of F if and only if there exists some y such that (x,y) is in F [that is, $F(x) = y$]. The *range* of the function F is the set of all objects y which are values of the function; that is, y is in the range of F if and only if there is an x for which the equation $F(x) = y$ is true.[6]

A relation is a set of ordered pairs

Table 10-2 gives another illustration of how a function may be defined. Here the set of ordered pairs of elements is (t,T), where t represents time and T represents temperature. The domain of the function is the set of even hours of the day from 2 A.M. to 2 A.M., and the range is the set of temperatures $(54°, 60°, 61°, 62°, 64°, 66°, 69°, 70°, 71°, 73°)$. Note that the set of ordered pairs (T,t) would not

---

[5] E. J. McShane, Operating with Sets, "Insights into Modern Mathematics," *Twenty-third Yearbook* (Washington, D.C.: National Council of Teachers of Mathematics, 1957), p. 57.
[6] *Ibid.,* pp. 57–58.

TABLE 10-2

Time	Temperature	Time	Temperature
2 A.M.	61	4 P.M.	70
4 A.M.	61	6 P.M.	66
6 A.M.	61	8 P.M.	62
8 A.M.	64	10 P.M.	62
10 A.M.	69	Midnight	60
Noon	71	2 A.M.	54
2 P.M.	73		

be a function, since for $T = 61°$ or $T = 62°$ there is not a *unique* determination of a value for t. However, the set of ordered pairs (T,t) is a *relation* in accordance with this definition: A *relation* is a set of ordered pairs (x,y) such that to each value for the first element x there corresponds at least one value for the second element y. Thus a function is a special kind of relation. The formula $y = \pm\sqrt{x}$ affords another example of a relation which is not a function. If the domain of the relation is the set of all positive real numbers, then to each value of x there correspond two values for y.

The first symbol in the ordered pair which defines a relation is the *independent variable*. It is the variable whose value is arbitrary so long as it is chosen from the domain of the relation. The second symbol is the *dependent variable*. It is the variable whose value is determined in the range merely by the assignment of an arbitrarily chosen value to the independent variable.

Use of independent and dependent variable

The terms "independent variable" and "dependent variable," though still very much in use, are used in secondary school much less than formerly. Their origin harks back to the time when a function was looked upon as a cause-and-effect affair. Consider the relation connecting the radius and circumference of a circle, $C = 2\pi r$. It is true that when the radius changes, the circumference changes, but it is equally true that when the circumference changes, the radius changes. In fact, to change either can only mean to transfer one's attention to another circle. The important consideration is the *interdependence of the two quantities*.

Translating verbal statements to mathematics

Attention has already been called to the practice of having students *translate verbal statements of relationships into formulas* by the use of letter symbols to represent the related elements in the situation. There can be little doubt that such practice in translating statements or laws into formulas is of great value in centering the students' attention upon the fundamental concepts which have been discussed and in clarifying these concepts. Probably the simplest and most effective way to give students an understanding start in this use of symbolism is to show them that it may be regarded as a sort of shorthand method of writing down what would otherwise have to be written in a less convenient verbal form. The contrast between the verbal and the symbolic forms and the advantage of the latter can be emphasized by actually writing down the verbal statements of relationships and then "for the sake of convenience" rewriting the statements by using merely the initial letters of the key words rather than the words themselves. The following examples illustrate this method.

Distance equals rate of speed multiplied by time
$$d \quad = \quad r \quad \times \quad t$$

Cost of gasoline equals number of gallons
$$C \quad = \quad g$$
multiplied by price per gallon
$$\times \quad p$$

A few such examples will serve to enable most students to get the idea of what is being done and learn to appreciate the significance of the symbolism and the expressed relationships. However, in order to ensure something distinctly beyond a mere threshold understanding of these concepts, the students should be given a substantial amount of practice in this work, and the practice should be spread over a considerable period of time.

TEACHING STUDENTS TO SOLVE LINEAR EQUATIONS

One of the most common and important activities of the first course in algebra is the solution of linear equations. Presumably, the student will bring to his study of algebra some understanding of what an equation means, since he will have had experience with simple equations in his previous work in arithmetic and informal geometry, and perhaps even with certain very simple equations in which the unknown quantity is represented by a literal symbol. In all probability, however, his experience in solving equations will have been barely above the intuitive level. For example, if confronted with the equation $3n = 24$ and required to find the number represented by n, he will probably conclude that, if three n's make 24, then "it stands to reason" that one n will have to be one-third of 24, or 8.

These intuitive reactions are generally sufficient and satisfactory so long as the situation is very simple, i.e., so long as it is possible for the student to keep in mind clearly and simultaneously all the pertinent elements and relationships which are involved in the problem. On the other hand, the moment the conditions become so involved that he is unable to keep all the elements and their proper relationships clearly in mind intuition breaks down; and

The student's experience with linear equations before formal algebra will probably not go beyond intuition

Logic must replace intuition

when this happens, logic must take its place. In such cases the only recourse is to more formal and powerful tools for the analysis of problem situations. Such a tool is the algebraic equation.

Since the turn of the century much criticism has been directed against formalism in secondary school algebra. It is undoubtedly true that the mechanical aspects of algebra have been heavily stressed and that the emphasis placed upon the formal operations has too often given little or no consideration to underlying meanings. There is a great difference, however, between formalism, conceived in this sense, and the formalization of mathematical procedures. Algebra really consists fundamentally in the generalization and formalization of these procedures, but this formalization need not and should not be divorced from meanings. Rather, it should be conceived as merely an extension of familiar procedures into an environment of number concepts more general and more powerful than those of elementary arithmetic. The student should bring to the algebra class an acceptance of the associative, commutative, and distributive properties when applied to numbers as an outgrowth of long experience with numbers. The algebra teacher may find it necessary to formalize this acceptance by naming the properties. He must also help the student extend his conception of the properties to include constants and variables.

> "Formalism" is not the same as formalization of content and procedures

The extension of the number system to include additive inverses (opposites) and multiplicative inverses (reciprocals) gives the student the tools with which to solve any linear equation. The above number properties, together with the properties of the equality relation, are sufficient. The student should learn to accept the definition of equality as a formalization of his conception of its meaning. The three properties that define equality are the following:

E_1 Equality is reflexive: $a = a$.
The sentence $2 + 3 = 5$ is an application of the reflexive property because "$2 + 3$" is a numeral for the number 5.
E_2 Equality is symmetric: if $a = b$, then $b = a$.
E_3 Equality is transitive: if $a = b$ and $b = c$, then $a = c$.

> The equality relation over a set of numbers

Two additional properties apply to equality of numbers:

E_4 Addition property of equality: if $a = b$, then $a + c = b + c$.
E_5 Multiplication property of equality: if $a = b$ then $a \times c = b \times c$.

Solution of an equation is no longer thought of as solving a puzzle where one discovers the unknown. The student's elementary school experience includes contact with mathematical sentences. A sentence that includes a variable is an *open sentence*; it is neither true nor false until a replacement is made for the variable. Solving the equation consists of finding the replace-

The solution of an
equation is finding
the truth set of the
sentence

ments for the variable that make the sentence true. This set of values is the *truth set*, or *solution set*, of the equation.

Linear equations in one variable assume a variety of forms, of which the following are illustrative:

$$ax = b \qquad x + a = b \qquad ax + b = c$$

$$\frac{x}{a} = b \qquad a - x = b \qquad x - a = b$$

$$ax + b = cx + d \qquad ax + bx = c$$

While these forms are all variations of a common form, the similarity is usually not immediately apparent to students encountering them for the first time. But they should not be classified and taught by type. A much sounder procedure is, first, to introduce the concept of *equivalent equations as two or more equations which*

Equivalent
equations have the
same solution set

have the same solution set. After this concept is clearly understood, the second step in the procedure becomes that of seeking a single unifying principle for use in the transformation of any given linear equation into an equivalent equation.

1 In solving *any* linear equation in one variable the object is to find an equivalent equation in which the variable stands alone in one member and is absent from the other.
2 To do this, first obtain an equation with all terms containing the variable, and only those terms, in one member of the equation. This can be done by applying the addition property of equality, adding the additive inverse of each term that is to be removed. Terms containing the variable are to be removed from one side of the equation, and terms not containing the variable removed from the other side.
3 Obtain an equation in which a multiple of the variable is equal to a constant. This can be done by applying the distributive property in the member containing the variable, and combining constant terms into one term on each side of the equation.
4 The equation sought in step 1 is obtained by using the multiplication property of equality, multiplying by the multiplicative inverse of the coefficient of the variable in step 3.

This principle gives a basis for the solution of linear equations without any recourse whatever to intuition, except the intuitive feeling of appropriateness of the number properties and properties of equality that are employed.

Although the formal study of number fields is no part of the responsibility of the first course in algebra, it is important that students at this level of instruction be made conscious of the field

Students must be
aware of the
properties of a
field

properties as they define the field of real numbers and the subfield of rational numbers. Although the field properties have been stated previously, they are of such great significance to the study of algebra that they are restated here.

Given the set of elements F and two operations, addition ($+$) and multiplication ($\times$).[7] The set F is called a *field* if, for every element $a,b,c,d, \ldots$ of F, the following postulates hold:

F1. *Closure.* $a + b$ and $a \times b$ are elements of F.

F2. *Uniqueness.* If $a = b$ and $c = d$, then $a + c = b + d$ and $a \times c = b \times d$.

F3. *Commutative.* $a + b = b + a$ and $a \times b = b \times a$.

F4. *Associative.* $(a + b) + c = a + (b + c)$ and $(a \times b) \times c = a \times (b \times c)$.

F5. *Distributive.* $a \times (b + c) = (a \times b) + (a \times c)$.

F6. *Additive identity.* There exists in F an element 0 such that $0 + a = a$ for every a in F. The element 0 is the *additive identity.*

F7. *Multiplicative identity.* There exists in F an element $1(\neq 0)$ such that $1 \times a = a$ for every a in F.

F8. *Additive inverse.* For each a in F there exists an element $-a$ in F such that $(-a) + a = 0$. The element $-a$ is called the *additive inverse* of a.

F9. *Multiplicative inverse.* For each nonzero element a in F there exists an element a^{-1} in F such that $a^{-1} \times a = 1$. The element a^{-1} is called the *multiplicative inverse* of a. An equivalent form for writing a^{-1} is $1/a$.

Field properties and properties of equality in solving equations

The justification of the steps outlined on page 283 is to be found in the field properties and the properties of the relation "equal." This can be illustrated by formal solution of the simple equation $ax - b = c$. First it should be stated that a, b, c, and x are all assumed to be elements of a field, and $a \neq 0$.

	Steps		*Reasons*
1	$ax - b = c$	1	Given
2	$ax - b = ax + (-b)$	2	Definition of subtraction, F_8, and F_6
3	$ax + (-b) = c$	3	E_2 and E_3
4	$[ax + (-b)] + b = c + b$	4	E_4
5	$ax + [(-b) + b] = c + b$	5	F_4
6	$ax + 0 = c + b$	6	F_8
7	$ax = c + b$	7	F_6
8	$a^{-1}(ax) = a^{-1}(c + b)$	8	E_5
9	$(a^{-1}a)x = a^{-1}(c + b)$	9	F_4
10	$1 \times x = a^{-1}(c + b)$	10	F_9
11	$x = a^{-1}(c + b)$	11	F_7
12	$a^{-1}(c + b) = (c + b)/a$	12	Definition of division, F_9, and F_7
13	$x = (c + b)/a$	13	E_3

Detailed justification of steps is not expected of students

This detailed presentation does not carry any implication that this sort of development should be expected of the students in the first course in algebra, although it is quite possible that there will

[7] Attention is called to the fact that, although the names and symbols of the two operations are the familiar ones, the nature of each operation is dependent upon its definition in each specific context. For example, if F is the set of integers, then addition and multiplication are defined in the familiar way, based on counting. If F is the set of rational numbers, then each element can be expressed in the form $a = p/q$ and $b = r/s$, where p, q, r, s are integers, with $q \neq 0$ and $s \neq 0$. In this case

$$a + b = \frac{p}{q} + \frac{r}{s} = \frac{(p \times s) + (q \times r)}{q \times s} \quad \text{and} \quad a \times b = \frac{p}{q} \times \frac{r}{s} = \frac{p \times r}{q \times s}$$

be students of sufficient understanding and ability to pursue solutions in such logical detail. Nevertheless, there should be inculcated in all students a basic understanding of what is taking place in such problem situations, that there is a basic structure to the algebra they are studying, and that it is not a mere aggregate of rules to be memorized and executed.

The foregoing illustrative example has attempted to point out the type of reasoning processes involved in solution of linear equations in one variable. Nothing has been said about the specific nature of the result. Is it the replacement of the variable that will produce a true statement of equality? One does not know until the substitution is made and the equality is tested. In the first example the reasoning is as follows: If $ax - b = c$, then $ax = c + b$, from which, in turn, it follows that $x = (c + b)/a$. (Note that even this statement does not follow if $a = 0$.) This reasoning simply states that if $ax - b = c$, then it is *necessary* that x have the value $(c + b)/a$.

Necessary and sufficient conditions

It *does not say* that $x = (c + b)/a$ is *sufficient* to make $ax - b = c$. This must be tested by substitution (we call it checking the work). The test will reveal that $x = (c + b)/a$ is *both a necessary and a sufficient condition* that $ax - b = c$.

Two further examples are given to illustrate this very important point. For the existence of a unique value of x which will satisfy $ax - b = c$, it is *necessary* that a be different from zero. That this is not sufficient can easily be demonstrated by the fact that if $a \neq 0$, then $1/a$ has a value, and $x = 1/a$ gives $a(1/a) - b = 1 - b$, which may or may not be equal to c. Furthermore, substitution will reveal that $x = k(c + b)/ka$, $k \neq 0$, is sufficient to give $ax - b = c$. Only $x = (c + b)/a$ is both necessary and sufficient to give $ax - b = c$.

A more homely illustration may be obtained from consideration of the following sentences:

1 To make a 20-cent purchase, it is necessary that one have x cents.
2 To make a 20-cent purchase, it is sufficient that one have y cents.
3 To make a 20-cent purchase, it is both necessary and sufficient that one have z cents.

Any number of cents less than 20 cents could be used to replace x, and statement 1 would be true.

Any number of cents greater than or equal to 20 cents could be used to replace y, and statement 2 would be true.

Only the number 20 could be used to replace z and make statement 3 true.

It is necessary to check every solution

The process is complete when the result $x = (c + b)/a$ is reached provided the solution consists of a series of equivalent equations (equations with identical solution sets). However, the student should never consider his solution complete until the obtained solution is checked in the original equation.

It is hardly necessary to give further illustrations. The single unifying principle of getting rid of the unwanted terms, divisors, and multipliers by the application of inverse processes results automatically in the solution of all forms of the linear equation in one variable. Approached intuitively in the beginning, its complete reasonableness can be made apparent to students without difficulty. Thereafter they should be led to focus their attention on the process per se and to give less and less attention to its concrete numerical setting. Thus, eventually, it will stand out as a general, abstract, mechanical principle of operation, not devoid of meaning (because it will have been built upon meanings in the beginning) but no longer dependent upon intuition, and therefore more certain and more powerful than the earlier and less formal procedures.

The process of solution becomes independent of intuition

THE EVALUATION AND SOLUTION OF FORMULAS

Theoretically, the *evaluation of formulas* presents no learning difficulties. Actually, however, students make mistakes in this simple process, and they are not always mistakes in computation. Mistakes in substitution occur with unexpected frequency. These are most often associated with the rewriting or recopying of the formulas, with the letters replaced by corresponding numerical values. This type of error can be offset to a considerable degree by having the students make a practice of enclosing in separate parentheses each numerical value which is substituted for a letter. This has a tendency to focus attention upon each quantity as a separate element in the formula, and so avoid the confusion of one such element with another. In chalkboard work it is helpful to have the students actually erase one by one the letters in the formula and write in the numerical value of each letter as that letter is erased. This makes them keenly conscious of the fact that *the letters are actually to be replaced by the numbers* and thus strengthens the appreciation of the real meaning of evaluation. While this practice of erasing and rewriting *in situ* cannot be followed so satisfactorily when the work is being done with pencil and paper, something of the same effect can be attained by having each substituted number enclosed in separate parentheses and written in a place which precisely corresponds to the place occupied in the formula by the letter for which the substitution is being made.

Much practice is needed

Students should replace letters with numbers

The *solution of formulas* often causes students much difficulty. This is because the students are not made consciously and specifically aware of the general principles underlying the solutions. Indeed, teachers themselves often seem to overlook the general principles. The principles do exist, however, and are quite simple and capable of being applied in an understanding manner by junior high school students. They are merely the principles which underlie the solution of all simple equations, whether numerical or literal, integral or fractional, rational or irrational.

Solving a formula is solving a literal equation

The general procedure may be illustrated by considering the formula $A = P + Prt$. Let it be required to solve for t in terms of A, P, and r. Since the letter t occurs in only one term, that term must be retained, and all other terms eliminated from that member of the equation. This elimination of elements from one member of the equation (or formula) is always accomplished by *undoing* the operation which binds that element to the rest of the given member of the equation. In this case P is related to Prt by addition. Hence, to eliminate P from that member of the equation, we must undo this addition; in other words, we must subtract P from the right-hand member of the equation. It therefore becomes necessary to subtract P also from the left-hand member of the equation. This (the equivalent of adding the additive inverse of P) gives the equation $A - P = Prt$.

To solve for one
term of a formula,
reverse the
processes involved

Now, since we wish to solve for t, we must eliminate Pr from the right member. But Pr is bound to t by multiplication. Hence, in order to eliminate Pr and make t stand alone, we must undo the multiplication by using a process which is the inverse of multiplication, namely, division. Therefore we divide the member Prt by Pr; and if we divide one member of an equation by a given quantity, we must also divide the other member by that same quantity. This is equivalent, of course, to multiplying both members by the multiplicative inverse of Pr. Thus we get

Solution is a logical
process

$$\frac{A - P}{Pr} = \frac{(Pr)t}{(Pr)} \qquad \text{or} \qquad \frac{A - P}{Pr} = t$$

This principle of "elimination by undoing" (or by applying inverse processes) is perfectly general and is not difficult once the students are brought to see it in its essential simplicity. It removes the solution of formulas from the status of a bag of tricks and places it upon a reasonable basis.

Apparent complications are introduced when the student is required to solve for a letter that occurs in two or more terms. In such cases, however, it should be pointed out that it is merely necessary to use the field properties as authority for grouping these terms and remove the required letter as a common factor. The procedure then follows the general pattern indicated above. To illustrate, let it be required to solve the foregoing formula for P in terms of A, r, and t. The steps are

$$A = P + Prt$$
$$A = P(1 + rt)$$
$$\frac{A}{(1 + rt)} = \frac{P(1 + rt)}{(1 + rt)}$$
$$\frac{A}{(1 + rt)} = P$$

Note that after using the associative and distributive properties to factor the right member, it remains merely to eliminate the factor $1 + rt$ by undoing the multiplication, i.e., by dividing both members of the equation by that factor or multiplying both members by the multiplicative inverse of $(1 + rt)$.

THE TEACHING OF GRAPHS

Importance of graphs

In recent years an increasing amount of importance has been attached to the study of graphs in junior high school mathematics. Among the several reasons for this may be mentioned the interesting character and the practical importance of graphical devices; the simplicity and power of the graph for presenting data in a condensed, understandable, and striking way; and the increasing prominence of graphical devices in newspapers, magazines, and other current publications.

Frequently, the assumption is made that the complete understanding of graphs is implied and guaranteed by the ability to construct them, but such an assumption is unwarranted. It is entirely possible for a student to plot a series of points whose coordinates satisfy a particular equation, draw a smooth line through these points, and call this the "graph of the equation" without having any clear realization of the meaning of what he has done. This is not to say that the construction of graphs is unimportant. On the contrary, not only is it extremely important in the development of a full understanding of the meaning of graphs, but it also gives valuable review and practice in understanding the meaning of the coordinates of a point and in the solution of equations and the substitution of numbers leading to the evaluation of algebraic expressions. The construction of graphs and the study of their meaning should go hand in hand.

Emphasis on interpretation accompanied by construction

The customary way of teaching students how to construct mathematical graphs is to give them an equation such as $2x + 5y = 9$ and have them build a table of number pairs which satisfy the equation. They are then shown how to locate points by means of the number pairs. After they have located a few points, they are instructed to draw a smooth line through them. Too often the subject is carried no further. Frequently, teachers fail to give adequate instruction even with reference to such fundamental matters as the dependence of one of the variables upon the other, the arbitrary assignment of values to the independent variables, the naming of the axes, and the selection of suitable scales.

Attention should be directed to important aspects

The construction of graphs can contribute little toward the development of adequate concepts of variation, continuity, and dependence if it is taught in this purely perfunctory fashion. These concepts are not likely to enter into the students' thinking unless they are specifically pointed out, not once but many times,

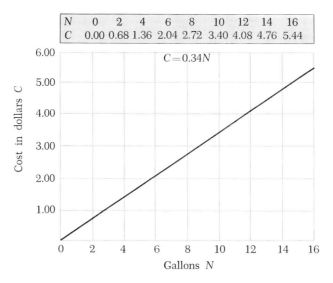

N	0	2	4	6	8	10	12	14	16
C	0.00	0.68	1.36	2.04	2.72	3.40	4.08	4.76	5.44

$C = 0.34N$

Figure 10-1
Cost of gasoline at 34 cents a gallon.

by the teacher. Many and varied illustrations should be used. The

Varied illustrations are important

students will find within their own common experiences many situations involving relationships among variable quantities that may be appropriately subjected to graphical treatment and which, because of their familiarity, will help materially in giving meaning to the graphs.

As an illustration, consider the relationship between the amount of gasoline that goes through a pump at a filling station and the total cost of the gasoline at 34 cents a gallon. This provides an excellent situation for emphasizing the *dependence* of one variable, the cost C, upon another variable, the number of gallons N, the price remaining constant. It can be expressed by the formula $C = 0.34N$. This formula can then be used as a basis for constructing the graph in Fig. 10-1. After the graph has been made, it should be carefully re-examined, with attention directed to the way in which it answers such questions as: What happens to the cost as the number of gallons increases? As the cost increases, does the number of gallons increase in the same ratio? Does a decrease in either of the variables bring about a corresponding decrease in the other? How does the price per gallon affect the direction of the graph? If the price were increased, how would the direction of the graph be changed? Approximately how many gallons of gasoline could be bought for $1? For $1.50? For $2? For $3? Does the graph show the cost of 8 gallons? For *any* point on the graph should the ordinate C give a number exactly

0.34 times as great as the number given by the abscissa N of that point? Would the same result be given by the formula? If a point were to move along the graph, would its ordinate or its abscissa change the more rapidly? How many times as rapidly? Explain how the graph shows that the cost *depends* on the amount of gasoline bought. Explain how the graph shows that the number of gallons of gasoline one can buy *depends* upon how much money he could spend for gasoline.

By such questions as the foregoing ones the students can be made conscious of the graph as a device which shows in a striking way the fact and the precise nature of the dependence of either of the variables upon the other, the meaning of dependent and independent variables, and the precise way in which a change in either variable inevitably brings about a corresponding change in the other variable. The students become more clearly aware of the meaning of coordinates. They learn to associate the relationships shown by the graph with those indicated by the formula or equation upon which the graph is based. They learn, in short, to understand what a graph means, and this in turn enhances their comprehension of dependence and functional relationship as a permeating principle, whether it is expressed graphically or by means of formulas or equations.

An associated problem calling for the graphs of two simultaneous equations could be set up as follows: One filling station sells gasoline at 34 cents a gallon; a competitor advertises 30 cents a gallon plus 30 cents service charge. Make cost graphs for both stations on the same set of axes.

Simultaneous equations

This problem involves writing a second formula, $C = 0.30N + 0.30$, and the construction of another graph along with the one already made and discussed. Questions similar to those heretofore indicated should now be discussed with reference to the new graph (Fig. 10-2).

In addition, such questions as the following should be discussed: With what amount of money could one purchase the same amount of gasoline at the second station as at the first? At which station could one get more gasoline for $1? For 50 cents? For $5? How much more gasoline could be purchased at one station for $4.00 than at the other station? At which station could one buy 10 gallons at the lower cost? At which station could one buy 2 gallons at the lower cost? How much could one save by buying 15 gallons at the station that offered the lower price on this amount? Show how to find this out from the graphs. Does the service charge made by the second station affect the direction of the graph? Does it affect its position? Explain. Does the price per gallon affect the direction of the graph? Explain. Would a change in the direction of the graph indicate a change in the price per gallon? Explain.

Consideration of the direction of a straight-line graph leads

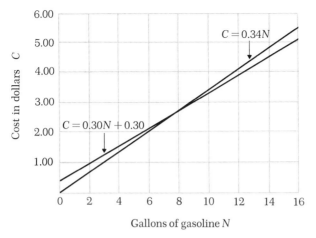

Figure 10-2
Comparison of the cost of gasoline at two prices.

naturally and easily to the concept of *slope*, which is the ratio of the

Concept of slope

difference between two function values $(y_1 - y_2)$ to the difference between the corresponding values of the domain $(x_1 - x_2)$. Similarly, the point where the graph crosses the function axis should be associated with the constant term in the equation, and the effect which any change in the constant term has upon the position of the graph should be studied. The students will be interested to know that when the equation is written as a linear function, $y = mx + b$, the b always indicates the point at which the graph crosses the function axis and m indicates the slope. Thus, by solving any linear equation of the form $ax + by = c$ for y ($b \neq 0$),

Slope-intercept form

the student has at his command a method for constructing the graph which is at once less tedious and more meaningful than the method described earlier in this section.

Attention should be called to the fact that the m and b, or the *slope* and the y *intercept*, are two conditions that determine the position of a straight line, just as two points determine its position. The method of determining the x intercept and y intercept from the equation of any line and the use of the two intercepts in

The first-degree relations

plotting the graph of the line should then be emphasized. All this discussion of the linear equation and its graph should lead to the summarizing generalization: To determine the position of a straight line in a plane, it is necessary to have two independent conditions.

Emphasis should be given to the fact that there are distinct cases to consider in analyzing the linear equation $ax + by = c$.

Case 1. $a \neq 0$, $b \neq 0$. Under these conditions the equation can be transformed into the formula for the *linear function* $y = mx + b$, where $m \neq 0$. The graph of the linear function is a straight line which intersects both coordinate axes. If $c = 0$, the graph passes through the origin.

Case 2. $a = 0$, $b \neq 0$. Under these conditions the equation can be transformed into the formula for the *constant* function $y = k$. The graph of the constant function is a line parallel to the x axis if $c \neq 0$ or is the x axis if $c = 0$. The constant function is *not* a special case of the linear function, since the slope of the graph of the constant function is zero ($m = 0$), while the slope of the graph of the linear function is different from zero ($m \neq 0$).

Case 3. $a \neq 0$, $b = 0$. Under these conditions the equation can be transformed into the formula for the *linear relation* $x = h$. This equation is that of the relation (h,y) in which all function values correspond to the single replacement h for x. It is not a function. For the linear relation the slope is undefined, and its graph is a line parallel to the y axis if $c \neq 0$ or is the y axis if $c = 0$.

There is no case for consideration if $a = 0$ and $b = 0$. Under these conditions c also is of necessity zero, since otherwise $ax + by = c$ is not a true statement. When $a = b = c = 0$, the statement of equality becomes a trivial relation satisfied by any set of values for x and y. Thus the equation $ax + by = c$ is the equation of a straight line if and only if a and b are not both zero (or $a^2 + b^2 \neq 0$).

Specific attention to these considerations not only adds interest and value to the study of graphs, but in an easy, natural, and understandable way provides the beginnings of a sound technical foundation for a real understanding of later work in analytic geometry and calculus. Obviously, more time is required for this sort of treatment of mathematical graphs than would be required for the mere construction of the graphs themselves. One may feel sure, however, that the thorough discussion of a few instances along the lines which have been indicated will do more to give the students a sense of functional relationships involved than will the mere rule-of-thumb construction of large numbers of the graphs.

Thorough study is a good preparation for future work

THE TEACHING OF DIRECTED NUMBERS

The study of directed numbers is an integral part of the study of algebra. Students will have already been introduced to the concept in the mathematics of the upper grades, but this work is quite incidental and not pursued to great length. The only safe procedure in the algebra class is to assume no prior knowledge of directed numbers.

The teacher should not assume that the students know directed numbers

The number line, or more properly, number ray, is quite familiar and has probably been used since the earliest grades to represent the positive real numbers. Students are familiar with the concept of diametrically opposite quantities such as profit or loss, above or below sea level, a bank balance or overdraft, above or below zero on the temperature scale, income or expenses. The idea that a quantity can apply in either of two opposite directions is sufficient for extending the number line in both directions from the zero point.

The concept of a quantity in a direction is necessary for the number line

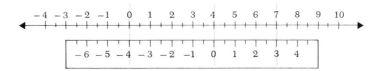

Figure 10-3

Adding on the number line.

A number of concepts should precede any attempt to formalize the operations with directed numbers. The meaning and role of opposites, absolute value, and order, all are intimately related to the number line.

Opposite is a symmetric relation. The opposite of a number is not necessarily a negative number. On the number line, two numbers are opposites if they are the same distance from the zero point but on opposite sides of it. The *absolute value* of a number is its distance on the number line from the zero point. *Order* is a relation

concerned with relative position; the position of the zero point is only incidental to this concept. On the Fahrenheit scale 23° is less than 41°. The same temperatures measured on the centigrade scale are −5° and 5°, respectively. Numbers are positive or negative according as they are to the right or to the left of the chosen zero point. Also, when any two numbers a and b are compared, $a > b$ or $a < b$ according to whether a is to the right or to the left of b on the number line. These concepts should be thoroughly mastered

relative to the number line before any attempt is made to define them independent of the number line.

The use of the number line is not just a crutch or visual aid. One acceptable approach to the real numbers depends on the assumption that every segment has a real-number measure and every real number is the measure of a segment. This is closely akin to the Dedekind cut approach to the real numbers.

When we add on the number line we are in fact combining the lengths of two segments. This can be highlighted by using two number scales, one fixed and one movable, somewhat like a slide rule. (See Fig. 10-3.) When zero on the sliding scale coincides with 4 on the fixed-number line, a segment 4 units long is indicated between the zeros on the two scales. With this setting we can add any segment to 4. For example, 3 on the movable scale indicates a segment 3 units long between zero on the movable scale and 3 on the same scale. Then, over against 3 on the movable scale, we find the sum $3 + 4$ on the fixed-number line. With the same setting we can find $4 + (−5)$ as the number on the number line facing −5 on the movable scale. It is an easy step from this to the more conventional method: to find $a + b$, locate a, then move $|b|$ units to the right if b is positive and to the left if b is negative. These activities

Figure 10-4

Subtracting on the number line.

should continue, along with those involving absolute value, opposites, and order, until the class can derive from the number line the following definitions:

Addition defined in terms of absolute value

1 If $a > 0$, $b > 0$, then $a + b = |a| + |b|$.
2 If $a < 0$, $b < 0$, then $a + b = -(|a| + |b|)$.
3 If $a < 0$, $b > 0$, and $|a| > |b|$, then $a + b = -(|a| - |b|)$.
4 If $a < 0$, $b > 0$, and $|b| > |a|$, then $a + b = |b| - |a|$.

There is more than one way to perform subtraction on the number line. The main objective in studying subtraction is to establish the identity

$$a - b = a + (-b)$$

for this identity encompasses the principal reason for extending number to include negatives. This objective should dictate what

Subtraction by finding the missing addend

approach to use in subtracting on the number line. The idea that $a - b$ is the number that must be added to b to obtain the sum a lends itself to the use of two number lines. (See Fig. 10-4.) If b on the movable scale is placed opposite a on the number line, then $(a - b)$ on the number line will be found opposite the zero point on the movable scale: $(a - b) + b = a$. In comparison, $a + (-b)$ on the two lines appears as in Fig. 10-5.

The similarity between this and the picture of $(a - b)$ should be made apparent to the students. In each case the result, indicated by the question mark, is the point b units to the left of a, provided b is positive. Similar sketches will show the solution point to be $-b$ units to the right of a if b is negative.

The additive inverse

The additive inverse property should receive concerted and deliberate attention. It should be emphasized that directed numbers were considered because it is not always possible to subtract in the set of positive numbers, but having created them, subtraction is never necessary in the enlarged set of directed numbers.

Multiplication using two number lines

It is possible to demonstrate the multiplication of directed numbers using two number lines, in a completely logical and satisfactory way. But the process depends upon the theory of proportional sides of similar triangles. In the first course in algebra there are better ways to rationalize multiplication. If both factors are positive, there is no problem. Students find no difficulty in

Figure 10-5
Subtracting on the number line.

accepting commutativity:

$-a \times b = b \times (-a)$

As a matter of fact, it usually comes as a surprise when a student makes first contact with a noncommutative operation. The two cases to consider, then, are (1) one positive and one negative factor and (2) two negative factors.

Rationalizing the rules for multiplication

The rule $(-a) \times (b) = -(ab)$ can be rationalized by resorting to the rule for positive integers,

$3 \times 4 = 3 + 3 + 3 + 3$

By analogy $(-a) \times (b) = (-a) + (-a) + (-a)$, until $(-a)$ is used as an addend b times. The result is $-(ab)$. The perceptive student will object that this holds only if b is a positive integer.

Another approach appeals to the desire for consistency.

Multiplicand	3	3	3	3	3	etc.
Multiplier	2	1	0	−1	−2	etc.
Product	6	3	0	−3	−6	etc.

In this array it is observed that decreasing the multiplier by 1 decreases the product by 3. If this pattern is consistently maintained throughout the integers, then $(-1) \times 3 = -3$, $2 \times 3 = 6$, and generalizing, $(-a) \times (b) = -(ab)$. If the above pattern is continued by decreasing the multiplicand

Multiplicand	3	2	1	0	−1	−2
Multiplier	−2	−2	−2	−2	−2	−2
Product	−6	−4	−2	0	2	4

the obvious generalization is $(-a)(-b) = ab$. The result $(-a)(-b) = ab$ can also be obtained by considering the fact that changing the sign of either factor in $a \times b = ab$ will change the sign of the product: $(-a)(b) = -(ab)$ and $a(-b) = -(ab)$. Also, if the signs of both factors in the latter equations are changed, the sign of the product is unchanged. $(-a)(b) = -(ab)$ becomes $a(-b) = -(ab)$, and $a(-b) = -(ab)$ becomes $(-a)b = -(ab)$. Many observations using specific numbers should be made. The students will probably be willing to accept the generalization: Changing the sign of one factor changes the sign of the product, and changing the signs of both factors leaves the sign of the product unchanged. Applying this generalization to $a \times b = ab$, the result is $(-a)(-b) = ab$; also, applying it to $(-a)(b) = -(ab)$, the same result $(-a)(-b) = ab$ is obtained.

The above approaches and others like them should be used as discovery techniques. They should not be considered proofs. If the students in their previous work have developed a genuine understanding of the structure of the nonnegative real numbers, the logically correct approach is the most satisfactory. In any event this approach should not be omitted. The demonstration is based on the acceptance of the associative and distributive properties. To show $(3)(-5) = -(15)$:

Proof of $-a \times -b = ab$ requires acceptance of associative and distributive properties

$$
\begin{array}{ll}
5 + (-5) = 0 & \textit{property of additive inverses} \\
3[5 + (-5)] = 3 \times 0 & \textit{multiplicative property of equality} \\
3 \times 0 = 0 & \textit{property of zero in multiplication} \\
3[5 + (-5)] = 0 & \textit{transitive property of equality} \\
(3)(5) + (3)(-5) = 0 & \textit{distributive property} \\
15 + 3(-5) = 0 & \textit{multiplication of (3)(5)}
\end{array}
$$

$3(-5)$ is the opposite of 15; therefore $3(-5) = -15$. Generalization of the result is obvious.

The same approach can be used to show $(-3)(-5) = 15$:

$$
\begin{array}{l}
(-3)[5 + \quad (-5)] = -3 \times 0 = 0 \\
(-3)5 + (-3)(-5) = 0 \\
-15 + (-3)(-5) = 0
\end{array}
$$

Therefore $(-3)(-5)$ is the opposite of -15:

$(-3)(-5) = 15$.

Since the quotient obtained by dividing one number by another is a number whose product with the divisor must give the dividend, it must follow that the law of signs for division is the same as that for multiplication. That is, if the signs of the divisor and the dividend are alike, the quotient will be positive; if they are different, the quotient will be negative. This explanation of the law of signs for division is usually quite satisfactory when illustrated by numerical examples, and ordinarily there is no material value in more elaborate attempts to rationalize it.

Rule of signs

SOLUTION OF INEQUALITIES
IN ONE VARIABLE

The inclusion of the order relation makes possible another kind of mathematical sentence, an inequality. After the students have mastered the properties of the relation "equal," the relation "greater than" should, in the same context, cause no undue diffi-

Solution of inequalities

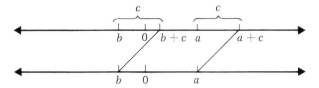

Figure 10-6

The addition property of order shown on the number line.

culty. It was necessary that the five properties of equality should serve as the definition of the relation. This is not true of "greater than." The students have learned that $a > b$ if and only if a is to the right of b on the number line. One way to describe subtraction $(a - b)$ on the number line is to find the number of steps required to go from b to a, that is, to find what must be added to b to get the sum a. Such questions as the following should elicit the correct definition of "greater than": If $a > b$, where is a relative to b on the number line? If a is to the right of b, which direction must you go from b to reach a? If you must add a positive number to b to get a, what kind of number is $a - b$? Are $a > b$ and $a - b > 0$ equivalent statements?

It is sometimes as important to know what properties the order relation fails to have as those it does have. Comparing with equality, it can be established from the definition that "greater than" is neither reflexive nor symmetric. Care should be exercised relative to the symmetric property, especially since the pupil is taught that $a > b$ and $b < a$ have the same meaning. If it were symmetric, any number would have to be greater than any other number. For example, under symmetry, if $10 > 3$, then $3 > 10$.

Properties of "greater than" contrasted with "equal to"

The transitive property of order can most easily be established on the number line: if a is to the right of b and b is to the right of c, then a is to the right of c.

The number line can also be used to advantage to establish the addition property of order. Adding c to each of a and b produces two new points, one the same distance and direction from a that the other is from b; see Fig. 10-6.

Multiplication of inequalities

The property most likely to cause trouble is the multiplication property of order. Probably the best way to proceed here is by examples. If $a > b$ and each is multiplied by c, the resulting statement depends on the value of c. If $c > 0$, then $ac > bc$; if $c = 0$, then $ac = bc$; and if $c < 0$, then $ac < bc$.

Equivalent inequalities

The above properties and the properties of a field are adequate for solving linear inequalities in one variable. The inequality is considered solved when an *equivalent inequality* in the form $x < c$ or $x > c$ is found.

Two or more inequalities are equivalent if they have identical

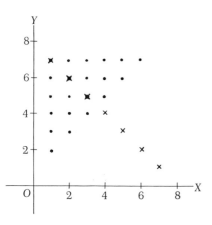

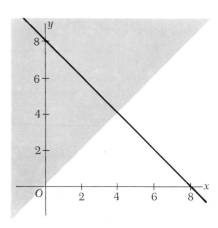

Figure 10-7

$y > x$ $\left.\begin{array}{l} 0 < x < 8 \\ 0 < y < 8 \end{array}\right\}$
$y = -x + 8$

Figure 10-8

$y > x$ $\left.\begin{array}{l} \textit{Domain and range are the} \\ \textit{set of all real numbers.} \end{array}\right.$
$y = -x + 8$

solution sets. An equivalent inequality can be derived by applying the field properties and the order properties to the given inequality.

TEACHING THE SOLUTION OF PAIRS OF SIMULTANEOUS LINEAR EQUATIONS

The systems of simultaneous linear equations of concern in elementary algebra are limited to only two equations in two variables.

Ways to solve simultaneous linear equations

The three commonly used methods for solving such systems are (1) the graphical method, (2) the method of elimination by substitution, and (3) the method of elimination by addition or subtraction.

The graphical method has many advantages, but it should be based on a clear understanding of what it is that the graph of a

Advantages of the graphic method

relation represents. For example, consider the two relations $y > x$ and $y = -x + 8$ under the following specifications:

Example 1: The domain and range of both relations are to be the same, namely, the set of all positive integers < 8. Under these restrictions the complete graph of $y > x$ is the set of points represented by dots in Fig. 10-7. The complete graph of $y = -x + 8$ is the set of points represented by the crosses in the figure. The solution set of the two relations considered simultaneously is therefore the set of points represented by the crossed-over dots in the figure, namely, the points $\{(1,7),(2,6),(3,5)\}$.

Example 2: The domain and range of both relations are to be the same, namely, the set of all real numbers. Under these restrictions the incomplete graph of $y > x$ is the set of points represented by the shaded portion of Fig. 10-8. The incomplete graph of $y = -x + 8$ is represented by the straight line. The solution set of the two relations considered simultaneously is represented by the portion of the straight line which crosses the shaded area of the figure.

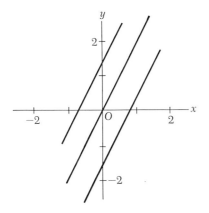

Figure 10-9
$y = 2x + b$

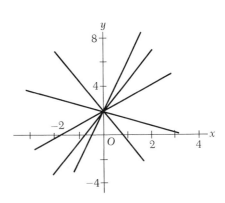

Figure 10-10
$y = mx + 2$

Furthermore, in consideration of the linear function

$$y = mx + b \qquad m \neq 0$$

Slope and y-intercept as parameters

it is important that there be a clear understanding of the part the parameters m and b play in determining the graph of the line. Since $(0,b)$ is a point on the line, it is evident that b is the y intercept of the line. In Fig. 10-9 the various lines all have the same slope ($m = 2$) but different y intercepts (b varies). The function represented in this graph is $y = 2x + b$. On the other hand, in Fig. 10-10, the various lines all have the same y intercept ($b = 2$) but different slopes (m varies). The function represented in this graph is $y = mx + 2$.[8]

The principal advantages of the graphical method lie in the fact that it is interesting and illustrates in a very convincing manner the reason why the solution set of such a system must consist of a pair (or set of pairs) of numbers rather than a single number. It affords a very effective method for demonstrating the significance of the relationships existing when the equations are consistent, inconsistent, indeterminate, dependent, or independent (see Fig. 10-11). This method also proves valuable in developing a clear understanding of just what is meant by *simultaneous linear equations*. Auxiliary advantages are that it gives an excellent review of graphs of linear functions and the associated concepts and procedures.

Disadvantages of the graphic method

Its main disadvantages are two. In the first place it is possible, in general, to get only approximate solutions instead of exact ones.

[8] For a more complete discussion of the graphs of such relations see the Report of the Commission on Mathematics, "Appendices" (New York: College Entrance Examination Board, 1959), pp. 8–27, 36–57. The chapters on the pages referenced are, respectively, Sets, Relations and Functions and The Linear Function and the Quadratic Function.

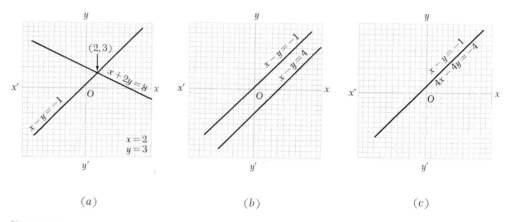

Figure 10-11

The graphical method demonstrates the relationships that exist when equations are consistent (a and c), inconsistent (b), indeterminate (c), independent (a and b), and dependent (c).

Second, it is a comparatively slow, tedious, and inefficient method for solving simple linear equations.

To assist students in interpreting the graphs, the teacher should remind them that every point in the plane represents an ordered pair of real numbers (x,y). Only those points on the graph of a line represent such ordered pairs which satisfy the equation of the line. Thus a point common to both of two graphs represents an ordered pair of numbers satisfying the equations of both of the lines. Since the solution set of a system of equations is the intersection of the solution sets of all the equations, if the graphs intersect, there is a nonempty solution set, and if the graphs are parallel, the solution set is the null set.

Interpreting a graphic solution

If the students have developed a thorough understanding of the meaning of substitution and how to solve and evaluate formulas and literal equations, there is nothing new for them to learn in solving a system of two equations in two variables by the method of substitution. Consider, for example, the system

Solution by substitution

$$3x - \ y = -13$$
$$2x + 3y = \ \ \ 17$$

The first step is to solve one of the equations for one of the variables in terms of the other. This is merely the solution of a literal equation or formula. The student should select the one which can be solved more easily. In this case he would probably solve the first equation for y and get the result $y = 3x + 13$.

He will now substitute this result for y in the second equation and get a resulting equation in which no term in y appears:[9]

[9] Note the use of parentheses.

$$2x + 3(\quad y \quad) = 17$$
$$2x + 3(3x + 13) = 17$$

Next he will perform the indicated operations and collect terms:

$$2x + 9x + 39 = 17$$
$$11x \qquad + 39 = 17$$

Then he will solve this equation for x:

$$11x \qquad + 39 = 17$$
$$11x \qquad\qquad = 17 - 39 = -22$$
$$x \qquad\qquad = \frac{-22}{11} = -2$$

Finally, he must substitute this value of x back in the first equation (the one which he originally solved for y) to get the numerical value of y:

$$y = 3(\ x\ ) + 13$$
$$y = 3(-2) + 13 = -6 + 13 = +7$$

The solution of the system can now be completed by substituting the values obtained in both of the original equations. The first equation is as follows:

$$3(\ x\ ) - (y) \overset{?}{=} -13$$
$$3(-2) - (7) \overset{?}{=} -13$$
$$-6 - 7 = -13$$

This checks. The second equation will be checked in the same manner.

The detailed steps in the foregoing illustration have been given for the purpose of showing how the principles and procedures discussed in connection with solution of a single equation in one variable are applied by the student to this new situation involving two equations in two variables. In particular, it is to be noted that the student does not need to learn or to use in this process anything that is new to him. He has merely to learn to use familiar mathematical tools in a new setting. In the process of doing so he receives a most valuable review and a fuller comprehension of the nature of these mathematical tools and, at the same time, gains added proficiency and facility in their use.[10] The student should be made fully aware of how the field properties provide the authority for the operations used in passing from one step to the next in finding the solution set of such a system.

It is well to make sure that the students understand the thinking that is back of the process of substitution. In the above discussion

$$y = 3x + 13$$

[10] In connection with the detailed steps in the foregoing illustration, the reader may well refer to the sections of this chapter dealing with symbols and formulas and the solution of equations.

gives a formula for finding a value of y which will satisfy the first of the two equations. This is true for any value which might be used for x, a fact that can be verified by experimenting with a few arbitrarily selected values of x and the corresponding values of y determined by the formula. When $3x + 13$ is used to replace the y in the second equation, the condition is imposed that whatever value of y satisfies the first equation must also satisfy the second equation. Imposing this condition on y removes the arbitrariness from x, a fact that should be made clear to the student. There is now only one value of x which can be chosen, and it is determined by the equation $2x + 3(3x + 13) = 17$ to be $x = -2$. The formula $y = 3x + 13$ associates one and only one value of y ($y = 7$) with this value of x. Thus the solution set of the system of equations is $\{(-2,7)\}$, which can and should be verified by checking in the two equations. Actually, the check in the first equation is no more than a check of the computation of the value of y from the determined value of x. This is due to the fact that $y = 3x + 13$ is but an equivalent form of the original equation $3x - y = -13$. The real check is the substitution in the second equation. The process of solving the two equations establishes that $x = -2$ and $y = 7$ is a necessary condition that the two equations be satisfied. The check establishes it as a sufficient condition.

A check should be made with second equation

The method of elimination by addition and subtraction is very effective if the method of substitution leads to the substitution of fractions, a complicated combination of symbols, or a maze of parentheses or signs of aggregation. It is a simple process, but the simplicity of the technique should not be allowed to camouflage its basic structure. Consider the same two equations,

Substitution sometimes leads to complicated expressions

$$3x - \ \ y = -13$$
$$2x + 3y = \ \ \ 17$$

The process of elimination by addition or subtraction would lead to the multiplication of the first equation by 3 and then to the addition of the transformed equation to the second equation. This process would produce $11x = -22$, which would then be solved to obtain $x = -2$, and the value would be used in either of the original equations to produce $y = 7$. Actually, when analyzed in its finality, the values $x = -2$ and $y = 7$ are produced as the solution set of the two equations

$$11x = -22 \qquad\qquad 11x = -22$$
$$3x - y = -13 \quad \text{or} \quad 2x + \ 3y = \ \ \ 17$$

The student should understand the logical basis for elimination by addition and subtraction

By what right can it be said that the solution set of either of these two systems of equations is the solution set of the original system? Of course, the simple answer to this question is that $\{(-2,7)\}$ can be verified as the solution set of the original equations merely by substituting these values in the two equations and seeing that the equations are satisfied. Such a check would justify the process used to find a solution set of any system of equations. A more fundamental question is: How can one be assured that the technique used will produce the solution set of a system of linear equations, if such a set exists? Consider the original system of equations written in the equivalent form

$$3x - y + 13 = 0$$
$$2x + 3y - 17 = 0$$

The process produced the following identity:

$$3(3x - y + 13) + (2x + 3y - 17) \equiv 11x + 22$$

For all values of x the expression on the left is equal to the one on the right. Hence any value of x which will simultaneously satisfy any two of the equations $3x - y + 13 = 0$, $2x + 3y - 17 = 0$, and $11x + 22 = 0$ will also satisfy the third one. Always the process of solving any equation or system of equations establishes the solution set as a necessary condition that the equations be satisfied. The check alone establishes that it is a sufficient condition. Why is this? For this reason one should never be satisfied with a determined solution set of a given equation or system of equations until it has been carefully checked. Again, students should be fully conscious of the part the field postulates play in such a solution process.

A check establishes sufficient condition

OPERATIONS WITH FRACTIONS

The ordinary operations with fractions which find a legitimate place in elementary algebra include reduction and "stepping up," multiplication and division, and addition and subtraction. The student's experience with arithmetical fractions will serve as a point of departure for beginning the work with algebraic fractions. It would be a mistake, however, to assume that familiarity with arithmetical fractions will eliminate all difficulty in working with algebraic fractions. Algebra lacks the familiar, concrete intuitive basis which characterizes a good deal of arithmetic, and the student must learn eventually to work almost entirely upon the basis of established rules or patterns of procedure rather than by intuitive methods. These patterns, of course, are merely generalizations of the methods used in arithmetic, and so may be developed and explained largely by means of analogy with arithmetical situations. The chief difference to be emphasized is that in algebra the student will find it necessary to confine his attention more and more specifically to the processes by which he works, and pay relatively less attention to the particular numerical values of the quantities involved.

Familiarity with arithmetic fractions is not sufficient to handle algebraic fractions

In algebra, the process is more important than the specific answer

Use simple
expressions at the
beginning of work
with fractions

Since the use of fractions in elementary algebra is confined largely to the solution of simple formulas and certain types of verbal problems and to the simplification of algebraic expressions, it is neither necessary nor desirable to include highly complicated fractional expressions in the work of the beginning course.

The best order of
introduction of
operations

Many textbooks, in both arithmetic and algebra, introduce the addition and subtraction of fractions before taking up the multiplication and division of fractions. There are those who contend that this plan is psychologically unsound. They argue that multiplication and division are the less difficult of the operations with fractions and hence should be studied first. In accordance with this point of view, the plan or organization followed in some texts is to consider first the reduction and stepping up of fractions, then the multiplication and division of fractions, and finally the addition and subtraction of fractions.

The student should acquire through his study of fractions the following abilities and understandings:

Goals in
studying fractions

Understanding of the different aspects of the meaning of a fraction
Understanding of what it means to reduce a fraction to lower terms or to change a fraction to higher terms
Understanding of the nature of the terms of a fraction and how the increase or decrease of the numerator or denominator affects the value of the fraction
Ability and skill in multiplying fractions together or in dividing one fraction by another
Ability and skill in adding or subtracting fractions

A rational
number is an
equivalence class
of ordered pairs
of integers

In arithmetic the student learns that a fraction is a numeral, two equivalent fractions being two names (numerals) for the same number. At a more advanced level, a rational number can be defined as an equivalence class of ordered pairs of integers. This same concept must be translated to the terminology and symbolism of algebra. There must also be given illustrations in which the precise numerical relations which provide the intuitive basis for the earlier meaning of a fraction are replaced in part or in their entirety by purely symbolic quantities, and students must be specifically trained to regard such expressions as a/b or $(x - 3)/2y$ as being fractions just as truly as $\frac{3}{4}$ or $^8/_{15}$. The meaning itself must be made to have the status of a definition, so that it may persist even when no intuitive basis exists. In this context such expres-

Rational
expressions obey
the laws
governing fractions

sions become, as it were, symbolic representations of rational numbers. They are known as *rational expressions* and are subject to the same laws of operation as those which govern rational numbers.

The *reduction of fractions,* as well as the inverse operation of changing fractions to higher terms, involves the general problem of changing the form of a fraction without changing the number it represents. Such changes can always be effected by the operation

Finding
equivalent
fractions

of a single simple principle: *The number which a fraction represents remains unchanged if its numerator and denominator are multiplied or divided by the same quantity.*[11] The new fraction is equivalent to the old by definition of equivalent fractions. Students generally are able to apply the principle quite successfully when working with arithmetical fractions, but they probably do so intuitively and without much conscious recognition of the principle itself. Evidence of this is found in the fact that, when they come to work with algebraic fractions, they often fail to apply the principle, and consequently get such erroneous results as

$$\frac{x+4}{4} = x \qquad \text{or} \qquad \frac{2n+a}{-3n+a} = \frac{2}{-3}$$

Results of this sort are almost certainly due to the failure of the students to realize that this procedure does not constitute division of numerator and denominator by a common factor. The undefined use of the word "cancellation" and the failure to place proper emphasis on the inverse relations between multiplication and division, and between addition and subtraction, probably are the major reasons for such looseness in thinking.[12]

Misunderstanding of "cancellation" leads to mistakes

Students must be kept aware of the fact that the addition or subtraction of like quantities (except zero) to or from the numerator and denominator of a fraction will certainly change not only the form but the value of the fraction, whereas in the reduction of fractions or in changing fractions to higher terms the value of the fraction must be kept intact. They must also be kept aware that in dividing numerator and denominator by a common factor, the factor must be a divisor of the *whole* numerator and of the *whole* denominator. Continued consciousness of this elementary principle will prevent the occurrence of such errors as this:

$$\frac{3a+5}{a+2} = \frac{3+5}{2} = \frac{8}{2} = 4$$

Common mistakes with fractions

Most of the mistakes which occur in the reduction of fractions could be avoided by the consistent practice of expressing (rewriting if necessary) the numerator and denominator of the fraction in factored form and enclosing each separate factor, no matter how simple, in its own parentheses. If this is done, the division, or cancellation, of common factors will be effected in a form which provides for real understanding of what is being done. Similarly, in changing fractions to higher terms, it is good practice to have the students immediately enclose the numerator and denominator of the original fraction in parentheses at the outset and then write

---

[11] Division by zero is, of course, excepted, and here multiplication by zero must also be excepted, since it would render the value of the fraction indeterminate.

[12] See pages 202–204 for similar discussion with respect to arithmetic.

the common multiplier also in parentheses as a multiplier of the numerator and as a multiplier of the denominator. The consistent use of parentheses in this way serves to keep all factors intact and to prevent students from treating a factor of a part as a factor of the whole.

The *multiplication of fractions* generally causes little difficulty. The principle governing this process is exceedingly simple: The product of two or more fractions is a fraction whose numerator is the product of the numerators of the original fractions and whose denominator is, similarly, the product of the denominators. It should be illustrated freely by examples drawn from arithmetic, and by analogy, the application to algebraic expressions can be made without difficulty.

Factors should be clearly identified

The fractional product can often be reduced to lower terms. Hence it is desirable to have it rewritten as a single fraction, the numerators and denominators of the component fractions being written in factored form, with every factor enclosed in its own parentheses. It should be stressed that the numerator of every component fraction must be regarded as a factor of the numerator of the product, and similarly for the denominators. The students will be more likely to keep this consciously in mind if they make a habitual practice of enclosing the individual numerators and denominators of the component fractions in parentheses at the outset, before doing anything else. Thus

$$\frac{4 - x^2}{2 + x} \times \frac{x}{2 - x}$$

would be rewritten

$$\frac{(4 - x^2)}{(2 + x)} \times \frac{(x)}{(2 - x)} = \frac{(2 - x)(2 + x)(x)}{(2 + x)(2 - x)} = x$$

When dividing two fractions, multiply by the inverse of one

In the *division of one fraction by another* it is necessary only to see that the students understand that division is always exactly equivalent to multiplication by the reciprocal of the divisor. They will probably be more or less familiar with this principle from their arithmetic, especially as regards division by a fraction. However, the principle should be clearly explained, and numerous illustrations should be given. The student should understand that dividing by a fraction means finding the number which, when multiplied by the divisor, gives the dividend. This is always the test of division. For example, if 7 is divided by $^3/_5$, the result must be such that the product of itself and $^3/_5$ will give 7 [or 7(1)]. We must therefore find a number q such that $q(^3/_5) = 7$. Evidently, q must equal $7(^5/_3)$, since $7(^5/_3)(^3/_5)$ equals 7(1), or 7. Thus 7 divided by $^3/_5$ equals 7 times $^5/_3$. Similarly, in the example $a \div (x/y)$, we have $a \div (x/y) = q$. But $q \times (x/y) = a$; whence $q = a \times (y/x)$. Thus $a \div (x/y) = a \times (y/x)$. The rationale of this process, of course, finds its authority in the definition of division and in the property of the multiplicative inverse. The student should be made fully aware of this fact.

As a rule the main difficulties to be anticipated are those incident to the multiplication and simplification of fractions, and these have been discussed in the foregoing paragraphs.

In introducing students to the *addition of fractions* care must be taken to prevent the occurrence of such errors at this:

$$\frac{5x}{a} + \frac{2}{n} = \frac{5x + 2}{a + n}$$

A clear understanding of the roles of numerator and denominator necessary for efficient addition

Mistakes of this kind reveal a lack of understanding of the real nature of a fraction and of the real meaning of the numerator (numberer) and the denominator (namer). Furthermore, rational expressions must conform to the definitions and operational properties of rational numbers. Such a result does not conform to the definition, which states that the sum of two rational numbers a/b and c/d is given by $a/b + c/d = (ad + bc)/bd$. This is obviously equivalent to finding the common denominator bd of the two fractions and then adding the numerators. This latter procedure allows for the simplification of finding the least common denominator. The two processes are equivalent, and neither supports the erroneous practice exhibited above. As an added precaution, attention should be redirected to the fact that addition is essentially a combining process. There is no occasion for such combination, nor can any sensible interpretation be given to the result unless the sets of objects to be combined are essentially sets of like objects. If students can really get the idea that the denominator of a fraction merely indicates what kind of things are being considered and that the numerator merely indicates how many of these are taken, they will have gone far toward heading off mistakes of the kind described above. Appropriate illustrations of arithmetical fractions are helpful in emphasizing this point because, if sufficiently simple illustrations are taken, the students can immediately check the correctness of their results. For example, they know that $3/4 + 1/4 = 1$, and they can at once see the discrepancy of saying that

Analogies to arithmetic are helpful

$$\frac{3}{4} + \frac{1}{4} = \frac{3 + 1}{4 + 4} = \frac{4}{8} = \frac{1}{2}$$

because $1/2$ is obviously not equal to 1, and they know that the correct answer must be 1. They should be trained to the habit of using some such simple numerical illustration to check on any doubtful operation to see whether or not it is legitimate and correct, and they should learn also to go back to the original meanings of the numerator and denominator to clarify their thinking. To this end it is often helpful to rewrite fractional expressions with the denominators written out in words. Thus $2/7 + 3/7$ can be written as 2 sevenths + 3 sevenths, in which case the expression becomes similar to the expression for the sum of any like denominate quantities, such as 2 dollars and 3 dollars. In other words, this process helps to make clear the idea that fractions are in a sense the same as denominate numbers, the denominator merely telling what kind of thing is being considered, and the numerator telling how many are being considered.

The tendency to add numerators and to add denominators is probably a carry-over from the operation of multiplying fractions. It is important that the students get the distinction between these processes clearly in mind so that they will not confuse them.

Careful instruction
in basic principles
is necessary

The first step in teaching students to add fractions is to have them recall the basic principle of addition: Addition should be used only for combining groups of like things. Thus fractions should not be added until they have been changed to fractions with a common denominator, for then, and then only, are they groups of like things. The denominator of the sum is the common denominator of the addends, and the numerator is the algebraic sum of their numerators. It is not sufficient, however, merely to tell students this. The teacher should give numerous carefully selected illustrations, working them out at the chalkboard and discussing them with the class while he works. The process is not difficult to understand or perform, but it needs to be explained very carefully and deliberately and to be firmly fixed in the minds of the students.

Well-chosen
practice exercises
are necessary

Such careful and adequate explanation can give the students an understanding of the addition of fractions, but the fixation of the ideas and the procedure requires that the students shall have a substantial amount of practice in doing the thing themselves. The practice exercises should be selected with great care. They should be very easy at first and become more difficult by gradual stages. The increasing complexity will be essentially in the numerators, since in this first stage only fractions having like denominators will be used. There should be no great difficulty if care is taken, because the only real algebraic work will be the algebraic addition of the numerators. Essentially, this will be nothing but a review of the algebraic addition of polynomials, with which the students should be expected to have considerable familiarity. The exercises should include fractions whose numerators are of varied types, including simple integers and literal monomials, binomials, and trinomials, some of the binomial and trinomial numerators being given in factored form requiring expansion in order to effect the simplification of the resultant sum.

Too much emphasis cannot be laid upon the principle that the transition to the more complicated forms should be made *gradually*. Teachers often assume that little attention need be given to the addition of fractions with like denominators. No greater mistake could be made; the assumption is entirely unwarranted. The fact is that when the students *really understand* the addition of fractions with like denominators, they are likely to have little difficulty in mastering the addition of fractions with unlike denominators.

When fractions with unlike denominators are to be added algebraically, the students should be firmly impressed with the guiding principle: *If the denominators are not alike, make them alike.* That is, the students should become clearly aware that the first thing to do is to change the given fractions into new fractions whose values are identical with those of the original fractions but whose forms are changed in such a way that they will all have the same denominator. After this has been done, the problem of the algebraic addition of these fractions becomes the already familiar one which has been described above.

Only like fractions
can be added

TEACHING THE SOLUTION OF
EQUATIONS CONTAINING FRACTIONS

Students often have difficulty in solving equations containing fractions even though they may readily solve equations without fractions. The difficulty generally can be traced to the complicated appearance which the presence of fractions gives to the equation. Lacking experience with such equations, the student tends to become confused at the outset because he does not know how to start the analysis of this problem.

The student needs to be taught two basic things to help him out of his difficulty: (1) He must come to understand that equations which contain fractions may be changed into equivalent equations which do not contain fractions and that, when so changed, equations in one variable frequently may be solved readily because they will then be in the same form as the equations he is used to. (2) He must learn how to change an equation containing fractions into an equivalent equation which does not contain fractions. After he has done this, in many cases he has merely to deal with ordinary linear equations, concerning which suggestions have been given.

A few illustrations should serve both to convince him that it is in general possible to change an equation containing fractions into an equivalent one which does not contain fractions and to make clear to him the method by which this is accomplished. The method of explanation should be substantially as follows:

Let us consider the equation $\frac{2}{3} + 3/x = \frac{5}{6}$, in which we are required to solve for x. We know how to solve equations without fractions; hence we could solve this equation if we could change

Finding equivalent
equations that are
not fractional

The method is to
multiply both
members of the
equation by the
common
denominator

it into one that contained no fractions. We could do so if we could get rid of the denominators. But the only way we can get rid of them is to have a factor in the numerator of each term which is exactly equal to the denominator of that term so that we may divide both numerator and denominator of each individual term by the whole denominator of that term.

We can get new factors in the numerators of all the terms if we

To multiply a fraction is to multiply its numerator

multiply every term in the whole equation by the same quantity, because multiplying a fraction means multiplying its numerator. We have a right to multiply all the terms in the equation by any common multiplier we wish, because while this changes the value of each individual term, it does not destroy the equation.

We wish, therefore, to find the smallest multiplier which can be exactly divided by the denominator of each fraction in the equation. This multiplier will be, as you know, the least common denominator of all these fractions. In the case of the equation which we are considering in this problem, the lcd will be $6x$, since this is the smallest quantity of which 3, x, and 6 are all exact factors.

Let us therefore multiply each term in the equation by $6x$; whence[13]

$$6x\left(\frac{2}{3}\right) + 6x\left(\frac{3}{x}\right) = 6x\left(\frac{5}{6}\right) \quad \text{or} \quad \frac{6x(2)}{3} + \frac{6x(3)}{x} = \frac{6x(5)}{6}$$

Now, if we reduce each term to its simplest form by dividing its denominator and numerator by whatever factor is common to both, we have the resulting equation $4x + 18 = 5x$, which has no fractions in it. We can easily solve this equation, since we have solved many others like it.

Multiplying both sides of a fractional equation is not addition of fractions

Sometimes students confuse the procedures involved in solving equations containing fractions with those involved in the addition of fractions. It is important to point out clearly that the two problems are fundamentally different. In the one case the aim is to find the algebraic sum of certain given fractions. This obviously makes it necessary to preserve the *original value* of each individual fraction, although its form may be altered. On the other hand, in solving an equation, both the form and the value of the individual terms may be altered if necessary, provided the *equality* of the two members of the equation is preserved. For this reason, in adding fractions, we may not multiply either the numerator or denominator of any fraction unless we multiply *both* by the same factor,

---

[13] Attention should be called to the fact that the multiplication of the equality gives

$$6x\left(\frac{2}{3} + \frac{3}{x}\right) = 6x\left(\frac{5}{6}\right) = \frac{6x(5)}{6}$$

The authority for this is the multiplicative property of equality (page 282). The distributive property and substitution then provide for the replacement of the left member by

$$\frac{6x(2)}{3} + \frac{6x(3)}{x}$$

whereas, in clearing an equation of fractions, the multiplicative property of equality gives us the authority to multiply the numerators of *all* the terms by *the same multiplier* without multiplying the denominators at all. It is important that illustrations of this point be presented to and discussed with the students and that they come to make a clear distinction between the meanings and the implications of these two fundamentally different problems.

The student must check the fractional equation for extraneous roots

Checking the solution takes on new significance when fractional equations are solved. Since to clear of fractions it is necessary to multiply by an expression containing the variable, it is possible for an *extraneous root* to be introduced. The derived equation may have as a root a replacement for the variable that makes the denominator zero. Checking should constantly be emphasized, but here the motivation is not merely to check on errors, it is also to check on the presence of extraneous roots.

SPECIAL PRODUCTS AND FACTORING

The amount of time and effort justified for the study of special products and factoring in the beginning algebra course is somewhat limited. The uses of factoring are mainly confined to work with fractions and to the solution of certain equations, and the uses of special products are mainly in the direction of facilitating factoring. The equations and fractions suitable to the first course are relatively simple, and the difficulty of the factoring and the special products studied should be in keeping with the difficulty and the requirements of these applications. The work in factoring should be confined to expressions involving a common factor, the difference of two squares, the square of a binomial, or the quadratic polynomial in the simple form $x^2 + px + q$ and also in the more general form $ax^2 + bx + c$, with $a \neq 1$. Consequently, the work in special products should include the product of a binomial by a monomial, the product of the sum and difference of two terms, the square of the sum or difference of two terms, and the product of two binomials of the form $(x + a)(x + b)$, or more generally, of the form $(ax + b)(cx + d)$. In all this work positive and concentrated effort should be directed toward having the student become consciously aware of the fundamental role played by the field properties of associativity, commutativity, and distributivity in all problems of multiplication or factorization of polynomials.

Students must be aware of the role of field properties

So far as the special products themselves are concerned, the aim is to enable one to save time by writing the products down without going through the details of multiplication. So far as their use in factoring is concerned, the aim is to suggest the factors and enable one to write them down without the need of going through the details of trying and checking. The attainment of either of these

It is helpful to know type forms and identify special cases with the forms

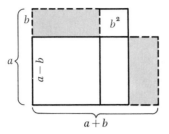

Figure 10-12
Geometric illustration of
$a^2 - b^2 = (a + b)(a - b).$

aims is conditioned primarily upon the following considerations:

1   Knowledge of the type forms of the products to which the various special sets of factors (in type form) give rise
2   Knowledge of the type forms of the factors to which the various sets of special products (in type form) give rise
3   Ability to identify a particular pair of factors as belonging to a particular type and as giving a type product of a particular form
4   Ability to identify a particular product as belonging to a particular type and as having factors of a particular form
5   Ability to identify each element in a special given factor or product with the corresponding element in the type form to which it belongs, and to make the appropriate substitutions

Thus the two fundamental requisites are knowledge of the type forms of the various special kinds of factors and their associated products and ability to recognize, identify, and associate particular cases and particular elements with the general types to which they belong or with the corresponding elements therein. Consequently, the two foremost pedagogical questions are: How can the student most effectively be brought to know these type forms, and how may he best become able to identify expressions in particular problems with the special types to which they belong?

Geometric and arithmetic illustrations are helpful

Geometrical and arithmetical illustrations will help to rationalize all these type forms and will provide a basis by which the student can easily reconstruct them. For example, consider the factorization of the difference of two squares:

$$a^2 - b^2 = (a + b)(a - b)$$

The geometric illustration (Fig. 10-12) shows clearly why the area represented by the product $(a + b)(a - b)$ is the same area as that represented by $a^2 - b^2$.

Now suppose a is 7 and b is 2. Then $a^2 - b^2 = 49 - 4 = 45$. But $a + b = 9$ and $a - b = 5$, and $(9)(5) = 45$. Thus we may also illustrate arithmetically the fact that $a^2 - b^2 = (a + b)(a - b)$. The other type forms may easily be illustrated in similar fashion.

To be of much use, the type forms must be learned thoroughly.

Type forms should
be memorized

They must be understood, and they must also be memorized. This means that the students must be shown in the beginning that the type forms either result from or are verified by actual multiplication. But it also means that in addition to this the students must have sufficient practice and drill upon these type forms to make the forms themselves become indelibly fixed in their minds.

THE SOLVING OF VERBAL PROBLEMS[14]

Word problems are
the most difficult
part of algebra

The solving of verbal problems is probably the most troublesome part of algebra for most students. This is not surprising, because here the student must analyze and set up the problem before he can solve it and, except for the dubious practice of classifying certain verbal problems by types, there is no definite pattern for this analysis. It is true, of course, that for the most part verbal problems involve relationships which may be cast in the form of one or more equations, and those problems to be found in algebra textbooks ordinarily involve relationships that can be represented by relatively simple equations which can be solved without any difficulty once they are set up. The trouble lies in setting up the equations, i.e., in translating the verbal statements into algebraic language. Therefore the principal effort of both teacher and students in connection with the study of verbal problems should be directed primarily toward developing the ability to translate the problems into equations.

A special kind of
reading is required
by word problems

The difficulty which students encounter in making such translation is quite understandable. In the first place, most students are not very careful analytical readers. The recent emphasis in the schools on rapid, cursory reading is doubtless appropriate and valuable for many purposes, but it does not lend itself well to the careful analysis of problems. Analysis is characteristically a slow and tedious process, and the ability to read analytically requires patience, as well as concentrated and sustained attention. These characteristics, generally, can be developed to a satisfactory degree only by special training in giving conscious attention to them. The teacher of algebra must assume responsibility for giving this special training in careful analytical reading if he expects to have his students become proficient in solving verbal problems.

Relationships in
word problems are
not always obvious

One of the material difficulties encountered by students in interpreting the verbal statements of problems lies in the fact that the relationships are not always stated explicitly but are often *implied*. For example, in the familiar distance-rate-time problems, relationships between units of measure are implied, such as the number of feet in a mile or the number of seconds in a minute. In the many problems that imply the use of money, the relationships

[14] It is suggested that the reader refer again to the discussion of this topic in Chapter 3.

between the various units of monetary value are always assumed as known. Such words as "complementary," "supplementary," and "right triangle" are used to imply pertinent facts or relationships which are not stated explicitly. Hidden implications of this sort may appear so obvious to the teacher that he will perhaps not even be consciously aware of the lack of explicit statement. Often, however, they constitute a real source of confusion to students. The students need to be trained specifically to be on the lookout for these hidden implications, to learn to detect them, and to take them into account in analyzing and setting up the problems.

Closely associated with the difficulties involved in this implicit manner of indicating facts or relationships is the difficulty which sometimes arises from the use of words or expressions whose meanings are not entirely clear to the students. For example, the expression "x less 5" means $x - 5$, while the expression "x less than 5" carries the ambiguous meaning of either $5 - x$ or $x < 5$, and students frequently fail to detect these differences because they do not recognize that the meanings to be attached to the word "less" are not the same in the two expressions.

In the second place, the careful analysis of problems requires much patience, concentrated attention, and the willingness to take the time to write down and organize all relevant data with painstaking care. These are not generally to be regarded as common characteristics of normal, healthy young students. Students tend to be impatient with problems they cannot organize intuitively in a moment. They want to get to the answer quickly and are often content to dismiss, with the remark "Too hard," any problem involving relationships that cannot be seen and organized at a glance. Development of the ability to give concentrated and sustained attention is not only desirable as a general trait, but absolutely necessary in the successful study of mathematics, and it is especially necessary in setting up verbal problems. The students need to be made and kept specifically conscious of this fact and to be trained in the habits implied.

Finally, and perhaps most important of all, students have difficulty with verbal problems because there is no single general pattern according to which all verbal problems can be set up. Certain "general methods" have been proposed and are doubtless helpful in systematizing the analysis, but there is, and can be, no formula which will obviate the necessity for alertness, care, ingenuity, and resourcefulness on the part of the student. The solution of equations, the addition of fractions, and many other operations with symbolic algebraic expressions can be reduced to mechanical laws which operate invariably. It is not so with the setting up of verbal problems. Every problem presents its own peculiar elements, relationships, and requirements which must be studied, interpreted, and organized strictly and solely in the light of the conditions and data stated or implied in the problem itself.

Ambiguous terms cause trouble

Perseverance is necessary

There is no one set method for setting up verbal problems

Use of type
problems

It is true that many of the problems customarily found in the textbooks tend to fall into certain general groupings or types. It is also true that several of these types have characteristic formulas which express the relationships involved. To this extent verbal problems may be classified and their solutions somewhat standardized, and for this reason some authors both advocate and practice the procedure of presenting verbal problems according to type. On the other hand, the component elements and the mathematical relationships involved in one type of problem may be entirely unlike those involved in other types. Thus, while a student may be able to set up and solve type problems when he knows to what types they belong, he may be completely at a loss when he attempts to classify problems by type. For this reason the advisability of teaching verbal problems by type seems questionable, at best. It does tend to produce specific classroom results more quickly than any other method, but they are results which are more in the nature of specific skills than general powers. Some authors suggest compromising the situation by supplementing the type lists of problems by unclassified lists of miscellaneous problems, holding that this secures the advantages of teaching problems by type and at the same time avoids the disadvantages. It would seem that this might be an effective compromise, provided that appropriate emphasis were given to the study of the unclassified problems.

In verbal problems,
one must find two
independent ways
to express the same
quantity

In general, verbal problems lead to equations. Therefore, somewhere in the problem, it should be possible to find at least one quantitative element for which two different mathematical expressions can be obtained. This element may be a particular distance, a particular volume, or any one of a variety of quantitative elements. The equality may be expressed specifically, or it may be merely implied. The search for such an element and for the two different ways of expressing it constitutes the analysis of the problem.

Example 1: How much alcohol must be added to a pint of 10 percent solution of iodine to make an 8 percent solution?

Here the quantitative elements in the problem are the amounts of alcohol, the amounts of iodine, and the total amounts of the solutions. If each of these is considered under both the initial and final conditions, it is seen that the element which

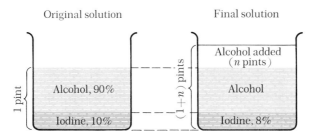

Figure 10-13
Diagram for the iodine-solution problem.

remains quantitatively the same in both cases is the amount of iodine. Thus we get the basic equation:

Original amount of iodine = final amount of iodine

By considering now the composition of each solution and designating by n the number of pints of alcohol to be added to the original solution, we may readily get two different expressions for the amount of iodine. A diagram will be helpful in this case.

It is seen from the diagram (Fig. 10-13) that the original amount of iodine is $^{10}/_{100}$ of 1 pint and the final amount of iodine is $^{8}/_{100}$ of $(1 + n)$ pints. By substituting these expressions in the basic equation given verbally above, we get the equation

$$\frac{10}{100}(1) = \frac{8}{100}(1 + n) \qquad \text{or} \qquad 10 = 8(1 + n)$$

from which the value of n can be found directly.

Example 2: Two trains, 350 miles apart, travel on double tracks toward each other until they meet. Train A travels at an average speed of 55 miles per hour, and train B travels at an average speed of 48 miles per hour. How long will it be after they start before they meet?

Here the elements involved in the two situations are distances, rates, and times. One element, which is the same in the case of both trains, is obviously the time. Thus we may set up our basic equation in words:

Time for train A = time for train B

It remains now merely to get two mathematical expressions representing the time in terms of respective distances and rates of speed. To this end the detailed data should now be tabulated in some such manner as in Table 10-3.

TABLE 10-3

Elements involved	Train A	Train B
Distance traveled, miles	x	$350 - x$
Rate, miles per hour	55	48
Time (distance/rate)	$\dfrac{x}{55}$	$\dfrac{350 - x}{48}$

The substitution of these two expressions for the time in the basic equation given verbally above gives the desired equation in algebraic form:

$$\frac{x}{55} = \frac{350 - x}{48}$$

This may be solved for x, the distance traveled by train A, and since the rate is known, the time can easily be computed.

Another, and perhaps easier, approach to this particular problem may be made by reflecting that the total distance is constant and that two expressions for this distance must be equivalent. One such expression is given explicitly in the problem, namely, $d = 350$ miles. Another may be inferred from the fact that the total distance is the sum of the distances traveled by the two trains. Thus we have a basic equation:

Total distance = total distance
(Miles traveled by train A) + (miles traveled by train B) = (350 miles)

TABLE 10-4

Elements involved	Train A	Train B
Rate, miles per hour	55	48
Time, hours	t	t
Distance traveled, miles	$55t$	$48t$

By again tabulating the data, recalling that the trains travel the same number of hours t, and making use of the relation $d = r \times t$, we have Table 10-4. By substitution in the basic equation, we get the simple equation

$$55t + 48t = 350$$

from which the required length of time can be found directly.

There is more than one way to analyze a problem

The alternative approaches to the above example make it clear that there is considerable latitude in the analysis of many verbal problems and that success depends largely upon the care and ingenuity of the student. The setup of the problem may involve implied relationships which the student must seek in his background of experiences. The student who in his earlier work in arithmetic and informal geometry has accumulated a rich store of ready information about such relationships will have a great advantage in the analysis of problems. It is often possible to make graphic or diagrammatic sketches which are helpful in making the relationships among the elements seem concrete and tangible.

EXERCISES

1 The two most frequent ways to begin the study of algebra are (a) through study of the formula and (b) through study of directed numbers. Give arguments for and against each point of view.

2 Make a formula for determining the score earned in a game of contract bridge by setting the opponents n tricks if the opponents were not vulnerable and not doubled.

3 Make a formula for determining the score of a team in a football game, in terms of t (number of touchdowns made), p (number of successful running or passing plays made after touchdowns), k (number of successful place kicks made after touchdowns), f (number of field goals made), and s (number of safeties made).

4 Let a distance be expressed as x yards, y feet, and z inches. (a) Make a formula that will give this distance in feet alone. (b) Make a formula that will give this distance in yards alone. (c) Make a formula that will give this distance in inches alone.

5 Evaluate the formula $s = (n/2)(a + b)$ for each of these sets of values of a, n, and b:

a	7	2.6	$^4/_5$
n	12	5	10
b	40	7.8	$6^4/_5$

6 Given the formula $w = dF/s$, what is the effect on w in each of the following circumstances? (a) d is doubled, and F and s remain unchanged. (b) Both d and F are doubled, but s remains unchanged. (c) d, F, and s are all doubled. (d) d and F remain unchanged, but s is doubled. (e) d is halved, s is doubled, and F is tripled.

7 In the two formulas $P = xy$ and $Q = x + y$, compare the effects on P and Q (a) of doubling x but leaving y unchanged, (b) of doubling y but leaving x unchanged, (c) of doubling both x and y.

8 Generalize your results of exercise 7 and state the generalization as a rule of action.

9 How would you make clear to a class the distinction between constants and variables? Between domain and range of a function?

10 Explain how the checking of solutions of equations gives good training in precisely the same kinds of mathematical activities as those used in the evaluation of formulas. Be specific.

11 In this chapter "formalism" in algebra is deplored, but the formalization of algebraic procedures is held to be important. Review the discussion of these two concepts, and make the contrast between the two clear.

12 Criticize or support the assertion that the very essence of algebra lies in the generalization of its concepts and the formalization of its procedures.

13 Which is the more important to the average student from the standpoint of later application, the ability to construct graphs or the ability to interpret graphs readily? Does the one imply the other? Discuss the pedagogical implications of your answers.

14 Do you think drill is needed in learning algebra? Give arguments in support of your viewpoint.

Prove each of the following theorems for real numbers:

15 $a - (-b) = a + b$

16 $(-a) + (-b) = -(a + b)$

17 $(-a) \times (b) = (a) \times (-b) = -(a \times b)$

18 $(-a) \times (-b) = a \times b$

19 For x an integer, let $S = \{x | 0 < x < 30\}$ and $T = \{x | 5 \leqslant x \leqslant 42\}$. What is the set $S \cap T$?

20 Use the definition $a > b$ if and only if $a - b$ is a positive number to prove that if $a > b$ and $b > c$, then $a > c$.

21 If X, Y, Z are sets, $X \subset Y, Y \subset Z$, is it necessarily true that $X \subset Z$ is true? Compare with exercise 20.

22 If a and b are real numbers and $a \neq b$, then either $a < b$ or $b < a$. If A and B are sets and $A \neq B$, is it necessarily true that either $A \subset B$ or $B \subset A$? (Note that sets are said to be equal if and only if they contain exactly the same elements.)

23 Make a careful large-scale graphic solution of the system of equations $2a + 5b = {}^{29}/_4$ and $7a - b = {}^{9}/_4$. Consider the domain of each of the variables a and b to be the set of real numbers. Explain your work, estimate the solution as nearly as you can from the

graph, and tell what the numerical values represent. Check your solution by substituting the values of a and b in both equations.

24 Consider the two relations $x + y \geqslant 2$ and $2x + y = 4$ with the domains of both x and y the set of integers such that $-3 \leqslant x \leqslant +4$ and $-2 \leqslant y \leqslant +5$.

   a. Draw the graph of each relation.

   b. What is the solution set when the two relations are considered simultaneously?

   c. What is the solution set for the two relations when the "is greater than" ($>$) is removed from $x + y \geqslant 2$?

25 Rework all parts of exercise 24, but this time let the domains of both x and y be the set of all real numbers.

26 Consider the following problem: The length of a rectangle is 2 inches less than twice its width, and its perimeter is 20 inches. What are its dimensions? Solve this problem by using just one equation in one variable. Then solve it by using two equations in two variables. Show that in the first case you really used two equations in two variables but solved one of them mentally.

27 It frequently happens that beginning algebra students who can combine numerical fractions have trouble in performing the same operations with fractions involving literal symbols. What, in your opinion, is the explanation of this?

28 Why is it important that students learn how to factor algebraic expressions before undertaking work with algebraic fractions?

29 In the process of reducing a fraction or changing it to higher terms, the original value of the fraction must be preserved. Explain why the value of a fraction is changed if the same nonzero number is added to or subtracted from both the numerator and the denominator of the fraction.

30 Point out the potential dangers of using the terms "cancel" and "cancellation" in elementary algebra. Give examples to illustrate.

31 In dividing one fraction by another, the rule generally used is: Invert the divisor, then multiply. Most students know this rule and know how to use it, but very few can justify it. If a student should ask you why the rule is valid, what explanation would you give him?

32 Explain as simply as you can the procedure

for converting fractions with unlike denominators into equivalent fractions having the same denominator. Give the reasoning that underlies and justifies the procedure.

33 If one of your students should write $a/x + 5/(x + 3) = (a + 5)/(2x + 3)$, just what would you do to get him to see his error and understand why it is an error? What would you do to help him understand how to correct his mistake and check his result?

34 If fractions are used in addition, it is necessary to preserve the original numbers represented by the fractions involved. Explain why this is not necessary in solving equations containing fractions. Explain what it is that must be preserved in such equations.

35 Students characteristically have difficulty in reading verbal problems with understanding, interpreting them correctly, and translating them into the symbolic language of the equation. How serious is the handicap imposed by these shortcomings? What, if anything, can be done about it?

36 Verbal problems usually are solved by solving one or more equations arising from the problems. Explain why, in checking the solutions, it is necessary to check them in the actual statements of the problems and why it is not enough merely to check them against the equations.

37 Rules and formulas of algebra can often be illustrated effectively by numerical examples. For instance, the general relation $a^2 - b^2 = (a - b)(a + b)$ can be illustrated by expressing 21 as $25 - 4$, or as $5^2 - 2^2$, and in turn as $(5 - 2)(5 + 2)$, or (3)(7). Select other algebraic rules and illustrate them in a similar manner. Do you think this practice would serve to clarify the meanings of the rules to the students?

BIBLIOGRAPHY

Adkins, Jackson B.: Goals in Algebra, *Mathematics Teacher,* **47** (1954), 368–370.

Alspaugh, John W.: The Relationship between High School Algebra and the Algebra of Computers, *School Science and Mathematics,* **68** (1968), 193–198.

Anderson, Rosemary C.: Let's Consider the Function!, *Arithmetic Teacher,* **14** (1967), 280–284.

Barnes, Ward Ewing, and John William Asher: Predicting Students' Success in First-year Algebra, *Mathematics Teacher,* **55** (1962), 651–654.

Beberman, Max, and Bruce E. Meserve: The Concept of a Literal Number Symbol, *Mathematics Teacher,* **48** (1955), 198–202.

_____ and _____: An Exploratory Approach to Solving Equations, *Mathematics Teacher,* **49** (1956), 15–18.

Bellman, Richard: On the Concepts of a Problem and Problem-solving, *American Mathematical Monthly,* **67** (1960), 119–134.

Bradford, Donald L.: The Majesty of Numbers, *Mathematics Teacher,* **60** (1967), 588–592.

Brown, C. Dale: Let's Prove It!, *Arithmetic Teacher,* **7** (1960), 154–155.

Brown, Stephen I.: Signed Numbers: A "Product" of Misconceptions, *Mathematics Teacher,* **62** (1969), 183–195.

Brumfiel, Charles: An Introduction to Negative Integers, *Mathematics Teacher,* **49** (1956), 260–266.

Butler, Charles H.: Home-made Problems for Algebra, *Mathematics Teacher,* **45** (1952), 384–386.

_____: A Note on Writing Fractions, *Mathematics Teacher,* **47** (1954), 527.

Calandra, Alexander: Teaching Signed Numbers in Grade 8, *Arithmetic Teacher,* **5** (1958), 259–260.

Clair, Harry S.: Factoring the Quadratic Trinomial, *Mathematics Teacher,* **51** (1958), 26–27.

Clark, J. F.: A Concrete Approach to Elementary Algebra, *Mathematics Teacher,* **53** (1960), 285–287.

Clements, C. Robert: Work Problems Made Easy, *Mathematics Teacher,* **48** (1955), 582–585.

Cohen, Louis S.: A Rationale in Working Signed Numbers—Revisited, *Arithmetic Teacher,* **13** (1966) 564–567.

Coltharp, Forrest L.: Introducing the Integers as Ordered Pairs, *School Science and Mathematics,* **66** (1966), 277–282.

Commission on Mathematics: "Concepts of Equation and Inequality" (New York: College Entrance Examination Board, 1958). (Sample classroom unit for high school algebra students.)

Condit, Martha C.: From Algebra to Geometry in Four Easy Lessons, *Mathematics Teacher,* **57** (1964), 40–41.

Crosby, Gwladys, and Herbert Fremont: Individualized Algebra, *Mathematics Teacher,* **53** (1960), 109–112.

Dolorsa, Mary A.: More on Factoring the Tri-nomial, *Mathematics Teacher*, **49** (1956), 304.

Entwhistle, Alice: Subtracting Signed Numbers, *Mathematics Teacher*, **48** (1955), 175–176.

Fogo, James D.: Linear Indeterminate Problems, *Mathematics Teacher*, **57** (1964), 223–225.

Forbes, Jack E.: The Most Difficult Step in the Teaching of School Mathematics: From Rational Numbers to Real Numbers—with Meaning, *School Science and Mathematics*, **67** (1967), 799–813.

Gold, Sheldon: Graphing Linear Equations: A Discovery Lesson, *Arithmetic Teacher*, **13** (1966), 406–407.

Green, Thomas M.: The Graphing of Absolute Value Inequalities, *Mathematics Teacher*, **60** (1967), 837–838.

Hannon, Herbert: A Device for Teaching Addition and Subtraction of Integers, *Mathematics Teacher*, **60** (1967), 860–861.

Henderson, K. B., and R. E. Pingry: Problem Solving in Mathematics, *Twenty-first Yearbook* (Washington, D.C.: National Council of Teachers of Mathematics, 1953), pp. 228–270.

Holder, Doyne: Factoring Trinomials $ax^2 + bx + c$ when $a > 1$, *School Science and Mathematics*, **58** (1958), 548–549.

———: Polynomials: Factorable or Non-factorable, *School Science and Mathematics*, **62** (1962), 22–25.

Hursh, Ronald E.: The Number Line in the Junior High School, *Arithmetic Teacher*, **13** (1966), 553–555.

Johnson, Donovan A., and William H. Glenn: "Sets, Sentences, and Operations" (New York: McGraw-Hill Book Company, 1960).

Kaner, P. A.: The Addition and Subtraction of Negative Numbers, *Mathematical Gazette*, **48** (1964), 183–185.

Klimczak, W. J.: The Solution of Linear Equations and Inequalities, *Mathematics Teacher*, **48** (1955), 460–463.

Kocher, Frank T., and Ralph T. Heimer: Techniques of Solving Rational Equations, *Mathematics Teacher*, **56** (1963), 486–489.

Koenen, William: Illustrating Simple Transformations, *Mathematics Teacher*, **49** (1956), 467–468.

Leake, Lowell: An Iterative Application for Elementary Algebra, *Mathematics Teacher*, **57** (1964), 12–15.

Lichtenberg, Don R., and Marilyn Zweng: Linear Programming Problems for First-year Algebra, *Mathematics Teacher*, **53** (1960), 171–176.

Mallory, Curtiss: Intuitive Approach to $x° = 1$, *Mathematics Teacher*, **60** (1967), 41.

Manheim, Jerome: Word Problems or Problems with Words, *Mathematics Teacher*, **54** (1961), 234–238.

McGarvey, Paul: Programmed Instruction in Ninth-grade Algebra, *Mathematics Teacher*, **55** (1962), 576–579.

Meadows, George C.: Let's Modernize Graph Teaching, *Arithmetic Teacher*, **10** (1963), 286–287.

Merriman, Gaylord M.: Sets and Some Elementary Problems, *Mathematics Teacher*, **53** (1960), 266–269.

Meserve, Bruce E.: New Trends in Algebra and Geometry, *Mathematics Teacher*, **55** (1962), 452–461.

——— and Max A. Sobel: "Mathematics for Secondary School Teachers" (Englewood Cliffs, N.J.: Prentice-Hall, Inc., 1962), pp. 77–173.

Messler, Dorothy L.: A Study of Pupil Age and Achievement in Eighth-grade Algebra, *Mathematics Teacher*, **54** (1961), 561–564.

"Modern Elementary Algebra" (Chicago: Society for Visual Education, Inc., 1963). (Two sets of filmstrips in color.)

"Modern Mathematics" (New York: McGraw-Hill Book Company, 1963). (Filmstrips on set theory.)

Moser, James M.: A Geometric Approach to the Algebra of Solution of Pairs of Equations, *School Science and Mathematics*, **67** (1967), 217–220.

Mueller, Francis J.: Building Algebra Readiness in Grades Seven and Eight, *Arithmetic Teacher*, **6** (1959), 269–273.

Murray, Pete: Intuitive Approach to $a^{-m} = 1/a^m$, *Mathematics Teacher*, **60** (1967), 737.

Myers, Sheldon S. (Editor): Applications, *Mathematics Teacher*, **45** (1952), 210–214, 522–524.

O'Brien, Katherine: Problem Solving, *Mathematics Teacher*, **49** (1956), 79–86.

Perisho, Clarence R.: A Non-commutative Algebra, *School Science and Mathematics*, **58** (1958), 727–730.

———: Curves with Corners, *Mathematics Teacher*, **55** (1962), 326–329.

Peskin, Anne S.: Geometric Representation of Binomial by Binomial—Laboratory Style, *Arithmetic Teacher*, **15** (1968), 40.

Rheins, Joel J., and Gladys B. Rheins: The Additive Inverse in Elementary Algebra, *Mathematics Teacher*, **54** (1961), 538–539.

Rich, Barnett: The Place of the Variable in

the Teaching of Mathematics, *Mathematics Teacher*, **48** (1955), 538–541.

Schaaf, William L.: "Basic Concepts of Elementary Mathematics" (New York: John Wiley & Sons, Inc., 1960).

School Mathematics Study Group: "Intermediate Mathematics" (New Haven, Conn.: Yale University Press, 1959).

———: "Elementary Functions" (New Haven, Conn.: Yale University Press, 1960).

———: "First Course in Algebra" (New Haven, Conn.: Yale University Press, 1960).

———: "Mathematics for Junior High School" (New Haven, Conn.: Yale University Press, 1960).

Singleton, Marilyn C.: An Approach to Solving Word Problems, *Mathematics Teacher*, **51** (1958), 212–213.

Swain, Robert L.: The Equation, *Mathematics Teacher*, **55** (1962), 226–236.

Taylor, Ross: First Course in Algebra—UICSM and SMSG: A Comparison, *Mathematics Teacher*, **55** (1962), 478–481.

Trine, F. Dawson: An Introduction to Algebra with Inequalities, *Mathematics Teacher*, **53** (1960), 42–45.

UICSM Project Staff: Arithmetic with Frames, *Arithmetic Teacher*, **4** (1957), 119–124.

Van Engen, Henry: Logical Approaches to $(-a)(-b) = ab$ and $x° = 1$, *Mathematics Teacher*, **40** (1947), 182–185.

Vavoulis, Alex: Teaching the Linear Equation in Intermediate Algebra, *School Science and Mathematics*, **62** (1962), 261–263.

Webber, G. Cuthbert, and John A. Brown: "Basic Concepts of Mathematics" (Reading, Mass.: Addison-Wesley Publishing Company, Inc., 1963).

Williams, Kenneth C.: The Three Faces of $(-)$, *Mathematics Teacher*, **55** (1962), 668–669.

Winthrop, Henry: The Structure of Simple Problems and Their Solutions, *School Science and Mathematics*, **63** (1963), 38–42.

Wollan, G. N.: What Is a Function?, *Mathematics Teacher*, **53** (1960), 96–101.

eleven | the teaching of algebra in the senior high school

The subject matter of algebra is very cumulative; hence at the higher levels it makes continual use of the concepts, principles, and operations developed in the first course at the same time that new concepts, new principles, and new operations are introduced and studied. From one standpoint the broader objectives of the instruction at the more advanced level offer certain points of contrast with the objectives of the junior high school. In particular, the elective status of the higher courses implies a somewhat different personnel in such classes. The students are likely to be inherently more interested and capable than typical junior high school students. It is also quite probable that they are studying algebra because of its usefulness in academic or professional fields. In view of these facts, the technical aspects of algebra may legitimately come to occupy a relatively more important place among the instructional aims. This, of course, does not imply any lessening of the emphasis upon understanding, but it does imply a progressively increasing insistence upon the mastery of the algebraic tools.

Contrast with junior high school algebra

REVIEW WORK IN BEGINNING INTERMEDIATE ALGEBRA

Review must be purposeful

In beginning the second course in algebra, teachers generally find it necessary to make some review of the work of elementary algebra. Indeed, most textbooks in the more advanced algebra courses begin with several chapters which are essentially reviews of various phases of the earlier work. Much time may be wasted in this review work, however, unless it is carefully and purposefully planned. It is well at the outset to take a rather careful inventory of the algebraic equipment of the class. This may be done by administering a comprehensive inventory test. If it is done at the beginning and if the results are immediately tabulated and analyzed, it is possible for the teacher to have very soon a fairly accurate picture of the needs of the class for review work. If these tabulated results are used as a basis for planning and conducting the review, it will be possible to concentrate attention on those topics for which the need is evident and to dispense with unnecessary work.

There is an advantage in spreading the review over some two or three weeks and giving it in small doses, interspersed with new work, instead of concentrating it all in the first few days and leaving it as finished business. When students get nothing but review work for several days, it becomes tiresome. Some new work offered along with the review provides both variety and incentive. The distribution of time in this way also makes for more effective learning. Among the things which are likely to need special attention in this review work may be mentioned the language of algebra, positive and negative numbers, easy formal work in the fundamental operations, review of the field postulates, the solutions of literal equations, and easy work with fractions.

Review should be spaced

Special attention should also be given to topics that must be extended or generalized. The ideas to be extended should be thoroughly reviewed in preparation for the extension: for example, the laws of exponents, in preparation for an extension of the domain of definition; and solution of two linear equations in two variables, in preparation for the study of systems of three and more equations in three and more variables.

Review should prepare for extensions and generalizations

A part of the continuing review will of necessity be an incidental part of the ongoing progress of the class. Many students find themselves confused, and their progress blocked, because of lack of understanding of some apparently minor point that is in fact a critical detail of the work. In many cases the difficulty can be removed by the teacher by merely calling attention to it. For example, students frequently fail to recognize equivalent or identical algebraic expressions merely because of their form. The following are illustrative:

Equivalent expressions are frequently not recognized

$$\frac{2}{3}\,xy, \ \frac{2x}{3}\,y, \ 2y\,\frac{x}{3}\ 2\,\frac{xy}{3}\ \frac{2xy}{3}$$

$$\frac{1}{2}\,h(b+B), \ \frac{h}{2}\,(b+B), \ \frac{b+B}{2}\,h, \ \text{and} \ \frac{(b+B)h}{2}$$

$\sqrt{7x}$ and $\sqrt{7}\times\sqrt{x}$

$\dfrac{\sqrt{x}}{\sqrt{y}}$ and $\sqrt{\dfrac{x}{y}}$

$\left(\dfrac{x}{y}\right)^3$ and $\dfrac{x^3}{y^3}$

x^3y^3 and $(xy)^3$

Such mistakes as

$$r(x+y)(a+b)=(rx+ry)(ra+rb) \qquad \text{or} \qquad 3\,\frac{a}{b}=\frac{3a}{3b}$$

undoubtedly stem from a misconception of the meaning of the distributive property. The former example is more inviting to mistakes than the latter. Both illustrate the misconception that multiplication is distributive over multiplication and division. Another type of error is also represented by

Meaning of laws is
sometimes not
clear

$$3\frac{a}{b} = \frac{3a}{3b}$$

Here the error has occurred in applying the definition of the product of two rational numbers. In this case the error is largely due to failure to recognize the integer 3 as a rational number:

$$3 = \frac{3}{1}$$

Mistakes such as these are common in the use of exponents, for example, $x^2 \times y^3 = xy^5$, $x^2 + x^3 = x^5$, $(a^2)^3 = a^5$, $a^2(b^2) = ab^4$. Many other illustrations could be given. The correct interpretations can be explained easily to the entire satisfaction of the students by dealing with them deliberately and specifically. This instruction, however, needs to be more than superficial; it needs to stress the basic principles that apply to the particular situation.

Emphasize under-
lying principles

EXPONENTS AND RADICALS

The first course in algebra should provide a thorough mastery of the laws governing positive integral exponents. Although negative and zero exponents may have been introduced, they should be reviewed in preparation for rational exponents and general radicals.

Students frequently have difficulty understanding why the definition must be extended whenever the domain of the definition for exponents is extended. This may stem from the fact that operations with positive integral exponents have become so routinized that the original justification for them is no longer evident.

Why it is necessary
to extend the
definition as the
domain is extended

Since

$$x^a \times x^b = x^{a+b}$$
$$x^0 \times x^b = x^{0+b} = x^b$$

But

$$1 \times x^b = x^b$$

Therefore

$$x^0 = 1$$

Why $a^0 = 1$ has
not been proved
yet

Why is this not a proof that $x^0 = 1$? This situation can be used to illustrate more than one point. The rule of exponents in multiplication, the first statement in the above "proof," was established only for positive integral exponents. This emphasizes the need for quantifiers. Unless the statement is universally true, the set of values for which it is true must be stated. The first statement does not justify the second. The correct statement for the rule is: For a any positive integer and b any positive integer, $x^a \times x^b = x^{a+b}$. It should be pointed out to the students that this rule must always lead to a positive integer as exponent since the positive integers are closed with respect to addition.

When natural numbers are taken as the basic elements, the commutative, associative, and distributive properties are usually taken as axioms. When the extension is made to signed numbers, two avenues of approach are open: (1) the axioms of commutativity, associativity, and distributivity are assumed for all "numbers" and the rules of signs can be proved, or (2) the rules of signs are imbedded in the definition of signed numbers, and the commutative, associative, and distributive properties are proved in the new number domain.

For example, the proof that $(-a)(-b) = ab$ is well known. If we accept the distributive property as an axiom and if the result

Proof of rules of signs

$a(-b) = -ab$ has already been demonstrated, the result $(-a)(-b) = ab$ can be shown as follows:

$$(-a)[b + (-b)] = (-a) \times 0 = 0$$
$$-ab + (-a)(-b) = 0$$

Therefore $(-a)(-b)$ is the additive inverse of $-ab$, which is ab.

$$(-a)(-b) = ab$$

Proof of distributive law

On the other hand, let a, b, c be natural numbers, $b < c$. The definition of integers includes the laws of signs, and the distributive property is accepted for multiplication over either addition or subtraction of natural numbers. If the commutative property has already been established for integers, one case of the distributive property can be established as follows:

If $b < c$, then $c - b$ is a natural number, and $b + -c = -(c - b)$ by definition of addition of integers with $c > b$.

$$-a(b + -c) = -a[-(c - b)]$$

and from the law of signs for multiplication,

$$-a[-(c - b)] = a(c - b).$$

But since the distributive law holds for subtraction of natural numbers,

$$a(c - b) = ac - ab$$

and

$$ac - ab = ac + -ab = -ab + ac$$

since the commutative law has been established for integers.

And from the law of signs for multiplication, we have

$$-ab + ac = (-a)b + -(-a)(-c)$$

Then, applying the transitive property,

$$-a(b + -c) = (-a)b + (-a)(-c)$$

The situation in regard to exponents is somewhat, but not completely, analogous to either of these approaches to signed numbers. Positive integral exponents are defined; then rules of operation *with positive integral exponents* are made plausible. Rigorous proof of the rules in the domain of positive integral exponents is possible, but it requires the use of mathematical induction. The domain of the original definition cannot be extended. If the exponent indicates the number of times the base is used as a factor, any exponent other than a positive integer is meaningless. If other kinds of numbers are to be used as exponents, they must be defined, in any meaningful way one chooses.

The choice of definition is dictated by the objective of permanence for the rules of operation. When the extended definitions are made, it can then be proved that the rules of operation are valid in the extended domain.

The motivation for the definition of negative integral exponents is similar to that for the definition of the exponent zero. If the restriction m, n positive integers and $m > n$ is relaxed, the rule for division,

$$a^m \div a^n = a^{m-n}$$

becomes, on substituting $m = 0$,

$$a^0 \div a^n = a^{-n} \qquad a \neq 0$$

But since $a^0 = 1$ by definition,

$a^0 \div a^n$ is equivalent to $1 \div a^n$

Hence

$$1 \div a^n = a^{-n}$$

Thus it immediately follows that a justified interpretation of a negative exponent is that it indicates the reciprocal of the same nonzero quantity raised to the corresponding positive exponent.

We cannot give meaning to fractional exponents until we define roots of numbers. The students should have gained from their arithmetic some understanding of the meaning of square roots and cube roots of numbers and of the symbols $\sqrt{}$ and $\sqrt[3]{}$. It is best, however, not to assume too much on this point. The square root of a number should be explicitly redefined as one of its two equal factors, the cube root as one of its three equal factors, etc., and the appropriate symbols should be carefully reassociated with their respective meanings.

A real problem, which frequently causes trouble at this point, is that of the proper interpretation of the radical symbols. Although there are two square roots of a number, the symbol $\sqrt{}$ represents only the positive square root. For example, $\sqrt{16} = 4$. Only the symbol $\pm\sqrt{16}$ can represent both square roots ± 4. Similarly, there exist n nth roots of any number, and the symbol $\sqrt[n]{}$ refers only to one such root, called the *principal nth root* in accordance with the definition.

Principal roots

Definition. For x any real number and n an integer greater than 1, the principal nth root of x^n is $\sqrt[n]{x^n}$, where

1 For n even: $\quad\begin{cases} \sqrt[n]{x^n} = x \text{ if } x \geq 0 \\ \sqrt[n]{x^n} = -x \text{ if } x < 0 \end{cases}$

2 For n odd: $\quad \sqrt[n]{x^n} = x$

Examples: $\sqrt{3^2} = 3 \qquad \sqrt{(-3)^2} = -(-3) = 3 \qquad \sqrt[n]{0^4} = 0$
$\sqrt[3]{(-2)^3} = -2 \qquad \sqrt[3]{2^3} = 2$

The n nth roots of the real number c may be obtained as the solution set of the equation $x^n = c$. If $c < 0$ and n is even, the above definitions do not define the principal nth root of c; for example, they leave $\sqrt{-4}$ undefined.

A number has n nth roots

From the definition of square root, $(\sqrt{y})(\sqrt{y}) = y$. Also, if there were a number represented by the symbol $y^{1/2}$ and if it were subject to the laws of multiplication by exponents, then we should have $(y^{1/2})(y^{1/2}) = y^1 = y$. Now since $\sqrt{y}$ is one of two equal positive factors whose product is y, and since $y^{1/2}$ may also represent one of two equal positive factors whose product is y, we may reasonably agree to think of $y^{1/2}$ and $\sqrt{y}$ as representing the same number. In other words, we may reasonably agree that $y^{1/2}$ shall have the same meaning as $\sqrt{y}$. Similarly, the corresponding meanings may be attached to such expressions as $y^{1/3}$, $y^{1/4}$, $y^{1/5}$, etc.

In accordance with these definitions $(x^n)^{1/n}$ may be used, synonymously with $\sqrt[n]{x^n}$, to represent the principal nth root of x^n. Thus $(3^2)^{1/2} = 3$, $[(-3)^2]^{1/2} = -(-3) = 3$, $(2^3)^{1/3} = 2$, and $[(-2)^3]^{1/3} = -2$.

Since these meanings have been arrived at by defining these fractional exponents in such a way that they will be subject to the laws of operation formulated for positive integral exponents, we may now apply those laws in such cases as $(y^{1/3})(y^{1/3})$. This obviously gives $y^{(1/3+1/3)}$, or $y^{2/3}$. It is equally clear that we have here $(y^{1/3})^2$. It is also clear that $(y^2)^{1/3}$ would give the same result, since $(y^2)^{1/3} = y^{2(1/3)} = y^{2/3}$.

Fractional exponents are consistent with rules of operation

By using numerous illustrative examples, carefully selected and arranged to bring out these analogies and identities, the students can be brought to understand what fractional exponents represent. In many cases the students themselves will be able to formulate the general relation that $x^{p/r}$ means the pth power of the principal rth root of x or the principal rth root of the pth power of x.

MORE ABOUT SIMULTANEOUS LINEAR EQUATIONS

Concept of a matrix

When more than two equations are involved in a system of linear equations, the most effective techniques for solving are based on the concept of a rectangular array of the coefficients of the system. Such a rectangular array is called a *matrix*. Consider the system of equations

$$x - y + 2z = 5 \tag{1}$$
$$4x - 2y + 3z = 9 \tag{2}$$
$$3x + 4y - 5z = -4 \tag{3}$$

There are basically two matrices associated with such a system of equations, the *coefficient matrix* and the *augmented matrix*. The coefficient matrix is merely the rectangular array consisting of the coefficients of the system. Here it is

Coefficient matrix

$$\begin{pmatrix} 1 & -1 & 2 \\ 4 & -2 & 3 \\ 3 & 4 & -5 \end{pmatrix}$$

The augmented matrix is obtained by annexing to the coefficient matrix the column of constant terms. The augmented matrix of the above system is

Augmented matrix

$$\begin{pmatrix} 1 & -1 & 2 & 5 \\ 4 & -2 & 3 & 9 \\ 3 & 4 & -5 & -4 \end{pmatrix}$$

The two methods to be discussed here are essentially methods of synthetic elimination in that the process is concerned with the detached coefficients of a system of equations as displayed in the augmented matrix of the system. No proof will be given of the validity of either technique, but a bit of careful examination will reveal the fact that each technique is closely related to the process of elimination by addition or subtraction.

The Pivotal-element Method

Consider the elements of the augmented matrix of the foregoing system of equations with a column in which each element is the sum of the numbers in the row in which it occurs (Table 11-1). In row 1, for example, $7 = 1 + (-1) + 2 + 5$. The technique of the pivotal-element method involves the selection of any nonzero element of the coefficient matrix as the pivotal element. If there is

TABLE 11-1

	x	y	z	c	S
(1)	1	−1	2	5	7
(2)	4	−2	3	9	14
(3)	3	4	−5	−4	−2
(2′)		2	−5	−11	−14
(3′)		7	−11	−19	−23
(3″)			(13	39)	52

a 1 among these coefficients, it should be used in order to simplify the computation as much as possible. Here the coefficient of x in the first equation is 1, and it is chosen as the pivotal element. The row and column to which this chosen element belongs are then

Equation of the pivotal element is eliminated

blocked out (here row 1 and column 1). The augmented matrix is then transformed in the following manner:

1 Each element of the augmented matrix, not included in either the row or the column which is blocked out, is replaced by a determinant of order two. The corresponding elements of the sum column are replaced in the same manner. For example, the elements of the second row in the matrix of the given system of equations, which are to be replaced, are −2, 3, 9, and 14.

If we use P to represent the pivotal element and R to represent the replaced element, then, for this illustration, P is 1 and R is, in turn, −2, 3, 9, and 14. For equation (3) R will be 4, −5, −4, and −2, respectively, while P, of course, remains 1. The symbol e_{pr} will be used to represent the element in the same row as the pivotal element and the same column as the replaced element, and e_{rp} will represent the element in the same row as the replaced element and the same column as the pivotal element.

2 Construct the determinant

Evaluating a second-order determinant

$$\begin{vmatrix} P & e_{pr} \\ e_{rp} & R \end{vmatrix} = PR - e_{pr}e_{rp}$$

for each element which is to be replaced. For example,

$$-2 \text{ is replaced by } \begin{vmatrix} 1 & -1 \\ 4 & -2 \end{vmatrix} = (1)(-2) - (-1)(4) = 2$$

$$3 \text{ is replaced by } \begin{vmatrix} 1 & 2 \\ 4 & 3 \end{vmatrix} = (1)(3) - (2)(4) = -5$$

$$9 \text{ is replaced by } \begin{vmatrix} 1 & 5 \\ 4 & 9 \end{vmatrix} = (1)(9) - (5)(4) = -11$$

14 is replaced by $\begin{vmatrix} 1 & 7 \\ 4 & 14 \end{vmatrix} = (1)(14) - (7)(4) = -14$

The elements in row 3 are replaced in a similar manner.

3 The new element in the sum column must be equal to the sum of the remaining elements in the same row. For example,

$$-14 = 2 + (-5) + (-11)$$

A running check This is a good rapid check, but it is not an infallible check. If the equality does not hold, there is an error. It should be evident, however, that owing to the possibility of compensating errors, the equality might still hold even in the event that errors were present.

4 Continue the process, each time choosing as the pivotal element a nonzero element from the transformed coefficient matrix. Each transformation has the effect of eliminating the variable for which the pivotal element was the coefficient. For example, if x were eliminated by subtraction from the above system of equations, the resulting system would be the two equations whose coefficients are displayed in rows 2' and 3'. Since 2, a coefficient of y, is chosen as the pivotal element in the second transformation, the row 3" represents the equation $13z = 39$.

5 From the final equation determine the value of one of the variables. Use this value in an equation of the immediately preceding system to evaluate a second variable. Use these two values to evaluate a third variable, and continue until values for all variables have been determined. For example, $13z = 39$ gives $z = 3$; use either 2' or 3' to find $y = 2$; use either 1, 2, or 3 to find $x = 1$. Check the results in the remaining equations of the original system.

In the above discussion of the pivotal-element technique, three equations with simple integral coefficients were chosen. All the computations can be made mentally in all such cases. The process is effective for any number of equations and with complicated coefficients. In such cases computing machines can make the computations effectively and rapidly, the most difficult problem being the control on the proper number of significant digits to retain in the rounding process that becomes necessary.

There are systems of equations which do not produce unique solutions. In such cases some of the variables may be expressed in *Interpreting the result* terms of the remaining variables. If a system of equations in n variables is such that r of the variables can be expressed in terms of the remaining $n - r$ variables, then the pivotal-element technique will produce proportional rows after $r - 1$ transformations.

For example, consider the system of equations

$$2x - 3y + z - u = -1 \tag{1}$$
$$3x + y - z + 2u = 5 \tag{2}$$
$$5x - 2y + u = 4 \tag{3}$$
$$5x + 9y - 5z + 8u = 17 \tag{4}$$

Table 11-2 shows the augmented matrix with the sum column.

TABLE 11-2

	x	y	z	u	c	S
(1)	2	-3	1	-1	-1	-2
(2)	3	1	-1	2	5	10
(3)	5	-2	0	1	4	8
(4)	5	9	-5	8	17	34
(2')	5	-2		1	4	8
(3')	5	-2		1	4	8
(4')	15	-6		3	12	24

One transformation has produced rows which are proportional; so two of the variables may be expressed in terms of the remaining $4 - 2$, or 2, variables. For example, from row 2', $u = 4 - 5x + 2y$. This value, used in equation (1), gives $z = 3 - 7x + 5y$. These values will check in equations (3) and (4).

The determinant that replaces each element

It is important to note that the determinant $\begin{vmatrix} P & e_{pr} \\ e_{rp} & R \end{vmatrix}$ is used to replace the element R, although the pivotal element P is not in the first column. The rows and columns in which P and R occur have no effect on the second-order determinant used to replace R.

In the illustrative example the number of equations is the same as the number of the variables. This is not necessary. Furthermore, if a system of m linear equations in n variables is inconsistent, this transformation procedure will result in an augmented matrix with nonzero elements only in the augmented matrix.[1]

The Sweep-out Process

This process is quite similar to the pivotal-element process. Again, consider the augmented matrix of the first system of equations. (See Table 11-3.) In each row divide all elements by the element which is the coefficient of x in the corresponding equation. (If this coefficient is zero, use the first nonzero element in the row.)

[1] For a more detailed discussion of this technique, see F. Lynwood Wren and John W. Lindsay, "Basic Algebraic Concepts" (New York: McGraw-Hill Book Company, 1969), pp. 255–272.

TABLE 11-3

		x	y	z	c	S
(1)		1	−1	2	5	7
(2)		4	−2	3	9	14
(3)		3	4	−5	−4	−2
(1′)		1	−1	2	5	7
(2′)		1	−1/2	3/4	9/4	7/2
(3′)		1	4/3	−5/3	−4/3	−2/3
(4)	[(2′) − (1′)]	1/2	−5/4	−11/4		−7/2
(5)	[(3′) − (1′)]	7/3	−11/3	−19/3		−23/3
(4′)		1	−5/2	−11/2		−7
(5′)		1	−11/7	−19/7		−23/7
(6)	[(5′) − (4′)]		13/14	39/14		26/7

This process produces equations (1′), (2′), and (3′). Subtract the elements of row 1′ from the corresponding elements of rows 2′ and 3′ to produce rows 4 and 5, respectively. This has, in effect, eliminated x from the three equations and produced two equations in two variables, y and z. Divide the elements in rows 4 and 5 by the leading nonzero coefficient to produce rows 4′ and 5′ and then subtract 4′ from 5′. This operation has, in effect, eliminated y from the two equations, leaving the one equation,

$$\frac{13}{14} z = \frac{39}{14} \text{ or } z = 3$$

This value of z can be substituted in row 4′, 5′, 4, or 5 to determine

TABLE 11-4

		x	y	z	c	S
(1)		5	−1	−2	11	13
(2)		3	−2	1	9	11
(3)		2	1	−3	7	7
(1′)		1	−1/5	−2/5	11/5	13/5
(2′)		1	−2/3	1/3	3	11/3
(3′)		1	1/2	−3/2	7/2	7/2
(4)	[(2′) − (1′)]	−7/15	11/15	12/15		16/15
(5)	[(3′) − (1′)]	7/10	−11/10	13/10		9/10
(4′)		1	−11/7	−12/7		−16/7
(5′)		1	−11/7	13/7		9/7
(6)	[(5′) − (4′)]		0	25/7		25/7

All but one
variable are
eliminated

a value for y. The values of y and z can then be substituted in any one of the three original equations to determine a value for x. The three values thus determined can then be checked in the remaining two equations.

The check column As in the pivotal-element method, each operation can be checked by the fact that the element in the sum column must be the same as the sum of the remaining elements in that row.

If the system of equations is inconsistent, either method will establish this fact. Consider the system

$$5x - y - 2z = 11$$
$$3x - 2y + z = 9$$
$$2x + y - 3z = 7$$

An inconsistent system produces a false final relation Using the sweep-out method, we have Table 11-4. In row 6 the matrix $(0 \quad {}^{25}/_7)$ represents the contradiction $0 \times x = {}^{25}/_7$.

Although the two techniques have been used to solve only one each of systems having a unique solution, solvable for $n - r$ variables in terms of r variables, or inconsistent equations, both techniques are general.

SOLVING QUADRATIC EQUATIONS IN ONE VARIABLE

Five methods for solving quadratic equations are commonly taught. They are (1) solving by the graphical method, (2) solving Five methods for solving quadratics: first, the graphical method by inspection (in the case of incomplete quadratics), (3) solving by factoring, (4) solving by completing the square, and (5) solving by use of the quadratic formula.

The graphical method is not very satisfactory as a means of determining the solution set. It is unduly tedious, and the results Shortcomings of the graphical methods are only approximate. But the method has its values. It helps the students get an intuitive feeling for the meaning of the roots of an equation and of the zeros of a function. It helps them develop the distinction between a quadratic function of x and a quadratic equation in x. To solve the equation $ax^2 + bx + c = 0$, one constructs the graph of the *quadratic function* $y = ax^2 + bx + c$. If the range of the function includes the value 0, the roots of the equation Find the intersection of graph of the quadratic with graph of y = 0 are the replacements for x corresponding to the function value 0. The graph shows the function value 0 where the graph crosses the x axis. Then the real solutions of the equation are the values of x where the graph crosses the x axis. These same values are also called the real *zeros* of the function. The graph also can be used effectively to show why two real and distinct roots may exist, why the roots are sometimes real and equal, and why, in certain cases, there are no real roots.

Just as in the case of the linear relations, it is important that the student have a clear understanding of just what is represented by a quadratic relation. Consider the two relations

$$x^2 + y^2 \leq 25 \tag{1}$$
$$y = x^2 - 5 \tag{2}$$

Graph of a quadratic relation depends on the domain

Example 1: Let the domain and range of $x^2 + y^2 \leq 25$ be the set of integers such that $-5 \leq x \leq 5$ and $-5 \leq y \leq 5$, and for $y = x^2 - 5$, let the domain be the set of integers such that $-4 \leq x \leq 4$, while the range is the set of integers such that $-5 \leq y \leq 11$. The *complete* graph for relation (1) consists of all those points marked by dots in Fig. 11-1, and the *complete* graph for relation (2) consists of all those points marked by crosses. When the two relations are considered simultaneously, the solution set consists of all those points common to the two graphs, namely, those marked by a crossed-over dot. It is the set $\{(0,-5), (-1,-4), (1,-4), (-2,-1), (2,-1), (-3,4), (3,4)\}$.

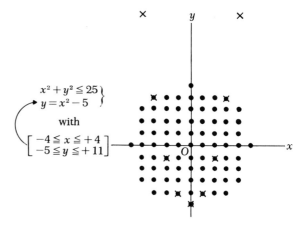

Figure 11-1
Complete graph of a system.

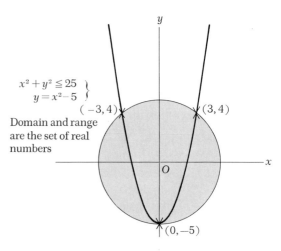

Figure 11-2
Incomplete graph of a system.

Example 2: Let the domain and range of $x^2 + y^2 \leq 25$ be the set of all real numbers such that $-5 \leq x \leq 5$ and $-5 \leq y \leq 5$. For $y = x^2 - 5$ let the domain be the set of all real numbers and the range be the set of all real numbers such that $y \geq -5$. The *complete* graph of the relation $x^2 + y^2 \leq 25$ will be the circle and the area which it encloses, as is indicated by the shaded portion of Fig. 11-2. An *incomplete* graph of the relation $y = x^2 - 5$ will be the portion of the parabola that is shown in the figure. When the two relations are considered simultaneously, the solution set will consist of all the points on the portion of the parabola that lies within the shaded part of the figure, including the three points it has in common with the circle. If the condition of "less than" ($<$) is removed from relation (1), then the graph of this relation becomes the circle. In this case the solution set of the two relations, considered simultaneously, becomes the set $\{(0,-5), (-3,4), \text{ and } (3,4)\}$.

Similar considerations are present when a quadratic relation and a linear relation are considered simultaneously.

The graph of $y = x^2 - 5$ is a special case of the graph of the quadratic function

General quadratic function of x

$$y = ax^2 + bx + c \qquad a \neq 0$$

The condition $a \neq 0$ guarantees that the function has the characteristics of a quadratic function; it also guarantees the possibility of certain operational procedures which are desirable in dealing with the function. For a proper understanding of the essential characteristics of this function it is necessary to examine the effect which each coefficient in the formula has on the graph. For the illustrative examples it will be sufficient to specify the set of real numbers as both the domain and range of the function.

The role of c in $y = ax^2 + bx + c$

Example 1: The effect of c on the graph of $y = ax^2 + bx + c$, Fig. 11-3. It should be evident that $(0,c)$ is always a point on the graph; that is, c is the y intercept of the graph. A comparison of the graphs of the functions $y = x^2 + 2$, $y = x^2$, and $y = x^2 - 5$ is sufficient to show that a change in the value of c merely shifts the position of the intercept on the y axis. Note that in each of these three cases the curve is open upward and the y intercept is the lowest point on the curve. It is a *minimum point;* that is, the function has a *minimum value* at this point.

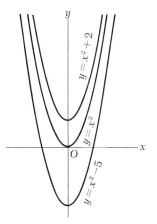

Figure 11-3
Incomplete graphs.

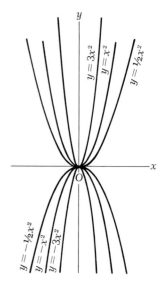

Figure 11-4
Incomplete graphs.

Example 2: The effect of a on the graph of the function $y = ax^2 + bx + c$. This effect is of two types. In Fig. 11-4, a comparison of the graphs of the functions $y = ax^2$, where the coefficients a are numerically equal but opposite in sign, will reveal the following facts: When $a > 0$, the curves are open upward and have a minimum

The role of a in $y = ax^2 + bx + c$

point. When $a < 0$, the curves are open downward and have a maximum (highest) point.

Furthermore, a comparison of curves for the equations in which the coefficients a have the same sign but differ in numerical value will reveal that, as a gets larger in numerical value, the curve tends to close up toward the y axis, and as a gets smaller in numerical value, the curve tends to stretch out away from the y axis.

In both of the above examples all the curves are symmetric with respect to the y axis. This means that $x = \pm k$ substituted into a quadratic function of the form $y = ax^2 + c$, where $a \neq 0$, will produce the same value for y, namely, $y = ak^2 + c$.

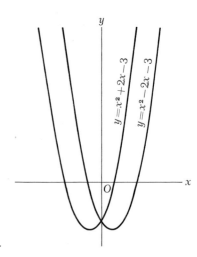

Figure 11-5
Incomplete graphs.

Example 3. The effect of b on the graph of the function $y = ax^2 + bx + c$. A simple illustration of the effect which a change in b will have on the graph of the quadratic function can be obtained from a comparison of the graphs of the two functions $y = x^2 - 2x - 3$ and $y = x^2 + 2x - 3$. Here simple values of a and c are used, but they remain the same for the two functions. The only difference is in the value of the coefficient b. The effect on the graph in Fig. 11-5 has been to shift along the x axis both the minimum point [from $(+1,-4)$ to $(-1,-4)$] and the axis of symmetry (from $x = 1$ to $x = -1$).

These special examples have depicted in simplified form the characteristic effects which the respective coefficients of the quadratic function $y = ax^2 + bx + c$ have on the shape and position of the graph of the function. Each case can be argued more rigorously for the general case by directing attention to the equivalent form of the function

$$y = a \left(x + \frac{b}{2a} \right)^2 + \frac{4ac - b^2}{4a}$$

which exhibits $x = -b/2a$ as the axis of symmetry of the graph and the point $[-b/2a, (4ac - b^2)/4a]$ as the minimum point (if $a > 0$), or the maximum point (if $a < 0$).[2]

Because it is slow and tedious, the graphical solution should not be required for many problems. Its purpose will have been served when it has been used in sufficient cases to clarify and amplify the students' understanding of quadratic equations and inequalities and their solution sets. The major part of the work with quadratic equations should be concerned with algebraic rather than graphical solutions.

The second method for solving a quadratic equation, mentioned at the beginning of this section, is that of solving by inspection. This method is so simple and obvious that often it is not even listed as a method of solution. The third offers little difficulty to students except possibly in the factoring, and this will merely require careful attention. There is nothing inherently new about the process, but there is one point that may need re-explanation. When an equation such as $x^2 + 5x - 14 = 0$ is given in factored form as $(x + 7)(x - 2) = 0$, it is not always clear to the students why one has the right to set the factors separately equal to zero and thus get two linear equations. This provides motivation for review of the field properties and two theorems that can be derived from them.

For all a	$a \times 0 = 0$	(I)
and *if*	$ab = 0$ $b \neq 0$	(II)
then	$a = 0$	

Statement (II) is a converse of (I), but they are not equivalent.

Marginal notes:

The role of b in $y = ax^2 + bx + c$

The purpose of studying the graphic method

The inspection method

Solution by factoring

Converse statements involving zero in multiplication

---

[2] For a more detailed discussion of the quadratic function see the Report of the Commission on Mathematics, "Appendices" (New York: College Entrance Examination Board, 1959), pp. 36–57. See also Wren and Lindsay, *op. cit.*, pp. 178–188.

However, they are both valid theorems about any elements of a field. By (I) we know that the equation $(x + 7)(x - 2) = 0$ is satisfied if either $x + 7 = 0$ or $x - 2 = 0$. By (II) we know that if $x + 7 \neq 0$, then $x - 2 = 0$ must be true; similarly, if $x - 2 \neq 0$, then $x + 7 = 0$ must be a true statement of equality. Students are sometimes confused by the fact that both -7 and 2 satisfy the equation, but it is impossible for both $x + 7 = 0$ and $x - 2 = 0$ to be true for the same value of x. Reference to the properties in (I) and (II) should clarify this. Much of the value of the factoring method in solving quadratic equations lies in its implication for polynomial equations of higher degree. Consequently, it is extremely important for the students to know why the method works.

The method of completing the square is of value primarily because it leads to the quadratic formula. To carry through this method, it is necessary for the students to have well fixed in mind the characteristics of the perfect trinomial square $x^2 + 2bx + b^2$.

The general quadratic formula is of such special importance and usefulness that it should be thoroughly mastered by every student. Its development requires the use of the method of completing the square and provides an excellent review of operations with literal symbols. The development should be carefully explained, and the students should be tested for their understanding of every step. The formula itself is indispensable, and every student should memorize it and use it until he is perfectly familiar with its form and meaning.

In connection with the study of this formula, the teacher should see to it that the students understand the meaning of the discriminant and that they understand why it is possible, in a quadratic equation under proper hypotheses of reality or rationality of the coefficients, to determine the nature of the roots from a study of the discriminant alone, without solving the equation. To this end it is desirable for the teacher and students to examine and discuss together a variety of quadratic equations with numerical coefficients, after which the students may well be given exercises such as the following.

Exercise. In each of the quadratic equations in Table 11-5, the coefficients are rational numbers. Indicate in each case the nature of the roots so far as this can be determined from the discriminant alone. Do not solve the equations.

Exercises of this sort demand and develop insight into the role of the discriminant in determining the nature of the roots and contribute materially to the understanding and appreciation of the generality of the formula. In any discussion of the use of the discriminant, exercises of the form (1) $x^2 - \sqrt{5}\,x - 5 = 0$ and (2) $2x^2 + 6ix - 9 = 0$ should be used by way of contrast to those listed in the table. The purpose is to place specific emphasis on the importance of the hypotheses of rationality and reality on the coefficients of the quadratic. In form 1 the discriminant is rational

TABLE 11-5

Exercise

Equation	Discriminant* $b^2 - 4ac$	Nature of roots		
		Real or imaginary	Equal or unequal	Rational or irrational
$x^2 + 7x + 6 = 0$				
$3y^2 + 7y + 2 = 0$				
$2x^2 - 2x + 11 = 0$				
$x^2 - 10x + 25 = 0$				
$5x^2 + x - 7 = 0$				

* In actuality, $b^2 - 4ac$ is not the discriminant of the quadratic equation $ax^2 + bx + c = 0$, but it is its value in terms of the coefficients of the equation. By definition the discriminant of the polynomial equation

$$a_0x^n + a_1x^{n-1} + a_2x^{n-2} + \cdots + a_{n-1}x + a_n = 0$$

is

$$a_0^{2n-2}(x_1 - x_2)^2(x_1 - x_3)^2 \cdots (x_1 - x_r)^2(x_2 - x_3)^2 \cdots (x_{n-1} - x_n)^2$$

where $x_1, x_2, \ldots, x_n$ are roots of the equation and the factor a^{2n-2} serves merely to render the discriminant an integral expression in the coefficients of the polynomial. For the quadratic equation the discriminant is

$$a^2(x_1 - x_2)^2 = a^2\left(\frac{-b + \sqrt{b^2 - 4ac}}{2a} - \frac{-b - \sqrt{b^2 - 4ac}}{2a}\right)^2 = b^2 - 4ac$$

but the roots are irrational. (The coefficients are *not* rational.) In form 2 the discriminant is positive but the roots are not real. (The coefficients are *not* real.)

Not infrequently students have difficulty in dealing with equations such as $x^6 + 13x^3 + 36 = 0$. The difficulty almost invariably lies in the failure to recognize that, while this, for example, is a sixth-degree equation in x, it may be regarded as a quadratic

Quadratics in f(x)

equation in x^3 and so may be solved easily for x^3, the values of x itself then being readily found by taking the cube roots of x^3. To help the students recognize the possibility of reducing such equations to quadratic form, a variety of examples should be given, the quadratic form being written out in each case. Thus $x^8 + 5x^4 - 2 = 0$ may be written $(x^4)^2 + 5(x^4) - 2 = 0$, or if preferred, a different letter, say z, may be substituted for x^4 so that the equation becomes $z^2 + 5z - 2 = 0$. The illustrations should include examples involving radicals and fractional exponents, such as $x + 3\sqrt{x} - 18 = 0$ and $2x^{2/5} + 8x^{1/5} + 12 = 0$. After a number of illustrative examples have been given, the principle may be generalized to help in subsequent recognition of such cases.

In work of the twelfth grade or of the first year of college algebra there should be extensive applications of the foregoing methods to the solution of quadratic equations in one variable. This work would necessarily involve the use of radicals and imaginary and complex numbers. The quadratic formula as a general solution should be stressed. Such work may be extended appropriately to include the investigation of certain other general properties of quadratic equations, particularly the relations existing among the roots and the coefficients. It should lead to the subsequent study of quadratic equations and systems of equations in two variables.

Many students who are able to apply the quadratic formula explicitly in determining the roots of a given equation find themselves at a loss when confronted with situations in which the formula is implicitly involved. The following illustrative examples are cases in point.

Implicit use of the formula

Example 1: In each of the following equations determine the real values of k for which the roots will be equal:

$$4x^2 - 12x + k = 0$$
$$2kx^2 + 5x + 1 = 0$$
$$x^2 - 8kx + 4 = 0$$

Usually, a few students will be able to sense for themselves the role of the discriminant in such cases, but for many it will need to be pointed out and illustrated specifically. In particular, it will be necessary to review the fact that the equality or inequality of the roots of such equations is determined solely according to whether the discriminant $b^2 - 4ac$ is or is not equal to zero, and consequently the condition for their equality is that k must be of such value as will make this discriminant zero. That is, the student must come to sense the fact that, in order to produce the required condition and to discover the required value of k, the discriminant of the particular equation must be set equal to zero, and the resulting equation solved for k.

The relations between the roots and the coefficients should be carefully developed. Most textbooks give the symbolic development of these formulas but are usually lacking in explanatory comment. To supply adequate explanation of the development and pointed comment with reference to applying these relations must be the task of the teacher. He must use a variety of problems which will provide the student with the opportunity of seeing the formulas applied both explicitly and implicitly.

Relationship between roots and coefficients

Example 2: Find the sum and product of the roots for each equation without solving.

$$5x^2 - 3x + 8 = 0$$
$$2x + 5 = x^2$$

Example 3: Given the equation and one root for each quadratic equation, use the relation between the roots and coefficients to find its other root without using any other method to solve the equation.

$$x^2 - 11x + 24 = 0 \quad \text{(one root is 8)}$$
$$2x^2 - 17x + 33 = 0 \quad \text{(one root is 3)}$$

Example 4: Given the roots as indicated, write the equations.

Roots are $5/2$ and -6

Roots are k and k/a

Other and varied examples will be found in any text in college algebra. Those which are to be used for illustrative purposes or for practice work should be carefully selected by the teacher. The main criterion should be the extent to which the exercise lends itself to clarifying and emphasizing the particular point in question.

SYSTEMS INVOLVING QUADRATIC EQUATIONS IN TWO VARIABLES[3]

The quadratic function $y = ax^2 + bx + c$ is but one form of the general second-degree relation in two variables. Since the graph of any such relation is some form of conic section, it is desirable

Quadratic relations in two variables are conics

that the study of systems of quadratic equations in two variables be approached through the use of equations of conics, at least those in standard position on a given frame of reference.

Two classes of quadratic systems

Systems of equations involving quadratics fall into two general classes: (1) systems containing one linear and one quadratic equation and (2) systems in which both equations are quadratic.

The graphical method of solving quadratic systems is a laborious method and, of course, gives only approximate solutions,

Value of the graphical solution

but it probably offers the average student more real intuitive insight into the nature of the solutions than any of the strictly algebraic methods of attack. In particular, it is useful in showing the possibilities for real roots.

The set of graphs in Fig. 11-6 includes representation of many types of solution sets that are possible in quadratic systems. Figure 11-6a is representative of systems involving one linear and one quadratic equation. A straight line always cuts a conic section

A straight line intersects a conic in no more than two points

in two distinct points, is tangent to the conic, or has no points common with the conic. Accordingly, such a system has two real distinct solutions, two real equal solutions, or two solutions involving imaginary numbers (imaginary solutions).

A system of two quadratic equations usually has a total of four solutions in one of the patterns of Fig. 11.6b to f. But this is not

Two conics intersect in not more than four points

universally true. A system of two quadratic equations may be inconsistent. For example, a system whose graph consists of two concentric circles has no solutions, real or imaginary. In the

[3] Wren and Lindsay, *op. cit.*, pp. 272–287.

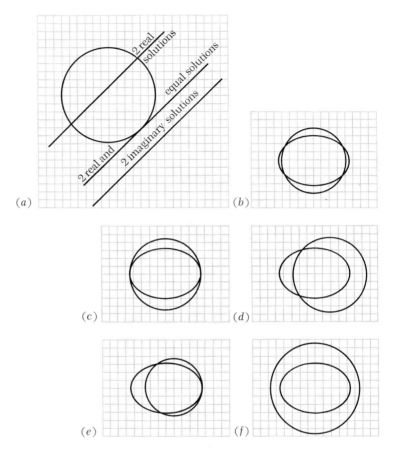

Figure 11-6

Quadratic systems: (a) Two distinct real solutions; two real and equal solutions; two imaginary solutions. (b) Four real solutions. (c) Four real solutions (equal in pairs). (d) Two real and two imaginary solutions. (e) Four real solutions (two equal). (f) Four imaginary solutions.

system

(1) $x^2 + y^2 = 25$
(2) $x^2 + y^2 = 16$

the relation obtained by subtraction

Two quadratic equations may be inconsistent

(1)–(2) $0 = 25 - 16$

is obviously false for all real or imaginary x and y.

On the other hand, the system

(1) $y = ax^2 + b_1 x + c_1$
(2) $y = ax^2 + b_2 x + c_2$

has one real solution. By equating the two values of y, we have

Two quadratic equations may have one real solution	(3) $ax^2 + b_1 x + c_1 = ax^2 + b_2 x + c_2$ (4) $x = \dfrac{c_2 - c_1}{b_1 - b_2}$

If this value of x is substituted in either (1) or (2), a unique value of y is obtained.

From the above examples, it should be evident that a system of two quadratic equations does not invariably have four solutions. But it can be said of any polynomial equation with real coefficients, and consequently of a system of two quadratics, that imaginary solutions occur in conjugate pairs.

A system of two quadratic equations always has an even number of imaginary solutions

The students' previous experience in solving simultaneous equations may be assumed to have been confined to systems of linear equations. In teaching the solution of such systems of equations there is a tendency on the part of many to overlook the method of substitution. The disadvantage of failing to give due emphasis to this method now becomes apparent, because it is generally applicable to the solution of systems involving quadratics, while other methods of solving systems of linear equations are not applicable. Therefore it may be advisable, in taking up the study of this topic, to give a *brief* review of the solution of systems of linear equations by substitution. The students should be made sensitive to the importance of the method as a general algebraic method for solving quadratic systems in two variables.

Review systems of linear equations

A system consisting of two quadratic equations in two variables may be further divided to advantage into homogeneous and nonhomogeneous systems. The special methods and devices used in the solution of these systems vary according to the forms of the equations involved in the particular systems under consideration. Teachers should make every effort to see that students do not use these various devices blindly, but are trained to look for the reasons why the devices work. In doing this they will be acquiring the ability to analyze systems of equations and to determine for themselves what procedures will be most likely to yield the desired solutions. It is highly important that the teachers use discretion and care in the selection of problems to be assigned.

Homogeneous and nonhomogeneous systems

Textbooks generally present these devices with appropriate illustrations but often without emphasizing either the peculiar characteristics of the forms to which the various methods are especially adapted or the *reasons why* a particular method is especially suitable for handling a particular form. It must be the teacher's primary task to see that the students are given insight into the reasons underlying the use of the various devices in particular situations, as well as a knowledge of the devices themselves. Otherwise rote work is inevitable.

Useful and economical as these special procedures are, the student should not be allowed to forget that as a rule they are merely means for reducing the tedious labor often involved in the more general method of solving one equation for one variable in terms of the other and then substituting the result in the other equation.

INEQUALITIES

One of the most significant characteristics that distinguish the algebra of the "new mathematics" era from that which it replaced is the extent to which inequalities are treated.

The properties of the relation of inequality should be contrasted carefully with the properties of equality. In particular, it should be emphasized that inequality is not a symmetrical relation. Also, care should be taken to ensure that students do not make false analogy with equality in regard to subtraction. It is easy to derive the proposition that equals subtracted from equals are equal. But we cannot say that unequals subtracted from unequals in the same sense are unequal in that sense. That is, if $a < b$ and $c < d$, one cannot conclude that $a - c < b - d$. For example, $9 < 10$ and $1 < 5$, but we cannot conclude that $9 - 1 < 10 - 5$.

Properties of the inequality relation

Another source of difficulty is the behavior of inequalities relative to multiplication. Although, if equals are multiplied by the same number, the products are equal, it does not follow that if unequals are multiplied by the same number, the products are unequal in the same sense. Many examples should be used to illustrate the fact that the sense of the inequality is preserved only if the multiplier is positive, while it is reversed if the multiplier is negative, and equality results when the multiplier is zero.

Behavior of inequality under multiplication

Inequalities involving absolute value require careful analysis. If a variable is involved in the absolute value, the solution set is, by definition of absolute value, the union of two solution sets.

Since $|ax + b| = ax + b$ if $ax + b \geqslant 0$ and $|ax + b| = -(ax + b)$ if $ax + b < 0$, the solution set of $|ax + b| < c$ is the union of solution sets $\{x | ax + b < c\} \cup \{x | -(ax + b) < c\}$, where the domain of x is $\{x | x \geqslant -b/a\}$ for the first set and $\{x | x < -b/a\}$ for the second. Since this is represented on the number line as one continuous segment, it can be described as the intersection $\{x | ax + b < c\} \cap \{x | -(ax + b) < c\}$, with no restriction on the domain of the variable. The original statement, $|ax + b| < c$, is equivalent to the compound inequality written in the form $-c < ax + b < c$.

The absolute value of inequalities is a compound sentence

On the other hand, the graph of $|ax + b| > c$ makes it quite clear that the solution set is the union of two sets. Here the graph is two disjoint half lines and cannot be expressed as the intersection of two sets.

Quadratic inequalities in one variable also require careful analysis. Inequalities of this kind should be expressed as the product

Inequality in-
volving a quadratic
is a compound

of two linear factors less than zero or greater than zero. If the product is less than zero, one of the linear factors must be positive and the other negative. An outline similar to the following one is helpful.

If $(ax + b)(cx + d) < 0$, then

$$(ax + b < 0 \text{ and } cx + d > 0) \qquad or \qquad (ax + b > 0 \text{ and } cx + d < 0)$$

The solution set is

$$\Big\{ \{x | ax + b < 0\} \cap \{x | cx + d > 0\} \Big\}$$
$$\cup \Big\{ \{x | ax + b > 0\} \cap \{x | cx + d < 0\} \Big\}$$

If the product is greater than zero, the factors must both be positive or both negative.

If $(ax + b)(cx + d) > 0$, then

$$(ax + b > 0 \text{ and } cx + d > 0) \qquad or \qquad (ax + b < 0 \text{ and } cx + d < 0)$$

The solution set is

$$\Big\{ \{x | ax + b > 0\} \cap \{x | cx + d > 0\} \Big\}$$
$$\cup \Big\{ \{x | ax + b < 0\} \cap \{x | cx + d < 0\} \Big\}$$

Inequalities in
linear
programming

Graphic solution of linear-programming problems in two variables requires the construction of the graph of a system of linear inequalities. If the graph is a convex polygon and its interior, the result is a *convex set*. In graphing such a system it is essential to know which half-plane is the graph of each relation. One way to determine this is to construct the graph of the corresponding linear equation, and then substitute in the inequality relation the coordinates of a point not on the line. If they satisfy the relation, the point is in the half-plane that is sought. Another method consists in solving the inequality for y. If the result is y less than a function of x, the solution set is the half-plane below the line. If the result is of the form $x < a$, then the solution set is the half-plane to the left of the line $x = a$.

RATIO, PROPORTION, AND VARIATION

Most students are
familiar with ratio
and proportion

Most students have a fairly clear understanding of the meaning of ratio and proportion by the time they reach the second algebra course. The concepts of ratio and proportion are used, at least intuitively and by implication, even in the arithmetic of the elementary school, and to a greater extent in the subsequent work of the junior high school. Most textbooks in elementary algebra or general mathematics contain some systematic, though elementary, treatment of this subject, and a more extensive treatment is found in the study of similar geometric figures in intuitive and demonstrative geometry and in numerical trigonometry. Consequently, students in the advanced courses may be expected to have some familiarity with the concepts and techniques of ratio and proportion.

Students' conception of variation is intuitive

The concept of variation also will be familiar to the students, but with intuitive rather than analytical implications. In all probability the form and meaning of the symbolic representation will be new. However, since it is often more convenient and effective to use the variation form of notation than the proportion form, the systematic analytic study of variation should undoubtedly find a place in the advanced work in algebra. It is not a particularly difficult topic to teach, but it needs to be taught thoroughly. Such explanation as may be given in the textbook will necessarily be condensed and will need to be materially supplemented by the teacher.

Objectives in presenting variation

The teacher should have in mind two specific objectives: (1) to see that the students get a clear understanding of what is meant by direct variation, inverse variation, joint variation, and combined variation and (2) to see that the students learn how to set up these relations in the form of equations involving a constant of variation or a proportion and understand why the equations necessarily represent the different types of variation. A variety of illustrative formulas, graphs, and problems can be used effectively to bring out the meaning of the equations $y = kx$, $y = k/x$, $x = kyz$, $y = kx^2$, $y = kx^2/z^3$, etc. Innumerable examples involving variation may be drawn from arithmetic, geometry, physics, and other sources. The following illustrative examples are designed to give the students training in translating verbal statements of relationships into equations of these types. In each case the students should be asked to translate the statement into an equation involving a constant k and to indicate the numerical value of k where they can.

Many applications are needed

1   The perimeter of a square varies directly as the side.
2   The area of a square varies directly as the square of a side.
3   The circumference of a circle varies directly as the radius.
4   The volume of a sphere varies directly as the cube of the radius.
5   The base of a rectangle of constant area varies inversely as the altitude.
6   The strength of an electric current (amperage) varies directly as the voltage and inversely as the resistance.
7   The amount of simple interest varies jointly as the principal, rate, and time.
8   The volume of a confined gas varies directly as the absolute temperature and inversely as the pressure.
9   The intensity of illumination from a given source varies inversely as the square of the distance from that source.

Many applications should be given in the form of problems in order that the students may become thoroughly familiar with these forms and acquire the ability to apply them correctly in appropriate situations and use them with proficiency and assurance. The students will realize, of course, that there are many situations involving variation in which the relationships are so complex that the mathematical laws governing them are not known. They should be impressed, however, with the fact that, whenever we can set up an analytical representation of the mathematical law governing such variation, we are thereby providing ourselves with a powerful instrument for studying and predicting the behavior of the variables.

The study of variation affords an excellent opportunity to clarify and emphasize the nature of functional relationship and functional thinking. In fact, the concept of variation is inseparable from the concept of function, and the two should be stressed together, both concepts being abstracted and clarified through the interweaving of graphic illustrations and numerical evaluation of formulas of polynomial functions. The concept of continuity should be emphasized in connection with the graphs of such functions. This concept should be associated with the concept of the *changing values* of the variables. These, in turn, are to be associated with the shifting coordinates of a point moving at will on the graph, and the graph itself should be associated, through these notions, with the formula or function which it represents. Proper attention to these concepts and associations of ideas will go far toward developing a real idea of the nature of variation at the same time that it gives clear emphasis to the general notion of dependence as an aspect of functionality.

Variation and function should be studied together

ARITHMETIC AND GEOMETRIC PROGRESSIONS

The first fundamental necessity in teaching progressions is to see that the students become really sensitive to the way in which the progressions are built up, i.e., the precise way in which each term after the first one is obtained from the preceding term. There are two approaches to this problem. Textbooks generally start by giving in each case a definition of the type of progression being discussed, calling attention to its distinguishing characteristic (the common difference between two consecutive terms or the common ratio of the one to the other), giving a few numerical illustrations, presenting the first few terms in symbolic form, and proceeding then to the development of the formula for the *n*th term. In this procedure the definition and the concept forms the starting point, and the numerical examples merely illustrate, supplement, and enrich the concept.

Some teachers feel, however, that better results are to be secured by more or less reversing this order of things. Under this plan various simple numerical illustrations of progressions are presented at the beginning, without any definite laws or conditions governing the relations among the terms being given. The students are merely asked to try to find the way in which each series is built up or to discover for themselves the characteristic relation governing each of the series. This approach obviously stresses discovery rather than definition as a starting point. After the student has discovered the relations governing several progressions, he is asked to formulate a statement expressing this relation for each type of progression, and finally to express these laws or relationships symbolically as formulas for the nth term of the series. It is held that many students can do this if the illustrative series are simple and appropriately chosen.

Students should try to discover the law of the progression

Advocates of this approach contend that students who discover the relationships for themselves are likely to understand the characteristic laws better, remember them more vividly, and apply them more readily than those who start with ready-made definitions and formulas. There are probably some grounds for this contention. There is no conclusive evidence, however, that either of these approaches is markedly superior to the other. In either case numerical illustrations are indispensable, and in either case it will probably be necessary for the teacher to help many of the students in setting up the symbolic formula for the typical nth term in the particular type of progression being considered.

Many illustrations are necessary

Derivation of the formulas for the sums of the first n terms demands careful attention. Some texts offer "simplified proofs" which avoid explicit application but require tacit assumption of the principle of finite induction. This does not seem to be justifiable practice. Rather, the proofs of these propositions afford simple, yet very effective, means for introducing the students to the important technique of proof by mathematical induction. The procedural pattern in the application of the principle of finite induction to these particular propositions is simple in content, but of sufficient general import to offer real opportunity for the development of basic understanding of this important mathematical technique.

Use mathematical induction to prove the rule

The most serious difficulty which most students encounter in the study of progressions is in knowing how to go about the insertion of a given number of arithmetic or geometric means between two given numbers. This difficulty can easily be dispelled, however, if the students can be made alert to the fact that all they need to do is to find the common difference or the common ratio and that they can do this in either case by taking the formula for the nth term and solving it for the common difference or the common ratio in terms of the other elements of the formula. For

Derive values of *d*
and *r* from the
general formulas
several reasons it is better for them to carry out these solutions as they are needed rather than to memorize the formula for *d* and *r*. Besides reducing the amount of memorizing, it enhances the students' understanding of the formulas and provides excellent practice in the solution of literal equations.

Arithmetic and geometric progressions have extremely interesting and important applications which should be pointed out to the students. In any linear function, for consecutive integral values (in terms of any real unit) of the independent variable, the corre-

There are many
interesting
applications
sponding values of the function form an arithmetic progression, and conversely. This may be illustrated both graphically and numerically. Doubtless, the most important general application of the geometric progression is the compound-interest law. Here the teacher has the opportunity to emphasize the usefulness of geometric progressions by showing that this law is applied not only to the computation of compound interest, but also to important problems in various fields. The following examples are illustrative:

Chemistry: problems associated with the disintegration of radioactive substances
Physics: the adiabatic law for gases; rates of cooling
Biology: problems associated with the growth of colonies of bacteria and abnormal tissue growth
Economics: problems of investment, insurance, debt funding, and installment buying
Sociology: problems associated with population growth

MATHEMATICAL INDUCTION

The technique of proof by mathematical induction is frequently a stumbling block even for good students. The term "mathematical induction" has an unfortunate connotation. It suggests inductive reasoning, yet the method is certainly deductive. One reason why good students have difficulty with the method is that, *as it has sometimes been presented,* it is not deduction. The method is fre-

Logical basis for
the method
quently introduced without any reference to the property of the natural numbers that justifies drawing the conclusion that the relationship to be established is true for all natural numbers. The logical basis for the technique is the principle of finite induction.

Principle of Finite Induction

If *P* is a set of positive integers that satisfy two conditions:

(1)   the integer 1 is an element of *P*
(2)   the integer $k + 1$ is an element of *P* if k is an element of *P*

then *P* is the set of all positive integers.

Any attempt to use the technique of mathematical induction without the benefit of this axiom, or its logical equivalent, is doomed to failure. The conclusion is not a justified implication. The principle should be clearly stated for what it is: an axiom, not a theorem, governing the positive integers. Any attempt to use proof by mathematical induction which does not include this axiom should and does leave the thoughtful student with a feeling of impropriety.

Domain of applicability

It is evident from the axiom that the method is applicable only to theorems concerning the positive integers. Each of the two conditions in the axiom is necessary, but neither taken alone is sufficient. The theorem to be proved by mathematical induction is a statement S about positive integers. Proving the theorem may be

There are two parts to the proof

thought of as investigating the set of integers for which the statement is true. The method requires that 1 is shown to be a positive number for which the statement is true, S_1. It also requires that the statement be true of the number $k + 1$, S_{k+1}, wherever it is true of the number k, S_k. When this is done, the axiom justifies the conclusion that the statement S is true for all positive integers. The procedure can be diagramed as a compound sentence,

$$[S_1 \wedge (S_k \longrightarrow S_{k+1})] \longrightarrow S$$

One part can be satisfied without the other

The following examples illustrate that neither part 1 nor part 2 of the axiom alone is sufficient for the conclusion that the set is the set of all integers. Suppose we make the statement that the formula $n^2 - n + 11$ gives a prime number for all positive integers. If this is a true statement, it certainly must be true for the positive integer 1; and it is, since $(1)^2 - 1 + 11 = 11$ and 11 is a prime number. If $n = 11$, however, we have $(11)^2 - 11 + 11 = (11)^2$, which is not a prime number. Here the second necessary condition fails, for the formula does give a prime for $n = 10$ but not for $n = 10 + 1 = 11$. Similar illustrations are found in the formula $n^2 - n + 41$, which renders a prime for all positive integers from 1 to 40, but not for 41, and in the formula $n^2 - 79n + 1,601$, which yields a prime for each positive integer from 1 to 79, but not for $n = 80$.

In the study of arithmetic progressions one of the important principles to be developed is that the sum of the first n consecutive positive integers is given by the formula $S = n(n + 1)/2$. It thus would be incorrect to say that this sum is given by the formula $S = [n(n + 1)/2] + 1 = (n^2 + n + 2)/2$. However, let us assume that there exists some positive integer k such that

$$1 + 2 + 3 + \cdots + k = \frac{k^2 + k + 2}{2}$$

It then follows from the additive property of equality that

$$(1 + 2 + 3 + \cdots + k) + (k + 1) = \frac{k^2 + k + 2}{2} + (k + 1)$$

$$= \frac{(k^2 + k + 2) + 2(k + 1)}{2}$$

$$= \frac{(k^2 + 2k + 1) + (k + 1) + 2}{2}$$

$$= \frac{(k + 1)^2 + (k + 1) + 2}{2}$$

It thus follows that if the formula is true for any positive integer k, it is also true for the positive integer $k + 1$.

If $n = 1$ is used, the formula produces 2, and $1 \neq 2$. In fact, we know that there is no positive integer for which this formula produces a correct result.

COMPLEX NUMBERS

In introducing students to the study of imaginary and complex numbers, it is well to review the previous steps in the extension of their number concepts from positive integers to common and decimal fractions, and later to irrational numbers and negative numbers. They will be interested in realizing that each of these extensions was made in response to a need; that when situations were encountered which could not be interpreted or explained adequately by use of positive integers alone, fractions were invented to do the job; and similarly for negative numbers. The point should be stressed that these new kinds of numbers have been sheer *inventions* made to serve a purpose and that they take their meanings from definition. This having been established, the students will tend to be in a receptive frame of mind for further extension of their number ideas.

Review of real numbers is necessary

The meaning of an imaginary number should be made clear at the outset. There should be no mystery about it, and there need be none. An explanation along the following lines will make clear the meaning which is to be attached to such numbers and will dispel much of the intellectual reservation, and even antagonism, that often exist with reference to this radically new concept.

Let us consider some negative number, say, -9. Can we find its square root? The square root of -9 cannot be $+3$, because $(+3)(+3) = +9$, nor can the square root be -3, because $(-3)(-3) = +9$. In fact, the square root of -9 cannot be any positive number, and it cannot be any negative number, because the square of either a positive or a negative number is positive. Obviously, it cannot be zero. What then can it be? The only kinds of numbers we know about up to now are real numbers. Since the square root of -9 cannot be any of these, we must *invent* another kind of number which we shall *define* as being the square root of a negative number and which we shall *call* an *imaginary number*. This is, in fact, what mathematicians have done. They have recalled that the square of either square root of any number gives that number [i.e., $\sqrt{7} \times \sqrt{7} = 7$, $(-\sqrt{7})(-\sqrt{7}) = 7$, etc.], and they have said that since this is the meaning of a square root, it must follow that $\sqrt{-9}\ \sqrt{-9} = -9$ and $(-\sqrt{-9})(-\sqrt{-9}) = -9$. Since they call both nonnegative and negative numbers *real* numbers, and since neither square root of -9 can be a real number, they call it a *pure imaginary* number. Such symbols as $\sqrt{-48}, -\sqrt{-2}, \sqrt{-1}, -\sqrt{-364}$, etc., represent other pure imaginary numbers. The special symbol i is used to designate the imaginary number $\sqrt{-1}$, which is used as the *imaginary unit*. Thus, if $i = \sqrt{-1}$, then $i^2 = -1$, and any negative number can be expressed as a positive number times i^2. For example, $\pm\sqrt{-9}$ can be expressed as $\pm\sqrt{9i^2}$, and this is equal to $\pm 3i$. The teacher should insist on expressing a negative radicand in this way; otherwise logical difficulties are very apt to arise. The rule for multiplying radicals, $\sqrt[n]{a} \times \sqrt[n]{b} = \sqrt[n]{ab}$, was justified only for the defined principal nth roots. If n is even and $a < 0$, $\sqrt[n]{a}$ was left undefined. Indiscriminate use of the rule for multiplication can lead to a contradiction. For example, applying the rule of multiplication,

$$\sqrt{-25} \times \sqrt{-4} = \sqrt{(-25)(-4)} = \sqrt{100} = 10$$

But writing the negative radicands as positive numbers times i^2,

$$\sqrt{-25} \times \sqrt{-4} = \sqrt{25i^2} \times \sqrt{4i^2} = 5i \times 2i = 10i^2 = -10$$

Under the foregoing definition of $\sqrt{-25}$, the rule for multiplication produces the correct result when $\sqrt{-25}$ is multiplied by $\sqrt{4}$:

$$\sqrt{-25} \times \sqrt{4} = \sqrt{-100} = \sqrt{100i^2} = 10i$$

which is the same result as obtained when $\sqrt{-25}$ is expressed as $\sqrt{25i^2}$. Thus

$$\sqrt{25i^2} \times \sqrt{4} = 5i \times 2 = 10i$$

Results of this sort occur because it is true that one of the nth roots of a multiplied by one of the nth roots of b does equal one of the nth roots of ab.

Any real number multiplied by the imaginary unit i is by definition a *pure imaginary*. It should be made clear to the students that in thus defining imaginary numbers, we make them subject to all the normal laws of operation that we use with real numbers. It is very important that students understand this clearly, and this understanding is facilitated, and confusion avoided, by the con-

Sidenotes (left margin):

Imaginary numbers were invented so that negative numbers might have square roots

It is essential to use i for $\sqrt{-1}$

The rule $\sqrt[n]{a} \cdot \sqrt[n]{b} = \sqrt[n]{ab}$ should not be used beyond its domain of definition

Pure imaginary numbers

sistent use of the symbol i in place of the radical $\sqrt{-1}$. Thus there is no difference between applying the laws of exponents, the law of signs in multiplication, etc., to numbers expressed in terms of i and applying these laws to numbers expressed in terms of x or y or a or any other literal symbol. The peculiar cyclic nature of the successive integral powers of i often makes it possible to simplify the results of such operations, but this characteristic itself is a direct consequence of the laws of exponents applied in the usual manner to the number i, and of the definition of that number.

Imaginary units are governed by the same rules as real units

The principal points at which difficulty may be anticipated are the establishment of the definition and meaning of imaginary numbers, the definition of the symbol i, the firm fixation of the principle that *operations* with numbers in terms of i are carried on in exactly the same fashion as operations with numbers expressed in terms of any other letter, and the establishment of the succesive positive integral powers of i which give a recurring series of numbers, $+i, -1, -i, +1$.

Any integral power of i is $i, -1, -i$, or 1

When these properties of imaginary numbers have been well established in the minds of the students, the subsequent definition of and work with complex numbers should present little difficulty. Care should be taken in defining complex numbers to make sure that the full significance of the definition is understood. A complex number is of the form $a + bi$, where a and b are real numbers. This is not clearly understood until one realizes that the real numbers can be put into one-to-one correspondence with the complex numbers of the form $a + 0i$, and the pure imaginary numbers with the complex numbers of the form $0 + bi$. Once this has been understood, the student is ready for the definition of conjugate complex numbers, equal complex numbers, and the four fundamental operations for working with complex numbers. The student should understand clearly that these definitions are such that the associative, commutative, and distributive properties are preserved. Furthermore, they are such that, when applied to numbers of the form $a + 0i$, the results are consistent with those obtained with real numbers.

Definitions of addition and multiplication of complex numbers are consistent with the rules for real numbers

The geometrical representation and treatment of complex numbers are extremely interesting to students and help to make their concepts of these numbers much more tangible. This work is not very difficult and may well be introduced even in the second course in algebra, at least to the extent of making the students familiar with the method of representing complex numbers graphically and with the basic principles of simple vector addition. For those students who have had trigonometry, this work may well be extended to include the representation of complex numbers in trigonometric form, multiplication of two numbers in polar form, De Moivre's theorem, finding the nth roots of a complex number, and the division of complex numbers expressed in polar form.

Geometric representation of complex numbers leads to consideration of vectors

LOGARITHMIC AND EXPONENTIAL FUNCTIONS

Logarithms as computational aids have been de-emphasized

The importance of logarithms as a computational aid has been much reduced in recent years. However, the rudiments of logarithms, including their use in computation, should be included as a part of the study of the logarithmic function.

Specifically, the students should know the definition of the logarithm of a number and how to use a table of logarithms. This implies understanding the role of the characteristic and of the mantissa. In short, the students should learn the theoretical basis for the use of logarithms.

Students should know the theoretical basis of logarithms

The major emphasis should be placed on the logarithmic function rather than logarithms of specific numbers.

Two functions f and g are inverse if and only if $f[g(x)] = g[f(x)] = x$. For example, if

$$f(x) = 7x + 2 \qquad \text{and} \qquad g(x) = (x - 2)/7$$

then

$$f[g(x)] = 7 \left[\frac{(x - 2)}{7} \right] + 2 = x - 2 + 2 = x$$

and

$$g[f(x)] = \frac{(7x + 2) - 2}{7} = \frac{7x + 2 - 2}{7} = \frac{7x}{7} = x$$

By definition of logarithms, the function $y = \ln x = \log_e x$ has as domain the set of positive real numbers, and the y corresponding to a given x is the power of e necessary to produce x. That is, y must satisfy the equation $x = e^y$ if $y = \log_e x$ is to be true. The two statements $y = \log_e x$ and $x = e^y$ are two forms for the same relationship. If x and y are interchanged in $x = e^y$, the result $y = e^x$ is the exponential function. The two functions $y = f(x) = \log_e x$ and $y = g(x) = e^x$ are inverse functions. For $f[g(x)] = \log_e e^x = x$. The last equation, $\log_e e^x = x$, is true because the power to which e must be raised to produce e^x is certainly x. Also, $g[f(x)] = e^{\log_e x} = x$ because $\log_e x$ is the power to which e must be raised to produce x; e is raised to that power; therefore the result is x. (See Figs. 11-7 and 11-8.)

Logarithmic and exponential functions are inverses

Attention should be called to the fact that this concept of inverse function is consistent with the concept of inverse element included among the properties of a number field. For each element a of a field there exists an additive inverse $-a$ such that $a + (-a) = (-a) + a = 0$, and for each nonzero element b there exists a multiplicative inverse b^{-1} such that $b \times b^{-1} = b^{-1} \times b = 1$. In each case the result of combining an element with its respective inverse is to produce the identity element. The analogous situation

The meaning of inverse function in relation to inverse element

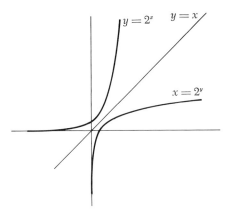

Figure 11-7
Inverse functions are symmetric to the line $y = x$.

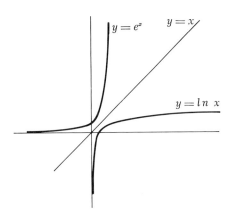

Figure 11-8
Logarithmic and exponential functions are inverses.

in the case of functions is that the composite function of a function and its inverse, in either order, is the identity function. That is, it is a function which may be represented by an ordered pair in which the first and second elements are the same, for example, (x,x).

As a part of mathematical literacy beyond the most elementary level, it is important for students to become aware of this inverse relationship between logarithmic and exponential functions. As an instrument in the study of analytic geometry, calculus, statistics, and subsequent courses, it is necessary for students to understand this relationship and be able to make interconversions with assurance and facility. This objective has often been sadly neglected, to the detriment of the students, who too often have been taught only how to use logarithms numerically.

OTHER TOPICS
IN ALGEBRA

In a volume such as this it is impossible to consider in detail the teaching procedures connected with all the topics of intermediate and college algebra. It is hoped that the preceding pages will in some measure have set a pattern for the study of such problems. It is hoped, further, that the discussion will encourage teachers to apply themselves assiduously to the task of specifying the major relationships and concepts to be developed in connection with each topic and discovering the main characteristic difficulties which the study of each topic presents to the students.

Among the topics which are of first-rate importance at their appropriate levels but which it has not been possible to discuss in this chapter may be mentioned the binomial theorem, special properties of functions and equations of degree higher than second, permutations and combinations, probability, determinants, general theorems on algebraic functions and equations, and the mathematics of investment and insurance. In concluding this chapter, a few general suggestions may be made with a view to helping teachers plan their instruction in these and other topics effectively.

Some important topics have been omitted from this discussion

Perhaps the most important objective of mathematical instruction at the higher levels is the development of the ability to understand *generalized* principles and concepts and to apply these generalizations properly to particular situations or problems. At the same time, this seems to present to students greater difficulty than almost anything else. It is therefore a matter to which special attention needs to be given very consistently. The following examples may be cited by way of illustration.

The importance of generalization

1   The recognition of type forms in factorable expressions which in themselves may be rather complicated, such as

$12y^3 - 4y^6 + x^{2a} - 9$ (difference of two squares)
$a^3 + 8b^3 + c^3 + 6a^2b + 12ab^2$ (sum of two cubes)

2   The recognition of possibilities for reducing equations or expressions to standard forms which can be more readily handled, such as

$x^{16} + 5x^8 + 6 = 0$ (quadratic equation in x^8)
$x^4 + x^2 + 1 = 0$ (factorable by difference of two squares)

3   Interpretation of the implications of consistency and inconsistency of a system of m linear equations in n variables

4   Understanding the generality of the relations given by the remainder theorem, the factor theorem, the fundamental theorem of algebra, the theorems giving relations between roots and coefficients, etc.

5   Understanding the significance of the procedures used in solving and checking literal equations and formulas

6   Applying the formula for the rth term in a binomial expansion for a given value of r, and similarly applying other generalized formulas to the determination of values in particularized cases

It is important that instruction be carried on at suitable levels of difficulty and expectation. At times there is an unwarranted, though not unnatural, tendency among teachers to assume that all the material in a textbook is suitable for the students in the grade in which the textbook is used. In connection with any given topic, the teacher should try to decide how far he can carry his particular class profitably in relation to that topic and what should be the nature and level of difficulty of the exercises he should use and the assignments he should make. It is to be expected that a spiral treatment of topics in algebra will generally produce better results than too intensive treatment, carried beyond appropriate levels, in any

Use good judgment in selecting textbook material

one year. Thus, instead of trying to teach all factoring in the first course, a few simple and easily understandable cases are given at that level. Later, at the more advanced level of instruction, these are reviewed and more difficult ones considered, and this process is repeated in subsequent years. The work should always challenge the best efforts of the students, but if it is carried beyond their capacities, it will lose its meaning and value.

Finally, the elements of time, practice, review, application, and maintenance are of extreme importance. They are all involved in a program of instruction that looks to a fundamental mastery of algebra. The great generalities do not emerge in an instant or a year; they are the result of a long process of assimilation and

Success is not instantaneous

familiarization. They require not hours but years of concentrated attention and sheer hard intellectual work, beginning with simple concepts and proceeding to ever more difficult and abstract relationships. Rome was not built in a day, nor is there any quick, easy short cut to a real mastery of algebra. Persistent review and practice, both in the skills of algebra and in their application, are re-

Continuous maintenance is essential

quired. Otherwise, the skills and understandings will deteriorate through disuse.

Under a program of subject matter selected to present a reasonable challenge to ability, to provide a gradual expansion of the horizon of mathematical understanding, and to demand an incessant program of maintenance, the student may expect to arrive at a *real mastery* of algebra. Such a mastery of appropriate subject matter of algebra not only will provide that student with a sound basis for exploring mathematics at its higher levels, but also will give him a richness of insight into the related fields of science.

PROVISION FOR
SUPERIOR STUDENTS

An advanced class is not a captive audience

Students who take algebra beyond the first course usually do so voluntarily, through some special interest in the subject. The problem of motivation is thus less acute, and some degree of selection with respect to mathematical aptitude will have been operative. At the same time the subject is sufficiently demanding so that the regular work of the course will call forth serious effort on the part of most of the students. There will be a few, however, for whom the regular work is easy, and there may be an occasional student for whom the regular course is not much of a challenge. These are the students who possess that rare combination of math-

Exceptional talent must be challenged to develop its potential

ematical insight and originality which marks them as potential leaders in mathematics, and the shortage of such leaders is regarded in high places as a matter of grave and increasing concern.

We cannot afford to let mathematical talent go to waste. Yet this will happen unless students of exceptional talent are given work which will call forth their interest and their best efforts. Students with marked ability and a taste for originality will often enjoy working on challenging problems which may be quite unrelated to the current work of the class. Such journals as the *Mathematics Student Journal,* the *Pentagon, School Science and Mathematics,* the *Arithmetic Teacher,* and the *Mathematics Teacher* are good sources of such problems, as are some of the books on mathematical recreations. For those students who are simply above average, varied assignments with perhaps less routine work and more emphasis on relatively difficult problems may suffice. It is usually easy to find some such problems in the regular textbook or in collateral textbooks. They may be oriented to the unit or to topics currently being studied by the class, but this need not be the case.

The teacher's responsibility concerning independent work

Once in a while one may find a student not merely superior but of truly exceptional insight and endowed with insatiable curiosity and the capacity for sustained effort. Such a student may work with more keen interest in carrying on independently an intensive investigation of some collateral topic than in working on short-term special assignments. Serious work of this kind should be encouraged, though with suitable safeguards. For high school students such topics as the following could serve as foci for such investigations: theorems about polynomials of higher degree; properties of determinants; exponential and logarithmic functions; mathematical induction and the binomial formula; permutations, combinations, and probability; notation for and operations with sets; elements of symbolic logic.

Only the student who is capable of a high order of independent and sustained work should be given this sort of collateral assignment. The teacher's role will be to recommend appropriate reference works, to receive and comment on the progress reports the student will make from time to time, and to appraise the final oral and written reports that should be presented. This will make extra work for the teacher, but if the assignment is well carried out, it can yield high dividends.

The capable student must not bypass mastery of skills and details

One caution is in order. Special projects of this kind should be regarded as complementing, but not replacing, the regular course in algebra, and such assignments should be made only with the most careful discrimination. Sometimes the enthusiasm of highly capable students makes them impatient with the need to master routine but necessary skills and details. But such neglect of fundamental groundwork imposes severe limitations on eventual progress, and it should not be tolerated. Talented students may not require as much time as their less capable classmates to acquire the necessary details and skills, but they should be held responsible for their mastery, just as the other students are.

EXERCISES

1 Explain in detail how you would make it clear and convincing to a class that the following definitions are consistent with the laws of operation with positive integral exponents.

$$x^{1/3} = \sqrt[3]{x} \qquad x^{-3} = \frac{1}{x^3} \qquad x^0 = 1$$

2 Does your explanation of the relations set forth in exercise 1 constitute a proof of these relations, or does it merely define fractional, negative, and zero exponents? Explain.

3 The rationale for the definition $a^{-n} = 1/a^n$ is usually developed with n a positive integer. Show that the rule applies to all rational numbers n except for $a = 0$. Show why $a = 0$ must be excluded.

4 For x a real number and n a positive integer, give illustrations to show that $\sqrt[n]{x^n}$ will be x if n is odd, but may be x or $-x$ if n is even.

5 The usual way of beginning the second year's work in algebra is to present a concentrated and extensive review of the fundamental operations. What are the reasons for this? What disadvantages does it entail? Can you suggest a better plan? What is it?

6 Use both the pivotal-element and sweep-out processes to solve these systems of equations:

(a)
$$\begin{aligned} x + y + z + u &= 5 \\ 2x - y + z - 2u &= -1 \\ x - 2y + z - 2u &= -1 \\ 3x + 2y - 2z + u &= 0 \end{aligned}$$

(b)
$$\begin{aligned} x + y + z + u &= 3 \\ 2x + 2y + 3z - u &= 8 \\ z - 3u &= 2 \\ 3x + 3y + 5z - 3u &= 13 \end{aligned}$$

7 Consider the two relations $y \geqslant x^2$ and $y^2 = 8x$ (1) with the domain for both x and y the set of integers such that $-3 \leqslant x \leqslant +8$ and $-5 < y < +10$, and (2) with the domain for both x and y the set of real numbers. (a) Draw the graph of each relation. (b) What is the solution set when the two relations are considered simultaneously? (c) What is the solution set for the two relations when the "is greater than" ($>$) is removed from $y \geqslant x^2$?

8 List the specific things you would want your students to know or be able to do as a result of their study of quadratic equations in their second year of algebra.

9 What difficulties would you expect your students to encounter in their work with quadratic equations? How could you help them avoid or overcome these difficulties? Consider each separately and be as specific as you can.

10 Make a list of the main outcomes you would strive for in teaching logarithms and exponentials in a second course in algebra. Why is it desirable to teach these two topics together?

11 What specific outcomes should be sought in work with radicals? What specific difficulties can students be expected to have in connection with this work?

12 Show that the equation $\sqrt{3x-5} + \sqrt{2x+3} + 1 = 0$ has no solution, although the derived quadratic equation does have two real solutions. (Such problems illustrate and emphasize the importance of thoughtful checking of algebraic work.)

13 Given: $f(x) = x^2 - 5x + 28$ and $g(x) = 12 - 5x + x^2$. Many students, if instructed to write the correct expressions for $f(12)$ and $g(h + 17)$, would report that they could not do it. Do you think this is due to lack of mathematical ability, or do you think it is due, mainly, to not knowing how to interpret the notation used? How important is this question? Discuss.

14 With reference to exercise 13, what are some steps you would take to remedy the situation?

15 The resistance of a wire to the passage of an electric current is directly proportional to the length of the wire and inversely proportional to the square of the diameter. Write this as a variation equation, using R, L, and D to represent resistance in ohms, length in feet, and diameter in mils, respectively, and K to represent the constant of variation.

16 A 24-gauge copper wire of diameter 20.1 mils and length 150 feet has a resistance of 3.85 ohms. Compute the constant of variation K, and determine the length of 30-gauge copper wire (diameter 10.0 mils) required to make a coil whose resistance is 75 ohms. Explain the part which the constant K plays in the solution.

17 Show how the compound-interest law, and

consequently the study of annuities and the mathematics of life insurance, is based upon a geometric progression. Give illustrations to show applications of the compound-interest law to fields other than finance.

18 The topic of inequalities formerly was ignored in high school algebra and given scant attention in college algebra. How do you account for the current changed attitude?

19 Graph each of the following expressions and discuss each graph: $y = 3$, $y \geq 3$, $y < 3$, $y < -1$, $y \leq x$, $y \geq x - 1$, $3y < 2x$, $y = x^2$, $y \geq x^2$, and $y < x^2$. Take the domains of x and y to be the set of real numbers.

20 Prove the remainder theorem, and show that the factor theorem is actually just a special case of the remainder theorem. Do you think students generally get the full significance of the remainder theorem? If not, why?

21 Explain to the class the principle of mathematical induction. As an illustration of this principle, prove that, if n represents any positive integer, then

$$\sum_{i=1}^{n} i(i+1)(i+2) = (\tfrac{1}{4})n(n+1)(n+2)(n+3)$$

22 Sometimes students are directed to remove all negative signs from square roots before any computation or other simplification by placing i outside the radical. A student sometimes objects that this is equivalent to

$$\sqrt{-8} = \sqrt{-1}\,\sqrt{8}$$

and that it violates the rule that

$$\sqrt{a}\,\sqrt{b} = \sqrt{ab}$$

is permissible only if a and b are nonnegative. How would you answer this objection?

23 Make a list of specific difficulties which

students may be expected to encounter in the study of one of the following topics and suggest ways to help them avoid or overcome the difficulties: progressions, logarithms, irrational roots, determinants, complex numbers, inequalities, quadratic equations, equations of third or higher degree, mathematical induction, binomial theorem, permutations and combinations, and probability.

24 What advantages, if any, accrue to students from the practice of checking their own solutions of, say, quadratic equations or equations involving radicals?

25 What advantages, if any, accrue to students from having printed answer lists available for some of the problems they are to solve? What disadvantages may attend this practice?

The next four problems were taken from the Problem Section of School Science and Mathematics. *Present your solutions.*

26 Solve for x: $\sqrt[3]{e^{2+x}} \times \sqrt[4]{e^{4-x}} \times \sqrt[5]{e^{5x-1}} = 1$.

27 If $\log(x+z) + \log(x-2y+z) = 2\log(x-z)$, show that x, y, and z are in harmonic progression.

28 Find two numbers such that their sum multiplied by the sum of their squares is 5,500 and their difference multiplied by the difference of their squares is 352.

29 Eliminate x and y from the following system of equations: $x^2y = a$, $x(x+y) = b$, $2x + y = c$.

30 Assume that you have discovered in your class a student of extraordinary ability who does the regular work of the class with little effort and who wishes also to carry on an independent study of transfinite numbers. Compile a list of suitable references which you would recommend for him.

31 Use mathematical induction to prove that $n^n > n!$ for every integer $n \geq 2$.

BIBLIOGRAPHY

Barnes, George: An Easily Constructed Chart for Finding the Roots of Quadratic Equations, *Mathematics Teacher*, **50** (1957), 40–42.

Barnett, I. A.: Introducing Number Theory in High School Algebra and Geometry, *Mathematics Teacher*, **58** (1965), 14–23.

Baumgart, John K.: Axioms in Algebra: Where Did They Come From?, *Mathematics Teacher*, **54** (1961), 155–160.

Beckenbach, Edwin, and Richard Bellman: "An Introduction to Inequalities" (New York: Random House, Inc., 1961).

Bellman, Richard: On the Concepts of a Problem and Problem-solving, *American Mathematical Monthly*, **67** (1960), 119–134.

Byrkit, Donald R.: Linear Indeterminate Equations: An Aid to Enrichment, *School Science and Mathematics*, **60** (1960), 627–631.

Coltharp, Forrest: Introducing Integers as Ordered Pairs, *School Science and Mathematics*, **66** (1966), 277–282.

Commission on Mathematics, Report of: "Appendices" (New York: College Entrance Examination Board, 1959), pp. 29–63, 74–93.

Dalton, Leroy C.: Complex Numbers and Loci, *Mathematics Teacher*, **54** (1961), 229–233.

Diamond, Louis E.: Introduction to Complex Numbers, *Mathematics Magazine*, **30** (1957), 233–249.

Fehr, Howard F.: "Secondary Mathematics: A Functional Approach for Teachers" (Boston: D. C. Heath and Company, 1951), pp. 36–73, 123–167.

Glickman, A. M.: Vectors in Algebra and Geometry, *Mathematics Teacher*, **54** (1961), 327–332.

Heinke, Clarence: Necessary and Sufficient Conditions, *School Science and Mathematics*, **65** (1965), 601.

Hohfeld, Joseph F.: An Analysis of the Quadratic, *Mathematics Teacher*, **54** (1961), 138–141.

Hoy, Dorothy H.: Reflexive, Symmetric, and Transitive Properties of Relations, *Mathematics Teacher*, **58** (1965), 205–210.

Jones, Phillip S.: Complex Numbers: An Example of Recurring Themes in the Development of Mathematics, *Mathematics Teacher*, **47** (1954), 106–114, 257–263, 340–345.

Kane, Robert B.: Linear Programming: An Aid to Decision Making, *Mathematics Teacher*, **53** (1960), 177–179.

Kocher, Frank: Techniques of Solving Rational Equations, *Mathematics Teacher*, **56** (1963), 486–489.

Lange, L. H.: Some Inequality Problems, *Mathematics Teacher*, **56** (1963), 490–494.

Law, Carol: Arithmetical Congruences with Practical Applications, *Mathematics Magazine*, **32** (1958), 221–227.

Lewis, Jesse C.: An Interesting Problem Involving Indeterminate Equations, *Mathematics Teacher*, **53** (1960), 540–542.

Maskewitsch, D.: On the Equation $ax + by = c$, *School Science and Mathematics*, **60** (1960), 288–290.

————: Geometric Solution of a Quadratic Equation, *School Science and Mathematics*, **61** (1961), 457–461.

McGaughey, A. W.: The Imaginary Number Problem, *American Mathematical Monthly*, **64** (1957), 193–194.

Meserve, Bruce E.: Foundations of Algebra, *Mathematics Teacher*, **50** (1957), 356–360.

———— and Max E. Sobel: "Mathematics for Secondary School Teachers" (Englewood Cliffs, N.J.: Prentice-Hall, Inc., 1962), 77–178.

National Council of Teachers of Mathematics: *Twenty-third Yearbook* (Washington, D.C.: The Council, 1957).

————: *Twenty-fourth Yearbook* (Washington, D.C.: The Council, 1959).

————: *Twenty-eighth Yearbook* (Washington, D.C.: The Council, 1963).

Niven, Ivan: "Numbers: Rational and Irrational" (New York: Random House, Inc., 1961).

Payne, Joseph H.: Self-instructive Enrichment Topics for Bright Pupils in High School Algebra, *Mathematics Teacher*, **51** (1958), 113–117.

Peters, Max: An Introductory Lesson in Logarithms, *New Jersey Mathematics Teacher*, **13** (1957), 3–6.

Praley, Arthur H.: A Radical Approach to $\sqrt{ab} = \sqrt{a} \cdot \sqrt{b}$, *Mathematics Teacher*, **58** (1965), 512.

Ransom, W. R.: Second Order Interpolation, *School Science and Mathematics*, **55** (1955), 460–461.

Ringenberg, L. A.: Numbers and Number Systems, *Mathematics Magazine*, **32** (1958), 265–276.

Rio, Sheldon T., and Walter J. Sanders: Interval Graphing, *Mathematics Teacher*, **54** (1961), 194–200.

Rosenberg, H.: Modern Applications of Exponential and Logarithmic Functions, *School Science and Mathematics*, **60** (1960), 131–138.

Schack, Arthur: Two Forms of Mathematical Induction, *Mathematics Magazine*, **32** (1958), 83–85.

School Mathematics Study Group: "Elementary Functions" (New Haven, Conn.: Yale University Press, 1959).

————: "Intermediate Mathematics" (New Haven, Conn.: Yale University Press, 1959).

————: "Introduction to Matrix Algebra" (New Haven, Conn.: Yale University Press, 1960).

Scott, C. H.: Dimensional Analysis, *School Science and Mathematics*, **57** (1957), 32–36.

Shuster, Carl N.: Graphic Solution of a Quadratic Equation, *Mathematics Teacher*, **54** (1961), 142–144.

Stewart, Lurline: The Binomial Theorem, *Mathematics Teacher*, **53** (1960), 344–348.

Strickland, Warren: Algebra of Complex Numbers, *School Science and Mathematics*, **58** (1958), 690–692.

Trine, F. D.: Introduction to Algebra with Inequalities, *Mathematics Teacher*, **53** (1960), 42–45.

Utz, W. R.: Maxima and Minima without the Calculus, *School Science and Mathematics,* **57** (1957), 263–266.

Wallin, D.: Applications of Inequalities, *Mathematics Teacher,* **53** (1960), 134–135.

Wendt, Arnold: A Simple Example of a Noncommutative Algebra, *Mathematics Teacher,* **52** (1959), 534–540.

Willoughby, Stephen S.: "Contemporary Teaching of Secondary School Mathematics" (New York: John Wiley & Sons, Inc., 1967), pp. 262–296.

Wren, F. Lynwood, and John W. Lindsay: "Basic Algebraic Concepts" (New York: McGraw-Hill Book Company, 1969).

twelve | the teaching of geometry in the junior high school

In the hands of an enthusiastic and competent teacher the geometry of the junior high school becomes for the students not only an important subject of study but a fascinating one as well. Children live and grow in a world that abounds in geometric form. They see circles in coins and wheels, angles in the hands of clocks and in gables of houses, and cylinders in tree trunks and tiles and tin cans. Cones are filled with ice cream, and cones are found on the ends of newly sharpened pencils. Doors and sheets of paper are rectangles. Kites are polygons. Marbles and oranges are spheres. Some figures are thin and flat, while others are not. Some are symmetrical, while others have very irregular outlines or surfaces. All children have countless times observed common geometrical forms such as those mentioned above, and often even very young children know the names of some of them.

Even familiar things may not be fully understood

But perhaps because of their very familiarity these geometric configurations are often seen without being sensed, and even when attention is focused upon them their properties may not be understood. This may well be due largely to the fact that until quite recently the mathematics of the elementary grades has given little or no overt attention to geometric ideas. But recent and current experimental work such as that done under the auspices of SMSG, the Madison Project, and other comparable groups is revealing possibilities for unlocking hitherto unsuspected reservoirs of ability and interest even in very young students. There is a clear and growing trend toward teaching a considerable amount of informal geometry in the elementary school as well as in the junior high school. Children have great curiosity, and well-conducted study of the properties of geometric figures seldom fails to capture their interest.

The main objective of geometrical instruction in the junior high school is to help the students learn to clarify, organize, and extend their understanding of geometrical concepts and relationships and to increase their interest in doing so. The approach is informal in the sense that it stresses understanding rather than formal proof and draws upon intuition and experimentation and conjecture as well as upon clear thinking.

Informal exploration and experimentation in measuring and in classifying, tabulating, and comparing original data and seeking for patterns can lead sometimes to the actual discovery of principles, and even if not to original discovery, at least to experimental confirmation. In either case such work provides an avenue to clear understanding and the fixation of concepts and relations, as well as being itself a powerful means of motivation. The purpose of this chapter is to consider some matters which seem important in connection with instruction in geometry at this preformal level.

THE OBJECTIVES OF JUNIOR HIGH SCHOOL GEOMETRY

The geometrical experience of most students upon entering the junior high school will have been casual rather than systematic. Students will have observed many geometric forms, some of which they can name, but they will not have thought much about the geometric properties of these forms. They will realize that some are smaller than others, but most will not have made any systematic study of geometric inequalities, and many of the concepts which these students have may be vague and perhaps con-

The objectives include extending and consolidating the geometrical background

fused. It is the function of the junior high school (1) to clarify and enlarge the student's store of geometrical concepts; (2) to systematize his geometrical information, and extend it to include some applications of geometry to everyday life; (3) to aid him in mastering the use of simple geometrical instruments and the techniques of geometric drawing, measurement, and construction; (4) to acquaint him with good geometrical notation and the application of set language to geometrical objects and relations; and (5) to bridge the gap between his largely informal early geometrical experiences and the concepts and procedures involved in the deductive proofs of geometric theorems. Such a geometry has been called "intuitive," but it is rather a geometry *sui generis*, which is characterized by intuition, experiment, conjecture, and an informal approach to the more formal processes of demonstrative geometry.

The list of objectives given above reflects broadly the more detailed recommendations for junior high school geometry published in 1959 in the Reports of the Secondary School Curriculum Committee[1] of the National Council of Teachers of Mathematics and of the Commission on Mathematics[2] of the College Entrance Examination Board. The recommendations contained in these two

[1] Report of the Secondary School Curriculum Committee, *Mathematics Teacher*, **52** (1959), 406ff.
[2] Report of the Commission on Mathematics (New York: College Entrance Examination Board, 1959), pp. 22–23.

important reports, together with numerous large-scale experimental projects that have been carried on, have exerted strong influence on modern curriculums and textbooks in mathematics, both for the junior high school and the senior high school.

More detailed
objectives

More specifically, the objectives of junior high school geometry include the ability to name, describe, identify, and draw the more familiar geometric objects and to discuss their more basic properties. Among such objects are acute, right, obtuse, and straight angles; complementary and supplementary angles; parallel, perpendicular, and oblique lines; intersecting lines, vertical angles, adjacent angles; transversal; alternate-interior and corresponding angles; the interior of an angle; interior and exterior angles of a polygon; circles, arcs, chords, central angles, and inscribed angles; and some simple three-dimensional figures such as right circular cylinders and cones, right prisms, and pyramids, and spheres. These objectives also will include the understanding of such concepts as locus, collinear and coplanar points or lines, betweenness, the interior and exterior of a simple closed-plane figure, line, line segment, interval, half-line, and ray; the measure of a quantity as a number; the measure of a line segment, an angle, an area, or a volume; congruent line segments or angles; congruent triangles and similar triangles; corresponding parts; perimeter, circumference, radius, diameter; simple geometric inequalities; the process of measurement, unit of measure, some standard units; the approximate nature of a measured value; precision and accuracy; and the metric system.

An important but more general objective is the understanding of the distinction between a conjecture based on experience or observation and a deductive proof. The technical vocabulary needed will include the names and nomenclature associated with any of the items mentioned above, concise and correct notation, and the application of set language and notation to the description of geometric objects and relations.

ANALYSIS OF THE CONTENT OF
JUNIOR HIGH SCHOOL GEOMETRY

The kinds of geometric configurations studied in the junior high school are relatively simple and relatively few. Line segments, angles, triangles and other polygons, and circles are about the only planar figures to be considered, while the list of solids includes only prisms, pyramids, cylinders, cones, and spheres. Thus, at first thought, it might seem that the instructional problems would be equally few and simple.

One must consider, however, that while a word may name a single kind of figure, it does not usually tell all that needs to be

Just to recognize
and name a figure
are not enough

known about that figure. The word "triangle" names a particular kind of configuration, but the study of triangles involves such concepts as the interior and the exterior of the triangle, betweenness, interior and exterior angles, altitudes, medians, area, etc. The word "circle" names only a single type of figure, but there are many concepts to be taught and learned about circles. Line segments and angles are not to be disposed of merely by defining or illustrating them. The mere naming and identification of these configurations are only a first step in studying them. Their properties must be investigated. Comparisons must be made. Ways of measuring them must be discovered, and means devised for making indirect measurements when direct measurement is not possible. The very meaning of "direct measurement" needs to be clarified, as also does the meaning of a "unit" and the need for and the definitions of certain standard units. Estimating and the approximate nature of measurement need to be stressed. In connection with measurement and estimating there should be some simple work involving inequalities and the associated conventional symbolism, as well as some work involving the concept and notation for vectors and simple exercises on the geometric addition of vectors.

A technical nomenclature and terminology needs to be mastered and associated with various geometric concepts. Measuring instruments need to be studied, and students need to acquire some skill and facility in their use. Properties of geometric figures and relations among such figures and their properties need to be formulated, both in words and in terms of equations or inequalities in which the variables are expressed by means of literal symbols. Formulas need to be evaluated. Symmetry, which characterizes many common geometric forms, should be given special study. The list could be extended, but enough has been said to make it clear that any analysis of the content of the informal geometry of the junior high school is a complex task.

The subject matter for study can be classified and organized in various ways. With each kind of figure are associated certain properties, concepts, and technical terms, and these need to be learned and associated with that type of figure. For example, many things need to be learned about angles: ways in which they are classified, how they are measured, conventional notation and symbolism, and contexts in which they are studied.

On the other hand, some properties, or characteristics, per se are associated with different kinds of figures. For example, all closed plane figures have characteristics which we call *perimeter* and *area*. The study of the perimeters and areas of such figures as rectangles, triangles, parallelograms, trapezoids, and circles forms an important part of the geometry of the junior high school. Similarly, volume and surface area are attributes of all solids, and the

Cross-association
of figures and
their properties is
necessary

study of these attributes of certain simple three-dimensional figures is important at this level of instruction.

Thus the analysis of the content of junior high school geometry solely according to types of figures would be incomplete, as would an analysis solely in terms of properties of figures. Certainly, each type of figure needs to be studied individually for determination of its properties, but this is not enough. Different types of figures sometimes are found to have similar properties, and this can be brought out only through comparisons. Yet the discovery of these similarities is no less important than discovery of the properties of the individual kinds of figures. Some of the significant generalizations of geometry emerge only through the cross association of the different properties of individual kinds of figures with the different types of figures which exhibit various particular properties.

ANALYSIS OF A UNIT OF INSTRUCTION: CIRCLES

An example of how a unit in geometry can be analyzed

The present section represents an analysis, such as a teacher might make, of a unit built around a particular type of geometric figure, in this case, circles. It cannot be considered complete, but it at least suggests some of the important objectives and activities.

Vocabulary and understandings to be mastered   Circle, arc, major arc, minor arc, semicircle, quadrant, radius, radii, diameter, chord, center, circumference, area, central angle, inscribed angle, compass, tangent, secant, segment, sector, locus, pi (π), ratio, congruent circles, concentric circles, intersecting circles, circle graph, inscribed circle, inscribed polygon, interior and exterior of a circle, degree, protractor.

Important facts, relations, and principles to be established   Value of the ratio

$$\frac{\text{circumference}}{\text{diameter}}$$

and how to find either of the terms when the other is known; how to find the area of a circle; circumferences of circles are proportional to their respective diameters or radii; measures of arcs on a circle are proportional to the measures of their central angles, and vice versa; measures of arcs or measures of central angles in a circle are not in general proportional to the lengths of their respective chords; doubling the radius length doubles the circumference but does not double the area; doubling the area does not double the circumference or the diameter; any angle inscribed in a semicircle is a right angle.

Constructions   Drawing circles with given radii or diameters; drawing central angles of given sizes, using protractor; constructing chords of given lengths; constructing perpendicular bisectors of line segments; constructing tangents at given points on circles; constructing angles equal to given angles; constructing angle bisectors; making circle graphs; making designs involving circles or arcs.

Types of activities and problems   Measuring diameters, radii, and chords; measuring angles with a protractor; measuring circumferences experimentally by rolling or string wrapping; determining experimentally the approximate value of pi (π); laying out circles experimentally on the ground by use of an angle mirror, and testing with tape; solving many numerical problems for determination of such values as circumferences, radii, central angles; areas of circles, sectors, or rings; arc lengths; ratios of areas, central angles, or arc lengths. At least some of the numerical problems should be based on data obtained by measurement.

Appreciations   The many places where circular forms are found in things we see in everyday life (coins, wheels, clock faces, dishes, etc.); the use of circular forms in designs; the use and the usefulness of circular forms in manufactured products; the role of the wheel (as a circle) in our civilization; the symmetries of the circle.

MEASUREMENT, MEASURE, AND NUMBER

Many excellent discussions of the meaning of measurement and of the approximate nature of physical measurements can be found in textbooks, journals, and other publications,[3] but there is one aspect of this topic which, though always implied, is not always specifically emphasized. This is the inseparability of measure and number.

Most people probably sense, in a vague sort of way, that a measure of any kind of magnitude is expressed as a *number* of units of the kind accepted for discussion of that kind of magnitude, but teachers and textbooks do not always give this identification of measure and number the explicit emphasis it should have. Yet it is important, because it is through measurement that number endows the field of geometry with a power and definiteness that it would otherwise lack.

We must distinguish between measurements and associated measures

Definitions of units of magnitude, of course, are arbitrary. Some, such as the standard units of length, time, weight, and angle measure, will already be familiar to many junior high school students,

[3] See Bibliography for this chapter.

for whom, also, some derived units appear, intuitively, to be "natural" units, such as the unit square (generally taken as the unit of area) and the unit cube (generally taken as the unit of volume). Sometimes other less familiar units are defined and used mainly for convenience in expressing the numbers associated with the measurements. But whether the measurements are those of length, area, volume, time, work, angles, weight, temperature, or what not, every measurement of any kind can be expressed only as a *number* of units of the kind accepted for the discussion. The scaled ruler and the protractor provide means of identifying linear and angular measures with numbers. The scale on a pan balance provides a way of expressing a measure of weight as a number, and the dials on clocks or on speedometers indicate numbers which express measures of time or of speed.

The measure of anything is the number of units in its measurement

In expressing a measurement, the kind of unit, as well as the number of units, is indicated. The measure, on the other hand, is simply the number. A distinction is made, for example, between a measurement of length as 15 feet and the measure as 15. A line segment has just one length, but it has as many measures as there are different kinds of unit in terms of which the measurement could be made. Consider a segment exactly 1 yard long. In terms of yards, its measure is 1. In terms of feet, its measure is 3. In terms of inches, its measure is 36.

The numbers which indicate measures may be integers, but they need not be. They need not even be rational numbers. If a number represents an actual physical measurement, it must be regarded, of course, as an approximation, but it will still be reported as a *number* (to some degree of precision), the name of the unit being either stated or implied.

Students should associate every measure with a number

It is important for even junior high school students to recognize and become alert to this identification of measure with number. It provides a precise and unequivocal means of representing any individual measure and of comparing measures expressed in terms of the same unit. Also, there are some situations in which it is useful to compare relations among sets of measures given in terms of different kinds of units, and number provides the common denominator needed. For example, sometimes tables are drawn up which involve measures of age, weight, and height, in which units of time, weight, and distance are used. Representation of the respective measures simply as numbers facilitates ranking and comparison of the sets of measures.

VECTORS IN A PLANE

It is probable that, prior to entering the junior high school, most students will not have become acquainted with the concept of vectors. On the other hand, the simplicity of the geometrical rep-

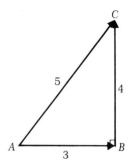

Figure 12-1
*Vector sum (resultant) of
vectors.*

Simple work with
vectors is feasible
and interesting

resentation, addition, and scalar multiplication of vectors ensures the feasibility of introducing this topic successfully even in the seventh grade. Moreover, the simple adaptation of these techniques to the solution of many interesting problems provides a good source of motivation at this level of instruction. Also, since the students are almost certain to encounter vectors in subsequent courses (geometry, physics, calculus) in high school and college, an early acquaintance with these fundamental concepts and with the associated terminology and notation seems highly desirable.

This is not to say that any extensive or abstract treatment of vectors in the junior high school is recommended. It is not. Formal treatment involves abstractions and algebraic procedures that would be totally inappropriate in the junior high school. Here the work should be concrete and intuitive. The aim should be to develop clear understanding of a few basic notions: of the distinction between a vector quantity with its dual properties of magnitude and direction and a scalar quantity which has magnitude

Some things about
vectors to be
studied

only; of just what scalar multiplication of a vector means; of the meaning of vector addition as contrasted with scalar addition; of the triangle law and the parallelogram law for finding the vector sum of two coplanar vectors; of what is meant by a set of components of a vector, by its rectangular components, and by the resultant (vector sum) of two vectors; of what is meant by the point of application of a vector and by the negative of a vector; and of the facts that under vector addition the set of coplanar vectors having the same point of application is closed, and that the commutative and associative laws hold.

Many students are fascinated to note, for example, that while in scalar addition $3 + 4 = 7$, the length of the vector sum of vectors $\overrightarrow{AB}$ and $\overrightarrow{BC}$ (as shown in Fig. 12-1), whose lengths are, respectively, 3 and 4 units, is not 7 units but 5 units.

Teachers can quickly and easily construct suitable problems by

Flexibility in
planning is
possible
the score, and can easily adapt these to students' individual differences. Copying diagrams of problems on graph paper gives
students good practice in concentrated attention and in careful
drawing and measuring, and they generally enjoy such problems.
If laboratory equipment is available, students can set up their
own experimental problems involving forces in equilibrium, and,
representing the forces by carefully drawn vectors, they can test
out their vector solutions experimentally.

PROBLEMS AND METHODS
OF INSTRUCTION

The particular instructional problems that will arise in connection
with any unit of subject matter will depend on the specific objectives of that unit. Many of these problems can be foreseen by a
careful, detailed listing of the particular understandings and abilities sought through the study of the unit. Every unit, whether it
is built around a particular kind of geometric configuration (e.g.,
angles or circles) or around a particular geometric property of cer-
Foreseeing learning
problems
tain figures (e.g., perimeters or areas) will aim at the understanding and mastery of several kinds of things. These will usually
include the mastery of an associated mathematical vocabulary;
clarification of certain geometrical concepts; understanding of relationships within and among particular geometric figures under
given conditions; the ability to make acceptable and helpful drawings and to use a suitable notation; the ability to make, interpret,
and evaluate formulas; and the ability to understand certain geometric "facts" which in the future will come to be known as
"theorems." These are the kinds of learning problems the student
will face in his study of informal geometry at this stage in his
education.

The teacher, of course, will face them too, but from a different
viewpoint. His concern must be to see that none of these problems
is neglected, to provide suitable learning situations and activities
through which the students will have optimal opportunity for
attaining the desired understandings and abilities, and to help
the students in appropriate ways to mastery of the objectives toward which the instruction is aimed.

Many approaches
can be used
The means at the teacher's disposal are numerous and varied.
Since the principal aim at this stage is knowledge and understanding rather than formal proof, any methods or devices that
will further such knowledge and understanding are appropriate.
Direct measurement with measuring instruments, including the
scaled ruler and protractor, may be used both to build clear understanding of the meaning and the approximate nature of measurement and to provide numerical data for experimental study of

geometric figures and their properties. Chalkboard drawings accompanied by suitable explanatory comment serve to clarify many ideas. Meter sticks and balances borrowed from the science laboratory can be helpful in comparing systems of measurement, in obtaining numerical information, and in making clear the principles of proportion and the solution of equations.

Experiments in paper folding can lead to discovery of principles about angles and lines. Cross-section paper facilitates understanding of relationships through the construction and interpretation of graphs. Hollow cylinders and cones filled with sand lead to conclusions about relative volumes. The principle that volumes of similar solids are proportional to the cubes of corresponding dimensions can be verified by weighing, say, wooden spheres of different sizes. Field work with simple instruments such as alidades, angle mirrors, and tapes, and even simple surveying equipment, provides interesting work in mapping small areas, and this, in turn, involves the use of many of the concepts, relations, and facts of geometry. In addition, it can contribute much to giving a sense of reality and importance to the classroom work in geometry. Indeed, there is no stage at which the mathematics laboratory plays a more important part than in connection with the informal work in geometry in the junior high school grades.

Thus the variety of means or methods of instruction appropriate to the subject and available to the teacher is large, and the ingenious teacher will find many ways of helping his students develop clear geometric concepts and understandings. Drawing, measuring, comparing, experimenting, discussing, explaining, questioning, conjecturing, verifying and testing—all these provide appropriate and helpful avenues for attaining the objectives of geometry at this stage of the students' education; so all are grist for the teacher's mill. Among them all, however, nothing is more

important than his ability to "chalk talk" well—to make good, clear chalkboard sketches and to accompany these with clear explanations of the ideas which he is trying to emphasize.

JUNIOR HIGH SCHOOL GEOMETRY
FROM A MODERN VIEWPOINT

The geometry in a modern course in junior high school mathematics gives increased attention to sharpness of definition, to new and more precise ways of thinking about geometric figures and their properties, and to the use of some modern terminology and

symbolism. The concept and notation of sets are prominent. Simple work with inequalities receives appropriate attention, as do the study of graphs and the association of ordered pairs of numbers with points in the coordinate plane. Geometric objects such as lines, line segments, half-lines, rays, planes, surfaces, and familiar geometric figures such as circles, triangles, etc., are at times described in terms of sets of points, and their descriptions given by formal set notation, terminology, and symbolism. Students are expected to make geometric interpretations of such symbolic expressions, and conversely, to be able to translate verbal descriptions of geometric objects into the notation of sets. They need to understand that $\overline{AB} \cap \overline{CD} = \{T\}$ means that T is the unique point of intersection of segments $\overline{AB}$ and $\overline{CD}$; that $\overrightarrow{SR} \cup \overrightarrow{ST}$ represents an angle whose vertex is at S; and that $l \cap m = \phi$ is simply a way of saying that two coplanar lines l and m are parallel. They need to learn to describe and illustrate what is meant by the interior of an angle, and to understand that this term applies only to angles less than 180°. They need to develop proper concepts of collinear and coplanar points, betweenness, and congruence, and they need to learn to think of ray, line segment, line, half-plane, circle, triangle, polygon, open and closed curves, and other geometric objects as sets of points to which the operations of union, intersection, and complementation can be applied. The familiar names of the common geometric figures are not discarded, but verbal descriptions may often be replaced or supplemented by statements in terms of set notation applied to sets of points. Measurement leads to situations involving inequalities, and students need to know the properties of these and to work with problems involving simple inequalities, using the conventional notation.

The introduction of a technical terminology and symbolism which were not found in the older textbooks will, of course, mean that hereafter junior high school students will have to learn to avoid vagueness in their study of geometry, to read statements very carefully, to interpret statements and symbols exactly, and to make their written work precise and unambiguous, using appropriate symbolism where it can be helpful. This of course increases the demands made on the students with respect to these matters, and one might be inclined a priori to expect that students would react to these increased demands in a negative fashion. Actually, however, this seems not to be the case. Testimony of experienced teachers who have used "modern" materials in the seventh and eighth grades indicates that for the most part students appear to take the new vocabulary and symbolism in stride and to enjoy using it.

The need to give geometric interpretation to symbolic statements, and vice-versa

Careful reading and precise written work are required

STUDENT PROBLEMS

On the whole, students in the junior high school grades who are well motivated should not be expected to have much difficulty with the informal geometry that they study. Normally, they can already identify by name some of the common figures: circles, triangles, rectangles, squares, cones, cylinders, and spheres. They will need to learn the meanings of some new words, such as chord, arc, central angle, degree, vertex, corresponding parts, perpendicular and parallel lines, intersection, altitude, base, diagonal, prism, pyramid, formula, perimeter, area, volume, and the like, as well as to associate these words with the concepts they represent. These, however, soon become familiar through illustration and repeated use in drawing, direct measurement, experimenta-

Laboratory work can help

tion, and discussion. Many kinds of laboratory exercises can be used to advantage in clarifying such concepts and in building skill and facility in direct linear and angular measurement. It is important that mastery of the fundamental concepts and associated vocabulary not be slighted, but it is easily motivated, and little difficulty need be anticipated. Estimating lengths and angles presents more of a problem. Considerable experience in drawing and measuring will usually be necessary to give students a basis for forming reliably good estimates, but through practice they can markedly improve their ability in this direction.

Formulas for the perimeters and areas of some of the simple plane figures and for the volumes of some of the common geometric solids need to be learned: in particular, the formulas for the areas of the square, circle, rectangle, triangle, parallelogram, and trapezoid, for the surface of a sphere, and for the volumes of prisms or cylinders (altitude times area of base), cones or pyramids (one-third altitude times area of base), and the volume of a sphere. With these in hand students should be able to see how to find lateral surfaces of right regular prisms and pyramids and of right circular cylinders and cones when the necessary component data are known. A good deal of practice will be needed, however, both for making the students reasonably adept in selecting or making correct formulas to fit given cases and for giving training in making numerical substitutions and performing correctly the computations involved.

Good drawings are important

Many students have difficulty in making good drawings of geometric figures, especially three-dimensional figures, yet good drawings are of key importance to students at this stage in their geometrical work. The teacher has considerable responsibility in this connection. He should take great pains to make his own chalkboard drawings correctly and carefully, so that they will really look like the objects they are supposed to represent. He can also give some specific suggestions to his students for making their drawings appear realistic.[4] A little time spent in efforts to help students improve their drawings of geometric figures will be well repaid in terms of their clearer insights into the geometric relations involved and quicker and better analyses of problems.

---

[4] Commission on Mathematics, *op. cit.*, Appendices, pp. 148–155.

HELPING STUDENTS DISCOVER RELATIONSHIPS

One of the aims in teaching any branch or any level of mathematics is to get students to try to investigate and to discover for themselves patterns which may lead to the formulation of rules or formulas which express generalized relationships. This is important for at least three reasons. First, the relationships may be useful things for the students to know. Second, a relationship which one discovers for oneself generally makes a stronger impression on one's mind and is more likely to be remembered and used than when it is presented ready-made. Finally, the *discovery* of a relationship invariably produces a sense of satisfaction and a quickening of interest, and thus provides the best kind of motivating stimulus to the student.

Three reasons why discovery is important

The geometry of the junior high school abounds in situations which can be presented in such ways as to provide students with opportunities for discovering the properties of geometric figures or relationships among these figures. These opportunities may often be used to advantage by setting them up as experimental exercises in making simple measurements, tabulating the results of these measurements, and then studying the tabulated results to see if any principle or relationship can be discovered. A well-equipped mathematics laboratory will allow for a considerable range of experimental investigation, but much can be done even if the students have available only such simple equipment as rulers and protractors.

An example of discovery by systematic measurement

For example, the sum of the measures of the angles of a triangle can be investigated in this way: Have each student in the class draw five triangles of different shapes, denoting the vertexes of each triangle by the letters A, B, and C for purposes of tabulation. Then have each student measure with his protractor (correct, say, to the nearest degree), and label, each angle of each triangle he has drawn, and tabulate his measurements in a form something like Table 12-1.

The teacher may well suggest a tabulation form

After this has been done, the measures of the three angles of each triangle can be added and the sum recorded in the fourth row

TABLE 12-1

Triangle / Angle	I	II	III	IV	V	
m∠A						Average of sums
m∠B						
m∠C						
Sum						

of the table. Most of these sums, of course, will be at least near 180°, but some will be a little less and some a little more than 180°. This is all to the good, since it will provide an appropriate occasion for a little discussion of the approximate nature of all measurement.

It would be well now to have each student compute the average of his five sums to, say, the nearest tenth of a degree, and then to list these averages on the chalkboard at the front of the room. Have the students examine this list of averages to see if any general statement can be made about them. Enough uniformity will doubtless be observed to lead some of the students to conjecture that the sum of the measures of each triangle would probably have been found to be 180° if the angles could have been measured exactly. The teacher can then point out that while the class has made measurements which are only approximations on only a few of the infinitely many triangles there are, the conjecture is indeed correct, and that in a later course the students will prove that it holds true for every plane triangle.

The fact that some of the students may already have known about this principle will hardly detract from the value of the experiment nor from their interest in it. For them it will have been an experiment in verification. For those who have not known about it before, it will represent a real discovery, which they will remember. For all, it will have provided interesting experience in measuring angles and some unsuspected and well-motivated drill in arithmetic. For further verification it can be suggested that other triangles of still different shapes can be investigated either in the manner indicated above or else by cutting out triangular pieces of paper, tearing off the corners, and fitting the pieces together with all the vertexes at a point, to see if the sum of the three angles appears in each case to be a straight angle.

The experimental procedure herein described for arriving at a general statement about the sum of the measures of the interior angles of a triangle can be extended to investigating the sum of the measures of the interior angles of other polygons as well. It will be instructive to the students to investigate the sums of the angles of quadrilaterals in the same way as for triangles. Then pentagons can be studied, and hexagons as well, if time permits. The measurements taken on the angles of these polygons will almost certainly produce agreement on the surmise that the measures of the

TABLE 12-2

Polygon	Quadrilateral	Pentagon	Hexagon
Number of sides	4	5	6
Sum of degree measures of its angles			

four interior angles of a quadrilateral probably total 360°; those of a pentagon, 540°; and those of a hexagon, 720°. If, as shown in Table 12-2, these totals are tabulated against the numbers of sides of the polygons, the ground is all prepared for the question: Can we find any relationship between the number of sides a polygon has and the probable sum of the measures of its interior angles? Some will see it immediately, and it will probably not be long before most or all of the class will have arrived at the conjecture that if 180 is multiplied by an integer which is two less than the number of sides, the product will probably be the sum of the degree measures of all the interior angles of the polygon. This conjecture can then be expressed as a rule by writing

Total number of degrees = 180 × (2 less than the number of sides)

or it can be expressed as a formula (using suitable notation):

$$S = 180(n - 2)$$

Some students may need help in this

This will represent a real discovery of a probable relationship, and it will be surprising if at least some students will not want to test it out with polygons of more than six sides. This may be suggested as an exercise, as may the question of whether this relationship holds for polygons that are not convex but have at least one interior angle greater than 180°.

Some may arrive at the conjecture by clear reasoning

It may happen that some bright student will hit upon the idea that since a polygon can be divided up into triangles by drawing appropriate diagonals, the sum of the measures of the angles of the polygon must be the same as the sum of the measures of all the angles in all these triangles, and that if the angles of each triangle total 180°, the angles of the polygon must total 180° multiplied by the number of triangles. Dissection of polygons of 4, 5, 6, 7, 8, 9 sides in this way will surely lead quickly to the discovery that in each of these cases the polygon has just two more sides than the number of triangles into which it is dissected. This provides another way for stating the conjecture as a rule:

$$\begin{pmatrix} \text{Sum of the degree} \\ \text{measures of the angles} \\ \text{of a polygon} \end{pmatrix} = 180 \times \begin{pmatrix} \text{2 less than the} \\ \text{number of sides} \end{pmatrix}$$

or

$$S \qquad\qquad = 180 \times \qquad (n - 2)$$

If this conjecture is agreed upon as reasonable, it should be pointed out that it is still only a conjecture, and that to be certain it holds true for *every* polygon it would still be necessary to *prove* beyond any doubt that (1) the sum of the measures of the angles of *every* triangle is exactly 180°, and (2) *every* polygon can be dissected in the manner indicated into exactly two less triangles than

Learning to dis-
tinguish between
a conjecture and
a proof

the number of sides of the polygon, though in the cases of some complicated concave polygons it may be helpful first to dissect the polygon into two or more simpler convex polygons and then to dissect each of these into triangles. This is a good place to discuss the meaning of a proof as contrasted with the meaning of a conjecture, no matter how convincing the conjecture may seem. Trouble in demonstrative geometry often arises from failure to keep this distinction always in mind. On the other hand, it can be pointed out that conjectures are often very useful both in suggesting probable relationships and in suggesting broad plans for their actual proofs. Thus, what started out as a simple measuring experiment can be made to yield several good educational dividends.

Some Other Opportunities

Suitable interesting
problems abound

The example discussed in the foregoing section is only one among numerous situations in the informal geometry of the junior high school which can be planned by the teacher in such a way as to guide the students toward discovery of patterns and toward conjecturing probable relationships. Space does not permit outlining any others in as much detail as the one discussed above, but a few more will be mentioned.

1 *Discovering that the sum of the degree measures of the exterior angles of a convex polygon is probably always the same (360) no matter how many sides the polygon has.* The measuring, tabulating, summing, and comparing technique can be used effectively here. By suitably defining the meaning of an exterior angle at a vertex where the interior angle is greater than 180°, cases of concave polygons could be included, but to avoid confusion it is advisable to confine the cases studied to convex polygons. Bright students may deduce the result from the conjecture about the interior angles of a polygon discussed in the preceding section.

Keep the
problems simple

2 *Discovering that the ratio of the circumference of a circle to its diameter is probably always the same, regardless of the size of the circle.* Use circular cylinders of different sizes. Have the students measure the diameters of the ends as closely as they can. Then have them wrap a string ten times around the cylinder, measure the length of the string, and take one-tenth of this length to be the circumference of the cylinder's circular end, repeating these measurements for each cylinder used. After the corresponding measures of the circumferences and the diameters have been tabulated, the ratios of the circumferences to their respective diameters should be computed and tabulated (see Table 12-3). These ratios should present only small variations, and each student can be asked to find the average of the five ratios he has found. If these

TABLE 12-3

Cylinder	I	II	III	IV	V	
Diameter						Average of ratios
Circumference						
Ratio: $\dfrac{\text{Circumference}}{\text{Diameter}}$						

Seek the pattern

averages are then listed on the chalkboard, the close uniformity may suggest the conjecture that if the measures could have been made exactly, the ratio probably would have been found to be the same in all cases. This represents an important discovery even though it still is only a conjecture, and it may well afford an appropriate occasion for some discussion by the teacher of the history and applications of the number *pi*. As always, systematic tabulation of measurements and calculations will help students to discover the pattern.

3 *Discovering relations between the areas of certain polygons and the lengths of certain lines associated with them.*

Rectangles   After the area of the unit square has been defined to be the unit of area, have the students draw several small rectangles with integral dimensions on cross-section paper, list the lengths of the sides, and count the unit squares in the rectangles.

The simplest area problem

Systematic tabulation of the resulting numbers will facilitate comparison. In the cases of small rectangles, this comparison should quickly suggest a general relation among the dimensions and the area of a rectangle, and this suspected relation can be tested out with some larger rectangles. The inevitable verification will surely bring agreement on the conjecture that this relation probably holds for all rectangles. This technique can be used also to point out that the formula merely provides an efficient method of counting the units of square measure.

Parallelograms   Parallelograms may now be studied. It may surprise some students to find that the products of the measures of two adjacent sides will not, in general, give the measure of the area of the parallelogram, as it did in the case of the rectangle, but the use of squared paper for drawings or cutouts will almost surely soon suggest that parallelograms can probably be transformed into rectangles having the same areas as the parallelograms by cutting

Dissecting and re-arranging parts

each parallelogram perpendicular to its longer sides and refitting the pieces as indicated in Fig. 12-2. If the resulting figure is indeed a rectangle, its area may now be found by using the relation found for rectangles, noting, however, that one of the sides of the rec-

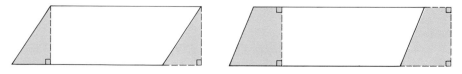

Figure 12-2
Finding the area of a parallelogram.

tangle will now have the length of the altitude of the parallelogram rather than the length of one of its sides.

From parallelo-grams to triangles

Triangles   Next, it may be noted by some students that a diagonal of a parallelogram divides the parallelogram into two triangles which appear to be alike. Cutting along the diagonal and fitting one of the triangles on the other will tend to confirm this idea, and this may suggest that the area of one of the triangles is probably half the area of the parallelogram. This should lead students to conjecture that the area of any triangle may be found by taking half the product of the measures of its base and its altitude.

From triangles to trapezoids

Trapezoids   Once a probable relation among the base, the altitude, and the area of a triangle is accepted, it can be noted that a diagonal of a trapezoid divides the trapezoid into two triangles whose altitudes have the same measure but whose bases may have different lengths. Most students will not be slow to note that if the areas of these triangles are found separately, the area of the trapezoid can be found by adding the areas of the two triangles. The way is now cleared for the students to try to formalize this into a rule or formula, thereby discovering the important generalized relation among the measures of the bases, the altitude, and the area of a trapezoid. As students try to formalize this general relation, it will be appropriate, and perhaps necessary, for the teacher to call attention to a common factor in two of the terms, and to suggest that the distributive law can be invoked in order to put the rule or formula into its most condensed general form.

Other relationships among geometric figures which can be investigated profitably by students include the probable relations between the areas of similar plane figures and the lengths of corresponding line segments in the figures; an approximate relation between the area of a circle and the length of its radius; the probable relation between the measures of central angles in a circle and of their intercepted arcs; the problem of finding a formula which would probably give the area of a sector of a circle in terms of the measures of its central angle and the radius of the circle.

The Pythagorean
theorem and some
applications

The Pythagorean relation for right triangles will probably have to be explained and illustrated by the teacher, but once it is understood and accepted by the students, the way is cleared for them to investigate some other relations in which it is involved. Among these may be mentioned the problems of finding relations between the length of a side and the area of the equilateral triangle or a regular hexagon, and the relations between the area of a circle and that of a circumscribed square, an inscribed square, and an inscribed or circumscribed regular hexagon.

Some students will be able to discover and state general rules for finding the volume and the lateral area or total area of a right circular cylinder in terms of the measures of its altitude and the radius of its base; a way for finding the volume of a right prism in terms of its altitude and the area of its base; and a way for finding the lateral area of a right prism in terms of its altitude and the perimeter of its base.

Still further opportunities for guiding students toward the discovery of geometric properties or relationships could be cited, but these will suffice. Any teacher who capitalizes on even a few of those mentioned will be encouraged by the increased student interest to seek other situations in which he can plan the work of the students to this end. Careful planning is very important.

Careful planning
is important

In experiments involving measurement, systematic tabulation of the numerical data is a great help to the students in making comparisons and seeking to discover patterns. The teacher may, without detriment to the students' initiative, suggest efficient tabulation forms. In other cases the suggestion, without comment, of drawing certain auxiliary lines may make it easier for students to discover relationships. Many students will need some such working suggestions, but beyond these they should be left pretty much on their own, so that when they do find patterns or relationships, they can feel with pride that they have discovered something for themselves. There is no stronger or better motivation than this.

SPECIAL WORK FOR
BRIGHT STUDENTS

The examples which have been suggested in the foregoing sections represent situations in which it can reasonably be expected that the majority of students in normal classes will be able to discover the principles or relations toward which the exercises are pointed, though some will make the discoveries more quickly than others. In some cases it is advisable for the teacher to lay out the general aim of the investigation, and sometimes to suggest methods of tabulating data to facilitate comparison, but in the instances given, the patterns or relations sought are fairly easy to discover.

It often happens that there will be one or more students in a class who have unusual capabilities and insights and who can work more independently and with fewer suggestions than the rest of the class may need. The following examples are suggested as being representative of kinds of geometrical problems which may appropriately be assigned for independent investigation by these bright seventh- or eighth-grade students.

Provide challenging work for bright students

1   See if you can discover a way, without using a protractor, to construct a line *l* which will be perpendicular to a given line *m* (*a*) at a given point *P* in line *m*, and (*b*) through a given point *P* that is not in line *m*.

2   Suppose *l* is a given line and *P* is a given point not in line *l*. See if you can discover a way, without using a protractor, to construct a line *m* which will contain the point *P* and be parallel to line *l*.

3   See if you can devise a way to determine the length of a diagonal of a rectangular solid in terms of the measures of its three mutually perpendicular edges.

Inequalities find a place

4   See if you can discover an order relation between the measures of the sides of a scalene triangle and the measures of the angles opposite those sides. If you can, try to formulate it as a rule.

5   A geometrical solid bounded by planes is called a polyhedron. Every polyhedron has a number of faces, a number of edges, and a number of vertexes. If we let *F* be the number of faces, *E* the number of edges, and *V* the number of vertexes, see if you can find a relation among *F, E,* and *V* that appears to hold true for polyhedrons in general.

6   Let *a* and *b* be the measures of a pair of corresponding sides of two similar rectangles, *A* and *B*. See if you can find a relation between the measures of the areas of *A* and *B* which can be expressed in terms of the measures of the sides *a* and *b*.

7   With the unit square defined as the unit of area, the measure of the area of any square is found by multiplying together the linear measures of two adjacent sides of the square. Suppose that a new unit of area were taken to be the area of an equilateral triangle with each side 1 unit in length. See if you can discover a way to find the area of any equilateral triangle in terms of this new unit of area and the lengths of two adjacent sides of the triangle. If you do discover a way, try to make it into a rule or formula, and compare it with the rule given above for finding the area of any square in terms of square units of area.

8   Draw four similar triangles, *R, S, T,* and *W,* such that the bases of *S, T,* and *W* are, respectively, two, three, and four times as long as the base of *R*. If the area of *R* is taken to be 1 unit of area, what are the respective areas of *S, T,* and *W*? These results may suggest a probable relation between the areas of *any* two similar triangles in terms of the lengths of pairs of corresponding sides of the two triangles. See if you can discover and state such a relation.

How a generalization may be approached

9   If you were successful with exercise 8, see if you can show that the relation you discovered there applies also to similar parallelograms, as well as to similar triangles.

10   Suppose that two congruent circles *A* and *B* are tangent to each other and that both are internally tangent to a larger circle *C*, as shown in

Fig. 12-3. See if you can find a numerical relation between the measures of area of circle C and circle A. If you can find such a relation, express it as a formula.

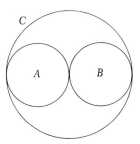

Figure 12-3
Exercise 10.

Translating verbal
statements into
set notation

11 Considering lines, rays, segments, etc., as sets of points, express the following verbal descriptions of geometric objects or situations as sets of points, using set notation. Draw a diagram to illustrate each.
 a. Lines $\overleftrightarrow{AB}$ and $\overleftrightarrow{CD}$ intersect in point P.
 b. Lines l and m are parallel.
 c. Lines m and n are parallel. Line l intersects line m at point A, and l intersects n at point B.
 d. The angle ABC.
 e. Lines l, m, and n exist, but do not all pass through the same point.

12 Illustrate each of the following geometric objects or situations by a diagram, and describe it in words. Let P and X represent points.

Interpreting set
notation

 a. S and T are sets of points, and $S \cap T = \phi$
 b. $\{P | P \in \overline{AB}\} \subseteq \{P | P \in \overline{AC}, \text{ and } AB \neq \overline{AC}\}$
 c. $T = \{X | X \in \overleftrightarrow{AB} \text{ and } X \in \overleftrightarrow{CD}\}$, and no three of the points A, B, C, D are collinear.
 d. $\{X | A \text{ and } B \text{ are distinct points, and } B \text{ is between } A \text{ and } X\}$
 e. Let S and T be intersecting circles and their interiors. Describe $\{X | X \in S \cup T \text{ and } X \notin S \cap T\}$

SPECIAL WORK FOR
SLOW LEARNERS

At the other end of the spectrum, most classes will have some students whose work, for various reasons, will not be as efficient as that of the majority of the class. Some have reading difficulties, and some may have had unfortunate experiences with mathematics in previous courses. Such students are likely to need more individual help than many of their classmates. They may need easier problems, or they may need to go more slowly and to take the work in smaller bits, with more leading questions and suggestions from the teacher. Experience has indicated that in many cases these slow learners can learn mathematics rather effectively if the work is taken at a leisurely pace and if their teachers get to understand

Don't force the pace

their learning problems and give them wise and sympathetic help where it is needed. These students need to have the encouragement engendered by success in their work. Never understanding and never being right is a deadening experience. Consequently, it is desirable to give them some tasks which they will find interesting and at which they can almost surely succeed, as well as some which they will find more challenging. Nearly all textbooks contain some work designed for slow learners, but at times special problems serve to increase their interest. Like all students, they get a "lift" when they can feel they have discovered something for themselves. Teachers can devise many situations in the informal geometry of the seventh and eighth grades to supplement the textbooks. The following list is merely suggestive of some such problems. In assigning them to slow learners, teachers should make sure that the students understand the meanings of the key words and concepts involved.

Discovery is good motivation

1   Express as a formula the relation of the time elapsed and the distance covered by a piece of heavy road machinery moving at a constant speed of 8 miles per hour. Then make a table and a graph representing this relation. If the speed were greater than 8 miles per hour, what effect would this have on the appearance of the graph?

Discovery of this kind spurs interest

2   See if you can discover any relation among the lengths of the sides of a triangle which you believe holds true for all triangles. If you can, explain what this relation is.

3   Draw several isosceles triangles of different shapes. In each of these measure the angles opposite the equal sides, and see if you can find any relation between the pair of angles that seems to be true in every case. If you can, state this relation and tell whether you think it probably holds true for all isosceles triangles.

4   Draw any triangle, and then see if you can find and describe a way (or perhaps more than one way) to construct another triangle congruent to (just like) the first one without measuring any distances or angles with your ruler or protractor. If you can discover any method or methods, describe it or them.

Conjectures formed in these ways will be remembered

5   Draw several triangles of different sizes in which the corresponding angles have, respectively, equal measures. You will note that these triangles have the same shape. Then measure and tabulate the lengths of all sides of these triangles. See if you can make any valid statement about the lengths of the *corresponding* sides of these triangles. If you can, do you think this statement would hold true for *all* triangles that have the same shape? Triangles that have the same shape are called "similar triangles."

This provides good practice in making generalizations

6   Draw a straight-line segment $\overline{AB}$ and label two points in it, P and Q. Now, using your protractor, draw segments $\overline{PR}$ and $\overline{QS}$ on the same side of $\overline{AB}$ and through P and Q, respectively, so that $\angle APR \cong AQS$. Do $\overline{PR}$ and QS appear to have any geometric relation to each other? If so, what is it? Repeat this exercise several times, and see if you can make any general statement about it which you think would be true in all such cases.

7   When two lines intersect, any pair of nonadjacent angles is called a pair of vertical angles. Draw several pairs of intersecting lines and measure all the angles in each diagram. See if you can discover any

general statement which you think probably holds true for *every* pair of vertical angles. Maybe you can even prove that it is always true. See if you can.

8 A rhombus is a quadrilateral all of whose sides have the same length. See what you can find out about the measures of the angles formed where the diagonals of a rhombus intersect.

9 See if you can find a way to construct the perpendicular bisector of a line segment without using your protractor.

10 Suppose the length of one diagonal and the length of one side of a rhombus are given. See if you can find one or more ways to construct the rhombus with straightedge and compass.

11 Draw several triangles of different shapes and sizes, and draw the perpendicular bisectors of the three sides of each triangle. See if you can make any statement about the three perpendicular bisectors of the sides of a triangle which appears to be true for all your triangles. If you can, tell what it is, and whether you think it probably holds true for all triangles.

12 Find out how to construct the medians of a triangle. Then repeat exercise 11, but using the medians of a triangle instead of the perpendicular bisectors of the sides.

Important geometric principles emerge from these problems

13 Find out how to construct an angle bisector if you do not already know how. Then repeat exercise 11, but using the bisectors of the angles of a triangle instead of the perpendicular bisectors of the sides.

14 When two straight lines intersect, four pairs of adjacent angles are formed. Draw several such pairs of intersecting lines, and in each case draw the bisectors of one pair of adjacent angles. See if you can find any relation between the two bisectors which seems to hold true in every case, and tell what it is. Do you think it probably holds true in all such cases?

15 Draw several circles of different sizes, and in each of them draw two chords of equal length. See if you can find any statement which you believe would be true in all such cases (*a*) about the lengths of the arcs which the two equal chords intercept; (*b*) about the central angles which these chords subtend; (*c*) about the distances of the equal chords from the centers of the circles.

16 Repeat exercise 15, but this time with one chord longer than the other.

17 Draw several pairs of parallel lines, each pair cut by a transversal. Measure each pair of alternate-interior angles. Does there appear to be any relation between the measures of each pair? Measure each pair of corresponding angles. Does there appear to be any relation between the measures of each pair? See if you can make any general statement that you think may be true (*a*) about the measures of any such pair of alternate-interior angles, and (*b*) about the measures of any such pair of corresponding angles.

Students will work with interest on problems like these

18 Draw two parallel lines cut by a transversal, and note the two angles formed between the parallel lines and on the same side of the transversal. Then draw the bisectors of these two angles. What geometric relation, if any, seems to be true about these bisectors? Repeat several times and see if you can discover any general relation of one bisector to the other which seems to hold true in all these cases. Do you think it would probably hold true in *all* such cases?

19 Each of the following triples of numbers represents the lengths of the three sides of a triangle. Use the Pythagorean theorem to determine in each case whether the triangle is a right triangle or not.

a. 3, 4, 5	*b.* 6, 8, 10	*c.* 12, 16, 20
d. 5, 12, 13	*e.* 10, 24, 26	*f.* 20, 48, 52
g. 4, 5, 6	*h.* 1½, 2, 2½	*i.* 10, 12, 15

Sound and painless learning results

20 Find out from your textbook or from your teacher what is meant by a convex plane figure and by its interior. Then draw three polygons each of which, with its interior, is a convex figure. Explain why your drawings satisfy this requirement.

21 Draw three polygons such that no one of them is a convex figure. Explain why your drawings satisfy this requirement.

22 Make ten interesting geometric designs, using only your straightedge and compass.

23 Make good drawings to represent (*a*) a triangular prism; (*b*) a rectangular prism with one of its diagonals shown; (*c*) a right circular cone showing its altitude from the vertex; (*d*) a right prism whose base is a pentagon; (*e*) a right circular cone cut by a plane parallel to the base.

EXERCISES

1 In this chapter there is an analysis of a unit of instruction organized about the study of circles. Make a similar analysis of a unit of instruction organized about one of the following types of figure: triangles, polygons, cylinders, prisms, cones, pyramids, or spheres.

2 Make an analysis of a unit of instruction organized for the study of perimeters of familiar plane figures.

3 Make an analysis of a unit of instruction organized for the study of the areas of simple plane geometric figures.

4 Make an analysis of a unit of instruction organized for the study of volumes of the simple geometric solids.

5 Make an analysis of a unit of instruction organized for the study of surface areas of right regular prisms and pyramids, right circular cylinders and cones, and spheres.

6 Construct a spelling list of fifty words encountered in the study of informal geometry. If you give it as a test to your classes, it is likely that you will get some misspellings.

7 In the junior high school how much emphasis should be placed on the approximate nature of measurement and on the results of computing with approximate data?

8 Explain how to find the relative error in a measured value, and give some illustrations.

9 Compile a conversion table for translating measurements of length and area and volume made in our common English system of units into units of the metric system, and vice versa.

10 Make a large 360° protractor by trimming a piece of polar coordinate paper around its largest circle and cutting a small hole in the center through which the vertex of an angle can be seen. This can be used satisfactorily as a chalkboard protractor.

11 In connection with symmetrical figures, explain and give examples to illustrate what is meant by "symmetry" with respect to a line, with respect to a plane, and with respect to a point.

12 Explain to your class what is meant by drawing to scale. What properties of similar figures are involved in a scale drawing? Is a map in effect a scale drawing? Discuss this.

13 Find at least one method of mapping small outdoor areas by use of simple field instruments, such as the plane table, alidade, and tape, and demonstrate or describe this to your class.

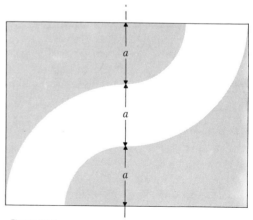

Figure 12-4
Exercise 14.

14 Figure 12-4 is a rectangular figure in which the curved lines are composed of quadrantal arcs of circles whose radii can be determined from the dimensions shown. Make a formula for the area of the shaded part of the figure in terms of a. Evaluate this area if $a = 5$.

15 Explain as you would to a seventh-grade class why the area of a trapezoid can be found to be half the area of a parallelogram the length of whose base is the sum of the lengths of the bases of the trapezoid, and the length of whose altitude is the same as that of the trapezoid. (See Fig. 12-5.)

Figure 12-5
Exercise 15.

16 Explain, as you would to a class, why the area of a triangle can be regarded as the area of a trapezoid one of whose parallel sides has a measure of zero.

17 Explain as you would to a seventh-grade class how to find the total surface and the volume of the tank shown in Fig. 12-6 in terms of the dimensions r, s, and t shown on the diagram. Make formulas for finding the total surface and the volume. What difficulties would you expect seventh-graders to have with this problem, and why?

18 Let the diameter of a circle be divided into a number of segments, not necessarily equal, and on each of these segments as a diameter let a small circle be made. If the circumferences of all the little circles were added together, would the sum be less than, equal to, or greater than the circumference of the original circle? How do you know? Is the answer intuitively evident?

19 If $ABCD$ is a trapezoid with bases $\overline{AB}$ and $\overline{DC}$, and with diagonals $\overline{AC}$ and $\overline{BD}$ intersecting at E, compare the areas of triangles AED and CEB, and write down the numerical ratio of these areas. Explain as you would to a junior high school class.

20 Using compass and straightedge only, construct some designs which you think would be interesting examples for a junior high school class. What values can be gained by having the students construct some such designs?

21 How would you get a seventh-grade class to understand what is meant by the statement that areas of similar plane figures are proportional to the squares of the lengths of corresponding line segments in the figures? Give some examples to illustrate this principle.

22 Find the lateral area, total area, and volume of a right circular cone whose base has a radius of 4.00 inches if the slant height of the cone is 7.00 inches. Explain.

23 Explain and illustrate the following terms as you would to a junior high school class: ray, coplanar, variable, ordered pair, locus, closed interval (on a number line), open interval, set, subset, union and intersection (of subsets), coordinate axes, coordinates of a point, and convex polygon.

24 In Figure 12-7, identify and describe each of the following:

a. $\overrightarrow{EA} \cup \overrightarrow{ED}$ *b.* $\overrightarrow{DE} \cup \overrightarrow{DA}$
c. $(\overline{AE} \cup \overline{ED}) \cup \overline{DA}$ *d.* $\overline{AE} \cup (\overline{ED} \cup \overline{DA})$
e. $\overline{AB} \cap \overline{CD}$ *f.* $\overline{RB} \cap \overline{TD}$
g. $\{H\} \cap \{K\}$ *h.* $\overline{EB} \cap \overline{HK}$

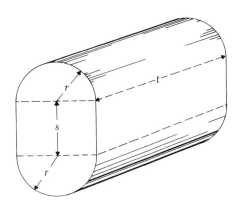

Figure 12-6
Exercise 17.

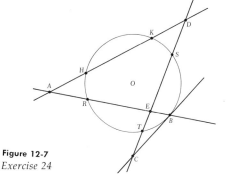

Figure 12-7
Exercise 24

25 Make graphs of the subsets R, S, and T of the set of numbers on the real number line if $S = \{n \,|\, 3 \leq n \leq 5\}$, $T = \{n \,|\, 0 \leq n \leq 3\}$, and $R = \{n \,|\, 4 \leq n \leq 6\}$. Describe and graph $(R \cup S) \cup T$.

26 Is $(7,2) \in S$, where $S = \{(x,y) \,|\, x$ and y real numbers and $3x - y = 1\}$? Translate this question into words, and explain and justify your answer as you would to a junior high school class. What difficulties might the students be expected to have?

27 Let $S = \{(x,y) \,|\, x, y$ real; $x^2 + y^2 = 25\}$. Make a good graph of S, and explain it as you would to a junior high school class.

28 Compare the sections on geometry in three different textbooks on junior high school mathematics published since 1970 with those found in textbooks published before 1960. In what ways are they alike, and in what ways do they differ? Report your findings to the class.

BIBLIOGRAPHY

Adler, Irving: "The Great Golden Book of Mathematics" (New York: Golden Press, 1960).

Auclair, Jerome A., and Thomas R. Hillman: A Topological Problem for the Ninth Grade Mathematics Laboratory, *Mathematics Teacher*, **61** (1968), 503–507.

Banks, J. Houston: "Elements of Mathematics," 3d ed. (New York: Allyn & Bacon, Inc., 1969), pp. 257–310.

Beckenbach, Edwin F.: Geometric Proofs of the Irrationality of $\sqrt{2}$, *Arithmetic Teacher*, **15** (1968), 244–250.

Brumfiel, Charles F., Robert E. Eicholz, and Merrill E. Shanks: "Fundamental Concepts of Elementary Mathematics" (Reading, Mass.: Addison-Wesley Publishing Company, Inc., 1962), pp. 237–303.

Dennis, J. Richard: Informal Geometry through Symmetry, *Arithmetic Teacher*, **16** (1969), 423–426.

Dotson, W. G., Jr.: On the Shape of Curves, *Mathematics Teacher*, **62** (1969), 91–94.

Egsgard, John C.: Geometry All around Us, *Arithmetic Teacher*, **16** (1969), 437–445.

Farrell, Margaret A.: Patterns of Geometry, *Arithmetic Teacher*, **16** (1969), 447–450.

"Geometry," Experiences in Mathematical Discovery Series (Washington, D.C.: National Council of Teachers of Mathematics, 1966), pp. 1–93. (Pamphlet.)

Hawley, Newton S.: Geometry for the Primary Grades, *Arithmetic Teacher*, **8** (1961), 374–376.

Homagh, Fritz: Concerning Plane Geometry in the Textbooks of Classes 7 and 8, *Mathematics Teacher*, **60** (1967), 165–172.

Keedy, M. L.: Areas, Volumes, and Sweeps, *School Science and Mathematics*, **68** (1968), 275–288.

Krause, Eugene F.: Elementary School Metric Geometry, *Arithmetic Teacher*, **15** (1968), 673–682.

Marx, Robert: Mathematics Can Be Fun, *School Science and Mathematics*, **68** (1968), 123–129.

Meserve, Bruce E., and Max A. Sobel: "Mathematics for Secondary School Teachers" (Englewood Cliffs, N.J.: Prentice-Hall, Inc., 1962), pp. 177–191.

————: "Introduction to Mathematics" (Englewood Cliffs, N.J.: Prentice-Hall, Inc., 1964), pp. 78–100.

Mikula, Thomas: The Trigonometry of the Square, *Mathematics Teacher*, **60** (1967), 354–357.

Neufeld, K. Allen: Discovery in Number Operations through Geometric Constructions, *Arithmetic Teacher*, **15** (1968), 695–700.

Ogletree, Earl: Geometry: An Artistic Approach, *Arithmetic Teacher*, **16** (1969), 457–461.

Payne, Joseph N., and Robert C. Seber: Measurement and Approximation, *Twenty-fourth Yearbook* (Washington, D.C.: National Council of Teachers of Mathematics, 1959), pp. 182–228.

Pearcy, J. F. F., and K. Lewis: "Experiments in Mathematics, Stages 1, 2, and 3" (Boston: Houghton Mifflin Company, 1967).

Ranucci, Ernest R.: A Tiny Treasury of Tessellations, *Mathematics Teacher*, **61** (1968), 114–117.

Rosskopf, Myron T.: Geometric Proof in the Eighth Grade, *Mathematics Teacher*, **54** (1961), 402–405.

Sanders, Walter A., and J. Richard Dennis: Congruence Geometry for Junior High School, *Mathematics Teacher*, **61** (1968), 354–369.

Schaaf, William L.: "Basic Concepts of Elementary Mathematics" (New York: John Wiley & Sons, Inc., 1960), pp. 50–64.

Sensiba, Daniel E.: Geometry and Transformations, *Twenty-seventh Yearbook* (Washington, D.C.: National Council of Teachers of Mathematics, 1963), pp. 302–311.

Smart, James R.: "Introductory Geometry: An Informal Approach" (Belmont, Ga.: Brook/Cole Publishing Company, 1967).

Sobel, Max A.: "Teaching General Mathematics" (Englewood Cliffs, N.J.: Prentice-Hall, Inc., 1967), pp. 26–52.

Strangman, Kathryn Besic: Grids, Tiles, and Area, *Arithmetic Teacher,* **15** (1968), 668–672.

Vigilante, Nicholas J.: The Address of a Point, *Arithmetic Teacher,* **15** (1968), 689–693.

Weiss, Sol: Junior High School Mathematics for the Low Achiever, *Texas Mathematics Teacher* (May, 1965), 1–3, 5.

Wren, F. Lynwood: "Basic Mathematical Concepts" (New York: McGraw-Hill Book Company, 1965), pp. 190–247.

the teaching of geometry in the senior high school

In this and the following chapter it is our intention to discuss some of the important elements of high school geometry, to call attention to some potential difficulties of students, and to offer suggestions which may be of practical help to teachers of high school geometry. If at times the discussion takes the form of direct substantive statements about the mathematical content or concepts or relations under consideration, our intention is, simply, that such statements represent matters which we feel need to be made clear to high school students, and which the teacher should emphasize in his own discussion with his students.

THE GEOMETRY COURSE AND THE TEACHER

The informal geometry of the junior high school will constitute the complete geometrical program for many students. For those who continue the study of geometry in the senior high school, the concepts and relations gained earlier through intuition, experiment, and conjecture will often be helpful, but the main objective of the course will not be the same. From this point on, in addition to extending the student's background of geometric concepts and facts, the course will aim mainly at giving the students deeper insight into how geometry may be structured; how a large body of geometric facts and relations can be made to grow by logical processes from a few simple statements made at the outset. It will continue the effort of the algebra program to develop habits of careful critical thinking and a feeling for the meaning of implication and for the roles of undefined terms, definitions, postulates, and theorems in the deductive process. It should also aim at developing insight into analogous properties and relations of geometric objects in two-dimensional and three-dimensional space, and it should exemplify and emphasize elements of mathematical structure which permeate not only geometry but other branches of mathematics as well, and which thus help to unify mathematics as a whole.

The primary objective of the geometry course is different in high school

The geometry course of the future will not be the same as the traditional course of the past. Many new topics are clamoring for inclusion, each with its proponents, and different approaches are being proposed and used in experimental programs. Textbooks will vary considerably in content and organization. This is a healthy state of affairs, because it makes for flexibility, allows for preferences, and provides teacher motivation. But no one-year course can include all the things that are being proposed.

Trends in pre-high-school work in geometry

Discernible trends for the elementary and junior high school years appear to include increased emphasis on the development of geometric concepts, visualization, and the recognition and naming of common geometric forms. There will be more informal experience with straightedge-and-compass constructions, and mensuration will be used to stress the continual interplay of geometric, algebraic, and arithmetic concepts. The formal high school course

Changes in the high school course are to be expected

in geometry will continue for still some time to give primary emphasis to postulational synthetic geometry, but greater attention will be paid to three-dimensional figures, along with their two-dimensional counterparts, as well as to the more basic ideas and techniques of coordinate and vector geometry.

Some things the teacher must know and do

The study of geometry will continue to present many students with difficulties, and each teacher should give careful attention to finding ways of helping his students attain the goals of the course. He needs to have a clear understanding of the nature of deductive reasoning and of the significance of demonstration if he is to help his students get this understanding. He needs to know the distinguishing characteristics of various techniques and patterns of careful reasoning, and he needs to be aware of difficulties that students are likely to have in their efforts to achieve understanding. He needs to keep in mind, as well as to remind his students, that mathematical proofs are not generally discovered in the elegant finished form in which they are presented in textbooks or treatises, and he needs to understand that unless care is taken, the technical terminology and symbolism may often be a barrier to understanding. It is most important that a teacher help his students become proficient in reading the mathematical discourse of their textbooks and in actually thinking in terms of the mathematical symbolism, as well as in writing out their own work.

HOW DEDUCTIVE GEOMETRY IS STRUCTURED

It is probably true that a good deal of the difficulty, frustration, and lack of interest which many students have experienced in high school geometry has stemmed from their lack of understanding of how it is structured, i.e., their failure to sense the fact that, like algebra and arithmetic, the development of its theorems follows a definite deductive pattern. In order to enjoy any game one has to understand the object of the game, the rules that govern it, and the meanings and implications of the terms used in talking about it. In a sense deductive geometry can be thought of as a sort of game. In order to pursue its study with real satisfaction, one needs to understand what its rules are, and how the superstructure of theorems grows as a continually expanding set of necessary consequences of a small number of primitive terms and statements which combine to give a point of departure. Unlike conjectures, which, although often suggestive, provocative, and pedagogically valuable, must still be regarded as tentative, the only logically acceptable end result in deductive geometry is the theorem: a proposition for which a valid proof has been given.

How geometry is like a game

The rules are simply that (1) the proof of every new statement (theorem) undertaken, in order to be valid, must be shown to be a chain of necessary consequences that begin with an accepted hypothesis (the "if" part) and end with the conclusion (the "then" part) whose proof is sought; and (2) every link in the chain must be, itself, the necessary consequence of some combination of accepted primitive statements and of theorems which have been proved previously. The object of the game is for the student to see if he can prove the theorem in question, keeping strictly within these rules.

The rules

The object

If teachers could get their students really to understand and be alert to these rules and to hold themselves responsible for not violating them, the students would be in a position to view the building of proofs as, indeed, a game in which they are matching their wits against the requirement previously stated, namely, that they must not leave any weak (unsupported) links in the chain of their argument leading to the conclusion. Working on a proof from this viewpoint of "seeing if you can do it" can actually be fun. It can provide intellectual stimulation and enjoyment of the highest order, and this is the best kind of motivation.

The game concept can be finest kind of stimulus

Unfortunately, it is to be feared that a good many students never get this viewpoint clearly established in their minds. When this is the case the fault may lie partly with the teachers. It is a responsibility of every teacher to try to give his students this view of demonstrative geometry as a sort of intellectual game—a testing of their ingenuity and knowledge in seeing if they can produce for each theorem a sequence of statements that will hang together and lead inevitably to the desired conclusion, with every step or link in the sequence justified by some combination of the accepted primitive terms and statements, the accepted special hypotheses, and theorems that have already been proved. The relative mathematical immaturity of most high school students makes it unrealistic to expect absolute rigor in this, and some allowance will

Clear thinking
and rigor

have to be made. A good line of reasoning is worth more than insistence upon a degree of rigor which may be inappropriate at this level and which may seem unnecessary to the students. But a growing appreciation of the role of rigor in a proof is an important element in developing a clear concept of what a deductive proof really is.

THE PRIMITIVE TERMS
AND STATEMENTS

It may be helpful to have some class discussion of the nature and role of what we have called the primitive terms and statements: undefined terms, definitions, and postulates. It should be explicitly pointed out to students that these are made in a somewhat arbitrary manner and are simply accepted in order to provide a starting point and a language for talking and reasoning about properties of the geometric figures to be studied and about relations among them. It should be made clear that these geometric figures are generally regarded as sets of points in a plane or in space, such as points, lines, rays, segments, polygons, circles, and prisms, and that most of them can be defined in terms of others. An angle is defined as the union of two rays with a common endpoint; a circle, as the set of all points in a plane that are at a given distance from a fixed point in the plane; a sphere, as the set of all points in space at a given distance from a fixed point in space; a triangle, as the union of segments $\overline{AB}$, $\overline{BC}$, and $\overline{CA}$ if A, B, and C are three noncollinear points.

The first building
blocks

Why some un-
defined terms and
postulates are
needed

These seem straightforward enough until we ask: What is a point? What is a straight line? What is a plane? What is space? Point out that to these questions we can find no satisfactory definitions in terms of still simpler concepts, so that these are left as undefined terms to be used in defining other terms and in talking about geometric figures. It might seem desirable to define *every* term, using only terms that have already been defined, but in the case of the *first* definition this would not work because there would not be any previously defined terms to use. Thus, for a start, it is necessary simply to assign words to represent a few of the most basic geometric concepts so that they can be used in defining other terms.

The case of postulates and theorems is somewhat analogous to this. The proofs of theorems usually involve the use of previously proved theorems, but this could not happen in the case of the *first* theorem because there would not be any previously proved theorems to use. Therefore, for a start, a few basic statements must be taken for granted without proof. These are the postulates of the system. By use of these postulates and the definitions and undefined terms, one or more simple theorems may be proved, and these, in turn, can be used in helping to prove other theorems.

It is important for students to understand how their geometry is structured, and teachers ought to make special efforts to ensure that they do. Postulates, in particular, ought to be given special attention. It should be made clear that although such terms as "set," "point," and "line" remain undefined, this does not prevent our talking about them, having common understanding of what they mean, and using synonyms and descriptions of them, so long as these are not confused with definitions. Similarly, although an axiom or postulate remains unproved, we can discuss its meaning, its reasonableness, and the implications of its denial.

A set of postulates
is arbitrarily but
purposefully
selected

In a sense the selection of a set of postulates for any mathematical system is arbitrary, but it is not merely random. The postulates of a geometry are selected to describe fundamental properties of the space in which that geometry has its setting. Since high school geometry has its setting in ordinary euclidean space (the idealized model of our familiar physical space, in which many geometric figures have familiar physical counterparts), the postulates are those which describe fundamental properties of that space. If different sets of postulates could satisfy that criterion equally well, one set might logically be used as satisfactorily as another. In this sense the selection of a set of postulates for a

The set must have
no gaps and no
contradictions

geometry is an arbitrary matter, so long as the set has no gaps and involves no contradictions. On the other hand, for either logical or pedagogical reasons, two sets might not be equally satisfactory logically, or might not be equally suitable at a given level of sophistication, and in that sense one set might be preferred over another. For example, the set of postulates given by Euclid has been used, with modifications, for centuries to form the basis of the traditional course in elementary deductive geometry. Defects and inadequacies in this set of assumptions have long been recognized by mathematicians, and many commentaries have been published in which these were considered. They will not be discussed here, except to say that the set contains no postulates that define separation and betweenness for points, lines, planes, or space, nor any which specifically associate measurement with the set of real numbers.

An early attempt
to repair defects in
the euclidean
system

In an effort to produce a set of postulates that could remedy these defects and that would be, at the same time, valid and suitable for high school students, Birkhoff and Beatley[1] proposed in 1930 a geometry course based on a different set of "fundamental principles." One of these, called the *Principle of Line Measure,* asserted that the points on a line can be numbered so that number dif-

---

[1] George D. Birkhoff and Ralph Beatley: A New Approach to Elementary Geometry, *Fifth Yearbook* (Washington, D.C.: National Council of Teachers of Mathematics, 1930), pp. 86–95.

ferences measure distance. Another, called the *Principle of Angle Measure,* asserted that all half-lines having the same endpoint can be numbered so that number differences measure angles. These later came to be commonly called *the ruler and protractor postulates,* or *the metric postulates.* This set of postulates was published later (1932) in the *Annals of Mathematics.*[2] It formed the basis for an experimental edition of a textbook which was published in 1933, and which was subsequently revised and published commercially a few years later.[3] This textbook, of course, differed radically in some ways from the traditional texts in use up to that time, and because of the inertia induced by established ideas and practices, it was so poorly received by teachers that it soon went out of print. It was simply ahead of its time. Since its publication, however, and especially since about 1960, teachers have become more receptive to new ideas, and a number of new textbooks have appeared in which the course is based substantially on the Birkhoff-Beatley postulates or their equivalent.

The main point for students to get

The point to be made here with students is simply that any set of postulates is merely a set of primary statements which are consistent and which are accepted without proof, to be used as working tools to establish other statements by deductive methods. No set of postulates is divinely ordained, but unless the postulates are consistent, the system is worthless, because conflicting implications will occur. Thus consistency is the one logical requirement for a set of postulates, which is also a requirement from a pedagogical point of view.

A LANGUAGE PROBLEM

The modern tendency to regard all geometric figures as sets of points, with the consequent introduction of set terminology and notation to describe properties of such figures or relations among them, does indeed make for greater precision and less ambiguity in statements, but it has somewhat complicated the technical language which students may find in their textbooks or reference books, and which they will need to be able to read and interpret. For students who may not have become well acquainted in earlier courses with the terminology and symbolism of sets, this creates a

The language problem arises again

language problem. The statements presented below are ways of saying certain simple things in terms of set notation that seem harder to interpret than the verbal statements. Each of the things

---

[2] G. D. Birkhoff, A Set of Postulates for Plane Geometry, Based on Scale and Protractor, *Annals of Mathematics,* **33** (1932), 329–345.

[3] George David Birkhoff and Ralph Beatley: "Basic Geometry" (Glenview, Ill.: Scott, Foresman and Company, 1940; New York: Chelsea Publishing Company, 1959).

could be said more simply, yet each statement, if properly interpreted, is correct. These statements are not to be taken as definitions, and statements so hard to interpret will hardly ever actually be found in high school textbooks. But statements involving set notation *will* be found. The statements given here have been deliberately exaggerated to point up the fact that students might run into problems of interpretation of even simpler statements made in set notation.

For example, if A, B, and C are distinct points, the statement $\overline{AB} \cup \overline{BC} = \overline{AC}$ is a way of saying (or at least implying) that these three points are collinear and that B is between A and C. The same implication could be inferred from the expression $\{A, B, C | \overline{AB} \subset \overline{AC}, B \neq A, B \neq C\}$. If A, B, C, X, Y, and Q are points in a plane such that A, B, and C are not collinear and X, Y, and Q are distinct, the expression $\{X, Q, Y | X \in \overrightarrow{BA}, Y \in \overrightarrow{BC}, \overline{XQ} \cup \overline{QY} = \overline{XY}\}$ is a way of indicating that Q is a point in the interior of angle ABC; and if l, m, and n represent lines in a plane, the pair of statements $l \cap m = \phi$, $m \cap n = \phi$, is a way of saying that lines l and n are both parallel to m and are also parallel to each other or coincident. Even so simple a concept as the point of intersection of two lines l and m might be expressed as $\{P\} = l \cap m$, or even as $\{P\} = \{X | X \in l, X \in m\}$. The expression $\overrightarrow{BA} \cup \overrightarrow{BC}$ is a way of indicating the angle ABC, and $\overline{AB} \cup \overline{BC} \cup \overline{CA}$ represents the triangle ABC if A, B, and C are not collinear. Otherwise the union is $\overline{CA}$. An angle bisector might be defined as follows: Given any $\angle ABC$ and a point D in its interior, the ray $\overrightarrow{BD}$ is the bisector of $\angle ABC$ if and only if $\overrightarrow{BD} \cup \overrightarrow{BA} \cong \overrightarrow{BD} \cup \overrightarrow{BC}$.

It is not necessary to give further examples to make the point that this symbolic language is quite different from the ordinary verbal statements which make up most ordinary discourse. It is clear, too, that if students have not learned to read and interpret the mathematical symbolism used in their books and actually to think in terms of this symbolism, they will not be able to get the correct meanings from what they read, and this precludes any meaningful work. It is true that many students (perhaps even most of those who take high school geometry) will have had some acquaintance with the notation and symbolism used for such concepts as sets, inequalities, lines, segments, rays, and angles before they get to this course. Every geometry teacher likes to hope that all his students have acquired reasonably good command

of this notation, but it is not safe to assume that this is the case. It may happen frequently that some have not. In any case teachers will be well advised to find out about this in their classes, and to take such remedial measures as may be necessary. If only a few students are found to have difficulties of this nature, individual help may be sufficient. If the difficulties are widespread, some time may need to be spent with the whole class in explanation and in drill, both in interpreting symbolic expressions and translating them into words and in translating verbal expressions into mathematical symbols. This is by no means a trivial matter, because to the students it may spell the difference between success and frustration in their work.

PLANNING PROOFS: THE ANALYTIC-SYNTHETIC APPROACH

A good many of the propositions and problems of elementary geometry are quite simple and involve proofs which are short and rather obvious. Others, however, are less simple, and the proofs of some are rather long and involved. In many cases, when no approaches seem intuitively evident, students are likely to have difficulty in getting started and in discovering and mapping out connected plans for their proofs. Yet a plan of proof is always important, and the less simple and obvious it is, the more important it is for the student to have his plan completely sketched out in his mind, and perhaps on paper, before starting to write out the formal proof of the proposition.

In cases where students have trouble in getting started or are unable to formulate a connected plan leading to the required conclusion, it may often be helpful to consider the proposition, as it were, in reverse. If a set of hypotheses implies a certain conclusion, then the conclusion *is implied by* the given set of hypotheses.

Approaching the problem in reverse may help

By supposing the conclusion to be true and then asking, "Under what circumstances would this be true?" or "By what is this implied?" one may be able to backtrack or blaze a trail of "is implied by" statements, leading without break backward from conclusion to hypotheses. If this can be done, then, since the conclusion is connected by a chain of "is implied by" statements to the hypotheses, it follows that the hypotheses are connected by an unbroken chain of "implies" statements to the conclusion. The plan of proof is then complete, and by reversing the order of the steps, the synthetic proof is established and can be written down formally.

As suggested in Chapter 3, the procedure can be represented schematically as follows:

Analysis and synthesis compared

Analysis:
Conclusion $\longleftarrow a \longleftarrow b \longleftarrow \cdots \longleftarrow m \longleftarrow n \longleftarrow$ Hypotheses
Synthesis:
Hypotheses $\longrightarrow n \longrightarrow m \longrightarrow \cdots \longrightarrow b \longrightarrow a \longrightarrow$ Conclusion

However, since schematic representations can often be clarified by concrete illustrations, the following example is given to illustrate such an analytic-synthetic attack upon a problem.

Suppose we wish to prove the following theorem.

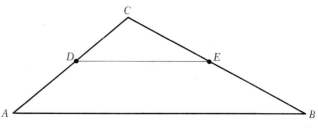

Figure 13-1
Construction for proving the theorem.

Theorem: If a straight line joins the midpoints of two sides of a triangle, then it is parallel to the third side (Fig. 13-1).

Given: ABC with $\overline{AD} \cong \overline{DC}$ and $\overline{BE} \cong \overline{EC}$.

Prove: $\overline{DE} \parallel \overline{AB}$.

An example of analysis

Since nothing is known initially about the angles in the figure, we cannot prove $\overline{DE} \parallel \overline{AB}$ directly by using any of the theorems about transversals and associated angles. An alternative method is to show that $\overline{DE}$ and $\overline{AB}$ are, or lie in, opposite sides of a parallelogram. Clearly, $ABED$ is not a parallelogram, and the figure does not appear to contain one. However, there might be a parallelogram having $\overline{AB}$ as one side and such that we could show that $\overline{DE}$ is part of the opposite side. If we could show that this is the case, our proposition would be proved.

Now, if we should construct a parallelogram $ABFD$ on $\overline{AD}$ and $\overline{AB}$ as adjacent sides (Fig. 13-2), then $\overline{DF}$ would be parallel to $\overline{AB}$ and would cut $\overline{BC}$ in some point H; so we would have $\overline{DH} \parallel \overline{AB}$. Then if we could show that points E and H coincide, this would make $\overline{DE}$ coincide with $\overline{DH}$, which is constructed parallel to $\overline{AB}$; whence $\overline{DE}$ would be parallel to $\overline{AB}$, as required. Moreover, the coincidence of points E and H would be established if we could prove $\triangle DHC \cong \triangle FHB$, because this would give $\overline{CH} \cong \overline{HB}$, making H the mid-point of $\overline{BC}$, whereas we know that E is the mid-point of $\overline{BC}$, and a line segment has only one mid-point. Finally, we see that we can actually accomplish all this because we can prove $\triangle DHC \cong \triangle FHB$ by use of the angle-side-angle theorem. That is, $\angle CDH \cong \angle BFH$, being alternate-interior angles of parallel lines; $\angle DCH \cong \angle FBH$ for the same reason; and $\overline{CD} \cong \overline{FB}$, since each is known to be congruent to $\overline{AD}$.

The analysis helps in two ways

This analysis of the problem has done two valuable things. It has given us a place to get started (proving $\triangle DHC \cong \triangle FHB$), and it has charted a sequence of steps through which we can pass from this starting point to the desired conclusion. If we start by proving $\triangle DHC \cong \triangle FHB$, we can show that H is the mid-point of $\overline{BC}$, and

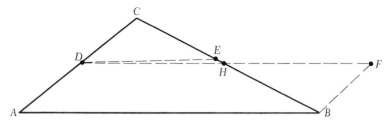

Figure 13-2

consequently is the same point as E. Thus $\overline{DE}$ coincides with $\overline{DH}$, which is constructed parallel to $\overline{AB}$; whence $\overline{DE} \parallel \overline{AB}$ as required. Once this plan is in mind, the students should have no difficulty in writing out the details of the formal proof. It may be remarked that this is not the only way of proving this proposition, but it is an interesting one.

Formulating a plan of proof is probably the most interesting, as well as the most demanding, part of the work in geometry. It

Planning proofs tests the student's ingenuity

is the creative part. It draws upon the student's store of information, and it requires him to exercise his ingenuity through speculation and conjecture and through testing his conjectures for validation or rejection. A plan that may appear plausible at first may sometimes be shown to be invalid by means of a counterexample. If a direct proof cannot be found, perhaps an indirect proof might work. If nothing else seems to provide a starting point, the analytic approach can be tried. The variety of possible approaches in the uncharted search for a plan affords play to the student's imagination and ingenuity in devising proofs and in testing them for validity.

ORIGINAL EXERCISES

For many years it has been recognized that original exercises provide probably the most effective means for the development of originality, ingenuity, and the power to do independent work in geometry. Here the student is on his own. Given a proposition to be proved or a construction problem to be solved, he needs first to interpret it so as to get his working conditions or hypotheses clearly in mind and to determine just what it is that he is to try

The student is on his own

to do. He then has to try to formulate a plan that will bring him to his objective. Finally, he must synthesize and formalize his work, justifying each step in his synthesis. He is thus faced with a variety of problems which may tax any or all of his mathematical resources. These will include not only his accumulated store of geometric facts (theorems), but also his quickness of insight, his power of analysis, his inventiveness, his ability to discriminate between relevant and irrelevant details and to synthesize those which are relevant into sound sequential argument, his tenacity and persistence, and his ability to write clear, lucid exposition. These are the characteristics which we like to see our students develop.

From careful study of the expositions of theorems that are proved in the textbook, students can learn much about correct synthetic form and, of course, can continually increase their store of important geometric facts and insights. But when they tackle

Creative thinking is required

original exercises they have to invent their own analyses and formulate their own proofs. This calls upon a higher order of insight and ingenuity than that which is required merely for following a demonstration that somebody else has worked out. When a student works out an original exercise, he is, in fact, engaging in creative mathematical activity. The proposition he proves or the construction he devises and validates will doubtless have been worked out by many people before, but to him it is new, and his accomplishment can bring the satisfaction that always accompanies the successful completion of a piece of original work. Hence original exercises furnish not only the most effective medium for developing the ability to do original work and independent thinking in geometry, but they also constitute a powerful built-in means of motivating students to put their best efforts into their work.

Moreover, teachers can probably learn more about the abilities and work habits and the strengths and weaknesses of their students (especially students with potential talent) by studying their work on original exercises than in any other way. In routine matters the student who is quick, curious, inventive, and self-reliant may often become bored and do only good ordinary but unimpressive work. On the other hand, his work on original exercises will almost certainly manifest these characteristics in a way and to a degree not usually reflected in the work of the conscientious but unimaginative plodder. Even the plodders, however, have an important stake in this creative aspect of geometry, because imagination and ingenuity can be cultivated, at least to a degree, and the cultivation as well as the recognition of these characteristics is a very important objective.

Problems should be graduated with respect to difficulty

For most students it is important that the original exercises be rather carefully graduated, and this is recognized by most textbook writers. A common practice is to divide sets of exercises into subsets on the basis of probable difficulty. Usually, authors do pretty well in such classification, but sometimes exercises will be found which seem to be placed in wrong categories. It is a good thing for teachers to check every exercise which is to be assigned to students to be sure that its level of difficulty is appropriate for the students who are expected to work on it and for the purpose of the assignment.

Some sources of students' troubles

It would be easy to make an extensive list of particular difficulties students have and particular errors they make in working on original problems in geometry, and such listings have been made. However, most of these detailed troubles will be found to stem from a few sources. Successful work invariably requires a well-organized fund of knowledge of the theorems that have been proved and of the postulates and definitions that have been accepted. Each exercise requires that the student get very clearly in mind precisely what he has given to work from and precisely what he aims to accomplish. Lacking any of these, the student is in trouble. Given all of them, success will depend largely upon his ingenuity in devising tentative plans of proof or tentative constructions and upon his ability to draw readily and extensively upon his funded information about geometry for hints and for supporting argument. Well-drawn diagrams may often suggest promising lines of attack. Careful notation and neat, orderly writing may appear to be peripheral considerations, but they are real assets. Many people feel that it is helpful to keep classified summary lists of ways of establishing particular properties or relations of geometric figures, such as the following:

1 Ways of proving triangles congruent
2 Ways of proving angles congruent
3 Ways of proving lines parallel
4 Ways of proving lines perpendicular
5 Ways of proving line segments equal in length
6 Ways of proving triangles similar
7 Ways of proving that an angle is a right angle
8 Ways of proving that a quadrilateral is a parallelogram
9 Ways of proving one angle greater than another
10 Ways of proving one line segment longer than another
11 Ways of proving chords of circles equal or unequal in length

Such classifications and lists can be made as detailed and as extensive as desired. They would probably prove useful to many students. It has long been fairly common practice among authors of geometry textbooks to include some such classified lists or summaries in their books.

MOTIVATION IN GEOMETRY

The best motivation in geometry, as in any mathematics course, lies in arousing the students' curiosity about aspects or details of the course to the point where they want to find out more than they already know about it, to work on interesting problems which may or may not be found in their textbooks, to discuss points of procedure or correctness, to question or defend statements, and in short, to become active participants in the course. This, of course, involves planning the work of the course within an appropriate range of difficulty, without allowing it to proceed at a dead level.

Some projects will be needed which will challenge the best students and some which even the poorer students will feel able to tackle with a measure of success.

It also requires of the teacher careful, correct, easy-to-follow discussion and skillful questioning. This latter, accompanied by a little adroit but casual chalkboard work, is a very effective means of eliciting opinions, and perhaps even controversies, adding zest to the discussion of a problem or theorem and producing genuine insight. Skillful questioning along the following lines may easily induce students to raise questions of their own, or to comment (perhaps argue) about statements made by their classmates: "How do you know that those two angles are congruent?" "What gives you the right to say that lines l and m are not parallel?" "Is there a theorem in solid geometry which is the counterpart of the plane geometry theorem that you have just proved?" "Jim, let's see if you can state a converse of the proposition stated in exercise 14 of today's assignment." "Mary, let's see if you can show whether or not Jim's converse is true." "Bill, see if you can state the inverse of Jim's proposition, and see if you can show whether your inverse is true or not." "John, you showed that if $AC > AB$, then $m\angle B > m\angle C$. What would be the relation between $m\angle B$ and $m\angle C$ if $AC < AB$? If $AC = AB$? Can you prove that you are right?" "Amy, you said you think Joe's last statement is wrong. Explain what you think is wrong about it, and why."

Use adroit questioning to get active participation

Interludes such as these are fine. Nothing could be better for the morale of the class, and nothing could do more to dispel the boredom which characterizes classes in geometry that are conducted in an atmosphere of dead-level monotony. Every class period in which there is any general discussion involving proofs, constructions, or conjectures will afford opportunities to raise provocative questions. If handled skillfully by the teacher, these generally can be channeled in such a way as to elicit reactions from the students, and when this occurs, it shows that the students are at least thinking profitably. The student who thinks seriously about his geometry will work at it, and most of those who work seriously at it will gain new or clearer insights into the structure and the details of geometry than they had before.

Try to elicit discussion by students

INEQUALITIES IN GEOMETRY

Congruence and equality have always played leading roles in high school geometry, and necessarily so. On the other hand, the important matter of inequalities has been given considerably less attention—probably less than it merits. If it is important to recognize conditions under which configurations would be congruent or measures would be equal, then it would also seem to be impor-

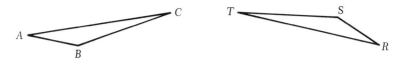

Figure 13-3

$A \rightarrow R, B \rightarrow S, C \rightarrow T.$

Simultaneous study
provides contrast
and impact

tant to recognize conditions under which such configurations would not be congruent or their measures would be unequal. The important concepts of locus, congruence, euclidean constructions, and dependence are closely associated with inequalities as well as with equalities. For all definitions, postulates, or theorems in which necessary and sufficient conditions for equality, congruence, or similarity are stated (and for many others in which only the sufficient conditions are given) there can be found other sets of conditions which will imply corresponding inequalities or lack of congruence.

Consider, for example, the two triangles ABC and RST (Fig. 13-3), for which the mapping $A \rightarrow R, B \rightarrow S, C \rightarrow T$ holds. The *s.s.s. theorem* (sometimes postulated) asserts that under this correspondence $(\overline{AB} \cong \overline{RS}, \overline{AC} \cong \overline{RT}, \overline{BC} \cong \overline{ST}) \Rightarrow (m\angle A = m\angle R, m\angle B = m\angle S, m\angle C = m\angle T)$. But in most textbooks the corresponding theorem involving the noncongruence of a pair of corresponding sides is not even mentioned along with the s.s.s. theorem. Although this and other theorems about inequalities of sides and of angles of triangles are proved subsequently, perhaps much further along in the course, it might be a good thing to at least mention these along with the s.s.s. theorem.

The isosceles triangle theorem usually appears early in the course, but in most textbooks there is no mention, along with its appearance, of the corresponding inequality theorem to the effect that, if the measures of two sides of a triangle are unequal, the measures of the angles opposite these sides are unequal in the same order. This theorem, or its separate parts, usually appears perhaps a hundred or more pages farther on. The theorem that chords of equal lengths in a circle are equally distant from the center of the circle is found as a major theorem in all textbooks, but the corresponding theorem about the measures of chords of unequal lengths and their respective distances from the center of the circle is usually not even mentioned along with the "equal chords" theorem. Most textbooks in high school geometry contain one or more chapters on coordinate geometry, but even here we find the emphasis placed on properties of equations and their graphs, with relatively little attention given to the graphs of inequalities.

There is too little
emphasis on
simultaneous study

In view of the importance which many people attach to the matter of integrating different parts or aspects of mathematics, this failure of textbook writers to tie together geometric inequalities with their counterpart equalities or congruences would seem to constitute an important oversight. Nearly all the geometric inequalities encountered in high school geometry are simple and intuitively rather evident. After the proof of any congruence theorem (e.g., the measures of chords equidistant from the center of a circle) some intuitive discussion of conditions under which the congruence would be replaced by an inequality or lack of con-

The teacher can
initiate profitable
discussion

gruence would almost always be profitable. It would provide powerful motivation, because it would stimulate the imaginations of the students and would provide for much conjecture in which even slow learners could participate adequately. It might, indeed, lead some students to suggest other geometric inequalities which they think might exist, or even to seek to establish these by deductive proof. In addition, it would certainly operate to clarify and fix in the minds of the students the conditions specified for the original equality or congruence.

CONVERSE, INVERSE (OPPOSITE), AND CONTRAPOSITIVE

The analysis of geometric theorems and their proofs is often facilitated by clear understanding of certain related theorems, known, respectively, as *converses, inverses,* and *contrapositives* of the given theorems. These types of theorems can be obtained from the original theorems to which they are related by the denial and/or interchange of hypotheses and conclusions of the original theorems. Because their statements often appear to be superficially similar to statements of the original theorems, casual reading may sometimes lead the reader to confuse them with the originals, whereas

Converses or in-
verses may or may
not be true

they are fundamentally different. The truth of an original theorem does not imply that a converse or an inverse is necessarily true; so care is necessary in drawing conclusions. An introduction to a clear understanding of these descriptive terms may be secured by examining a simple theorem containing only one hypothesis and one conclusion.

Theorem. If a triangle is equilateral, then it is isosceles. (Obviously true.)

Converse theorem. If a triangle is isosceles, then it is equilateral. (Not necessarily true.)

Inverse theorem. If a triangle is not equilateral, then it is not isosceles. (Not necessarily true.)

Contrapositive theorem. If a triangle is not isosceles, then it is not equilateral. (Obviously true.)

In this simple case the method of derivation of the different types of theorems is rather evident. For a theorem with one hypothesis and one conclusion:

1   The converse theorem is obtained by interchanging the hypothesis and conclusion.
2   The inverse (or opposite) theorem is obtained by taking the contradiction of the hypothesis as the new hypothesis and the contradiction of the conclusion as the new conclusion.
3   The contrapositive theorem is obtained by taking the contradiction of the conclusion as the new hypothesis and the contradiction of the hypothesis as the new conclusion.

If H represents the hypothesis of a given theorem and C the conclusion, the above definitions may be stated diagrammatically as follows:

Theorem. If H is true, then C is true.
Converse theorem. If C is true, then H is true.
Inverse theorem. If H is not true, then C is not true.
Contrapositive theorem. If C is not true, then H is not true.

It was mentioned earlier, in Chapter 3, that a theorem and its contrapositive are equivalent theorems; i.e., if one is true, the other is true, and if one is false, the other is false. Attention was also called to the fact that the truth of a theorem makes no implication as to the truth or falsity of the converse theorem. The same holds true for the inverse theorem. Each is really a conjecture which must be investigated independently.

The above definitions must be modified for theorems that involve more than one hypothesis or more than one conclusion. The following definitions have been suggested as satisfactory generalizations:

How these related
theorems are
formed

1   A converse of a theorem may be obtained by interchanging *any* number of conclusions with an *equal number* of hypotheses.
2   An inverse of a proposition having one conclusion may be formed by contradicting one of the hypotheses and the conclusion.
3   A contrapositive of a theorem containing more than one hypothesis and only one conclusion may be obtained by the interchange of the contradictory of one of the hypotheses with the contradictory of the conclusion.[4]

It will be noticed that the definitions given here for inverses and contrapositives of theorems are somewhat more restrictive than the one given for converses. Less restrictive definitions could be given, but logical difficulties which would then be encountered suggest that the definitions given here are more desirable for elementary geometry.[5]

As an illustration of the nature of converse propositions, consider the following theorem.

[4] N. Lazar, The Importance of Certain Concepts and Laws of Logic for the Study and Teaching of Geometry, *Mathematics Teacher*, **31** (1938), 107ff.
[5] *Ibid.*

Theorem. If two right triangles have the hypotenuse and a leg of one congruent, respectively, to the hypotenuse and a leg of the other, the triangles are congruent (Fig. 13-4).

Hypotheses	Conclusions
$\triangle ABC$ and $A'B'C'$ (Fig. 13-4)	$\triangle$ are $\cong$
$H_1:\angle C$ and $\angle C'$ are right $\angle s$	$C_1:a=a'$
$H_2:c=c'$	$C_2:\angle B=\angle B'$
$H_3:b=b'$	$C_3:\angle A=\angle A'$

Figure 13-4

The immature student may be tempted to consider the statement that the triangles are congruent as the one conclusion of the theorem. Upon analysis, however, it is seen that there are in fact many conclusions, since congruence of any pair of corresponding parts of the two triangles follows as a consequence of the three stated hypotheses. Only the three basic conclusions are listed above for purposes of the desired illustration. Symbolically, the above theorem may be written

The general conclusion subsumes several detailed ones

$$(H_1)(H_2)(H_3) \longrightarrow (C_1)(C_2)(C_3)$$

It is then evident that the following converses can be obtained by the interchange of one hypothesis and one conclusion.

1 $(H_1)(H_2)(C_1) \longrightarrow (H_3)(C_2)(C_3)$
2 $(H_1)(C_1)(H_3) \longrightarrow (H_2)(C_2)(C_3)$
3 $(C_1)(H_2)(H_3) \longrightarrow (H_1)(C_2)(C_3)$
4 $(H_1)(H_2)(C_2) \longrightarrow (C_1)(H_3)(C_3)$
5 $(H_1)(C_2)(H_3) \longrightarrow (C_1)(H_2)(C_3)$
6 $(C_2)(H_2)(H_3) \longrightarrow (C_1)(H_1)(C_3)$
7 $(H_1)(H_2)(C_3) \longrightarrow (C_1)(C_2)(H_3)$
8 $(H_1)(C_3)(H_3) \longrightarrow (C_1)(C_2)(H_2)$
9 $(C_3)(H_2)(H_3) \longrightarrow (C_1)(C_2)(H_1)$

Careful examination of these nine theorems reveals the fact that in each case but one, there is a combination of hypotheses sufficient to give congruent triangles. The exception is theorem 6, where the hypothesis would imply the ambiguous case for a triangle. In each theorem, however, which involves H_1 as one of the conclusions, there is not necessarily a true statement. Thus, of the nine converse theorems, only six (1, 2, 4, 5, 7, 8) are necessarily true theorems.

Since converse theorems may be obtained by the interchange of two hypotheses with two conclusions and of the three hypotheses with the three conclusions, we have the following additional converses of the original theorem:

10 $(H_1)(C_1)(C_2) \longrightarrow (H_2)(H_3)(C_3)$
11 $(H_1)(C_1)(C_3) \longrightarrow (H_2)(C_2)(H_3)$
12 $(H_1)(C_2)(C_3) \longrightarrow (C_1)(H_2)(H_3)$
13 $(C_1)(H_2)(C_2) \longrightarrow (H_1)(H_3)(C_3)$
14 $(C_1)(H_2)(C_3) \longrightarrow (H_1)(C_2)(H_3)$
15 $(C_2)(H_2)(C_3) \longrightarrow (C_1)(H_1)(H_3)$
16 $(C_1)(C_2)(H_3) \longrightarrow (H_1)(H_2)(C_3)$
17 $(C_1)(C_3)(H_3) \longrightarrow (H_1)(C_2)(H_2)$
18 $(C_2)(C_3)(H_3) \longrightarrow (C_1)(H_1)(H_2)$
19 $(C_1)(C_2)(C_3) \longrightarrow (H_1)(H_2)(H_3)$

As above, it is evident that no theorem which has the clause H_1 as a part of its conclusion is necessarily a true theorem. Furthermore, the hypothesis of theorem 12, $(H_1)(C_2)(C_3)$, is not sufficient to establish congruence. Hence, of the above converse theorems, only theorems 10 and 11 are necessarily true theorems. Thus, out of the total of 19 possible converse theorems to the original true theorem, there are only eight (1, 2, 4, 5, 7, 8, 10, 11) which are necessarily true theorems.

For an illustration of inverses and contrapositives of a theorem consider the following theorem.

Theorem. If two sides of one triangle are respectively congruent to two sides of another but the measures of the included angles in the two triangles are unequal, then the measures of the third sides of of the two triangles are unequal in that same order (Fig. 13-5).

Hypotheses	*Conclusions*
$\triangle ABC$ and $A'B'C'$	$C : b > b'$
$H_1 : a = a'$	
$H_2 : c = c'$	
$H_3 : m\angle B > m\angle B'$	

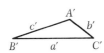

Figure 13-5

This theorem is well adapted to the consideration of inverses and contrapositives because it has only one conclusion. In the discussion which follows, we shall use $\overline{H}_1$ to represent the contradiction of H_1, $\overline{H}_2$ of H_2, $\overline{H}_3$ of H_3, and $\overline{C}$ of C. Thus $\overline{H}_1$ becomes

$a \neq a'$ (or $a \gtrless a'$); $\overline{H}_2$ becomes $c \neq c'$ (or $c \gtrless c'$); $\overline{H}_3$ becomes $m\angle B \ngtr m\angle B'$ (or $m\angle B \leq m\angle B'$); and $\overline{C}$ becomes $b \ngtr b'$ (or $b \leq b'$). From the definition of the inverse of a theorem it is evident that there are three inverses to the given theorem:

1 Hypotheses: $\overline{H}_1, H_2, H_3$; conclusion: $\overline{C}$
2 Hypotheses: $H_1, \overline{H}_2, H_3$; conclusion: $\overline{C}$
3 Hypotheses: $H_1, H_2, \overline{H}_3$; conclusion: $\overline{C}$

Analysis of these three theorems establishes that theorem 3 is the only true theorem.

Similarly, there are three contrapositives of the given theorem:

1 Hypotheses: $\overline{C}, H_2, H_3$; conclusion: $\overline{H}_1$
2 Hypotheses: $H_1, \overline{C}, H_3$: conclusion: $\overline{H}_2$
3 Hypotheses: $H_1, H_2, \overline{C}$; conclusion: $\overline{H}_3$

By the contrapositive law all three of these theorems should be true theorems. Careful analysis reveals that this is the case.

THE CONCEPT OF LOCUS

The concept of locus is one of the most pervasive ideas in geometry. Explicitly or tacitly, loci are involved in all geometric constructions, and the very descriptions of many figures are in effect the descriptions of loci which satisfy certain given conditions.

Constructions and loci are interactive

Seventh-grade students learn how to make simple constructions in which they continually apply intuitive ideas about loci, even though they may not have had any formal definition of the word.

Conversely, an effective approach to a clear understanding of locus can be made with the aid of some of these elementary constructions. Through their use the student can frequently be made aware of the truths of certain locus theorems before he actually comes into formal contact with them. The proper use of experimental geometry in the junior high school provides for just such an approach to an understanding of the meaning of a locus. The construction of circles, angle bisectors, perpendicular bisectors of line segments, and perpendiculars to a line from any given points provides the basis for constructing the lines involved in the concurrence theorems for triangles (medians, angle bisectors, altitudes, and perpendicular bisectors of the sides), and thus for constructing the inscribed and circumscribed circles of a triangle.

The language of sets often affords a good way of describing a locus. For example, the perpendicular bisector S of a line segment $\overline{AB}$ (Fig. 13-6) can be expressed as $S = \{P | \overleftrightarrow{DP} \perp \overleftrightarrow{AB}, AD = DB\}$, and it will be proved subsequently that it can be defined simply as

The language problem once again

$S = \{P | AP = PB\}$. This expression for S would represent either a line or a plane, depending on whether the locus is considered in two- or three-dimensional space.

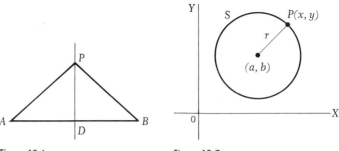

Figure 13-6   Figure 13-7

In a coordinate plane a circle S with center at a fixed point (a,b) and radius r (Fig. 13-7) might be represented as

$$S = \{(x,y)|(x-a)^2 + (y-b)^2 = r^2\}$$

Both concepts of loci should be stressed

Set notation and terminology are especially useful in connection with coordinate systems. However, both the static concept of locus ("a set of points") and the dynamic concept ("the path of a point") should be introduced and developed. The concept of motion makes possible the dynamic interpretation of a locus as the path of a point moving in such a way that at all times its position satisfies certain prescribed conditions. Clearly, when both apply, the two interpretations are in no sense contradictory or inconsistent, though there are some loci to which the term "path" is hardly applicable. The "set of points" interpretation, of course, applies in all cases.

Seven basic locus theorems

As an aid to general construction problems in plane geometry there are seven basic locus theorems which should be thoroughly understood by everyone. Stated for the plane only, these are as follows:

1 A *circle* is the locus of points which are at a fixed distance from a fixed point called the center.
2 The locus of points at a fixed distance d from a straight line m is a pair of lines parallel to m, one on each side of m and at the given distance d from m.
3 The locus of points equidistant from two fixed points A and B is the perpendicular bisector of $\overline{AB}$,
4 The locus of points equidistant from two fixed lines which intersect at R is a pair of lines m and n, each bisecting a pair of vertical angles formed at R by the original intersecting lines. It will be shown subsequently that in all such cases $m \perp n$.
5 The locus of points equidistant from two fixed parallel lines m and n is a single line parallel to m and n and midway between them.
6 The locus of the vertex of the right angle of a right triangle is a circle of which the hypotenuse of the right triangle is a diameter.
7 The locus of any vertex C of a given triangle ABC is a pair of congruent arcs, one on each side of $\overline{AB}$, such that each is an arc of a circle of which $\overline{AB}$ is a chord, and each is an arc in which $\angle ACB$ can be inscribed.

Three-dimensional counterparts of most of these loci are intuitively rather obvious, and for lack of space they will not be listed or discussed here. The study of loci, however, offers many rich opportunities for exhibiting relations and counterparts of plane and solid geometry, providing a correlating link between them. Thus, for example, the locus of points in space which are equidistant from two fixed points might well be examined in connection with the locus of points in a plane which are equidistant from two fixed points in the plane. The result of studying these loci together could hardly fail to enrich the student's conception of both. Many other similar cases are readily found. By using motion in space as the generalizing technique, two- and three-dimensional loci can be shown, in many cases, to be closely associated with each other, and each may be used effectively to supplement the discussion of the other.

The traditional method of proving a locus theorem has been to prove a theorem and one of its converses or one of its inverses. If the seven fundamental locus theorems listed on page 409 are established by this two-way method, or merely postulated, then a one-way proof can be used effectively in practically all the other locus situations. In order to avoid the two-way proof, some recommend that the seven fundamental loci be postulated. As illustrations of the one-way proof, two locus problems will be considered.

Problem 1. Find the locus of the mid-point of a rod whose ends always touch two fixed rods which are perpendicular to each other.

Given: Rods $\overline{XX'}$ and $\overline{YY'} \perp$ each other at O and $\overline{AB}$ a rod moving so that end A is always on $\overline{YY'}$ and end B is always on the rod $\overline{XX'}$ (Fig. 13-8).

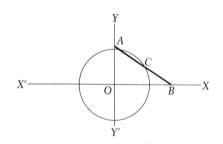

Figure 13-8

To find: The locus of C, the mid-point of AB.

Solution:

1 $\overline{AB}$ in any position forms a right $\triangle$ with $\overline{AB}$ as hypotenuse.

2 $\overline{OC} \cong \overline{AC} \cong \overline{CB}$.

3 $\therefore$ The locus of C is a circle with O as center and $\overline{OC}$ as radius.

1 $\overline{XX'}$ and $\overline{YY'}$ given $\perp$ each other.

2 *The mid-point of the hypotenuse of a right $\triangle$ is equidistant from the three vertexes.*

3 *The locus of points lying in a plane and at a fixed distance from a fixed point in the plane is a circle.*

Problem 2. Find the locus of the points of contact of tangents drawn from a given point to concentric circles.

Given: Concentric circles with center at O and tangents drawn from fixed point P (Fig. 13-9).

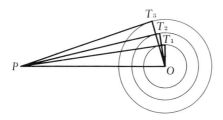

Figure 13-9

To find: The locus of the points of contact of these tangents.

Solution:

1 In any position $\overline{OT}$ will pass through O.

2 In any position $\overline{PT}$ will pass through P.

3 In any position the $\angle PTO$ is a right $\angle$.

4 $\therefore$ The locus of the point T is a circle on $\overline{PO}$ as diameter.

1 *In each case $\overline{OT}$ is a radius of a circle.*

2 *Given condition.*

3 *The radius of a circle is always $\perp$ a tangent at the point of contact.*

4 *The locus of the vertex of the right $\angle$ of a right $\triangle$ with a given fixed hypotenuse is the circumference of the circle with the hypotenuse as diameter (theorem 6, page 409).*

Each of the above problems can be established by a two-way proof, but the directness and simplicity of the one-way method make it very desirable.

After a locus problem (especially one that involves intersecting loci) has been investigated by the students, a critical discussion can help to clarify insights and is a potential source of fine motivation. Unless teachers capitalize on this and plan for such discussion, they will be overlooking a valuable opportunity for stimulating interest and careful thinking. The following is just one of countless examples that could be given to illustrate and emphasize this fact.

Example. Discuss the locus X of points in the plane π which are 3 inches from a given line l in π and 5 inches from a given point P in π.
Designate the locus

$X = \{x \,|\, x \in \pi,\ x \text{ is 3 inches from } l\} \cap \{x \,|\, x \in \pi,\ x \text{ is 5 inches from } P\}$

Let $d = $ distance from P to l.

In this case the locus turns out to be a function of the distance d, and d can take on all nonnegative values. It seems intuitively clear, too, that for some values of d the locus will not exist, and that when it does exist, it will consist of a set of discrete points. It seems appropriate, then, that the discussion should center around such questions as these:

1 For what values of d, if any, is $X = \phi$?
2 For what values of d, if any, will X consist of a single point?
3 For what values of d, if any, will X contain exactly 2 points?
4 For what values of d, if any, will X contain exactly 3 points?
5 For what values of d, if any, will X contain exactly 4 points?
6 For what values of d, if any, will X contain more than 4 points?

The discussion, if well conducted, should prove to be stimulating and productive of careful thinking on the part of the students. They should be asked to defend their answers to these questions and to any others that may arise. As a final step, relative to the foregoing questions, they may be asked to decide whether the following summary is correct and complete:

1 $X = \phi$ if and only if $d > 8$.
2 X consists of a single point if and only if $d = 8$.
3 X contains exactly 2 points if and only if $2 < d < 8$.
4 X contains exactly 3 points if and only if $d = 2$.
5 X contains exactly 4 points if and only if $d < 2$.
6 For no value of d can X contain more than 4 points.

CONSTRUCTION PROBLEMS

There is no more fascinating or provocative activity in school mathematics than the solution of construction problems in geometry by euclidean methods. This aspect of the subject brings into play all the geometrical assets which students possess: their knowledge of the accepted postulates, stated definitions, and proved theorems; their ability to analyze problems; their ingenuity in making plausible conjectures and in seeking for methods of verification; their skill in planning formal proofs; their ability to recognize, in carrying out the synthesis, whether the proposed proof is valid or not; their care in considering all the possible cases that might arise under the given hypotheses; and their ability to

(margin notes:)

Critical discussion: a most productive device

Well-chosen questions stimulate student participation

Construction presents a real challenge

determine whether or not the construction is unique or, indeed, whether or not it is possible. Thus construction problems form an extremely valuable part of the experience of students in geometry.

Most students in plane geometry will have had some experience in making simple constructions empirically and without proofs in their work in the junior high school. This is a helpful start and serves to give the students an intuitive feeling for certain loci and combinations of figures. It is sufficient for making interesting designs, but it is not sufficient to meet the objectives we have in mind in proposing construction problems for students in demonstrative geometry.

Most of the construction problems which occur as principal "problems" along with the sequence of principal "theorems" in the textbooks are quite simple of analysis and proof. For example, it is relatively easy to devise a method for constructing a tangent to a circle at a given point on the circle and to prove that this method is valid. However, there are many interesting problems whose solutions are far from obvious and which do tax the ingenuity and ability of the students. Such problems provide valuable experience, especially for the better students, and can do much to stimulate interest in the course.

There are four main things to be done

There are four aspects of any construction problem in geometry: (1) Determine how to use the given elements to construct the required figure. (2) Construct the figure. (3) Prove that the construction is correct; i.e., prove that the constructed figure has the given elements in it, either directly or indirectly. (4) Discuss the possibilities of construction, i.e., the conditions under which the construction is possible and whether the construction, when possible, is unique. These four aspects might be more briefly labeled: (1) analysis, (2) construction, (3) proof, and (4) discussion. To illustrate, let us consider the following problem.

Problem. Construct $\triangle ABC$, given $m\angle(A+C)=m\angle A+m\angle C<180°$, a, and $(b+c)$, with a, b, and c representing the lengths of the sides respectively opposite $\angle A$, $\angle B$, and $\angle C$, as well as designating these sides.

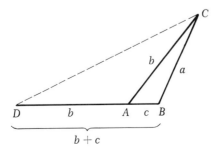

Figure 13-10

Planning the attack

Analysis   See Fig. 13-10. Suppose $\triangle ABC$ is the required triangle. We know that $\angle B$ can be constructed because $\angle B$ is the supplement of $\angle(A + C)$, which is given. Also $a \cong \overline{BC}$ can be laid off on one side of $\angle B$. How can $b + c$ be used to get the required triangle? Is there an auxiliary triangle using $b + c$ which can be constructed and by means of which $\triangle ABC$ can be obtained? It can be observed that if $\overline{BA}$ is extended to D so that $\overline{BD}$ has the length $b + c$, then $\triangle DBC$ is constructible (s.a.s.). Also, it is seen that $\overline{DA} \cong b \cong \overline{AC}$, so that $\triangle DAC$ is isosceles; whence $m\angle DCA = m\angle CDA$. Thus $\angle DCA$ is constructible. This construction would give a line which would intersect $\overline{BD}$ in A, and so complete the construction of the required triangle.

Construction   See Fig. 13-11.

Making the construction according to plan

With one side lying in a working line $\overleftrightarrow{BX}$, construct $\angle B$ as the supplement of $\angle(A + C)$.

Lay off $BC = a$ on one side of $\angle B$, thus locating C.
Lay off $BD = b + c$ on $\overleftrightarrow{BX}$, thus locating D.
Draw $\overline{DC}$.
Construct $\overrightarrow{CQ}$ in the interior of $\angle DCB$, making $\angle DCQ \cong \angle BDC$ and intersecting $\overline{DB}$ at A.
Then $\triangle ABC$ will be the required triangle.

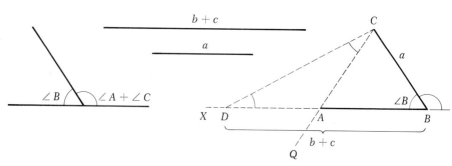

Figure 13-11

Proof:

Proving its validity

1	$\angle B$ can be constructed	1 *Supplement of $\angle(A + C)$ which is given $< 180°$*
2	$\overline{BC} \cong a$	2 *By construction*
3	$\overline{DB} \cong b + c$	3 *By construction*
4	$\overline{DC}$ can be drawn	4 *Any two points determine a line*
5	$\overrightarrow{CQ}$ can be constructed to make $\angle DCQ \cong \angle CDB$	5 *An angle can be constructed congruent to a given angle*

6	$\overleftrightarrow{CQ}$ intersects $\overline{DB}$ at A, between D and B	6	$\overrightarrow{CQ}$ drawn in interior of $\angle DCB$
7	$\triangle DAC$ is isosceles	7	$\angle ACD \cong \angle ADC$
8	$AD = AC$	8	Sides opposite congruent $\angle$s of isosceles triangle
9	$BA + AD = b + d$	9	Given
10	$BA + AC = b + c$	10	Step 8
11	$\triangle ABC$ is the required triangle	11	Constructed from given elements and satisfies requirements

Extensive discussion, with the class participating, is important

Discussion   For the construction to be possible, $b + c$ must be greater than a, since the sum of the lengths of two sides of any triangle must be greater than the length of the third side. Also $m\angle(A + C)$ must be less than 180°, because the sum of the measures of all three angles of any triangle is only 180°. If $b + c = a$, or equivalently, $m\angle(A + C) = 180°$, the triangle is degenerate, merely the segment $\overline{CB}$. If $b + c < a$ or if $m\angle(A + C) > 180°$, no construction is possible. Thus $b + c > a$ and $m\angle(A + C) < 180°$ are necessary conditions for the construction. They are also sufficient, because, by using the given elements under this set of conditions, we have been able to construct a unique triangle that satisfies the requirements of the problem.

For all except very simple cases, the analysis of a construction problem usually is the hardest step for the student; but it is important. This is the step in which he formulates his plan for the construction and lays the basis for the proof of its correctness or validity. Many construction problems require the use of auxiliary lines or figures, the need for which may not be obvious at the outset. Students require discussion of many examples and original exercises in construction to sharpen their space imagination and their facility, and also to help them organize their geometrical information so that it may be more useful to them in solving construction problems.

Once a plan for a required construction has been formulated, the proof should not be difficult if the analysis has been correct. Here care is the main requisite. Standards of rigor in these proofs should be comparable with those used in connection with the proofs of theorems.

Discussion is too often neglected by teachers

No construction problem should be considered a finished product until it has been subjected to the complete treatment outlined above. Much of the most important information concerning a construction is frequently hidden until discussion brings it to light. It should be emphasized that such procedure as this gives system to the attack on construction problems and eliminates a great deal of the futile effort expended and the feeling of helplessness developed in the hit-or-miss, trial-and-error technique so frequently used.

GENERALIZATION AND
SPECIAL CASES

Mathematicians like to generalize because generalizations show interconnections. Whenever they can prove general theorems that include other theorems already established as special cases, they do so. This is good mathematics.

Sometimes in high school geometry groups of theorems can be found such that all of them can be shown to be special cases under a single inclusive theorem. In such cases teachers should call attention to the fact, because recognition of this relationship can benefit students in several ways. It forces them to examine and compare the geometric properties of the configurations involved, and to test critically each of the special cases to determine whether or not it actually is a special case under the general theorem. The close attention this demands of students and the element of dis-

Attention to generalization has several desirable results

covery it involves are almost sure to enlist and hold their interest, and thus to provide strong motivation. It serves to fix more clearly in mind both the general theorem and the included special theorems, and thus to make them less likely to be forgotten and easier to recall. Above all, it helps to connect and give organization to sets of separate but related theorems and to clarify the concept of generalization. It has received little emphasis in textbooks in geometry, but it can be used to advantage by any good teacher.

The two examples which follow will serve to illustrate how certain groups of theorems can be generalized so that each proposition in the group can be shown to be a particular case under a single general theorem.

Two examples from plane geometry

First, consider the familiar formulas usually defined or developed separately for the areas of the square, rectangle, parallelogram, triangle, and trapezoid. If we relax the restriction that one pair of sides of a trapezoid must be nonparallel, then the formula for the area of a trapezoid is a generalization covering all the other cases. They can be subsumed as special cases, and their areas can all be determined by the same formula. In the case of the triangle it must be noted that the measure of one of the "parallel" sides is zero.

A second, and perhaps more interesting, case involves a group of theorems giving the measures of angles formed by lines associated with a circle. These measure formulas are always developed separately, commonly in the following order:

1 The measure of a central angle
2 The measure of an angle formed by two chords intersecting inside the circle
3 The measure of an inscribed angle
4 The measure of an angle formed by a tangent and a chord
5 The measure of an angle formed by two secants intersecting outside the circle

6 The measure of an angle formed by a secant and a tangent which intersect outside the circle

7 The measure of an angle formed by two tangents to the circle

As they are usually given in textbooks, the formulas for the measures of angles formed under the several conditions described above all imply that only the absolute values of all arcs involved are to be considered. Under this restriction there is no single theorem which would include all the cases. But by introducing the notion of *directed* arcs (counterclockwise, positive; clockwise, negative), each of these separate measure formulas can be subsumed under the general theorem: The angle formed by two lines, each of which cuts or is tangent to a circle, is measured by half the *algebraic* sum of the intercepted arcs. It is very possible that students will not find this generalized theorem stated in their textbooks, but this may make it all the more interesting to them. They will find that testing the separate theorems against this generalization is an interesting and valuable experience.

Not all theorems fit into such patterns of generalization, and the cases cited above admittedly represent unusually large groupings. There are a good many cases, however, both in plane and solid geometry, in which two or three theorems can be subsumed under a single covering theorem. Consider, for example, to cite a very simple case, the theorem: The degree measure of each interior angle of a regular polygon of n sides is $(n - 2)180/n$. This theorem includes, among others, as special cases, the two propositions: (1) Each interior angle of a square has a measure of 90°. (2) Each interior angle of an equilateral triangle has a measure of 60°.

The Pythagorean theorem generalized

The law of cosines (which has an exact geometric analog) is a generalization which subsumes the Pythagorean theorem as a special case. It asserts that in any triangle ABC, $(AB)^2 = (AC)^2 + (BC)^2 - 2(AC)(BC) \cos \angle ACB$. When $\angle ACB = 90°$, then $\cos \angle ACB = 0$, the last term of the formula drops out, and the result is the Pythagorean theorem.

Another generalization of the Pythagorean theorem is the following theorem. Let a, b, and c be, respectively, the two legs and the hypotenuse of the right triangle ABC (Fig. 13-12). Let R, S, and T be three similar figures of any shape such that a, b, and c are corresponding line segments in R, S, and T, respectively. Then (area of T) = (area of R) + (area of S). This theorem is completely general and is easily proved by elementary methods for circles, for similar parts of circles, and for similar polygons, though proof of its complete generality must make use of the theory of limits. Evidently, three squares having a, b, and c, respectively, as sides qualify as special cases of the similar figures R, S, and T, and the areas of the three squares are, respectively, a^2, b^2, and c^2; whence $a^2 + b^2 = c^2$; and the Pythagorean theorem thus emerges as a special case of the more general theorem.

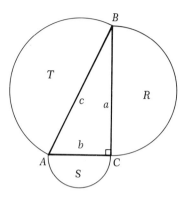

Figure 13-12
Area T = area R + area S

Congruence as a
special case of
similarity
On a broader scale congruence itself is a special case of similarity. Pairs of both similar and congruent figures are characterized by the condition that pairs of corresponding angles have equal measures. In any pair of similar figures we have the further condition that the measures of corresponding line segments are in the ratio of $k:1$ (k being some constant), while in any pair of congruent figures the measures of any pair of corresponding line segments are in the ratio of $1:1$. Thus a pair of similar figures for which $k = 1$ is a pair of congruent figures. Similarity is simply a more general property which includes congruence as a special case when the ratio of similitude is $1:1$.

AREAS AND VOLUMES
AND THEIR MEASURES

Students, like most people, tend to think of areas and volumes more or less as hybrid geometrical-quantitative concepts. That is to say, for example, they think of the area of a closed figure on a plane or surface as the amount of surface space which the figure occupies, and of the volume of a three-dimensional object as the amount of three-dimensional space which the object occupies. This is altogether natural and not to be discouraged, and the authors of some textbooks do not go further in explaining these concepts. Generally, there is little reason to expect that this will lead to any confusion in the minds of the students, and usually it does not. Yet some of these same authors are very particular about distinguishing between an angle and the measure of the angle, between a line segment and the measure of that line segment, etc. To be consistent, they should make corresponding distinctions

Authors should
distinguish be-
tween area and
measure of an area

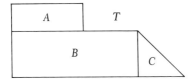

Figure 13-13

between an area and the measure of that area, and between a volume and the measure of that volume. Some authors are more meticulous about this than others, illustrating the geometric or spatial concepts by examples and then carefully defining the measures as *numbers* associated with these spatial concepts.

While alternatives could be used, the unit of area is generally taken to be the area of a unit square, and the unit of volume to be the volume of a unit cube. With these conventions the measure of the area of a closed planar region can be defined as the unique nonnegative number which indicates the amount of surface space (in terms of nonoverlapping unit squares) the region occupies. More precisely, though perhaps no more clearly, it is defined as the greatest lower bound of the sum of the areas of a set of unit squares which completely cover the region. Similarly, the measure of the volume of a closed solid can be defined as the unique non-negative number which indicates (in terms of nonoverlapping unit cubes) the amount of three-dimensional space the solid occupies.

Actually, since the concepts, terminology, and notation of sets are now widely used, there is good reason for making the distinction between the spatial concepts of area and volume and their measures in terms of numbers. Suppose, for example, that in Fig. 13-13 the region T consists of the nonoverlapping component regions A, B, and C. Then T would be represented in set notation as $T = A \cup B \cup C$. However, if it is desired to express the measure of T, it will be necessary to indicate the measures of the component regions A, B, and C as numbers and then to find the sum of these numbers. But numbers, as such, cannot be combined by the operation $\cup$, and sets, as such, cannot be combined by the operation $+$. To represent the measure of the area of T as a single number, it would be necessary to set up a correspondence between the regions A, B, and C and a set of numbers which denote their respective measures (say, S_1, S_2, and S_3) so that $S_1 = m(A)$, $S_2 = m(B)$, $S_3 = m(C)$. Then, making use of the axiom that the area measure of the union of two nonoverlapping regions is the sum of the area measures of the component regions, we may replace the set composition $T = A \cup B \cup C$ by its numerical counterpart, $m(T) = (S_1) + (S_2) + (S_3)$. Thus, if the measures S_1 and S_2 and S_3 are known or can be determined, they can be summed into a single number which is the measure of the composite figure *T*.

Some teachers may feel that there is no need to be so fussy about making the distinction between the measure of an area or of a volume and the area or volume itself. Others will feel that a treatment which does not make the distinction is too casual and may lead to careless thinking and sloppy work. It is probably true that most students would make the distinction tacitly, without even being aware of it and without sensing any difficulty in doing it.

Why the distinction is important   However, as one progresses in mathematics, precision in technical language and in notation becomes increasingly important. Casualness begets casualness. On the other hand, the practice of precision and consistency strengthens the habits of precision and consistency, and such habits of self-discipline, with respect to language and notation, become increasingly important in subsequent work.

EXERCISES

1   In the junior high school, students learn to understand a good many facts or principles of geometry which they later encounter as theorems in high school geometry. Sometimes they ask, in effect, and in good faith, "Why do we have to prove this now when we have already learned it?" How would you answer this question if you were the teacher?

2   Discuss the roles and importance of intuition, experiment, speculation, and conjecture in the attempt to *discover* general properties of, or relations among, geometric figures, or in trying to discover a way of proving a theorem. Illustrate by examples.

3   Explain why, in general, an intuitive discussion of a plan for proving a theorem should be given before exhibiting the detailed formal proof. Give two or three examples to illustrate and support your argument.

4   Take three standard textbooks on high school geometry published in the half decade 1950–1955 and three published in the half decade 1965–1970. Compare the tables of contents of the first set with those of the second set, and comment on the differences you find.

5   Enumerate five sources of difficulty which students are likely to have in their work in geometry. Discuss the one you consider the most critical. Explain why you think it is critical, and what you think a teacher might

do to help students avoid or overcome the difficulties that stem from this source.

6   Sometimes students do not know how to get started at finding proofs of theorems. Explain how an analytic-synthetic attack may help them to discover for themselves a correct synthetic proof. Illustrate by at least one example.

7   Exhibit an analytic-synthetic proof of this theorem: If *ABC* is an equilateral triangle inscribed in a circle, and if *P* is any point on the arc $\overset{\frown}{BC}$, then $PA = PB + PC$.

8   Explain the nature of each of the following elements, and the role of each in the process of deductive thinking: (*a*) undefined terms, (*b*) definitions, (*c*) assumptions (axioms or postulates), and (*d*) theorems.

9   Examine three or more textbooks in high school geometry published since 1960 and compare the definitions given for each of these terms: angle, interior of an angle, straight angle, reflex angle, interior of a straight angle, interior of a reflex angle. Note and discuss any lack of agreement you find in these definitions.

10   Take two recent texts in high school geometry and make a list of all the theorems on geometric inequalities that you can find in these books. See if you can state any additional ones that are valid but not given in either of these books.

11   See if you can give a geometric derivation of this inequality (for two variables): geometric mean $\leq$ arithmetic mean.

12 State a theorem which has a converse that is not true in all cases. State this converse and disprove its generality by a counter-example.

13 State and prove the converse of the Pythagorean theorem.

14 Give several reasons why it is desirable to have students do a great deal of work with original exercises.

15 Consider the theorem which states that two right triangles are congruent if the legs of one are congruent, respectively, to the legs of the other. Is this a special case under another more general theorem? If so, state it and justify your answer.

16 Show that the Pythagorean theorem is a special case of the law of cosines.

17 Show that similarity of geometric figures is a general property which subsumes congruence as a special case of similarity.

18 Prove the following theorems:

   a. The areas of two similar triangles are proportional to the squares of any pair of corresponding sides of the triangles.
   b. The areas of two similar polygons are proportional to the squares of any pair of corresponding lines in the two polygons.
   c. The areas of two circles are proportional to the squares of the diameters or the radii of the two circles.

19 The theorems of exercise 18 all deal with the measures of the areas of pairs of similar figures. See if you can formulate a statement of a more general theorem which you think might include all these as special cases. If you can, write it down and test each of the given theorems against it to see whether the given theorem really is a special case under your general theorem.

20 Do you think your generalized theorem of exercise 19 would hold for the surface areas of two similar solids? Test it out on some pairs of cubes, spheres, similar prisms, and similar cylinders.

21 See if you can find or formulate a theorem by which the measures of the volumes of two similar solids can be compared. If you can, test it out with some pairs of similar solids whose volumes you can compute easily.

22 Select ten theorems of plane geometry for which you can give analogies or counterparts in solid geometry, and state these three-dimensional counterparts.

23 Show how to construct a line which is parallel to the base of a triangle ABC and which divides the triangle into two parts whose areas have the same measure. Discuss fully, and explain how you discovered the solution.

24 Given a plane figure bounded by a straight-line segment $\overline{AB}$ of length c and two circular arcs of radius c, $\overarc{AC}$ centered at B, and $\overarc{BC}$ centered at A. Construct a circle that is tangent to $\overline{AB}$ and to $\overarc{BC}$ and $\overarc{AC}$. Prove that your construction satisfies the requirements, and explain how you discovered how to make it.

25 Construct a triangle ABC, given the lengths of the three medians. Explain your construction, and prove that it does the job. Is this construction always possible? Explain why or why not. Try to explain how you discovered how to make the construction.

26 Consider a triangle of base b and altitude h. If a rectangle of height x is inscribed in the triangle with the base of the rectangle in the base of the triangle, express the area of this rectangle in terms of b, h, and x.

27 What difficulties do you think high school students would be likely to have with exercise 26?

BIBLIOGRAPHY

Adler, Irving: "A New Look at Geometry" (New York: The John Day Company, Inc., 1966).
———: What Shall We Teach in High School Geometry?, *Mathematics Teacher*, **61** (1968), 226–238.
Allendoerfer, Carl B.: Angles, Arcs, and Archimedes, *Mathematics Teacher*, **58** (1965), 82–88.
———: The Dilemma in Geometry, *Mathematics Teacher*, **62** (1969), 165–168.
Alspaugh, John W., and Robert P. Giese: An Unestablished Conjecture, *School Science and Mathematics*, **68** (1968), 455–456.
Altshiller-Court, Nathan: The Dawn of Demonstrative Geometry, *Mathematics Teacher*, **57** (1964), 163–166.
Becker, J. P.: Geometry Achievement Tests in NLSMA, *American Mathematical Monthly*, **75** (1968), 532–538.
Bell, Max: High School Geometry via Ruler and Protractor Axioms: Report on a Classroom

Trial, *Mathematics Teacher,* **54** (1961), 353–360.

Birkhoff, George D., and Ralph Beatley: A New Approach to Elementary Geometry, *Mathematics Teacher,* **61** (1968), 765–771.

Brossard, Roland: Metric Postulates for Space Geometry, *American Mathematical Monthly,* **74** (1967), 777–788.

Buck, Charles: What Should High School Geometry Be?, *Mathematics Teacher,* **61** (1968), 466–471.

Dye, David L.: What is a Trapezoid?, *Mathematics Teacher,* **60** (1967), 727–728.

Eves, Howard: "A Survey of Geometry," vol. I (Boston: Allyn & Bacon, Inc., 1963).

Fehr, Howard F.: Reform of Instruction in Geometry, *American Mathematical Monthly,* **70** (1963), 323–327.

Hirsch, Martin: Pythagorean Converse, *Mathematics Teacher,* **54** (1961), 632–634.

Huffman, David C.: Independence of the Incidence Postulates, *Mathematics Teacher,* **62** (1969), 269–276.

Jeger, Max: The Present Conflict in the Reform of Geometry Teaching, *Mathematics Teaching,* Autumn, 1965, pp. 23–32.

Johnson, Paul B.: Are Circles Similar?, *Mathematics Teacher,* **59** (1966), 9–13.

Keedy, M. L.: What is a Trapezoid?, *Mathematics Teacher,* **59** (1966), 646.

Keller, M. Wiles: Semantics and Mathematics, *School Science and Mathematics,* **68** (1968), 103–113.

Klamkin, Murray S.: On Some Geometric Inequalities, *Mathematics Teacher,* **60** (1967), 323–328.

Klingler, Donn L.: Structuring a Proof, *Mathematics Teacher,* **57** (1964), 200–202.

Leake, Lowell, Jr.: Axiom or Theorem?, *Mathematics Teacher,* **59** (1966), 107–109.

Marks, John L., and James R. Smart: Using the Analytic Method to Encourage Discovery, *Mathematics Teacher,* **60** (1967), 241–245.

Menger, Karl: "You Will Like Geometry" (Chicago: Museum of Science and Industry, 1961).

Meserve, Bruce E.: Euclidean and Other Geometries, *Mathematics Teacher,* **60** (1967), 2–11.

Moise, Edwin: Some Reflections on the Teaching of Area and Volume, *American Mathematical Monthly,* **70** (1963), 459–466.

————: "Elementary Geometry from an Advanced Standpoint" (Reading, Mass.: Addison-Wesley Publishing Company, 1963).

Moore, Charles G.: Pierced Polygons, *Mathematics Teacher,* **61** (1968), 31–34.

Poincaré, Henri: Mathematical Definitions and Teaching, *Mathematics Teacher,* **62** (1969), 295–304.

Ranucci, Ernest R.: Jungle-gym Geometry, *Mathematics Teacher,* **61** (1968), 25–28.

Rising, Gerald R.: A Reaction to "Definitions without Exceptions," *Mathematics Teacher,* **60** (1967), 343–344.

Rosskopf, Myron F., Joan L. Levine, and Bruce R. Vogeli: "Geometry: A Perspective View" (New York: McGraw-Hill Book Company, 1969).

Ryoti, Steven: Congruency of Triangles by AAS, *Mathematics Teacher,* **59** (1966), 246–247.

————: What Is an Isosceles Trapezoid?, *Mathematics Teacher,* **60** (1967), 842.

Scheid, Francis: Square Circles, *Mathematics Teacher,* **54** (1961), 307–312.

Schor, Harry: Altitudes, Medians, Angle Bisectors, and Perpendicular Bisectors of the Sides of Triangles, *Mathematics Teacher,* **56** (1963), 105–107.

————: An Introduction to the Angle Measurement Theorems in Plane Geometry, *Mathematics Teacher,* **56** (1963), 107–108.

Shuster, Seymour: If Not Solid Geometry, Then What?, *Mathematics Teacher,* **54** (1961), 313–315.

Sitomer, Harry, and Howard F. Fehr: How Shall We Define Angle?, *Mathematics Teacher,* **60** (1967), 18–19.

Smith, Stanley A.: What Does a Proof Really Prove?, *Mathematics Teacher,* **61** (1968), 483–484.

SMSG: "Geometry with Coordinates" (Pasadena, Calif.: A. C. Vroman, Inc., 1965).

Stover, Donald W.: Auxiliary Lines and Ratios, *Mathematics Teacher,* **60** (1967), 109–114.

Szabo, Steven: An Approach to Euclidean Geometry through Vectors, *Mathematics Teacher,* **59** (1966), 218–235.

————: Some Results on Quadrilaterals with Perpendicular Diagonals, *Mathematics Teacher,* **60** (1967), 336–338.

Usiskin, Zalman: A New Approach to the Teaching of Constructions, *Mathematics Teacher,* **61** (1968), 749–757.

Veblen, Oswald: The Modern Approach to Elementary Geometry, *Mathematics Teacher,* **60** (1967), 98–104.

Wiseman, John: Some Related Theorems on Triangles and Circles, *Mathematics Teacher,* **54** (1961), 14–16.

Wren, F. Lynwood: "Basic Mathematical Concepts" (New York: McGraw-Hill Book Company, 1965), pp. 190–247.

Wylie, C. R., Jr.: What Are Perpendicular Lines?, *Mathematics Teacher,* **60** (1967), 24–30.

| fourteen | the teaching of geometry in the senior high school (continued) |

MAPPINGS

"Mapping" is no longer an unusual word to find in high school geometry textbooks. Considerable prominence is now given to the explicit treatment of the concept of mappings and associated ideas, terminology, and notation. This practice will almost certainly become more prevalent in the future, but the conventional language and notation used in the discussion of mappings are not yet found in all high school textbooks. For this reason we shall consider the topic in a rather detailed manner, discussing many of the key concepts and some of the important terminology which we believe should become familiar to students.

The concept of a mapping is simple. Given two sets R and S, the mapping of $R \rightarrow S$ is *into* if it is a one-way correspondence set up by some procedure whereby each element x of R is associated with a unique element y (called the image of x) in S. In such a mapping of R into S these images may or may not be distinct. The set R is called the *domain* set of the mapping, and S is called the *range* set. As noted, each element of R has a unique image in S. However, an *into* mapping $R \rightarrow S$ may be either a *many-to-one* or a *one-to-one* mapping.

Some technical terminology

It may also happen that each element of S is the unique image of some element in R. In this case the mapping $R \rightarrow S$ is called an *onto* mapping, as distinguished from an *into* mapping. This is an important distinction, and care should be taken to ensure that students understand it.

If R is mapped onto S, and if the elements x in R have *distinct* images in S, then there is said to be a *one-to-one correspondence* between the elements of R and those of S, and the mapping is said to be a 1:1 mapping of R onto S. These 1:1 onto mappings are the ones with which high school geometry is most likely to be concerned.

We may also think of a mapping $R \rightarrow S$ as a set of ordered pairs: $\{(x,y) | x \in R, y \in S\}$. If R is mapped into S, then each $x \in R$ is the first element in exactly one of these ordered pairs. If R is mapped onto S, then each $y \in S$ is the second element in at least one of these ordered pairs. If R is mapped onto S in a 1:1 mapping, then each $x \in R$ is the first element *and* each $y \in S$ is the second element in exactly one of these ordered pairs. Thus this mapping is a proper subset of $R \times S$.

Defining a
particular mapping

For any particular mapping $R \rightarrow S$, there must be given some definitive procedure whereby each element of R can be associated with its own image in S. There are many such procedures. For example, we might think of or define a particular mapping $R \rightarrow S$ by letting the elements of R and S be real numbers and defining the mapping $R \rightarrow S$ as $\{(x,y)|x \in R, y \in S, y = x^2 - 2\}$. The defining formula $y = x^2 - 2$ enables us to determine, for each x in R, its image y in S. Again, the ruler postulate, already discussed, provides a way of defining a mapping of a set of points on a line onto the set of real numbers. This is a very important mapping, because it gives us an explicit way of bringing the powerful methods of arithmetic and algebra into the service of geometry.

Some authors use Greek letters to denote mappings. If θ represents the mapping $R \rightarrow S$, and if θ has an inverse mapping $S \rightarrow R$, it is customary to denote the inverse mapping by θ^{-1}.

It is sometimes desirable to consider mappings (transformations) which may be composite as well as single. Let R, S, and T be

Notation

sets, and let Γ, θ, and ψ be mappings such that Γ maps R onto S, and θ maps S onto T. In order for this to be possible, the range of Γ must clearly be the domain of θ. If we assume this property, then for each ordered pair (x,y) in Γ, there is an ordered pair (y,z) in θ, so that the composite mapping $\psi = \Gamma\theta$ (meaning Γ followed by θ) in effect maps each x in R onto a unique z in T. Thus ψ is a two-stage transformation (an onto mapping) which takes the elements of R into the corresponding elements of T.

Suppose, for example, that R, S, and T are sets of real numbers

Composite
mappings

such that $R = \{x|0 < x < 2\}$, $S = \{y|y = 3x + 2\}$, and $T = \{z|z = y^2\}$. Designate the mappings $\Gamma : R \rightarrow S$, $\theta : S \rightarrow T$, and the composite mapping $\psi : \Gamma\theta$. Then ψ is, in effect, an association of the elements of R with the corresponding elements of T.

Composite geometrical mappings are implied, for example, in theorems about congruent figures, Γ and θ being the transformations of translation (parallel shift, or sliding) and of rotation about a point, respectively. By means of either of these transformations or of their composite, any geometric figure can be mapped onto another figure congruent to it. When that is the case, it is customary to say that "congruence is preserved" under the mapping. A geometrical mapping under which congruence is preserved is sometimes called *motion* in the plane or in space.[1]

[1] Paul J. Kelly and Norman E. Ladd, "Geometry" (Glenville, Ill.: Scott, Foresman and Company, 1965), p. 372.

An invariant is a property of a set, function, equation, or geometric configuration which is not altered by a particular transformation, and geometry has been described as the study of invariants under a group of transformations. Among the invariant properties under some mappings are the lengths of line segments, the measures of angles, parallelism, perpendicularity, and the shapes of geometric figures (e.g., similarity, which includes congruence as a special case). The transformations (mappings) most often used in elementary geometry are those of translation (or parallel shift, or sliding); rotation about a line or point; reflection *Congruence-pre-* in a line, plane, or point; and expansion (stretch or compression) *serving mappings* of lengths of segments in a given ratio. Under any one of the first three of these transformations a figure is mapped onto another figure congruent to it. If two congruent figures are arbitrarily located in a plane or in space, some combination of these transformations can be made to map one of the figures onto the other. If a particular property of a figure is unchanged when that figure is subjected to a particular transformation, it is customary to say that that property is *preserved* under that transformation. For example, the lengths of segments and the measures of angles are preserved under translation, under rotation, and under the composite of these mappings. The same is true for the congruence of triangles. Similarity is preserved under any composite of any congruence-preserving mapping taken together with mapping of the expansion of lengths in a given ratio. Congruence and similarity are also preserved under the mapping of reflection in a plane, line, or point (the center of similitude), and symmetry is preserved under the mapping of reflection in a line or plane. The intersection of figures is preserved under any combination of the mappings mentioned above, and examples of still other geometric properties which are preserved under these mappings could be given.

Probably the most important mappings used in elementary geometry are distance-preserving and similarity mappings. Distance-preserving mappings map lines onto lines, segments onto segments, rays onto like-directed rays, half-planes onto half-planes, triangles onto congruent triangles, and circles onto congruent circles. Under distance-preserving mappings the properties of collinearity of points, betweenness of points, parallelism, perpendicularity, symmetry, and congruence of angles, segments, polygons, and circles are preserved. Distance-preserving mappings can be produced by any one or any combination of these three basic mappings: (1) translation (parallel shift, or sliding), (2) rotation about a point or line, and (3) reflection in a plane, line, or point (the plane, axis, or center of symmetry).

Similarity-pre- Similarity mappings, on the other hand, may be, but need not *serving mappings* be, distance-preserving mappings. Suppose a geometric figure is in the domain of a mapping θ, and that any two points A and B

in the figure are carried by the mapping into their images A' and B'. Then, if the distances AB and $A'B'$ are in the ratio $1:k$, where k is some real number, the mapping θ is called a similarity mapping, and k is called the similarity ratio, or the ratio of proportionality. Under such a mapping angle measure is preserved (invariant) but distance is not preserved. Similarity mappings can be produced by any combination of the distance-preserving mappings, combined with the additional basic mapping of expanding lengths of line segments in the given ratio $1:k$.

Space does not permit further elaboration of the concepts and terminology related to mappings, nor is it necessary. All that has been attempted here is to point out these concepts in the belief that they form an important chapter in contemporary high school geometry which should not be neglected. Teachers can help their students to understand the meaning and language of mappings by giving careful explanations, many specific examples and practice exercises, and perhaps the proofs of some theorems. The concepts involved in setting up a theory of geometric mappings are fairly simple, and most of the theorems are not difficult to understand or to prove.

The problem of language and notation again

The principal difficulty is not in the mathematics but simply in becoming familiar with the language and the notation of mappings and in learning to use this language to express ideas that are already familiar.[2]

CONVEXITY

Traditionally, the study of convexity and of convex sets has received little formal attention in high school geometry textbooks. Some authors talked about convex polygons without even defining them, and some merely defined them as polygons in which each interior angle is less than 180° and made no mention of convex figures as point sets. By the early 1960s, however, a few authors had begun to talk about convex point sets, and to define convex polygons, in effect, as plane figures whose sides are line segments,

Convex polygons

and such that for any two points in the region consisting of the union of the polygon and its interior, the segment joining these two points is wholly contained in this polygonal region. This trend toward treating convex sets (especially convex point sets in general) from a modern viewpoint has become more pronounced, and by 1965 at least one textbook for high school geometry[3] had included a whole chapter of fifty-two pages on "convexity." This is perhaps a precursor of things to come, and teachers should be

---

[2] *Ibid.*
[3] Kelly and Ladd: *op. cit.,* Chapter 6.

prepared to discuss with their classes the subject of convex point sets with familiarity and ease.

Intuitively, the concepts of a convex plane figure and some of its properties are easy for students to grasp through illustrations; for example, triangles, parallelograms, circles, and ellipses or ovals are convex plane figures, while stars, crescents, and figures bounded by irregular curves are not. An axiomatic treatment of convexity, however, can become quite involved. For example, even to define a plane or solid convex figure requires some care. First, it must be made clear just what is meant by a convex set of points. A point set S is called a convex set if, for every two points A and B in S, every point on the line segment $\overline{AB}$ lies in S. Next, we note that a convex plane *figure* must have a boundary, while a convex set need not be bounded. Moreover, a bounded figure has an interior, an exterior, and the boundary itself. Clearly, any set of points defining a figure must be nonempty and it is customary to exclude straight lines and line segments from the category of convex figures, though they are convex sets of points. Therefore a convex plane figure is defined, in effect, as a non-empty, nonlinear, convex, and bounded set of points in a plane such that the set contains both the points of its boundary and those of its interior but no other points. Thus it is easily shown that the boundary of a convex figure is not a convex set of points, but that the set of interior points with or without the boundary is a convex set.

Then there is the concept of a supporting line of a convex plane figure. This is defined as a line in the plane of the figure which contains at least one point of the figure's boundary, and such that the figure is contained wholly in one of the closed half-planes of the line. (See Fig. 14-1.) If a convex figure is a polygon or if its boundary contains a straight-line segment, then the line which contains this segment, or which contains any side of the polygon, is a supporting line. Also, each line which contains a vertex of the polygon but no other points of the figure is a supporting line. Every convex plane figure has exactly two supporting lines in any given direction, and the perpendicular distance between these is called the width of the figure in the direction perpendicular to these supporting lines. For figures other than circles, the width of the figure, defined in this way, will vary with different directions of the supporting lines, and the term "width," used in this nonunique way, may seem unfamiliar and confusing to students. There are other cases, too, of familiar words to which unfamiliar meanings are attached. The words "center" and "diameter" take on new and more general meanings than those generally associated with the center and diameter of a circle. Under the new and more general definitions of these terms, many convex figures other than circles have centers, while all plane convex figures have di-

Defining a convex figure

Supporting lines

New meanings for old words

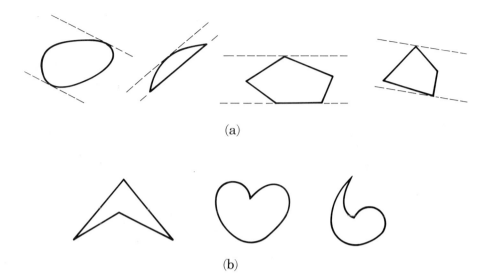

(a)

(b)

Figure 14-1

(a) Some convex figures, with pairs of supporting lines (dotted) in certain directions. (b) Some nonconvex figures.

ameters, so that one can speak, for example, of the center of a parallelogram or the diameter of a triangle.[4]

One important advantage of an axiomatic treatment of convexity is that practically all the properties developed for plane convex figures have analogous counterparts in three-dimensional geometry for the properties of convex solids. A convex solid is defined as a point set which is nonempty, nonplanar, convex, and bounded and which contains the set of points that form the boundary. The sphere is the three-dimensional counterpart of the circle, and the tetrahedron takes over that role with respect to the triangle. An interior point of a convex solid is, as with planar figures, any point that belongs to the solid but is not in the boundary set. A supporting line of a convex plane figure has for its three-dimensional analog a supporting plane of a convex solid, and a plane separates space into two half-spaces, just as a straight line separates a plane into two half-planes. Neither a half-plane nor a half-space is a convex geometric *figure* because neither is bounded, but both are convex point sets. Similarly, definitions of other properties of convex plane figures have their complete analogs in definitions of corresponding convex solids, and the same is true for numerous theorems that can be established for convex plane and solid figures and point sets.

Counterparts of plane figures in 3-space

[4] *Ibid.,* pp. 330–331.

Another advantage of some axiomatic study of convexity in high school is that, for the increasing number of students who go on to pursue college mathematics, a prior understanding of convexity may make some parts of their college mathematics easier to under-

Axiomatic study is a help in later mathematic courses

stand than it might otherwise be. At least the language and the concepts and definitions of the basic properties of convex sets and figures will not be new to them. This can be of considerable help. The greatest difficulty in connection with convexity lies not in the mathematics involved, but in getting to know the language and in learning to use it and to think in it with fluency and ease.

DEPENDENCE

In high school mathematics most of the emphasis on dependence, functionality, and variation has been confined in the past to the study of interdependent variation by means of algebraic techniques. In synthetic geometry this has resulted, unfortunately, in a tendency to overlook those aspects of dependence which may not be expressible in the conciseness of algebraic formulation but which still are deeply significant to an enriched understanding and appreciation of the geometrical relations under consideration.

In any geometric configuration there are intrinsic interrelationships among its constituent elements. Some of its elements are dependent upon others, and study of such dependence provides a powerful means of discovering and expressing characteristic properties of the configuration. These interrelations of elements are implied, it is true, in nearly every theorem, but as a rule noth-

Study of interdependence of elements is an enrichment: don't leave this to chance

ing is said explicitly about the interdependence of the elements. The phrase "depends on" is seldom used, yet this phrase is a meaningful part of the vocabulary of every student. While the "depends on" statement lacks the definiteness of an algebraic formula, it has a verbal definiteness which drives home in the minds of immature students the implication of the formula.

We prove that the measure of the area of a triangle is found by taking half the product of the measures of the base and the altitude, and we write the formula $A = \frac{1}{2} bh$. Logically, this implies that the measure of the area depends on the measures of the base and the altitude, but the textbooks do not bother to say so in words. Yet pedagogically, such a statement would probably be helpful to many students, and its omission may be a lost opportunity to clarify and clinch a generalization. It is recommended that in discussing theorems, teachers should try to make use of appropriate "depends on" statements in verbal form.

Some illustrations

The following examples are additional illustrations. The perimeter and the area of a triangle depend on the measures of an angle and the two sides that include it. The volume and the surface area of a sphere depend on the length of the radius. The equation of a line in a coordinate plane depends on its slope and on its intercept on the vertical axis. The length of a chord in a circle depends on its distance from the center. The volume of a right circular cone depends on its altitude and the radius of its base. The set of points in which two spheres intersect depends on the lengths of the radii of the spheres and the distance between their centers. The area of a right section of a right circular cone depends on its distance from the vertex. When two coplanar lines are cut by a transversal, their parallelism or obliquity depends on the congruence or the noncongruence of a pair of corresponding angles. Hundreds of such examples could be given.

The study of dependence has two faces. There is the formal study of the interdependence of certain elements of a given (fixed) geometric configuration. For this the instrument is deductive proof, properly within the province of high school geometry. Then there are certain aspects of dependence which can be approached informally, on a conjectural basis, and which, though contributing conjectures rather than theorems, for the most part, and thus being properly in the province of junior high school geometry, still can contribute materially to the enrichment of even the high school students' understanding of dependence. These two aspects of dependence will be discussed here in the order mentioned.

Since it takes only two points to determine a line, we say that three points are dependent if they are on the same line. But three noncollinear points are not dependent. They determine a triangle. On the other hand, the sum of the measures of the three angles of a triangle is always 180°; so the measure of any one of them is determined by the measures of the other two, and the three angles are dependent. The area of a triangle depends on the measures of its base and its altitude; so the base, the altitude, and the area form a set of dependent elements. The volume of a sphere depends on the length of its radius; so the radius and the volume are dependent elements. We establish dependence whenever we prove theorems, the conclusions being dependent upon the hypotheses.

In some cases the dependence of certain elements, or properties, on others is readily established, by definition or by proof. In addition to dependence among what may be regarded as primary elements of the configurations studied, it may also be possible to discover some less apparent secondary sets of elements which are also dependent. Thus, in the inscribed triangle ABC in Fig. 14-2, it is clear that angles A, B, and C are dependent elements. But we may note also that any angle inscribed in the arc BAC will be congruent to angle A, and so, evidently, a, A, r (radius of the circumscribed circle) are dependent elements of the configuration; i.e., given any two of them, the third is determined. Also, if x and

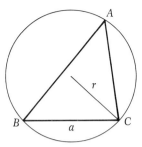

Figure 14-2
*Dependent elements of an
inscribed triangle.*

y represent, respectively, the circumference and the area of the circumscribed circle, it is clear that a, A, x and a, A, y are sets of dependent elements. In some geometric configurations it is possible to discover numerous sets, including such indirect, or secondary, elements, which are dependent. The search for such sets of elements is interesting, and it can be used as a profitable instructional device, especially for supplemental work for superior students.

There is another aspect of dependence whose study really comes within the purview of the junior high school, since it must be largely intuitive and since in most cases conjectures rather than proved theorems will be obtained. This is dependence in the sense of related change. Most people associate the notion of dependence with the idea of the change in one thing (a dependent variable) which corresponds to given changes in its independent variable or variables.

Dependence and change—the dynamic aspect

The volume of a cube depends on the length of an edge. Does the length of a diagonal depend on the length of an edge? What about the volume of the inscribed sphere? Of the circumscribed sphere? Which, if any, of these varies directly as the edge of the cube? If the length of the edge were doubled, by what factor would the surface be increased? By what factor, the volume?

The volume of a right circular cone depends upon both its altitude and the radius of its base. Which would increase the volume more: to double the altitude or to double the radius of the base? If both were doubled, what would be the ratio between the new volume and the original volume?

Consider a rectangle which has a fixed width of 5 units but whose length x increases continuously from 3 to 6 units. If n represents the number of axes of symmetry of the rectangle, then n depends on x and n is a function of x. Make a graph of n plotted against x over the interval [3,6].

The area of a regular polygon of n sides inscribed in a given circle depends on the number n. As n increases, what happens to the area of the polygon? To the length of its perimeter? To the length of one side?

Questions such as these may often help to bring to light important dependence relations among elements of the figures under consideration. The algebra and the arithmetic of variation can be tied in effectively with this aspect of dependence, and even though it will be mainly intuitive and conjectural, some study of dependence from this dynamic viewpoint can do much to clarify the insights of both junior and senior high school students.

Don't neglect discussion of these matters

SYMMETRIES

The study of symmetries affords some interesting excursions into geometry which are somewhat off the beaten track, but which can serve as worthwhile supplements to the material commonly found in textbooks on school geometry. Symmetries are defined in terms of certain transformations: (1) reflection in a point, line, or plane and (2) rotation about a point or a line. The study of symmetries is a good vehicle for motivation in geometry. At the intuitive level symmetry can be examined adequately even by seventh-grade students, while good senior high school students may find that the proofs of some of their conjectures will challenge them.

Symmetries are suitable for study in both junior high and senior high school

For planar configurations symmetry with respect to a line l is a property of figures each of which consists of two sets of points: a set A and a set A' (the image of A) such that, if l separates the plane into two closed half-planes L and M, then A and A' lie, respectively, in $L \cup l$ and $M \cup l$. A further property of A and A' is that, for every point $P \in A$ and its image $P' \in A'$, the line l is the perpendicular bisector of $\overline{PP'}$. The line l is called the *line*, or the *axis*, of symmetry. Symmetry with respect to a plane is similarly defined, except that here A and A' lie, respectively, in two closed half-spaces into which a plane π (called the *plane* of symmetry) separates three-dimensional space, with the further property that the plane is the perpendicular bisector of the segment $\overline{PP'}$ for every point $P \in A$ and its image $P' \in A'$.

Symmetry with respect to a point requires only that A and A' shall lie, respectively, in two closed half-spaces of one, two, or three dimensions, and that there be some point C which is the bisector of $\overline{PP'}$ for every $P \in A$ and its image $P' \in A'$. The point C is called the center of symmetry. What has been said clearly implies that symmetry is a property of reference *which exists only with respect to something*, some plane, line, or point.

Reflection of any geometrical configuration A of one, two, or three dimensions in a plane, line, or point produces an image A'

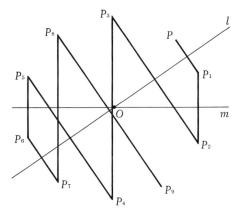

Figure 14-3
Successive reflections.

such that not only are A and A' symmetrical with respect to the point, line, or plane in which A is reflected, but also $A' \cong A$. Thus reflection is both a symmetry-producing and a congruence-preserving transformation, or mapping. Correlative to this we observe that distances and measures of angles are also preserved under this transformation. Rotation of a plane figure through a dihedral angle of 180° about a line l in its plane also produces symmetry and preserves congruence. In this case A and A' are symmetrical with respect to the line l and to the plane which contains l and is perpendicular to the plane of A. If the rotation is through a dihedral angle $\alpha \neq 180°$, then A and A' are symmetrical with respect only to the plane which bisects the dihedral angle α.

Most students will be interested in examining numerous geometrical configurations and physical objects for the purpose of determining for each one how many lines, points, and planes of symmetry (if any) it has. We list here a few of the innumerable figures which are suitable for such investigation: rectangle, square, circle, arc, isosceles triangle, equilateral triangle, and scalene triangle, regular polygons having either an even or an odd number of sides, right circular cylinder and cone, oblique cylinder, cube, line segment, a house, a leaf, a bird, a football, an airplane. It is also interesting and worthwhile to have students note what happens to the number of axes and planes of symmetry when a variable figure such as a "stretchable" rectangle suddenly becomes a square, or when a variable ellipse becomes a circle.

Another interesting excursion in symmetry is the examination of the result of successive reflections of a point in a pair of oblique lines (see Fig. 14-3). If P is reflected in l, its image is P_1. Then if P_1 is reflected in m, its image is P_2. If P_2 is reflected in l, its image

Some properties are preserved by reflection and rotation

Topics for investigation

is P_3. Proceeding in this way to form successive images of images for a large number of reflections, it may appear to the students that the original point and all its successive images formed by these successive reflections alternately in l and m seem to lie on a circle which contains P and whose center is at O, the intersection of l and m. Actually, it can be easily shown that this is the case, regardless of the measure of the angle formed at O by l and m. What can you say about the number of images P_i $(i = 1, 2, 3, \ldots)$ of P if l and m are oblique to each other? If they are perpendicular to each other? What can you say about the number and location of the images if $l \parallel m$? Exercises such as these can help students sharpen their space perceptions and space imaginations.

Graphs and symmetry

Many interesting symmetries can be studied by coordinate methods. The graphs of some functions and relations have symmetries of their own. In other cases pairs of graphs of related functions form symmetrical patterns. Certain symmetries can be noted in the graphs of the trigonometric functions and of the ellipse and the hyperbola. Power functions of the form $y = x^n$ are symmetrical about the Y axis when n is an even integer but have center symmetry when n is an odd integer. The function $y = 1/x$ has a center of symmetry and two axes of symmetry. The even functions are symmetrical with respect to the Y axis. For any function $y = f(x)$, the graphs of $y = f(x)$ and $y = -f(x)$ form a symmetrical pattern with respect to the X axis, while the pattern formed by the graphs of $y = f(x)$ and $y = f(-x)$ is symmetrical about the Y axis [provided $f(-x)$ exists], and that formed by the graphs of $y = f(x)$ and $y = -f(-x)$ is symmetrical with respect to the origin. If $y = f(x)$ and $y = f^{-1}(x)$ are inverse functions, such as the logarithmic and exponential functions, then the graphs of $y = f(x)$ and $y = f^{-1}(x)$ form a pattern that is symmetrical with respect to the straight line $y = x$.

In the polar-coordinate plane the equations $r = f(\theta)$ and $r = f(-\theta)$ represent curves which are symmetrically located with respect to the polar axis, while the equations $r = f(\theta)$, $r = f(-\theta)$, $r = -f(\theta)$, and $r = -f(-\theta)$ represent curves which either singly or combined in pairs have various axes, or centers of symmetry, depending on the functions represented by f. For students who have had work with coordinate geometry, some study of symmetries by coordinate methods provides motivation and can clarify insights.

VECTORS

Why study vectors in geometry?

An examination of high school textbooks indicates that the study of vectors has not yet come to occupy a prominent place in high school geometry. The principal motivation for the study of vectors in high school lies in the fact that vectors afford clear and interesting illustrations of many physical phenomena involving forces and velocities, and that they are associated with coordinates and complex numbers in interesting and natural ways. Thus an introduction to vectors can serve to illuminate both physical and mathematical relationships and concepts. Because of the close connection with coordinates and complex numbers, and because of the simple visual graphic representation and the many practical applications, the study of vectors has an appeal both to theoretically minded students and to those who are especially interested in applications. High school geometry certainly is not the place for any exhaustive treatment of vector theory, but some of the concepts are quite simple and appealing, and can perhaps offer a welcome note of variety to the geometry course.

Topics studied could well include the following: scalar and vector quantities; geometrical representation of a vector (magnitude and vectorial angle); free vectors and the distance-preserving mapping of translation; centered vectors; equivalent vectors; zero vector; components of a vector; resolving a vector into rectangular and other components; vector sum or resultant of two vectors; the triangle law; the parallelogram law; resultant of several centered vectors; additive inverse of a vector; subtraction of vectors; commutativity and associativity of vector addition; rectangular coordinates and vectors; vectors and polar coordinates; vectors and complex numbers; solving numerical problems by vector diagrams; and proofs of a few theorems of plane geometry by vector methods. An excellent discussion of the treatment of vectors in high school geometry can be found in the "Appendices" volume of the Report of the Commission on Mathematics, published in 1959 (see Bibliography at the end of this chapter).

The following illustrative examples represent types of problems that would be suitable for high school students. The notation is that commonly used in electrical engineering to denote vectors. It is a modification of the usual form for polar coordinates. The symbol $23\underline{/78°}$ denotes a vector whose magnitude is 23 units and which acts at a vectorial angle of 78° with the polar axis. The polar-coordinate symbol for this vector is (23, 78°).

Some examples

Example 1. A force of 15 units acts at an angle of 50° above the horizontal. Plot the vector for this force carefully to a large scale, and determine as accurately as possible the values of its horizontal and vertical components.

Example 2. One of two force vectors is $5\underline{/60°}$, and the other is $8\underline{/150°}$. Find the resultant graphically, and give the approximate measures of its magnitude and its vectorial angle.

Example 3. Determine from a diagram the approximate measures of the vertical and horizontal components of the force represented by the vector $25\underline{/200°}$.

Example 4. Four force vectors are represented as complex numbers as follows: $\mathbf{v}_1 = 5 + 0i$; $\mathbf{v}_2 = 2 + 5i$; $\mathbf{v}_3 = -3 + i$; $\mathbf{v}_4 = 7 - 3i$. Without graphing these, represent the vector sum of these four vectors as a complex number. Then draw it as a vector in the rectangular-coordinate plane.

Example 5. Find the approximate measures of the magnitude and the vectorial angle of the vector $25 + 12i$.

Example 6. Illustrate by a diagram the fact that the commutative law holds for the addition of vectors.

Example 7. Prove by vector methods that the diagonals of a parallelogram bisect each other.

Problems such as the foregoing examples can be made up easily and proposed by the teacher, or they can be made up and proposed by students for other students to solve. The latter is an excellent device for stimulating interest. The variety can range from very simple problems to fairly difficult ones. Slow-learning students can handle the simple problems because the drawings give visual help in analyzing the problems and sensing what is required. This in turn serves to give these students a feeling of success in their work, with a consequent increase of interest. Superior students may be challenged to pursue their study of vectors further, and perhaps even to inquire into the multiplication of vectors. Because of its intrinsic mathematical interest and its many physical applications, some study of vectors in high school geometry has the potential for providing good motivation for all the students, as well as for extending their mathematical horizons.

Some material dealing with introductory work on vectors for use in connection with high school geometry is available in printed form. The section in the "Appendices" volume of the Report of the Commission on Mathematics (1959) has already been mentioned. In 1961 an introductory course of about fifty pages was prepared by A. M. Glicksman of the Bronx High School of Science for use in that school. This course has been published as a pamphlet by the National Council of Teachers of Mathematics and has been through several printings. More recently (1964), a pamphlet of about the same length, entitled "The System of Vectors," has been published under the auspices of the School Mathematics Study Group as one of its Supplementary and Enrichment Series for high schools. Since 1962 the UICSM has developed a whole two-year course in which euclidean geometry is approached through vector methods. This course is intended for superior students. It has been taught experimentally, with apparent success, in several high schools in different states. Reference to these materials and to some others can be found in the Bibliography for this chapter.

INDIRECT PROOF

Most proofs in school geometry involve arguments that start with an accepted hypothesis and proceed directly from that by a sequence of steps through which the desired conclusion is reached as a necessary consequence. Indirect proof, on the other hand, is a method of establishing a conclusion C by showing that any conclusion different from C must involve an inconsistency or a contradiction of known facts or accepted hypotheses, and so must be rejected; whence C must be accepted as the correct conclusion. In other words, it establishes C by ruling out every other possibility. It is a method used extensively in all branches of higher mathematics, as well as in much thinking about everyday matters. The alibi is a perfect example.

Students'
difficulties

But until they get to really see and appreciate the essence of indirect proof and how it works, young students, accustomed to "hammer-and-tongs" direct methods, may often fail to see why it *is* a proof, or they may feel that it is a sort of sneaky way of going about the job. In years past many teachers of high school geometry have tended to shy away from indirect proof, but this form of argument is a powerful method of deduction and deserves more attention than it gets. Some theorems for which direct proofs have not been found have been established rather easily by indirect proof. Logically, indirect proof is just as valid as direct proof, but it follows a different pattern, and high school students need careful explanation of its pattern and experience in its use. The following discussion suggests the main ideas that they should get, and the examples which are presented illustrate how the method is employed to establish theorems.

The usual form of indirect proof employs a pair of contradictory propositions. The truth of either one implies the falsity of the other, and the falsity of either one implies the truth of the other. Therefore, if we wish to establish the truth of one of them, it is sufficient to prove the falsity of the other. This, in summary, is the essence of indirect proof. It is based upon two fundamental laws, or axioms, of logic: (1) *the law of contradiction,* which asserts that at a given time a thing cannot both be and not be, and (2) *the law of the excluded middle,* which asserts that a thing must either be or not be. The properties of a pair of contradictory propositions, indicated above, are corollaries to these two axioms of logic.

The technique of indirect proof in mathematics may be conveniently set forth in four specific steps to be followed.

How to make an
indirect proof

1 Set up a pair of contradictory propositions, one of which you desire to prove true. Select the latter at the outset.
2 Assume, for the time being, that the other of the two is true, and test the consequences by deductive reasoning to see whether this assumption leads to a contradiction or an inconsistency.
3 If the assumption of step 2 does lead, by correct reasoning, to an inconsistency or a contradiction, conclude that it was a false hypothesis.
4 Under the conditions of step 3, conclude that the contradictory proposition selected in step 1, i.e., the one you want to prove true, is necessarily true, since the only alternative proposition has been shown to be false.

Let us first use indirect proof to establish an algebraic inequality.
Prove that if a and b are real numbers, then $a^2 + b^2$ can never be less than 2ab.

Possibilities: $a^2 + b^2 \geqslant 2ab$ (I)
                   $a^2 + b^2 < 2ab$ (II)

We wish to prove that (I) is true, so let us try to disprove (II).

Proof: If $a^2 + b^2 < 2ab$, then $a^2 - 2ab + b^2 < 0$, or $(a - b)^2 < 0$. But this contradicts the algebraic principle that the square of any real number is either zero or positive, and $(a - b)$ is a real number. Hence we must discard possibility (II) and accept (I) as being true, since it is the only other possibility.

We shall now exhibit some examples from geometry. Many theorems undertake to establish the necessary and sufficient conditions under which certain geometric facts or relations can be validated as general theorems. These are the "if and only if" theorems, or the "one and only one" theorems. Every such theorem necessarily splits into two parts, or two theorems: one in which the "if" part is established, the other in which the "only if" part is established. Indirect proof can often be used to advantage in establishing the "only if" theorem after the "if" theorem has been proved. Consider, for example, the following theorem.

Theorem.   Given a line l and a point P not on that line. Then there is one and only one plane π which contains both l and P.

We are required to show (1) that there is at least one plane π that contains both l and P, and (2) that there is no other plane different from π which contains both l and P.

Figure 14-4

Proof: See Fig. 14-4. By presupposing the postulates that three noncollinear points determine a unique plane and that two distinct points determine a unique line, and that if two points lie in a plane, the line containing these two points lies in the plane, part 1 can be proved directly by taking two points S and T on l; whence P, S, and T, being noncollinear points (since P is not contained in l), determine a plane π, and since S and T lie in π, therefore l also lies in π. This proves the *existence* of a plane π which contains l and P.

Part 2 requires a proof that there is only one such plane. We can invoke an indirect proof to establish part 2 as follows: Suppose that there were another plane, π', different from π, containing l and P. Then π' would contain, and thus be uniquely determined by, the three noncollinear points P, S, and T. On the other hand, we know that P, S, and T also lie in and determine the plane π. Hence the supposition that π' is different from π would give us two different planes determined by the same three noncollinear points, and this contradicts the postulate that three noncollinear points lie in one and only one plane. We are thus forced to conclude that π' and π are not different planes, but that there is *only one* plane containing l and P. This establishes the *uniqueness* of the plane which contains l and P.

As a third example of indirect proof, consider the following theorem.

Theorem.   If two angles of a triangle are congruent, then the sides opposite these angles are congruent. (See Fig. 14-5.)

Hypothesis: $\angle B = \angle C$
Conclusion: $AB = AC$

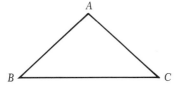

Figure 14-5

Establishing a converse by indirect proof

Proof: There are only three possibilities: (1) $AB > AC$; (2) $AB = AC$; and (3) $AB < AC$. If we can show that possibilities 1 and 3 are false, then we have to conclude that possibility 2 must be true. We can show that this is the case as follows: If $AB < AC$, then $m\angle C < m\angle B$, and if $AB > AC$, then $m\angle C > m\angle B$. Both of these statements are justified by the theorem that if two sides of a triangle have different measures, then the angles opposite these sides also have different measures, the greater of the two angles being opposite the greater of the two sides. This eliminates possibilities 1 and 3, thus forcing us to accept the remaining possibility 2, and to conclude that $AB = AC$. This is what we were required to prove.

In this connection it will be well to call attention again to the use of counterexamples as a way of showing the falsity of some propositions. This method of proof (or rather, of disproof) is, in fact, a kind of indirect proof; but it is not stressed, and gener-

Disproof by
counterexample

ally it is not even mentioned, in geometry textbooks. The reason for this is that the theorems and exercises given in the books are nearly always theorems that are true or valid generalities, which call for proofs, not disproofs. Some converses of some theorems, however, do not hold true for all cases, but sometimes students use converses uncritically as supporting reasons without confirming their general validity. If, in investigating the generality of a statement, *a single example* could be adduced in which it can be shown that the statement is untrue, then no more is needed to disprove the generality or the truth of the statement.

Consider, for example, the general statement: If two triangles are congruent, then they have the same area. A converse would be: If two triangles have the same area, then they are congruent. This obviously is not true in general, and it can be disproved simply by exhibiting two triangles which do have the same area but which have different shapes.

In the same vein, consider the true theorem: If a triangle is equilateral, then it is isosceles. A converse would be to the effect that: If a triangle is isosceles, then it is equilateral. In order to show that this is not always the case, one has only to cite, for example, the case of an isosceles triangle in which the measure of the base is only half the measure of one of the legs. By citing a single case in which the statement does not hold true, its generality is thereby disproved.

Other cases could be given of statements that are not true generalities although they are converses of general theorems. Consider the true general theorem: If a quadrilateral is a rhombus, then its diagonals are perpendicular to each other. Then consider the converse: If the diagonals of a quadrilateral are perpendicular to each other, then the quadrilateral is a rhombus. As an exercise, disprove the generality of this converse by exhibiting a counterexample.

The counterex-
ample is a helpful
tool in analyzing
statements

Perhaps the most important use of the counterexample, from the standpoint of instruction, lies in analyzing the validity of careless statements given by students as supporting reasons for steps in proofs of theorems or exercises.

It can be argued with complete validity that a theorem can be established in an indirect manner by giving a direct proof of an equivalent theorem, usually, though not necessarily, a contrapositive of the given theorem. Certainly, since a proposition and its contrapositive are equivalent, a direct proof of either does imply the validity of the other. But as with the method of counterexamples, a direct proof of a contrapositive does not make use of the *form of argument* involved in the typical indirect proof. It is this form of argument that we have tried particularly to emphasize in this section.

COORDINATE GEOMETRY IN THE
HIGH SCHOOL COURSE

In line with contemporary trends, nearly all high school textbooks now give some attention to coordinate geometry. This work is by no means intended to take the place of a full course in analytic geometry. Rather, it is a brief introduction to some of the fundamental concepts and techniques involved in the treatment of geometry by coordinate methods. The major emphasis is on a few of the basic properties and key relations of lines and circles considered as geometric entities oriented within a coordinate system.

Topics in co-ordinate geometry

A composite list made by examination of several textbooks published since 1960 includes the following topics treated by coordinate methods in one or more of these books: graphs on one axis; absolute value; graphs as loci; graph of an equation; graph of a condition; plotting points in a coordinate plane; slope of a nonvertical line; parallel and perpendicular lines; writing the equation of a line; the distance formula; the mid-point formulas; intersection of lines; equation of a circle; intersection of circles; choosing axes for convenience in proofs; systems of equations; proving theorems in coordinate geometry; symmetry; and polar coordinates. These topics are given varying degrees of emphasis in different textbooks, and several (e.g., symmetry, polar coordinates) appear in only a few of the texts examined. In most of the texts, however, many of these topics are considered in enough depth to provide the basis for a good understanding of the simple concepts, relations, and procedures involved.

Helpful assets

Success in solving problems and making proofs by coordinate methods will depend largely on the student's ability to translate the geometric conditions involved into algebraic symbols, his competence in handling these algebraic expressions as such, and his ability to retranslate or reinterpret his algebraic results back into the concepts and language of geometry. Thus he must become familiar both with the standard equations representing simple types of geometric forms with which he is dealing, and with the types of geometric forms identified with certain algebraic equations or inequalities. In short, in the simple cases that are considered, he must be able to infer algebraic representation from given geometric conditions, and also geometric properties from certain algebraic representations. This fusing of geometry with algebra poses a new type of problem for high school students, and it is one that will need to be pointed out explicitly to them time after time in connection with many examples and exercises. Questions such as the following would lend themselves to these ends: What kind of geometrical locus is represented by the equation $3x + 7y = 4$? By the equation $3x^2 + 3y^2 = 27$? What is the slope of the line represented by $x + 7y = 2$? What is the equation of the line through (2,5) and (8,1)? What is the equation of the line whose slope is $3/2$ and which contains the point (2,3)? What is the distance between the points (5,−1) and (−3,6)? How long is the radius of the circle whose equation is $x^2 + y^2 = 49$? What are the coordinates of the center of the circle whose equation is $(x − 2)^2 + y^2 = 2$? What is the equation of the circle whose center is at (4,5) and whose radius is 5 units long?

Problems involving the intersection of loci require not only the ability to identify geometric loci with their algebraic equations or inequalities, and conversely, but also the recognition that a point of intersection of two loci lies on both of them, and so must have coordinates that satisfy both of the equations or inequalities that

Problems about
intersecting loci—
the key

represent the respective loci. In other words, such problems require that the student recognize that the algebraic counterpart of a pair of intersecting loci is a system of equations or inequalities, and that the solution set of this system yields the coordinates of the point or points in which the loci intersect. This is another new idea for high school students, and it cannot be assumed that it will become clear to all from a single explanation. Here again the teacher should be careful to give lucid explanations, using numerous examples, and the students should be given many practice exercises. Exercises should be selected or devised so that they will have simple solution sets, to prevent algebraic complications from obscuring the main issue, which is identification of the coordinates of the point or points of intersection with the solution set of the algebraic system.

Proofs of theorems by coordinate methods sometimes follow different patterns from the patterns generally used in synthetic proofs. For example, consider the theorem which asserts that the diagonals of a parallelogram bisect each other. The synthetic proof is based on the establishment of the congruence of two triangles, and the conclusion is inferred from the fact that corresponding sides of these triangles must have equal measures. In contrast to this, the proof of this same theorem by coordinate methods is made by determining the coordinates of the mid-points of the two diagonals separately, and then showing that these mid-point coordinates are identical in the two cases.

This important method of establishing separately the identity of coordinates of points or of the measures of line segments or of

Adequate illus-
tration and practice
are needed

angles in different cases and then using the fact that the properties in question *are* identical in the different cases is a method often used in coordinate geometry. Teachers should take special care to explain and illustrate this to their classes, and to assign numerous simple exercises to give their students practice and to focus their attention particularly on this method or pattern of proof.

In some cases proofs of theorems can be simplified by judicious choice of the coordinate axes and/or by use of the properties of symmetry. For example, in proving that the diagonals of an isosceles trapezoid have the same measure, the equations yielding the lengths of the respective diagonals will be in simplest form if one coordinate axis is taken to contain one of the parallel sides of the trapezoid, with the origin taken to be at the mid-point of that side. There is no loss of generality in this, and the algebraic work can sometimes be materially simplified.

Polar coordinates need not be omitted

The topic of polar coordinates is given little, if any, attention in textbooks on high school geometry, probably because of limitations of time and because this topic is treated in depth in later courses. However, the fundamental concepts associated with polar coordinates and their use can be very simply explained provided the students understand the definitions and the basic properties of the trigonometric functions. The equations of some loci can be written more concisely and handled more easily in polar form than in rectangular form. Moreover, the relation between polar and rectangular coordinates and between polar coordinates and complex numbers would seem to make an introduction to polar coordinates a useful, as well as interesting, excursion in connection with the work on coordinate methods in the high school geometry course.

The fundamental relations

The main underlying idea to bring out is, of course, the fact that a point in a plane can be represented just as well by a direction and a distance as by two distances. This gives rise to the relation between the rectangular coordinates (x,y) of a point P in a plane and the polar coordinates (r,θ) of the same point, and provides the basis for the translation formulas $x = r \cos \theta$, $y = r \sin \theta$, $r = \sqrt{x^2 + y^2}$, $\theta = \arctan y/x$. With these in hand, exercises in translating expressions from rectangular to polar form, and vice versa, can easily be undertaken. A few simple illustrative examples explained and discussed by the teacher should clear the way for students to try some on their own. Algebraic and trigonometric complications should be avoided in this introductory treatment, and about all that should be undertaken is translating equations or inequalities from one form to the other and some simple graphical representations in polar coordinates.

A little trigonometry is needed

It must be noted that any study of polar coordinates requires some understanding of the trigonometric functions and of right-triangle trigonometry. Most modern high school geometry textbooks, and even junior high school textbooks, include as much trigonometry as is required for some simple work with polar coordinates. Before taking up such work, however, teachers should make sure that their students have had enough work in trigonometry to enable them to understand the fundamental concepts of polar coordinates. Perhaps, even if the whole class is not ready for it, some work with polar coordinates can serve as an interesting project for certain superior students.

Some people have questioned the propriety of including any work on coordinate geometry in the high school geometry course, on the grounds that most students who take the beginning course in geometry will have had only one year of algebra and very little systematic work in trigonometry. This is undoubtedly the case. On the other hand, this work on coordinate geometry certainly does not envisage any extensive coverage of analytic geometry. The concepts presented are few and simple, and the algebra required is not beyond the normal scope of a beginning course. No trigonometry is required except a little for polar coordinates, and this topic is not included in most high school geometry books. The brief introduction to coordinate geometry which is coming to be a typical feature of the newer textbooks in high school geometry is not beyond the level of maturity and of algebraic preparation of the tenth-grader who has a good mastery of the course in beginning

This work is
feasible and
appropriate if
time permits

algebra. It seems probable that the propriety of this work for tenth-grade students poses less of a problem than the matter of finding time for it in a crowded schedule. For the exceptional student who may have had one or two extra semesters of algebra or who takes a special interest in the work with coordinates, independent investigation of some topics of analytic geometry beyond those included in his textbook may provide a well-motivated and worthwhile project.

GEOMETRY FOR THE
LOW ACHIEVER

The problem of providing a *satisfactory* program in demonstrative geometry for the slow learner and the low achiever is a difficult task. Perhaps it is an impossible one. One of the main objectives of high school geometry is to have the students attain a good working understanding of the essential meaning of a proof, and at least a modicum of skill in actually making some proofs. Some low achievers have potential ability to understand and apply this concept but at a lower level or a slower rate than the majority of the

Some causes of
low achievement

students in their classes. These are, characteristically, the plodders. Others, who simply do not have the requisite mental ability, may never attain much understanding of geometry beyond the intuitive level. Such students should not be encouraged to take demonstrative geometry at all. There are still others who may have enough ability but who lack interest in geometry and who have failed to build up a background of geometric concepts, vocabulary, and facts adequate for pursuing profitably the course in high school geometry. Occasionally, among these there will be a "late bloomer" who suddenly wakes up to the fact that geometry can have meaning and be fun. But all these types of students will be handicapped, in comparison with their classmates, in doing really satisfactory work in demonstrative geometry. The teacher's problem is what to do for them and what to have them do in order that they may get as much profit from the course as possible.

Probably the best the teacher can do lies in (1) trying as hard as he can to motivate these students so as to draw out their best efforts, and (2) trying to provide them with work at levels of abstraction and rigor which will stretch their capacities within reason and strengthen their understanding and insight, and still let them feel that they have attained a measure of success. This will be largely a matter of working with them as individuals. Motivation, effort, and success are interactive. For the slow learner it may often be necessary to relax usual standards of rigor, but it must be considered that insights are more important than rigor. Even intuitive insights are valuable, but rigor without understanding is barren. For the slow learner there is no better motivation than to be able to feel that he has tried hard and has attained some degree of success which has been recognized as being creditable.

Success breeds interest and spurs effort

For the student who has reasonable ability but who just has not built for himself an adequate store of geometric concepts, facts, insight, or vocabulary, it may be necessary at the outset to give considerable work at the intuitive level. Numerous examples of this sort of work can be found in the last section of Chapter 12. Exercises designed for building the necessary background should involve various kinds of geometric figures and should have the aim of building technical vocabulary and understanding of the main properties of the geometric configurations commonly studied in high school geometry.[5]

Select exercises with care

Also, in almost every class there will be a few students who have reasonable ability but who just do not gain insights as rapidly or as completely as their classmates do. These students may not be able to keep up with the assignments made for the rest of the class, but they need to be encouraged to do as well as they can, and they need to have considerable work at which they can succeed. Moreover, they need to have their successes recognized by the teacher, so that they can feel some pride of accomplishment. It is worth mentioning again that this constitutes the highest and most effective of all forms of motivation. For students such as these the work should involve proofs, but not necessarily all the proofs expected of the rest of the class, and not necessarily the same proofs. Exer-

[5] For an excellent discussion of this kind of work, with examples and diagrams, see Max A. Sobel, "Teaching General Mathematics" (Englewood Cliffs, N.J.: Prentice-Hall, Inc., 1967), pp. 26–35.

Suggestions to
teachers

cises to be assigned to them should be selected with care and, for
the most part, should not be such as to require long or involved
proofs, though at least intuitive understanding of all the theorems
assigned to the class should be expected. As with all slow learners,
standards of rigor will have to be relaxed, and the teacher will
need to give them special individual attention and help. Careful
efforts to diagnose individual troubles and to spot key difficulties
through a few well-chosen questions may save a good deal of time
for both the teacher and the students.

The main problem teachers will face in working with under-
achievers in a regular class is lack of time. Much of their work
will need to be specially planned, assigned, supervised, and
checked for these students individually, and the teacher will
still have his responsibility to the rest of the class. It therefore
seems clear that this type of provision could not be made, in a
regular class, for more than a few students.

TOPICS FOR BRIGHT STUDENTS

Some students are able to master the usual course in high school
geometry with so little effort that their full mathematical potential
is hardly more than tapped. These are the students who, with
proper motivation, could go furthest in mathematics but who are

The bright student
needs intellectual
challenge

often neglected, in the sense that they are not given work which
will "stretch their minds," but are allowed to coast along with
the rest of the class and are not forced to extend themselves very
much. These students need, and usually like, work that will challenge their best intellectual efforts. The discussion which follows
suggests a few examples of topics that could serve this purpose.
Others could be given. With suitable reference books available,
and with some guidance and perhaps some help from the teacher,
either of these topics could be investigated with interest and
profit by high school students of exceptional insight and ability.

Mirror Geometry

This is a geometry in which the basic mapping, or transformation,
is the reflection of points in a straight line or plane, or the construction of images of points and figures, so that the points and
their images are symmetric with respect to a straight line or a
plane. The concept of symmetry with respect to a line or a plane
is central, and the construction of images is achieved through the
definition of this concept. To construct the image P' of a point P
with respect to a line l or a plane π, one need only construct a line
segment from P perpendicular to l or to π and prolong this line
segment through l or π to a point P' such that P' and P are equi-

distant from l or from π. The image F' of a figure F is simply the aggregate of the images P' of all the points P in F. Thus little is required from the usual euclidean geometry except the construction of a perpendicular to a line or plane from a given point; the theorem which asserts that each such perpendicular is unique; and the definition of congruent figures and a few congruence theorems.

By constructing carefully a number of plane figures and their images (reflections), certain general observations soon become intuitively evident. Repeated reflections (reflections of images in the same line or in other lines) yield other and more interesting observations which the student may set down as conjectures and for which he may then seek proofs. Observant and ingenious students may be able to discover and prove several theorems in such a "mirror geometry." More importantly, their understandings of transformations will be somewhat generalized and clarified, and they will almost certainly get a sense of achievement and a high degree of motivation through investigation of this special topic.

Important side products

Inversion

In plane geometry the fundamental transformation which, in effect, defines mirror geometry is reflection in a line. Another fundamental transformation which bears some resemblance to reflection in a line is that of inversion with respect to a circle. This transformation is sometimes referred to as "reflection in a circle," just as reflection in a line is sometimes referred to as "inversion in a line." When a point P is reflected in a line l, the point and its image P' are endpoints of a line segment PP', of which l is the perpendicular bisector (see Fig. 14-6a). But when a point P is reflected in a circle (called the circle of inversion) whose center is at O and whose radius is r (Fig. 14-6b), the point P and its image P' are not in general equidistant from the circle. Instead, the mapping which locates P' for a given P is defined as follows: P' lies on $\overrightarrow{OP}$, and $OP \times OP' = r^2$. Thus, if P lies outside the circle of inversion, then P' must lie inside the circle, and conversely. If P lies on the circle, then P' coincides with P. This mapping is called "inversion with respect to the circle O."

A new kind of mapping

Inversion with respect to a circle leads to a number of interesting results and to some interesting contrasts. Reflection in a line l is a 1:1 mapping of the plane onto itself in that, for every point P in one of the half-planes of l, reflection assigns a point P' in the plane, but in the other half-plane, as the image of P. Each half-plane thus is mapped 1:1 onto the other. Inversion in a circle O also is a 1:1 mapping of the plane onto itself in that, for each point P which lies outside the circle, the image P' lies inside the

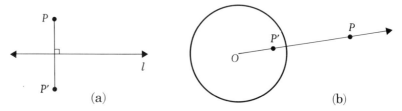

Figure 14-6
Reflection (inversion) (a) in a line and (b) in a circle.

**Test of insight and
ingenuity**

circle, and conversely. Each point on the circle is its own image. Thus inversion is a 1:1 mapping of all that part of the plane lying outside the circle onto the interior of the circle, and conversely. Other interesting facts that can be brought to light without difficulty include the following theorems: A line through the center of the circle O is its own inverse. The inverse of a line which does not contain O is a circle which passes through O; and conversely: the inverse of a circle not through the center of inversion is a circle not through the center of inversion.

For most of the theorems on inversion, good mathematical acuity on the part of the student is required, but the algebra and the geometrical concepts needed do not go beyond those with which good high school sophomores should be familiar. In view of the interesting theorems and constructions that may be investigated, some study of inversion in a circle would appear to be a good topic for independent study by the exceptional student in the latter part of the course in high school geometry. One or more reference books of the type of Altshiller-Court's "College Geometry" should be made available to the student who undertakes such a project.

Finite geometries

In euclidean plane geometry it is assumed that there are infinitely many lines in the plane and infinitely many points on each line. In a finite geometry, by contrast, it is stipulated at the outset that only a finite number of points and lines are to be considered and that for purposes of this geometry there are no other points or lines. Such terms as "parallel" or "perpendicular lines," "bisector," "triangle," "congruent," and other concepts to be involved are not to have the usual meanings intuitively attached to them, but must be defined explicitly in terms of admissible points. Likewise, all assumptions must be stated categorically and without ambiguity. These conditions are very important because, ex-

A strange-looking
geometry, strictly
axiomatic

cept for its axiomatic structure, such a geometry will have little in common with ordinary plane geometry. Unfamiliar meanings will be attached to familiar terms. The definitions and graphic or physical models will seem strangely different from those of euclidean plane geometry, and intuition can play no part in arriving at conclusions. Even theorems which may sound verbally familiar cannot have the familiar interpretations.

On the other hand, the very necessity of working without the aid of intuition can do much to clarify the sense of what the axiomatic method is and how it operates. Because most students depend considerably on intuition, working with such a geometry would likely have little appeal to them, except, perhaps, as a puzzle. But to those who have a natural liking and flair for abstractions, the search for proofs of theorems in a finite geometry can be a fascinating and truly productive experience.

The foregoing examples are but three taken from a considerable list of topics that would be suitable for investigation by exceptionally able high school students. Others might include such topics as incidence geometry; geometry and perspective; traversable networks; inequalities in geometry; generalization and special cases; making and testing converses and inverses for certain theorems; geometric mappings, or transformations; rigid motion; vectors, and proofs of selected theorems by vector methods; convexity and convex figures; proofs of selected theorems by coordinate methods; and regular polygons.

Many challenging geometrical problems can be found in the "Problem Department" of the *Mathematics Student Journal.*

EXERCISES

1 Give a careful definition of a convex set of points and of a convex geometrical figure. Exactly what is meant by the *width* of a convex solid in a direction perpendicular to a supporting plane?

2 Characterize each of the following point sets as a convex point set, a convex figure, both of these, or neither of these, and explain your answers: (*a*) a circle; (*b*) the interior of a triangle; (*c*) the union of a sphere and its interior; (*d*) a line segment; (*e*) a plane; (*f*) an open ray; (*g*) a tetrahedron; (*h*) a paraboloid; (*i*) an angle; (*j*) the region bounded by a cube.

3 Explain, illustrate, and discuss the meaning of the following definition: A point *A* is an inner point of a two- (three-) dimensional set of points *S* if and only if there exists a circle (sphere) with center at *A* whose interior consists entirely of points belonging to *S*.

4 Consider the following planar point sets: (*a*) an open half-plane; (*b*) a polygon; (*c*) a circle together with its interior; (*d*) the interior of a triangle. Which of these point sets contain inner points? Which contain only inner points? Which contain only boundary points? Why can a boundary point not be an inner point?

5 Explain the distinction between an *into* mapping and an *onto* mapping. Give examples of (*a*) an into mapping that is not an onto mapping, and (*b*) an onto mapping that is not a 1:1 onto mapping.

6 In a given plane *E* let α be the translation mapping (parallel shift, or sliding) and let β be the mapping of rotation about a point in *E*. Both are congruence-preserving mappings. However, if *R* and *S* are congruent figures in *E* but arbitrarily placed, then α or β alone may not be sufficient to map *R* onto *S* or *S* onto *R*. Explain why. Would the composite mapping $\theta = \alpha\beta$ be sufficient? Explain.

7 Let α, β, and θ be the mappings named, respectively, by these letters in exercise 6, and let γ be the mapping achieved by stretching line segments in a given ratio. Show that the composite mapping $\psi = \theta\gamma$ is a similarity mapping. Give five examples. Describe how the mapping ψ could be used to map a given figure A in plane E onto A', a figure similar to A but arbitrarily placed in E. Describe in words the inverse mappings γ^{-1}, θ^{-1}, and ψ^{-1}, if they exist.

8 Describe and illustrate (a) a procedure by which a 1:1 onto mapping can be set up between the set of points on a 1-inch line segment and the set of all nonnegative real numbers; (b) a procedure by which a 1:1 onto mapping can be set up between all angles having measures of between 0° and 180° and the set of all real numbers.

9 Consider a right circular cone whose altitude is h and the radius of whose base is r. (a) If r is held constant so that $r = 3$, make a graph of the volume V of the cone against h as the independent variable over the closed interval $0 \leqslant h \leqslant 5$. (b) If h is held constant so that $h = 5$, make a graph of V against r as the independent variable over the closed interval $0 \leqslant r \leqslant 3$.

10 Consider the triangle ABC in which the sides $\overline{AB}$ and $\overline{AC}$ have fixed lengths of 7 and 3 units, respectively, and in which the side $\overline{AC}$ is rotated about A so that the degree measure of $\angle A$ varies continuously over the closed interval $[0,180]$. Make graphs of the measures of $\overline{BC}$ and of the area k of the triangle as $\angle A$ varies over this interval. Use these graphs in discussing the dependence of $\overline{BC}$ and of k on $m\angle A$. Also discuss the variation of each.

11 Let x and y be the respective lengths of the axes of an ellipse. Let n represent the number of axes of symmetry. Discuss the set of values of n: (a) when $x < y$; (b) when $x = y$; (c) when $x > y$.

12 Take five theorems involving geometric figures and restate them in a form in which you use the phrase "depends on." Discuss each of them from this standpoint.

13 Give good definitions of symmetry (a) with respect to a line; (b) with respect to a point; (c) with respect to a plane. Illustrate your definitions with careful drawings.

14 Explain why reflection in a point, line, or plane is a congruence-preserving mapping.

15 For each of the following objects (or its geometrical idealization) tell (1) how many axes of symmetry it has, (2) how many planes of symmetry it has, and (3) whether or not it has a center of symmetry: (a) a right circular cone; (b) a tomato can; (c) a football; (d) a baseball; (e) a cube; (f) a rectangular prism that is not a cube; (g) a fish; (h) an ordinary light bulb; (i) a glove; (j) an apple.

16 Consider two oblique lines l and m intersecting at O, another point P (different from O) in the plane of l and m, and the images $P_i(i = 1, 2, 3, \ldots)$ formed by reflecting P and its successive images alternately in l and m. (a) Prove that P and its infinitely many images P_i lie on a circle whose center is at O and whose radius is OP. (b) Show that reflection first in l, then in m, etc., gives a different set of images from those obtained by reflecting first in m, then in l, etc. (c) If l and m are perpendicular to each other, how many distinct images are obtained?

17 Consider the points $A(-2,-2)$, $B(1,-5)$, $C(4,-1)$, $D(-3,1)$, and $E(-1,3)$. The vectors $\overrightarrow{AB}$, $\overrightarrow{BC}$, $\overrightarrow{CD}$, and $\overrightarrow{DE}$ are one set of components of the resultant vector $\overrightarrow{AE}$. Explain, as you would to a class, how to use the horizontal and vertical components of these component vectors to find the horizontal and vertical components of the resultant vector $\overrightarrow{AE}$, and thus to determine its magnitude and its amplitude, or vectorial angle. Would the same resultant be obtained by using $\overrightarrow{AC}$ and $\overrightarrow{CE}$ as components of $\overrightarrow{AE}$? What about $\overrightarrow{AD}$ and $\overrightarrow{DE}$? Explain.

18 Explain graphically why the commutative and associative laws hold for vector addition. If $\mathbf{v}$ and $\mathbf{w}$ are vectors, explain graphically the meaning of $\mathbf{v} - \mathbf{w}$.

19 Prove by vector methods that the diagonals of a parallelogram bisect each other.

20 Prepare an outline and present a good discussion of "vectors and complex numbers" as you would in introducing this topic to a class.

21 Describe the essential steps in the indirect proof of a proposition. Illustrate by this example: Let $ABCD$ be a quadrilateral with vertexes A, B, and C on a circle. If $m\angle A = m\angle B = m\angle C = 75°$, show by an indirect proof that the vertex D cannot lie on this circle.

22 Suppose that two coplanar lines m and n are cut by a transversal l, making a pair of corresponding angles unequal. Show by an indirect proof that m and n are not parallel.

23 Let triangles ABC and ABD have a common side $\overline{AB}$, and let D be an interior point of $\triangle ABC$ with $AD = AC$. Show by an indirect proof that $BD < BC$, and discuss your proof.

24 Let a, b, and m be real numbers with $0 < m < a < b$. Show by an indirect proof that $(a - m)/(b - m) < a/b$.

25 In the coordinate plane let r and s be two straight lines having slopes of m_1 and m_2, respectively. Give the necessary and sufficient condition for $r \perp s$, and show how you would prove this to a high school geometry class.

26 Give both a synthetic proof and a proof by coordinate methods of the theorem that the line segment joining the mid-points of two sides of a triangle is parallel to the third side, and that its length is half that of the third side.

27 Explain the meaning of the polar coordinates (r,θ) of a point in a plane, and their relation to the rectangular coordinates (x,y) of the same point. Show how the formulas for translating polar into rectangular co-ordinates, and conversely, are arrived at, and give some examples of how they are used.

28 Show why it is simple to plot the locus of the equation $r = 3 \cos \theta$ in polar coordinates, while if it were translated into rectangular coordinates, the plotting would not be at all simple.

29 Select three special topics which you think could be investigated independently and with some success and interest by students who have trouble keeping up with the regular work of the class. With respect to one of these topics, write down some suggestions which you think would be helpful to the student, and prepare a small but good list of references for him to use.

30 Select three supplementary topics which you think would be good ones for investigation by an exceptionally good student in geometry. For one of these topics outline what suggestions you would give for undertaking an independent study of the topic, and prepare a suitable bibliography for the student.

BIBLIOGRAPHY

Adler, Irving: What Shall We Teach in High School Geometry?, *Mathematics Teacher,* **61** (1968), 226–238.

Ash, Carol: Locus Proofs, *Mathematics Teacher,* **55** (1962), 175–176.

Athen, Herman: The Teaching of Vectors in the German Gymnasium, *Mathematics Teacher,* **59** (1966), 382–393, 485–495.

Barnett, I. A.: Introducing Number Theory in High School Algebra and Geometry, *Mathematics Teacher,* **58** (1965), 14–23, 89–101.

Barry, Edward H.: "Introduction to Geometrical Transformations," vol. 3 (Boston: Prindle, Weber & Schmidt, Inc.), chap. 3.

Beckenbach, Edwin F.: On the Positive Square Root of Two, *Mathematics Teacher,* **62** (1969), 261–267.

Byrkit, Donald R.: Distance from a Point to a Line—Revisited, *School Science and Mathematics,* **68** (1968), 145–147.

Commission on Mathematics: "Appendices" (New York: College Entrance Examination Board, 1959), 116–139, 159–179.

Coxford, Arthur F., Jr.: Geometric Diversions: A 25-point Geometry, *Mathematics Teacher,* **57** (1964), 561–564.

———: Geometry with Transformations: An Alternative for High School Geometry, *Mathematics in Michigan,* **22** (1968), 3–12.

Einhorn, Erwin: Graphing and the Centigrade-Fahrenheit Relationship, *School Science and Mathematics,* **69** (1969), 89–91.

Elkin, J. M.: A Deceptively Easy Problem, *Mathematics Teacher,* **58** (1965), 194–199.

Eves, Howard: "A Survey of Geometry," vol. I (Boston: Allyn & Bacon, Inc., 1963).

———: A Geometry Capsule Concerning the Five Platonic Solids, *Mathematics Teacher,* **62** (1969), 42–44.

Forsythe, Alexandra: What Points Are Equidistant from Two Skew Lines?, *Mathematics Teacher,* **62** (1969), 97–101.

Garfunkel, J.: Solving Problems in Geometry by Using Complex Numbers, *Mathematics Teacher,* **60** (1967), 731–734.

———: A Project in Mathematics, *Mathematics Teacher,* **61** (1968), 253–258.

———: Explaining Geometric Maxima and Minima, *Mathematics Teacher,* **62** (1969), 85–90.

——— and B. Plotkin: Using Geometry to Prove Algebraic Inequalities, *Mathematics Teacher,* **59** (1966), 730–734.

Glicksman, Abraham M.: Vectors in Algebra

and Geometry, *Mathematics Teacher*, **58** (1965), 327–332.

_____: "Vectors in Three Dimensional Geometry" (Washington, D.C.: National Council of Teachers of Mathematics, 1966). (Pamphlet.)

Haddock, Glen, and David Moon: Isometries in Euclidean 1-space, *Bulletin of the Kansas Association of Teachers of Mathematics*, April, 1968, pp. 26–27, 31.

Hardesty, James: On Similarity Transformations, *Mathematics Teacher*, **61** (1968), 278–283.

Heidlage, Martha: A Coordinate Approach to the 25-point Miniature Geometry, *Mathematics Teacher*, **58** (1965), 109–113.

Hicken, Baron B.: Some Interesting Mathematical and Optical Properties of Parabolas and Parabolic Surfaces, *School Science and Mathematics*, **69** (1969), 109–117.

Hood, Rodney T.: A Chain of Circles, *Mathematics Teacher*, **54** (1961), 134–137.

Johnson, Paul B.: Are Circles Similar?, *Mathematics Teacher*, **59** (1966), 9–13.

Jones, Burton W.: Reflections and Rotations, *Mathematics Teacher*, **54** (1961), 406–410.

Kalman, Karl (Editor): "The System of Vectors" (Ann Arbor, Mich.: Cushing-Malloy, Inc., 1964). (Lithoprinted SMSG pamphlet.)

Kelley, Paul J.: Plane Convex Figures, *Twenty-eighth Yearbook* (Washington, D.C.: National Council of Teachers of Mathematics, 1963), pp. 251–264.

Klamkin, Murray S.: On Some Geometric Inequalities, *Mathematics Teacher*, **60** (1967), 323–328.

Levy, Harry: The Role of Geometry in the Eleventh and Twelfth Grades, *Mathematics Teacher*, **57** (1964), 130–138.

Meserve, Bruce E.: Euclidean and Other Geometries, *Mathematics Teacher*, **60** (1967), 2–11.

_____: "Geometry in the Secondary School" (Washington, D.C.: National Council of Teachers of Mathematics, 1967), pp. 1–7. (Pamphlet.)

Perisho, Clarence R.: The Use of Transformations in Deriving Equations of Common Geometric Figures, *Mathematics Teacher*, **58** (1965), 386–392.

Schaaf, William L.: Mathematics for the Gifted, *Twenty-fifth Yearbook* (Washington, D.C.: National Council of Teachers of Mathematics, 1963), pp. 6–16. (Bibliography.)

Scheid, Francis: Square Circles, *Mathematics Teacher*, **54** (1961), 307–312.

Spencer, Richard V.: Discovery of Basic Inversion Theory by Construction, *Mathematics Teacher*, **57** (1964), 303–306.

Szabo, Steven: An Approach to Euclidean Geometry through Vectors, *Mathematics Teacher*, **59** (1966), 218–235.

Troyer, Robert: Rotations, Angles, and Trigonometry, *Mathematics Teacher*, **61** (1968), 123–129.

Vaughn, Herbert E.: An Illustration of the Use of Vector Methods in Geometry, *Mathematics Teacher*, **58** (1965), 696–701.

Walter, Marion: Polynominoes, Milk Cartons, and Groups, *Mathematics Teaching*, no. 43, pp. 12–19, Summer, 1968.

Wernick, William: Variations on a Theme: $y = 2x - 3$, *Mathematics Teacher*, **59** (1966), 251–256.

| the
teaching
of
trigonometry

Trigonometry is a very old subject, but there was a time when few people other than mathematicians, engineers, surveyors, and astronomers studied the subject or knew anything about it. This is no longer the case. It is common practice now to introduce some of the simple ideas and applications of right triangle trigonometry even in the seventh grade. The more comprehensive and systematic study of the subject, although it is still offered in most colleges (often without credit) has come to be regarded as essentially a high school subject and is usually offered in the eleventh or twelfth grade. More and more students are taking trigonometry in high school, often not as a separate course, but as an integral part of the second course in algebra or of a program in Elementary Functions in the eleventh and twelfth grades.

The emphasis has changed

The systematic course in trigonometry has undergone a profound change since the middle of this century. The numerical aspect, as represented by the solution of triangles by laborious logarithmic methods, has faded from prominence, and primary attention now is focused on the analytical properties of the circular, or trigonometric, functions and their relations.

Trigonometry draws heavily upon ideas and procedures of arithmetic, elementary algebra, and geometry, and by synthesizing these with a few new ideas, concepts and relations are opened up beyond the scope of the earlier courses. It is not inherently a very difficult course, but there are some important and fairly definite problems of learning which will inevitably be encountered and of which teachers should be aware. The purpose of this chapter is to consider some of these instructional problems.

TRIGONOMETRY IN THE JUNIOR HIGH SCHOOL

The justification of some work in numerical trigonometry in the junior high school lies partly in its propaedeutic value, but more in its contribution to the general enrichment of the mathematics course at this level. It includes extension and application of the concept of ratio and the properties of similar figures; use of the conventional terminology and notation associated with the sub-

ject; appreciation of the power of indirect measurement; understanding of methods of accomplishing such measurement through
the use of the right triangle and the tangent, sine, and cosine
ratios; correlation of ideas and procedures drawn from arithmetic,
algebra, and geometry; and the solution of simple problems. It
offers opportunities for experimental activities and inductive
reasoning, and it aims at stimulation of interest in mathematics
as a whole.

The subject matter of the numerical trigonometry of the junior
high school is simple. It consists primarily of instances dealing
with the indirect measurement of distances and angles. Impetus
can be given to this work through experimental laboratory activities involving such measurements, and perhaps even by outdoor
activities. But before these things can be undertaken, considerable preliminary groundwork needs to be done. It is necessary
that the students have clear concepts of the meaning of similar
figures (especially similar triangles), of a ratio as a comparison
of two quantities, in the sense that one is a certain fraction of the
other or that one is a certain number of times the other, and also
of a ratio as a single number (fractional or integral) which may be
used as a multiplier. They also need to understand the particular
meanings of the tangent ratio, the sine ratio, and the cosine ratio;
and they must know how to use the table of natural functions
either to find the value of a particular function of a given angle
or to find the value of an angle if the numerical value of one of its
functions is known. They need to know the meaning of such terms
as "angle of elevation" and "angle of depression." They need practice in analyzing problem situations, in making working drawings, in selecting the appropriate functions to use, in setting up
and solving equations involving these functions, and in substitution and evaluation. These things need to be carefully and clearly
explained by the teacher. In order to develop comprehensive understanding of the techniques used in field projects, the students
should work a large number of illustrative problems. Furthermore,
the teacher should carefully discuss the full implications of such
problems with the students.

DEVELOPING THE MEANING OF
A TRIGONOMETRIC FUNCTION

In teaching numerical trigonometry to junior high school students
the teacher should keep in mind that his two fundamental objectives are (1) to give the students a clear understanding of the meanings of the tangent, sine, and cosine functions as *ratios* and as
numbers, and (2) to teach them how to use these functions and

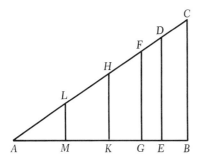

Figure 15-1
Finding tangent ∠A.

their numerical values to solve simple numerical problems in which right triangles are involved. Obviously, they must be undertaken in this order.

The initial approach, then, is to make clear the meanings of each of these functions, first as a ratio, and then as a number. Probably the best way to accomplish this is to have the students actually make careful measurements of the angles and sides of right triangles and compute the numerical values of the ratios representing the tangent, sine, and cosine. It is well to have several students compute the values of these functions for angles of a given size so that they may compare their results. Generally, their results will show a fairly close correspondence, and the fact that they may not agree exactly offers a good opportunity to emphasize the approximate nature of measurement. Thus any discrepancies may be attributed either to mistakes in computation or to errors in taking the measurements. This approach, through measurement and computation, to the meaning of a trigonometric function emphasizes the concept of the function both as a comparison of the lengths of two sides of a right triangle and as a single numerical quantity or quotient. Common agreement on the value to be accepted may be reached by averaging the values found by several students.

Two concepts of a function: meaning, and numerical value

A variation of the foregoing procedure might be to have each student make several sets of measurements and computations leading to the determination of the values of the functions of a particular angle, such as angle A in Fig. 15-1. Thus the value of the tangent of angle A might be determined by using several different ratios, such as CB/AB, DE/AE, FG/AG, HK/AK, or LM/AM. This would emphasize the principle that the value of a given function of any angle is independent of the actual lengths of the sides of the triangle and depends only on the *ratio* of the lengths of the two sides involved.

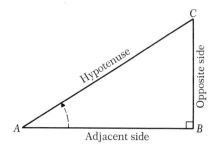

Figure 15-2
Functions of acute ∠A.

The functions that are introduced in the study of trigonometry in the junior high school are generally limited to the tangent, sine, and cosine. The others would add nothing toward making the meaning of a function clear, and they are not needed for the solution of the simple applied problems that make up the work of this period. For obvious reasons this work is limited to situations that involve functions of acute angles. With this in mind, the functions of an acute angle may be defined in terms of the sides of a right triangle containing that angle. Let angle *BAC* be the given angle of Fig. 15-2.

$$\text{Tangent } \angle BAC = \frac{\text{length of opposite side}}{\text{length of adjacent side}}$$

The three functions used first

$$\text{Sine } \quad \angle BAC = \frac{\text{length of opposite side}}{\text{length of hypotenuse}}$$

$$\text{Cosine } \angle BAC = \frac{\text{length of adjacent side}}{\text{length of hypotenuse}}$$

An interesting and valuable exercise can now be introduced by having the class as a whole make measurements and computations necessary for the compilation of a table of sines, cosines, and tangents for the acute angles, say, which are integral multiples of 5°. This exercise would provide well-motivated practice in accurate drawing and measurement of lines and angles and in careful computation. Diagrams for the measurements should be rather large and very carefully drawn. For each of the angles considered, at least two or three students should make determinations of the functions for purposes of comparing, checking, and averaging the results. The values of the functions as shown by the computed results should be expressed to three significant figures.

Care in drawing is important

TEACHING STUDENTS HOW TO USE
THE TRIGONOMETRIC FUNCTIONS

The meanings of the trigonometric functions and the ways in which they are to be used will be more quickly and adequately comprehended if the meanings and uses are illustrated in problem situations. There need be no delay about this. As soon as the meaning of the tangent ratio has been explained to the point of understanding, the teacher should show how it is used in finding distances or angles without direct measurement. Hypothetical or "made-up" problems will serve for this purpose quite as well as "real" problems, and perhaps better, because the assumed elements (an angle and a distance or two given distances) can be selected at will and with a view to convenience, and there will be no extraneous details of actual measurement, the manipulation of instruments, or unnecessarily difficult computations to draw the students' attention from the main ideas and procedures involved. Substantial mastery of the basic theory and procedure should be assured before the students are presented with situations in which they will have to provide their own data. Initial interest is usually

Illustrative ex- high, and the artificial motivation afforded by field projects is
amples are needed unnecessary at the outset. Thus such problems as the following serve well to introduce students to the applications of the functions. The fact that convenient data are arbitrarily chosen in no way lessens the value of the problems. The steps in the solution are about in the form in which they should be explained to the students.

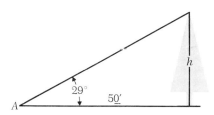

Figure 15-3
Find h.

Example. From a point 5Q feet from the base of a tree, the angle of elevation A of the top of the tree is found to be 29°. Find the height of the tree. (See Fig. 15-3.)

1 First we shall make a picture or diagram to represent the problem. On this diagram we shall indicate all data that are given, such as the distance from point A to the base of the tree and the size of the angle of elevation at A. (The diagram is made and data are indicated as shown; see Fig. 15-3.)

2   Since the height of the tree represents the unknown distance, we should designate it by some letter; for example, let us use h.

3   We know that the ratio $h/50$ represents the tangent of angle A; so we may now write the equation $h/50 =$ tangent of 29°.

4   We know that the tangent of an angle can be expressed as a number. From our table of tangents we find that the numerical value of the tangent of 29° is 0.5543. Therefore we may substitute this numerical value for the expression "tangent of 29° and write the equation $h/50 = 0.5543$.

5   Now, if we solve this equation for h, we shall get the equation $50(h)/50 = (0.554)(50)$, or $h = 27.72$ feet, i.e., about 28 feet. Thus we know that the tree is about 28 feet high.

Two things to stress   In presenting this explanation, the students' attention should be deliberately focused both upon the particular activities and the basic concepts presented in each of the various steps and upon the order in which the steps are taken. The order reveals to the students a pattern for their work. This pattern not only helps them to systematize their written work and their computations, but also to analyze such problems and organize their thinking about them. Each step stresses one important element in the analysis and solution of the problem. Drawing and lettering the figure and indicating the given data (step 1) give the problem a concrete setting and facilitate the job of translating it into an equation. The selection and indication of a literal symbol to represent the unknown part of the figure (step 2) direct attention to the fact that the object of the work is to determine the magnitude of this particular part. Writing the equation (step 3) requires analysis of the problem to determine which of the trigonometric functions is the appropriate one to use.

In this connection the following points should be stressed: (1) If one side and an angle of the triangle are given and it is required to find another side, that function should be selected which is represented by the ratio that involves both the unknown side and the **Selecting the** known side. (2) If two sides are given and an angle is required, **function to be used** then that function should be selected which is represented by the ratio of one of these known sides to the other. A scheme that is slightly mechanical yet rather helpful in selecting the proper function is to emphasize that the sine and cosine should be used if one of the given sides is the hypotenuse. It should further be emphasized that the hypotenuse occurs in the denominator of the fraction representing either of these functions.

The transition from the ratio concept to the quotient and numerical concepts of a trigonometric function and the substitution of the numerical value for the ratio (step 4) are of vital importance in understanding the use of the functions in indirect measurement. The actual solution of the equation for the unknown part and the reinterpretation of this in terms of the diagram or of the original problem situation (step 5) bring a realization of how the laws of algebra operate to find the required information by giving explicit form to a relationship which was merely implicit before. In the calculations involved, care should be taken to observe the rules for computation with approximate data. The order in which these steps have been indicated is the order in which they logically occur in the analysis and solution of the problem. Fortunately, there is no conflict between this logical order and the natural, or "psychological organization," of the analysis from the standpoint of the immature student.

The plan of procedure

The problem upon which the foregoing discussion is based involves the use of the tangent. Similar illustrative problems involving the sine and the cosine should also be used. Such problems should be selected or devised with care, but they are available in countless numbers and with many variations. The following are examples involving, respectively, the sine and cosine.

Example 1. A ladder 22 feet long is placed against a vertical wall so that it makes an angle of 62° with the ground. At what height above the ground does the ladder touch the wall (Fig. 15-4)?

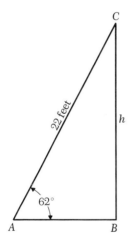

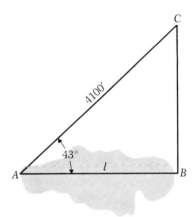

Figure 15-4
Find h (*distance CB*).

Figure 15-5
Find l (*distance AB*).

Example 2. To find the distance across a lake, some surveyors sighted an east-west line *AB* across the lake and then a north-south line *BC*. Then they measured the distance *AC* and the angle *BAC*. They found that *AC* = 4,100 feet and that angle *BAC* = 43°. Find how far it was from *A* to *B* (Fig. 15-5).

A useful work pattern

In setting up the earlier problems care should be taken to arrange the data so that, when the equations are set up, the symbols for the unknown parts will occur in the *numerators* of the fractions representing the trigonometric ratios or functions to be used. Later on it will be desirable to introduce some problems in which the unknown will occur in the *denominator* of the fraction. The following example will illustrate this.

Example. In order to find the distance between two points *P* and *Q* on opposite sides of a small lake, two boy scouts decided to set up a right triangle with $\overline{PQ}$ as the hypotenuse (Fig. 15-6). They used an angle mirror to locate a point *O* such that the lines of sight *OP* and $\overrightarrow{OQ}$ formed a right angle. The distance from *O* to *Q* could not be measured directly, but the distance from *O* to *P* was measured and found to be 218 feet. By sighting from *P* to *O* and then from *P* to *Q*, the size of angle *P* was established as 52°. From these data the boys found the distance from *P* to *Q*. How far was it? (Call this distance *d*.)

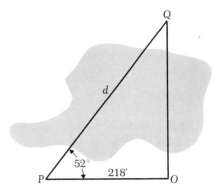

Figure 15-6
Find d (distance PQ).

This problem leads to the equation

$$\frac{218}{d} = \cos 52° = 0.6157$$

Simplifying the arithmetic

To simplify the solution, it may be suggested to the students that the equation can be written $218/d = 0.616/1$, that by inverting both of these fractions, the equation $d/218 = 1/0.616$ will result, and that, if both members are now multiplied by 218, the equation is solved for *d*, the required distance, by performing the indicated division.

The work in trigonometry in the junior high school will scarcely go beyond these simple applications of the functions to the general problem of finding certain unknown parts of right triangles. If desired, the cotangent may be introduced, but it is unnecessary, and little is to be gained by its use. The secant and cosecant should not be discussed.

TRIGONOMETRY IN THE SENIOR HIGH
SCHOOL AND THE JUNIOR COLLEGE

The systematic course in trigonometry in the senior high school and the junior college will be in marked contrast to the work offered in the junior high school, both in complexity and in emphasis. It will also differ from the old-time traditional course, which gave excessive emphasis to the solution of triangles. Relative emphasis on this aspect of the course, and upon the massive numerical work that formerly was considered so important, has diminished, while increasing importance is being attached to the analytic aspects of the subject.

There will still be triangles to be solved, of course, but in view of the changing demands of the physical sciences, engineering, and higher mathematics, there is need today for increased study of such analytic considerations as the variation, graphs, and composition of the trigonometric functions, the inverse functions, proofs of identities, solution of trigonometric equations, polar coordinates and complex numbers in trigonometric form, and a trigonometry of numbers and circular functions. Of the students who take trigonometry today, relatively few will have much occasion later in life to solve oblique triangles, but many will take mathematics and science in college and will need a good understanding of the analytic aspects of trigonometry. In the interests of these students it is important that the course should provide increased emphasis on the analytic side of trigonometry.

The modern emphasis

Such a course will demand of students more intellectual alertness, ingenuity, and insight than the traditional triangle-solving course did, and students will have to accept more responsibility for the analysis and understanding of an expanded theory of the subject. The teacher has the obligation both of keeping them aware of this responsibility and of assisting them in their efforts. There are parts of trigonometry which most students would find pretty difficult to "dig out for themselves," but which can easily be made clear and meaningful by a skillful teacher. The teacher of trigonometry has the same obligation to help his class to a clear understanding of the basic principles and techniques of the subject as has the teacher of arithmetic, algebra, or geometry in the earlier years of the secondary school. With this in mind, the remainder of this chapter will be devoted to a discussion of teaching problems that arise in connection with the development of certain concepts and procedures in trigonometry. The topics which will be discussed have been selected on the basis of three criteria: (1) they are fundamental; (2) they are often troublesome; (3) they are based upon relatively simple fundamental principles which, if not properly emphasized, are easily obscured by the mass of detail

The teacher's role includes important responsibilities

attending their development, but which, if set forth and perceived at the outset, will furnish a clear and helpful guide to the development. In the discussion of these topics the aim will be to present suggestions for developing them in a manner calculated to make clear the underlying principles and thus provide a basic framework around which the details of the development may be organized effectively.

THE GENERAL ANGLE: DEGREE
AND RADIAN MEASURE

It has become customary in high school geometry to define an angle whose degree measure is x as the union of two noncollinear rays having a common endpoint, with the further provision that $0 < x < 180$, and this definition is sufficient for the purposes of that course. The definition, however, is restrictive. It would exclude the notions of straight or reflex angles, the zero angle, the general angle (having any size whatever), and sensed (or directed) angles. But these concepts are needed in trigonometry; so the students must now revise their thinking to include these concepts in the set of objects which we shall call angles.

A broader definition of an angle is needed now

Perhaps the best way to develop this more inclusive idea of *angle* is to get the students to think of an angle as being formed when a ray is rotated about its endpoint from one position to another which may or may not be different from the first, with the conventional agreement that angles generated by counterclockwise rotation shall be considered positive, and those generated by clockwise rotation, negative.

The essential groundwork for this concept of the general angle and its measure will normally have been laid in the junior high school. There the protractor furnishes a means for associating with each angle not greater than a straight angle a nonnegative real number k ($0 \leq k \leq 180$), called the degree measure of the angle.

The general angle

Now it becomes desirable to extend the concept of angle to the more general one based on rotation about a point. For such a general angle the domain of permissible measures is the set of all real numbers. Careful explanations illustrated by use of a circular protractor and accompanied by illustrative examples and exercises will serve quickly to enable students to sketch positive or negative angles of any given measure and to measure any given angle.

The concept of radian measure should be developed along with that of the general angle. In order to understand radian measure clearly, the students must first of all have a thorough understanding of the definition and meaning of a radian. The geometrical explanation and illustration should be given repeatedly until the students can readily form a mental picture similar to the one

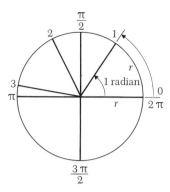

Figure 15-7
Radian measure.

shown in Fig. 15-7. This will provide them with a concrete basis for thinking in terms of radians and for understanding the definition. It will provide a means for recalling instantly why the angle π is the same as 180°, why $\pi/2$ is the same as 90°, why $\pi/3$

Radian and degree measure

is the same as 60°, why 2π is the same as 360°, etc. With this sort of picture in mind for reference, the student will have no need to memorize the relations between degree measure and radian measure because he can easily figure out these relationships for himself. He is thus equipped not only with a knowledge of the facts and relationships he will need, but also with an understanding of how they are determined.

After the students have gained an understanding of the meaning of radian measure, it is well for them to have some special practice in determining the degree equivalents of angles expressed in radians and the radian equivalents of angles expressed in degrees. For the special angles 0, $\pi/2$, $\pi/3$, π, 2π, 45°, 120°, etc., the students should soon become able to give the corresponding equivalents at sight. The teacher should explain that, in expressing angles in terms of radian measure, it is customary to omit the word "radians." The student needs to be told this so that, when he encounters in his reading such expressions as $\sin \pi$, $\tan 2$, and $\cos 3\pi/4$, he will understand that the angles are given in radians rather than in degrees. It may be pointed out that in

Need for interconversion

higher mathematics radian measure is used almost exclusively.

TRIGONOMETRIC FUNCTIONS
OF ANY ANGLE

An angle is said to be in standard position with respect to a rectangular coordinate system if its vertex is at the origin and its

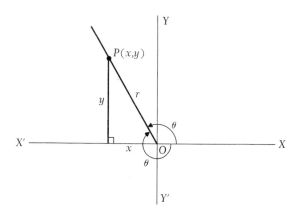

Figure 15-8
Angle in standard position.

initial side lies along the positive half of the X axis. Then if $P(x,y)$ is any point in the XY plane, the distances x, y, and r ($= OP$) and the angle XOP ($= \theta$) are determined. (See Fig. 15-8.) Except for multiples of $360°$, the measure of angle θ is determined solely by the position of the terminal side $\overrightarrow{OP}$, and θ may be either positive or negative.

In this context the trigonometric functions of the general angle θ are defined as follows:

The ratio definitions

$$\sin \theta = y/r \longleftarrow \text{reciprocals} \longrightarrow \csc \theta = r/y$$
$$\cos \theta = x/r \longleftarrow \text{reciprocals} \longrightarrow \sec \theta = r/x$$
$$\tan \theta = y/x \longleftarrow \text{reciprocals} \longrightarrow \cot \theta = x/y$$

These definitions are general in that they apply both to positive and negative angles of any size for which they are defined. They have clear meanings, except when the divisor is zero, in which case the functions are simply undefined. They are entirely consistent with the definitions of the functions of acute angles in terms of the sides of a right triangle, learned earlier in the junior high school. Since they define the fundamental concepts on which all trigonometric work is based, they must be learned to the point of perfection through repeated drills and exercises, both formal and numerical, and much practice based upon sketches such as that shown in Fig. 15-8.

Some authors and teachers prefer to define the sine and cosine functions in terms of the coordinates of a point on a unit circle, as shown in Fig. 15-9. In this frame of reference the sine and cosine functions are identified, respectively, with the x and y coordinates themselves, rather than with ratios. This may have some advantage in studying the variation of these functions, but it may

The unit circle definitions

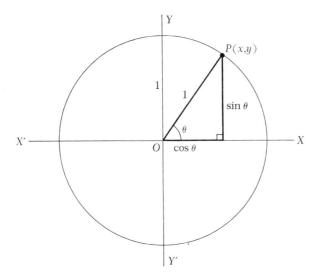

Figure 15-9
Functions in terms of coordinates of a point on a unit circle.

also complicate and confuse the interpretation for students. For example, the terminal side of an angle θ may pass through $Q(5,7)$, but in this case Q does not lie on the unit circle. On the other hand, the ratio definitions offer no problem of interpretation and, if desired, can easily be reduced to the "unit circle" definitions simply by dividing each of the coordinates of such a point $Q(u,v)$ by $\sqrt{u^2 + v^2}$. This, if Q is the point $(5,7)$, the coordinates of the point P, where $\overrightarrow{OQ}$ intersects the unit circle, are seen to be $5/\sqrt{74}$ and $7/\sqrt{74}$.

Since tables of trigonometric functions generally include only values of functions of angles from $0°$ to $90°$, it is necessary to have some means of expressing functions of any angle whatever in terms of functions of some angle not less than $0°$ and not greater than $90°$. The method of making such transformations may be effectively explained to students somewhat as follows.

The tables of functions are adequate if used with the triangle of reference

Let A be the given angle in standard position, as shown in Fig. 15-10. If we take a point $P(x,y)$ on the terminal side of angle A and drop a perpendicular to the X axis, a right triangle will be formed, called the "triangle of reference." The absolute values of the functions of A are determined by the lengths of the sides of this triangle, since its sides are x, y, and r, that is, the abscissa, ordinate, and distance of P, respectively.

Now, if $m\angle A$ is known, we may also find $m\angle\theta$, without regard to sign. θ is the smallest angle formed by $\overline{OP}$ and the X axis. $\angle\theta$

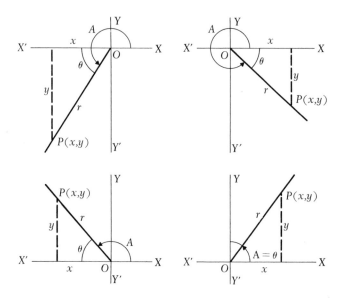

Figure 15-10
Functions in terms of a triangle of reference.

will always be the angle *XOP* or *X'OP* in the triangle of reference
(see Fig. 15-10); so its measure can never exceed 90°. Then the
values of the functions of ∠*A* will be the same as the values of the
functions of ∠*θ*, except perhaps for sign. Since $0° \leqslant m\angle\theta \leqslant 90°$, the
values of the functions of ∠*θ* can be found in the tables, and the
signs of the corresponding functions of ∠*A* (whether positive or
negative, and regardless of size) can be determined by noting the
signs of *x* and *y* (*r* is always positive) in the triangle of reference.

The conversion is easy

Example 1. Find the value of cot 112°5′ (Fig. 15-11). From the tables, cot 67°55′ =
.40572. But in the triangle of reference, cot *θ* is negative. Therefore cot 112°5′ is
negative also, and its real value is −.40572.

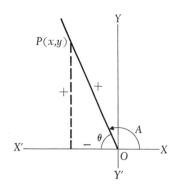

Figure 15-11
Find cot 112°5′.

Example 2. Find the value of cos 312°.

Let $A = 312°$. Thus $\theta = 48°$ (Fig. 15-12). From the tables, cos 48° = .66913.

Therefore the value, except for sign, of cos 312° = .66913. But in the triangle of reference, cos θ is positive. Therefore cos 312° is positive also, and its real value is + .66913.

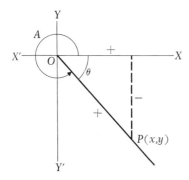

Figure 15-12
Find cos 312°.

If the matter is explained and illustrated in this way, the students should have little difficulty in understanding how to find the functions of any given angle from the tables. It is well for them to work out numerous examples of the type given above and to build for themselves tables showing the signs of each of the functions when the angle is in standard position and the terminal side lies in the following eight positions:

Working out examples promotes both understanding and facility

In the first quadrant   Along the positive X axis
In the second quadrant   Along the positive Y axis
In the third quadrant   Along the negative X axis
In the fourth quadrant   Along the negative Y axis

When the students have acquired the ability to do this for themselves, they will have attained a real understanding of how the tables can be used to find the functions of any angle whatever. They should experience no further difficulty in this respect, and there will be no need for them to memorize the signs of the functions for the various positions of the terminal side of the angle as indicated in the list given above.

THE CIRCULAR FUNCTIONS: A
TRIGONOMETRY OF REAL NUMBERS

Freedom from reference to angles is desirable

The increasing emphasis on the analytic properties of the trigonometric functions makes it desirable to have a way of interpreting these functions and their properties as functions and properties of real numbers, quite apart from any direct reference to angles at all. The need for such interpretation occurs often, both in mathe-

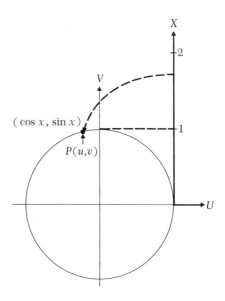

Figure 15-13
Wrapping process.

matical and physical contexts, particularly in connection with periodic phenomena.

The circular functions

Such an interpretation is readily available and is easily accomplished through the concept of a "wrapping function," or wrapping process, whereby the real-number line is wrapped around the unit circle. Such a process establishes the ordered pair (cos x, sin x), where x is a real number, as the coordinates of points on the unit circle. (See Fig. 15-13.) The complete "trigonometry" of these functions can be developed without having to make any reference to angles at any point in the development. However, if at any time it should become desirable to compare the circular functions of real numbers with the trigonometric functions of angles, the comparison can be effected through the medium of radian measure. The one-to-one correspondence which can thus be set up affords a simple method for the evaluation of the circular functions of real numbers. The point should be made, however, that this is a method of evaluation used through convenience, and not through necessity. The circular functions can be evaluated without any reference to angles whatsoever.[1]

Under this one-to-one correspondence the wrapping process guarantees the same domain, range, and periodicity for the cir-

[1] For a more detailed discussion of circular functions of real numbers see the Report of the Commission on Mathematics, "Appendices" (New York: College Entrance Examination Board, 1959), pp. 206–213. See also the booklet "Circular Functions" in the SMSG Supplementary and Enrichment Series, 1964.

Validity of the
circular functions

cular functions of real numbers as for the corresponding trigonometric functions of angles, and the same relationships and identities among the functions can be established in the two cases.
Functions of real numbers and their inverse functions are evaluated from tables precisely as functions of angles (in radians) and
their inverses are evaluated. Indeed, the trigonometry of real
numbers is in all respects the exact counterpart of the trigonometry
of angles.

It is not difficult to explain all this to students. A good discussion of it can be found in the "Appendices" volume of the Report
of the Commission on Mathematics.[2] Some, however, will almost
certainly want to know why we should bother with a trigonometry
of numbers, when we already have a perfectly good trigonometry
of angles. To answer this it may be pointed out that there are at
least two good reasons. One is that a trigonometry of numbers

Why use the
circular functions?

can be interpreted more flexibly than a trigonometry based only
on angles. In many problems in physics and higher mathematics
it is necessary to work with circular functions of numbers apart
from any explicit reference to angles. A second reason is that the
structure of mathematical systems is a primary concern of mathematicians. It is therefore a matter of great mathematical interest
to note that our trigonometry of numbers and circular functions
has exactly the same structure as the trigonometry of angles.

TRIGONOMETRIC OR CIRCULAR
FUNCTIONS: WHICH APPROACH?

Because of the close connection between circular motion and many
periodic phenomena, and because trigonometric functions are
periodic, many authors and teachers now prefer to approach the
whole subject of trigonometry analytically through the circular
functions. Others prefer the older geometric approach through the
medium of triangles. Each has its advantages and its disadvantages, and since the same trigonometry is developed through the
one as through the other, the issue of which approach is better
is sometimes raised.

The geometrical approach is the traditional one. It has the advantage of building upon initial familiarity through the students'
acquaintance with some geometry and perhaps some numerical
trigonometry in the junior high school. It employs familiar defi-

The old and the
new approaches—
pros and cons

nitions of the functions, and greater use of geometrical figures for
reference. This lends tangibility and concreteness to the discourse,
and makes it easier for some students to read and to follow than
the more abstract development through the circular functions. On

[2] *Op. cit.,* pp. 208–210.

the other hand, it affords less training in this analytical aspect of the subject, and from the standpoint of later work this may be a detriment.

By contrast, the approach through the circular functions has a more analytic and "modern" aspect. Its development eliminates the need for any reference to angles or triangles at all. The domains of the functions are numbers rather than angles, so that the mappings for the functions are from numbers to numbers rather than from angles to numbers. Some, of course, may feel that this is a trivial point because the numbers in the domain are determined by, and associated with, central angles of the unit circle, being in fact the radian measures of these angles. More importantly, the approach through the circular functions is an *analytical* approach. Most students of trigonometry are now taking it because they plan to take further courses in mathematics. These courses are becoming increasingly condensed, abstract, and sophisticated, and the training students may receive through analytical work in trigonometry could be of considerable help to them in their later courses.

Whether the functions are called trigonometric functions or circular functions is of little importance. Since this chapter deals with the teaching of trigonometry, we shall generally refer to them as trigonometric functions.

VARIATION AND GRAPHS OF THE TRIGONOMETRIC FUNCTIONS

Just as the concept of variation enriches the study of geometry and algebra, so it enriches the study of trigonometry. It is important for the students to sense the fact that any *change* in the size of an angle is accompanied by a corresponding characteristic change in each of the functions of the angle. This fact should be repeatedly emphasized by the teacher and should be illustrated with great care. One effective method is a thoughtful examina-

A point to be stressed

tion of the tables of functions. It will be immediately noted that increases in the size of the angle are accompanied by characteristic increases or decreases in each of the functions. It should be specifically pointed out that the values given in the tables merely represent particular stages in a continuous variation and that, between any two successive values given in the tables, there exists an infinitude of intermediate values. This concept of variation of the functions can be strengthened by certain mechanical devices which are available commercially or which can be made by the teacher or students. Perhaps the most commonly used and most effective device is the construction and study of graphs of these functions (Fig. 15-14).

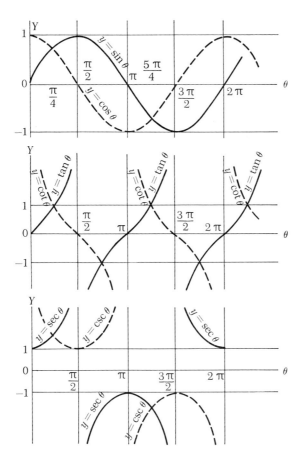

Figure 15-14
Graphs of the functions.

A real understanding of these graphs makes clear several important things about the variation of the functions. In particular, the following considerations are worthy of note and comment:

1 There is a general similarity in the shape of the graph of any function and its corresponding cofunction.[3] This may be explained by the fact that, for example, the cosine of a given angle is the sine of some other angle (in general, the complement of the given angle), and similarly for the other functions and their corresponding cofunctions.

The students must understand why these functions differ in these ways

2 The functions $\sin \theta$ and $\cos \theta$ are always finite and continuous over the entire domain of values of θ, while for certain values of θ the other functions become infinite and have points of discontinuity. This may be explained by the fact that each of the other functions is the reciprocal of some function which may take on the value zero, and when

---

[3] Here we speak of $\sin \theta$ and $\cos \theta$, for example, as *cofunctions of each other.* Like reference is made to $\tan \theta$ and $\cot \theta$ and to $\sec \theta$ and $\csc \theta$.

this happens, the reciprocal function is undefined. It should also be noted that, at each value of the angle for which a given function becomes discontinuous, the function also changes sign.

3   The sine or cosine of an angle can never be greater than 1 nor less than -1, and the secant and cosecant can never have values between these bounds. This is explained by the fact that sec $\theta = 1/\cos \theta$ and csc $\theta = 1/\sin \theta$. Since the range for both sin θ and cos θ is the closed interval $[-1,1]$, the range for their reciprocals must consist of the union of the two half-open intervals $(\leftarrow,-1] \cup [1,\rightarrow)$. Numerical and graphic illustrations should be given, using the number line.

4   From the graphs it will be seen that when $\theta = k\pi + \pi/4$ for all integral values of k, each function has the same value as its corresponding cofunction. The students may be asked to explain this.

Practically all textbooks contain graphs of the functions for reference, and in many cases the students are required to construct their own graphs. Too often, however, such study and analysis is perfunctory. If the graphs are to contribute much toward understanding the nature of the variation of the functions, considerable time will have to be spent in the interpretation of the graphs and in the discussion of their implications.

Emphasis on interpretation of the graphs is needed

VALUES OF FUNCTIONS OF SPECIAL ANGLES

The trigonometric functions of the special angles (numbers) 0, $\pm\pi/6$, $\pm\pi/4$, $\pm\pi/3$, $\pm\pi/2$, $\pm2\pi/3$, $\pm3\pi/4$, $\pm5\pi/6$, and $\pm\pi$ are of great importance. They occur so frequently in both analytical and numerical trigonometry that students should be able to write them down without having recourse to tables. Some teachers prefer to have them memorized, but this is not necessary, because they can be recalled so easily from the definitions of the functions and from even a mental diagram of a circle with center at the origin, radius 2 (or $\sqrt{2}$, for convenience), and with the angle drawn in standard position.

The basic diagrams

For example, in Fig. 15-15, if $m\angle\theta$ is $\pi/6$ radians, or 30°, we can use a circle with radius $r = 2$, and let the terminal side of θ intersect the circle at a point $P(x,y)$. If a perpendicular is drawn from P to the X axis, a right triangle MOP is formed, and since $m\angle\theta = 30°$, this triangle is easily seen to be the upper half of the equilateral triangle TOP. Thus y (or MP) $= \frac{1}{2}r$ (or $\frac{1}{2}OP$), and by the Pythagorean theorem x (or OM) $= \sqrt{r^2 - y^2}$. Since for simplicity we took $r = 2$, we thus have $y = 1$ and $x = \sqrt{3}$. Thus sin 30° $= y/r = \frac{1}{2}$, cos 30° $= x/r = \sqrt{3}/2$, and tan 30° $= y/x = 1/\sqrt{3}$. The only numbers needed in these ratios are 1, 2, and $\sqrt{3}$. The values of the cosecant, secant, and cotangent of 30° can now be written down immediately, since these are merely the reciprocals of the sine, cosine, and tangent, respectively.

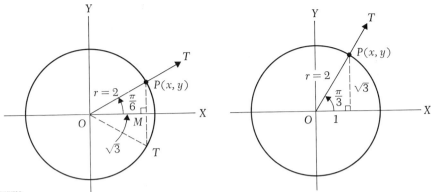

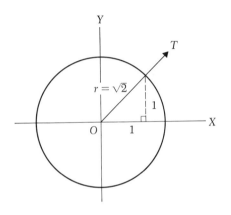

With such diagrams
as these there is no
need to memorize
the function values

Figure 15-15
Trigonometric functions of the special angles.

Since the functions of 60° are the corresponding cofunctions of 30°, these can be written down at once, and we have

sin 30° = ½ = cos 60°   cot 30° = √3/1 = tan 60°
cos 30° = √3/2 = sin 60°   sec 30° = 2/√3 = csc 60°
tan 30° = 1/√3 = cot 60°   csc 30° = 2/1 = sec 60°

Geometric considerations similar to the foregoing will yield the values of the functions of 45°. In this case, however, the use of a circle of radius $r = \sqrt{2}$ will give the simplest set of values for x, y, and r. Clearly, if $m\angle\theta = 45°$, the point (1,1) will lie on the circle; whence $x = 1$, $y = 1$, and $r = \sqrt{x^2 + y^2} = \sqrt{2}$. The definitions of the functions then give immediately the values

sin 45° = cos 45° = 1/√2
sec 45° = csc 45° = √2/1
tan 45° = cot 45° = 1/1

Values of the functions of the quadrantal angles are immediately obvious if the angle is put in standard position with its vertex at the center of a unit circle, as in Fig. 15-9. For any point $P(x,y)$ on this unit circle we have $x = \cos\theta$ and $y = \sin\theta$. These considerations, together with the definitions of the other functions, give us the values in Table 15-1.

These function values are needed continually

TABLE 15-1

Functions of quadrantal angles

	0°	90°	180°	270°
sin	0	1	0	−1
cos	1	0	−1	0
tan	0	undefined	0	undefined
cot	undefined	0	undefined	0
sec	1	undefined	−1	undefined
csc	undefined	1	undefined	−1

These considerations can be explained easily and are not hard to understand. Students, however, need considerable practice in giving the values of functions of these special angles. This is probably best attained by having them make sketches of many of the special angles in standard position and build tables of values based on their sketches. Teachers tend to underestimate, rather than overestimate, the amount of practice needed to gain familiarity, facility, and assurance in this.

INVERSE TRIGONOMETRIC FUNCTIONS

Make it clear that the inverse of a function is a relation, not a function

It must be made clear that the inverse of any trigonometric function is a relation but not a function. The function-to-angle correspondence is not one-to-one but one-to-many. For example, there are infinitely many angles x for which $\sin x = \frac{1}{2}$. On the other hand, it is desirable to have a way of defining the inverse of a function as a function itself, so that for a given value of a function there will correspond exactly one angle instead of many. This is accomplished by restricting the domain of the angle and by designating this restricted domain or interval as the set of *principal values* of x. This restriction is made separately for each function. Reference to either the trigonometric function or its inverse within this restricted domain is generally indicated by capitalizing the initial letter, e.g., $\text{Sin}^{-1}\ 0.8$ or Arctan 3. The intervals defining the restricted domains for the principal values are in a sense arbitrary, but are usually taken as follows:

Arcsin: [−90°,90°]   Arctan: (−90°,90°)
Arccos: [0°,180°]   Arccot: (0°,180°)

**Principal values;
notation**

In an analogous manner, Sin x is defined to mean sin x, where
$-90° \leqslant x \leqslant 90°$.

Two notations are commonly used for the inverse trigonometric
functions. For example, the angle whose sine is 0.8 is written
either as Arcsin 0.8 or as Sin^{-1} 0.8. This is sometimes a little confusing to students at first, but since they will certainly encounter
both notations, it is advisable that they become accustomed to
both. The matters discussed above need more than casual attention in the classes. The concepts and notation should be made
clear through careful definition, pointed questions, and many
examples using graphical interpretation. Any difficulties which
students may have in working with inverse trigonometric functions are almost sure to have their origins either in wrong interpretations of the meaning of an inverse function and its relation
to the parent function or else in failure to attach clear meanings
to the terminology and notation employed.

If we consider the graph of any function, say, $y = \sin x$, we note
that it is a device which will map any number (or angle) x in its
domain into the corresponding number y in its range. If we should
take y as the independent variable, with $-1 \leqslant y \leqslant 1$, then the
same graph would map any number y into the corresponding
number (or angle) x, where $-\pi/2 \leqslant x \leqslant \pi/2$, and we could write
$x = \text{Arcsin } y$. In this sense the same set of points could be used
as the graph of both the trigonometric function $y = \text{Sin } x$ and of

**How the graphs
are related**

the inverse function $x = \text{Arcsin } y$, depending on whether x or y
is regarded as the independent variable. However, since the letter
Y is so often used to represent the axis of the range, and so seldom
to represent the axis of the domain, this inverse function is generally written $y = \text{Arcsin } x$, in which case its domain is the set
of numbers x, where $-1 \leqslant x \leqslant 1$, and its range is the set of numbers (or angles) y, where $-\pi/2 \leqslant y \leqslant \pi/2$.

If the graphs of the trigonometric function $y = \text{Sin } x$ and of the
inverse trigonometric function $y = \text{Arcsin } x$ are drawn on the same
set of axes scaled to the same unit, it will be noted that they are
symmetrical to each other with respect to the straight line $y = x$.
The use of the unit circle in drawing the graphs is helpful in bringing out the contrast between the properties of the trigonometric
functions and the properties of their respectively related inverse
functions.

Expressions such as cos (Tan^{-1} 1/3) or csc (Cos^{-1} 1/2) sometimes
turn up in applied work involving trigonometry. Very often stu-
dents have trouble in evaluating such expressions because they
do not know how to read and interpret them. After they do learn
how, the trouble usually disappears, and quickly. But while this

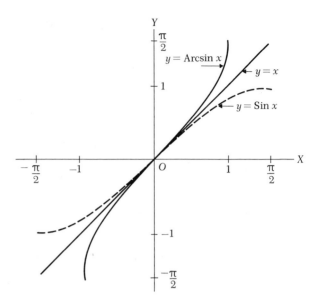

Figure 15-16
Graphs of y = Sin x and the inverse function y = Arcsin x.

The reading problem again

matter of clearing up the meaning of such expressions can be done easily by the teacher, it is by no means trivial, and should not be neglected. It is a matter of teaching the students how to read this mathematical symbol, or shorthand, and to understand precisely what it means. Explain, for example, that tan (Cos⁻¹ ½) simply means the tangent of the angle (or number) x in the interval $0 \leqslant x \leqslant \pi$, for which cos $x = $ ½, and that once the measure of x has been determined, the value of its tangent can be found. To illustrate, using this example, we find that Cos⁻¹ ½ $= \pi/3$, or 60°, and that tan $\pi/3 = \sqrt{3}$. Thus tan (Cos⁻¹ ½) $= \sqrt{3}$.

SOME SPECIAL FUNCTIONS
AND THEIR GRAPHS

Functions such as 3 sin x, sin 3x, ½ cos x, and cos ½x occur at times. The function 3 sin x of course is not at all the same as the function sin 3x, yet sometimes students confuse them unless the difference has been pointed out. Therefore it is important to give some special attention to the interpretation of functions expressed in forms such as those indicated above.

Effect of the constant: term or coefficient

The thing that tends to confuse students in considering, say, sin 2x and 2 sin x, is the effect of the constant in the two expressions. Failure to interpret such expressions correctly is usually

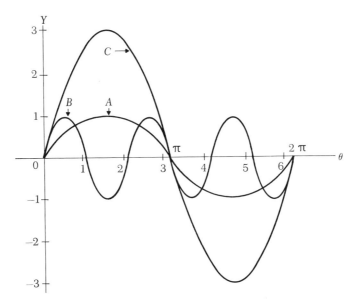

Figure 15-17
Graphs of some sine functions. A: $y = \sin \theta$. B: $y = \sin 3\,\theta$. C: $y = 3 \sin \theta$.

due to lack of careful reading, and it can be corrected, but teachers as a rule will need to give students some help in learning to determine the effect of the constant in each case. To make students aware of the distinction, have them construct graphs of both functions on the same set of axes, as is done in Fig. 15-17. Comparison of the graphs points up the fact that in one case the constant is a multiplier of the argument (independent variable) and so affects the period of the function but not the amplitude, while in the other case the constant is a multiplier of the function itself and so affects its amplitude but not its period. By constructing the separate graphs on the same axes students should be able to note these effects clearly. They should also become aware of which effect is associated with which position of the constant in the expression. This is the key to proper interpretation. Subsequently, additional experience in this can be given by having students consider and perhaps graph some functions, such as $3 \sin 2x$, in which constants are present that affect both the amplitude and the period. Illustrations can be found in most textbooks.

Practice in graphing helps understanding

Along with this topic it may be well to mention the construction of graphs of composite functions by addition of ordinates. Students as a rule have little difficulty in making such graphs and usually seem to enjoy it, but they should be given some instruction in interpreting their graphs. They will sometimes be a little

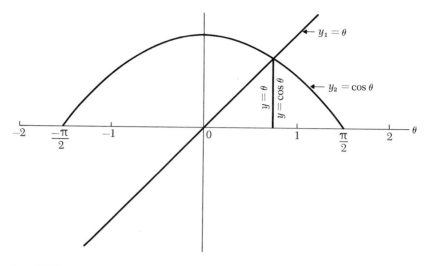

Figure 15-18
Graph showing method of obtaining an approximate solution of the equation $\cos \theta = \theta$.

surprised when they come to realize that if the graphs of any two functions, no matter what kind, can be made on the same axes, the graph of their sum or difference can be immediately and easily made by this simple method. It will not require much work to develop understanding of the idea, but on the other hand, such understanding should not be taken for granted. Teachers should explain and illustrate the procedure, and students should be expected to make at least a few such graphs. As a matter of interest it can be pointed out that approximate solutions for such equations as $\cos \theta = \theta$ can be found by this method (see Fig. 15-18), although solutions cannot be obtained by either algebraic or trigonometric methods, and exact solutions are not available in any case.

Solving problems graphically

TEACHING THE FUNCTIONS OF THE SUM OR DIFFERENCE OF TWO ANGLES

Since there are times when the students will need to use the functions of the sum or difference of two angles, a double angle, a half angle, and perhaps certain other formulas involving two angles, it is necessary that these formulas be developed in terms of the original angles and listed for reference. This is done in practically all textbooks. It is not necessary that students memorize all these formulas. It might be desirable at times for them to memorize all for ready reference, but actually, it is only necessary to memorize one and to know the simple technique of immediate derivation of the others. A few which are frequently needed, and which should be derived, include

$\sin (A + B)$ $\cos (A + B)$ $\tan (A + B)$
$\sin (A - B)$ $\cos (A - B)$ $\tan (A - B)$
$\sin 2A$ $\cos 2A$ $\tan 2A$
$\sin \frac{1}{2}A$ $\cos \frac{1}{2}A$ $\tan \frac{1}{2}A$

Different branches of mathematics contribute to the derivation

The development of these formulas exemplifies the nice working together of algebraic techniques, geometrical facts, and trigonometric relations to a common end. Consider, for example, the formulas for $\sin (A + B)$, $\sin (A - B)$, $\cos (A + B)$, and $\cos (A - B)$. It is interesting and rather remarkable that after any one of these has been established, the other three can be derived therefrom, as can many extensions and specializations of them, through appropriate interplay of algebra, geometry, and trigonometry.

The traditional approach was essentially geometrical, and the formulas for $\sin (A + B)$ and $\cos (A + B)$ were usually developed first by the use of triangles and the definitions of trigonometric functions of a right triangle. Most contemporary authors prefer to employ a more analytical approach, using circular functions and usually developing first the basic formula $\cos (A - B) = \cos A \cos B + \sin A \sin B$. Development of this formula is not difficult, and the others can all be derived from it. For example, by replacing B by $-B$, we get $\cos (A + B) = \cos A \cos B - \sin A \sin B$. Then, recalling that $\sin x = \cos (\pi/2 - x)$, we get

$$\sin (A + B) = \cos \left[\frac{\pi}{2} - (A + B) \right] = \cos \left[\left(\frac{\pi}{2} - A \right) - B \right]$$
$$= \cos \left(\frac{\pi}{2} - A \right) \cos B + \sin \left(\frac{\pi}{2} - A \right) \sin B$$
$$= \sin A \cos B + \cos A \sin B$$

One formula yields the others

Again, replacing B by $-B$, we get at once the formula $\sin (A - B) = \sin A \cos B - \cos A \sin B$. The formulas for $\tan (A \pm B)$ follow, with a little algebraic work, from the definition $\tan x = \sin x / \cos x$.

Table 15-2 indicates lines of association through which many other identities can be derived from this beginning.

If teachers would lay more stress on the interrelations suggested by the table, they might bring additional motivation to this work and at the same time give students a sense of the organic relationship and interplay among different parts of trigonometry and, indeed, among different parts of mathematics.

Apart from the derivation of these special formulas or identi-

TABLE 15-2

Reduction formulas

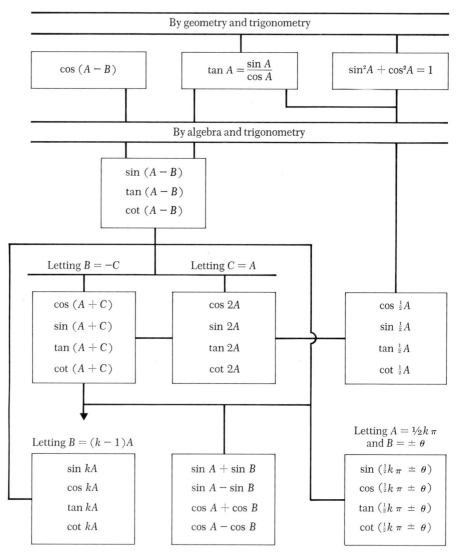

Organizing the
formulas is a real
difficulty

ties, the main difficulty which students have is in organizing them
to the point of ready recognition and recall and of useful association. The teacher can probably give some help in this by suggesting a method or order for classifying the formulas. There are
different schemes of classification, and each teacher will probably
have some scheme which he has found helpful and which he may
wish to recommend to his students.

PROVING TRIGONOMETRIC IDENTITIES

What it means to prove an identity

In this section we shall be concerned with trigonometric identities involving a single independent variable (angle or number). To prove a trigonometric identity means to prove that a given expression involving one or more trigonometric functions can be transformed by legitimate means into the precise form of another given expression. If this can be done, the two expressions are said to be identically equal for all admissible values of the variable.

In most textbooks the trigonometric identities proposed for proof are stated in the form of equations. In a way this is unfortunate, because with this form of statement students sometimes misinterpret the problem and, by treating it as an equation, may arrive at a statement that two expressions are equal. From this they sometimes conclude that they have proved the identity of the original expressions, failing to realize that they had, essentially, assumed this very thing at the outset. The fallacy involved in this sort of reasoning can be shown by taking a case which is evidently absurd on the face of it but which illustrates the point in question. Let it be required to test to see whether or not $\sin x = -\sin x$ is an identity. By treating this as an equation and squaring both members we do get an identity: $\sin^2 x \equiv \sin^2 x$. Clearly, however, this does not justify the conclusion that the original expressions ($\sin x$ and $-\sin x$) are identically equal for all values of x.

A few examples of this sort may serve to clarify the matter for students and to alert them to this type of pitfall. They need to sense clearly that in proving two trigonometric expressions identically equal, we may work with only one of them at a time. Either may be changed in form by trigonometric substitutions from known identities or by permissible algebraic operations, and if it can be put in the same form as the other, the identity of the two original expressions will have been established. It is convenient at times to change the forms of both expressions *separately* into other expressions known to be identically equal. Such a procedure establishes a valid proof of the identity of the original expressions if, but only if, all the steps are reversible.

A pattern for procedure

Once the students have the essential problem and method clearly in mind, their only other need is for a close familiarity with the basic relations among the functions. The eight fundamental identities most commonly needed are

$$\sin^2 x + \cos^2 x \equiv 1 \qquad (1) \qquad\qquad \sec^2 x - \tan^2 x \equiv 1 \qquad (2)$$

$$\csc^2 x - \cot^2 x \equiv 1 \qquad (3) \qquad\qquad \tan x \equiv \frac{\sin x}{\cos x} \qquad (4)$$

$$\cot x \equiv \frac{\cos x}{\sin x} \qquad (5) \qquad\qquad \cot x \equiv \frac{1}{\tan x} \qquad (6)$$

$$\sec x \equiv \frac{1}{\cos x} \qquad (7) \qquad\qquad \csc x \equiv \frac{1}{\sin x} \qquad (8)$$

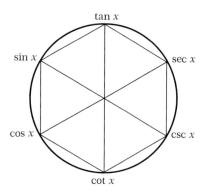

Figure 15-19
The function hexagon.

These should be thoroughly memorized. The student should already be familiar with formulas (6) to (8), since they are merely the reciprocal relations pointed out in connection with the definition of the functions, and his attention should be called to the fact that formulas (2) and (3) follow immediately from formula (1). In addition to these, the student should also be familiar with the functions of the double angles.

A useful mnemonic   Other relationships are sometimes needed, but are so numerous and so much alike that it is difficult to memorize them all. The mnemonic device of Fig. 15-19, which we shall call "the function hexagon," provides an easy means for recalling all these fundamental identities except the first three listed above and the functions of double and half angles. The arrangement should be made exactly as shown. This is easy to remember because the sine, tangent, and secant appear in this order from left to right, and each is directly above its corresponding cofunction.

1 The two functions at the ends of any diagonal are reciprocals of each other.
2 Any function is the product of the two functions between which it lies. Thus $\sin x = \tan x \cos x$; $\cot x = \cos x \csc x$; etc.
3 Any function may be expressed as a quotient in which the numerator is either of the adjacent functions and the denominator is the one beyond that. Thus

$$\tan x = \frac{\sec x}{\csc x} \qquad \cos x = \frac{\cot x}{\csc x}$$

and so on.
4 The product of any three alternate functions is 1. Thus

$$\sin x \cot x \sec x = 1 \qquad \text{and} \qquad \cos x \tan x \csc x = 1$$

This mechanical device is so simple, economical, and powerful, giving, as it does, twenty-six separate identities for reference, that students will find it extremely helpful in making trigonometric transformations in their work with trigonometric identities and equations. It does not, of course, *prove* any of these identities, but the proofs are all simple and should be made by the students.

Two-way student participation

Much interest and motivation can be added to the work on identities by the alternative device of asking students to make up some identities of their own. Have them take some expression involving one or more trigonometric functions of an angle and see how many different expressions they can write that are identically equal to the one they started with. These may then be given to other students to prove. Exercises in making up identities seem to provide a psychological stimulus even for students who may have shown little enthusiasm for proving the ready-made identities in the textbook, and at the same time they provide a valuable learning experience for the students as they become more familiar with the basic identities themselves.

SOLVING TRIGONOMETRIC EQUATIONS

What the goal is

In contrast to trigonometric identities, which are valid for all admissible values of the independent variable (angle or number), the term "trigonometric equation" is applied in general to an equation involving one or more trigonometric functions of a variable such that the equation is satisfied, if at all, by some, but not all, values of the variable. Thus a trigonometric equation is a conditional equation, and the task one faces in finding its solution is that of determining the value or values of the variable which satisfy the equation. It is wise to explain and illustrate this to students at the outset in order that their thinking and their efforts may not be misdirected. Trigonometric identities may at times be invoked to advantage in solving trigonometric equations, but their involvement is intermediate and incidental to the solution.

Trigonometric equations really are equations, and they are therefore subject to treatment under the algebraic laws of the equation, besides being subject to the algebraic transformation of either member separately or to the trigonometric transformation of the trigonometric elements involved.

Example. Let it be required to solve $\sin 2x = \tan x$. The problem is to find the solution set S of all angles (numbers) for which this relation holds. A complete solution is shown here.

$\sin 2x = 2 \sin x \cos x$	*Trigonometric transformation*
$\tan x = \dfrac{\sin x}{\cos x}$	*Trigonometric transformation*
$2 \sin x \cos x = \dfrac{\sin x}{\cos x}$	*Substitution*
$2 \sin x \cos^2 x = \sin x$	*Both members multiplied by cos x*
$2 \sin x \cos^2 x - \sin x = 0$	*Using additive inverse*
$\sin x\,(2 \cos^2 x - 1) = 0$	*Commutative law for multiplication and distributive law*

This will be true if and only (1) if $\sin x = 0$ or (2) if $2 \cos^2 x - 1 = 0$. Thus, in the interval $0 \leq x < 2\pi$, we find that

$$S = \left\{ x \mid x = 0, \pi, \frac{n\pi}{4}, \text{ where } n = 1, 3, 5, 7 \right\}$$

Substitution in the original equation verifies this set of values as the required solution set.

Note that the algebraic transformations employed to find the solution set are all entirely legitimate, because we started with an admitted equation and sought merely its solution set.

What variable to solve for?

Students are sometimes confused or uncertain as to the variable for which they are to solve. This arises from the fact that the problem really involves two main parts. The students need first to solve for an intermediate variable which is typically a trigonometric function of an ultimate independent variable (angle or number). Then, having obtained a solution for this intermediate variable (e.g., $\cos x = \pm 1/\sqrt{2}$), there still remains the task of determining the value or values of x for which this is true. This is illustrated in the foregoing example. It is an easy thing to understand once it is pointed out, but it should be made clear to the students that the problem is not completed until they have found the set of values for the angle or number which satisfies the original equation.

It should also be pointed out that expressions may sometimes be encountered which appear in the form of trigonometric equations but which really are not, because they have no real solutions. Their solution sets are empty. For example, there is no number x for which $\sin^2 x + 2 \cos^2 x = 3$. If this were treated as an equation, it would yield $\cos x = \pm \sqrt{2}$, which is impossible, because $|\cos x| \leq 1$ for all values of x. It is probably advisable for

Numerous illustrative examples are needed

teachers to give full and detailed chalk-board explanations of the solutions of several typical trigonometric equations and to make clear, as each step is taken, why it is taken.

Authors of textbooks are not always careful to graduate the difficulty of the problems given for solution. Students, however, often learn to see patterns and get their insights a step at a time. A set of problems arranged in a sequence or order such that complications are introduced gradually can be a most helpful learning device. Teachers will do well to examine sets of trigonometric equations given in textbooks and, if necessary, rearrange them in reasonable order of difficulty when they assign the problems to their students for solution.

POLAR COORDINATES AND COMPLEX NUMBERS IN TRIGONOMETRIC FORM

It is likely that a good many students in trigonometry classes will not have had any previous experience in working with polar coordinates, though some may have done so. Therefore it is advis-

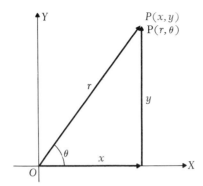

Figure 15-20
Polar coordinates.

able, in taking up the study of complex numbers in trigonometric form, to begin with a careful explanation of the polar-coordinate system, using diagrams and the conversion formulas to clarify the basic relations between polar and rectangular coordinates.

The definition of the polar coordinates of a point is based on superimposing directly on a conventional rectangular-coordinate system a polar system with pole, polar axis, vectorial angle, and standard position properly defined. This is motivated by the fact that, with respect to an initial point and direction, any point in the plane can be defined as well by a distance and a direction (its polar coordinates) as by two distances (its rectangular coordinates). The relations between these two coordinate systems is easily made clear by reference to a diagram such as Fig. 15-20. Evidently, $x = r \cos \theta$ and $y = r \sin \theta$. Also, $r = \sqrt{x^2 + y^2}$ and

Conversion formulas

$\tan \theta = y/x$; whence $\theta = \arctan y/x$. These conversion formulas are so simple and so easily reconstructed that there is no need for students to memorize them.

Once these basic relations are established, numerous exercises should be given for the purpose of strengthening understanding and developing facility in applying them. These exercises should include conversions both from rectangular to polar coordinates and from polar to rectangular coordinates. The following are samples: (1) Give the polar coordinates of the point (7,10). (2) Give the rectangular coordinates of the point (12,π/3).

Extension of the idea of polar coordinates to polar representation of complex numbers requires setting up a one-to-one correspondence between the complex numbers and the points in a plane. This is accomplished by representing all complex numbers as vectors, or rather, as vector sums. Since each complex number

Polar representation of complex numbers

is of the form $x + yi$, where x and y are real numbers (not excluding zero), it is necessary to designate one of the axes (usually, the X

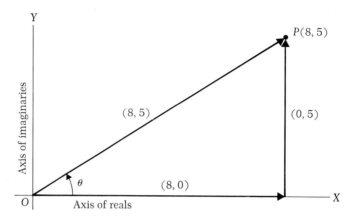

Figure 15-21
Complex numbers represented as vector sums.

axis) as the *axis of reals* and the other (the Y axis) as the *axis of imaginaries.* Then any complex number such as $8 + 5i$ can be represented by a vector drawn from the origin (or pole) to the point (8,5) as referred to the axes. See Fig. 15-21. The length, or absolute value, of this vector is known as the *magnitude,* or *modulus,* of the complex number. In this case the modulus is $\sqrt{8^2 + 5^2} = \sqrt{89}$. The positive angle θ which this vector makes with the polar axis is called the *vectorial angle,* or the *amplitude,* of the complex number. In this case $\tan \theta = 5/8$; so the amplitude, or vectorial angle, is *arctan* $5/8$. Hence the polar representation of the complex number $8 + 5i$ in the complex plane is ($\sqrt{89}$, arctan $5/8$).

Two new terms: modulus and amplitude

None of these ideas should cause any serious difficulty to students if they are carefully explained and adequately illustrated by the teacher. The only new elements are the terms "modulus" and "amplitude" and the designation of the y axis as the *axis of imaginaries,* against which the coefficients of the imaginary parts of complex numbers are plotted. It will probably be necessary to recall to students the methods of forming the sum and product of two complex numbers and the fact that two complex numbers $a + bi$ and $c + di$ are equal if and only if $a = c$ and $b = d$. Then they need only be reminded that (1) the sum of $a + bi$ and $c + di$ can be represented by the vector drawn from the origin to the point corresponding to the complex number [$(a + c), (b + d)i$], which is in fact their sum, and (2) the product of $a + bi$ and $c + di$ can be represented by the vector drawn from the origin to the point corresponding to the complex number [$(ac - bd), (bc + ad)$], which is in fact their product.

Transition to trigonometric representation is now easily accomplished by recalling that in the rectangular form $x + yi$ the real numbers x and y have the polar representation $x = r \cos \theta$ and $y = r \sin \theta$, with $r > 0$. Therefore, by direct substitution, $x + yi$ becomes

$$r \cos \theta + (r \sin \theta)i = r(\cos \theta + i \sin \theta)$$

From this, the passage to the formula for the product is made by direct multiplication. Thus, let $A = r(\cos \theta + i \sin \theta)$ and

$$B = s(\cos \phi + i \sin \phi)$$

Show the steps in full detail

Then it needs to be shown that $AB = rs[\cos (\theta + \phi) + i \sin (\theta + \phi)]$. Similarly, the quotient formula

$$\frac{A}{B} = \frac{r}{s} [\cos (\theta - \phi) + i \sin (\theta - \phi)]$$

needs to be worked out directly and in detail.

The detailed work involved in developing these formulas is straightforward, but it is somewhat long and tedious. It also requires that certain trigonometric expressions be recognized and replaced by their equivalents as sines and cosines of the sum and difference of two variables. This latter step is not likely to be obvious to students until it is pointed out to them. Therefore it is probably desirable for the teacher to go through all the details of the derivations with the class. Students should eventually memorize the formulas for facility in using them, but not until the derivations have been thoroughly explained and understood.

De Moivre's theorem: roots and powers

The product formula effectively provides the foundation upon which De Moivre's theorem is established, and so leads to a way of finding rational powers and roots of complex numbers in trigonometric form easily and quickly. Students may be helped to a clearer understanding of the procedures implied by the formula if they are asked to state the formula verbally and to answer such questions as these: If two complex numbers are given in trigonometric form, what is the amplitude of the product? What is the modulus of the product? Similar questions about the modulus and the amplitude of the quotient of two complex numbers and about the modulus and the amplitude of a power and a root of a complex number should be raised.

Graphical methods should be used freely in all work with complex numbers in trigonometric form, and students should be expected to make graphical representations of sums and differences, products, quotients, powers, and roots of such numbers.

THE SOLUTION OF TRIANGLES

The trigonometric solution of the right triangle is discussed in the first part of this chapter. The methods are so simple, obvious, and direct that they offer no difficulty and need not be discussed further here. The solution of the oblique or general triangle, however, is not so simple. It requires the development of certain special formulas and a discriminating analysis of the given data in each particular problem to determine the method and the formulas to be used.

There are four different combinations of independent parts, any one of which, with one exception, mentioned later, may uniquely determine a triangle. These are often referred to as the "four cases of the general triangle."[4] The four combinations of parts are as follows:

Conditions for
solvability

Case 1. Given two angles and any side
Case 2. Given two sides and an angle opposite one of them
Case 3. Given two sides and the included angle
Case 4. Given the three sides

To handle the solution of these cases of the general triangle, various special formulas are developed; the most fundamental of them are the law of sines, the law of cosines, and the law of tangents. In addition to these, there are numerous more specialized formulas connected with the triangle, including the half-angle formulas in terms of the sides and Heron's formula for the area of the triangle.

The mastery of these formulas and their use in solving the various cases of the general triangle cause a good deal of difficulty to students. The most common difficulties may be enumerated under five main types as follows:

Some troubles
students have

1 Difficulty in following and understanding the derivation of the formulas
2 Difficulty in remembering the various formulas and keeping them in mind without confusing them
3 Difficulty in knowing what formulas to use in particular cases
4 Difficulty due to lack of systematic preplanning and layout of written work
5 Difficulty in checking the solution

Many teachers fail to appreciate either the seriousness of these difficulties or the extent to which failure to master them may impair the effectiveness of the students' work. Yet the teacher has a serious obligation to see that the students are adequately equipped with respect to these points.

The development of the fundamental trigonometric laws is not inherently difficult or complicated. It can be understood without great difficulty by most students if properly presented. The teacher, however, should point the way by laying out the main steps in the development in quick, bold outline, just as one lays out the plan of

Laying out a plan

---

[4] The term "general triangle" is used here instead of "oblique triangle" because the general formulas developed for these cases apply to right triangles as well as to oblique triangles.

proof for a proposition in geometry before proceeding to write down the complete synthetic proof in finished form. Some geometry teachers and textbook writers have recognized the importance of setting forth the main plan of a proof before proceeding to details. For the most part, trigonometry textbooks have not stressed this; so the responsibility must be accepted by the teacher. For example, most students find it difficult to take the bare facts set forth in the proof of the law of cosines and to extract from them much understanding of a plan whereby the proof could be reconstructed without being literally memorized. On the other hand, a rapid chalk talk explanation of the *plan* of development by the teacher will leave the student with a basis of understanding which he can fill in with the necessary details and reconstruct at will.

The teacher should give the students criteria for determining which formulas to use in particular cases. One criterion is as follows: The formula to be used must be one which expresses, either implicitly or explicitly, an unknown part of the triangle completely in terms of the given parts. By adopting a standard system of notation, listing the fundamental formulas, and setting down the given parts of the triangle in a particular problem, the student may readily determine by inspection which of the formulas should be used. If he is required to do this consistently, he will soon learn that the law of sines is the appropriate formula to use if he is given either two angles and any side or two sides and an angle opposite one of them,[5] and that the law of cosines will enable him to solve triangles in which the given parts are either two sides and the included angle or the three sides. The teacher may want to point out that, in place of the law of cosines, the alternative formulas for the law of tangents and for the tangents of the half angles in terms of the sides may be used when the given parts are, respectively, two sides and the included angle or the three sides, and that these formulas are more amenable to logarithmic treatment than is the law of cosines. The association of the appropriate formulas with the different cases would be strengthened if each formula were developed and immediately applied when the case requiring it is first taken up. In many textbooks, however, the formulas are developed as in an intact body of theory, and the applications are left until later.

In teaching the solution of the general triangle, the teacher should show the students how to make a layout for the work and should give specific training in doing so. Students generally are inclined to start computing as soon as they get hold of two numbers with which they can work. However, since most problems in solving oblique triangles are somewhat long and complicated, this

Catalog the formulas for reference

Plan before computing

---

[5] The ambiguous case (given two sides and an angle opposite one of them) should be discussed at length, and its geometric and trigonometric possibilities pointed out.

is uneconomical and unwise, for several reasons. There is great advantage in thinking the problem through completely and planning the entire solution in detail, but as a whole, before doing anything else. This will ensure an understanding analysis of the problem as a whole. It will prevent the student from becoming confused in a heterogeneous mixture of analysis and computation. It will provide a specific step-by-step guide for all necessary computation and use of the tables. It is economical of time and labor. Finally, it is conducive to orderliness, which in turn is always conducive to effective work.

EXERCISES

Several of the exercises in this list call for explanation or discussion. It is intended that you give these as you would in teaching a high school class.

1 Explain what a radian is, and explain how to convert the measure of an angle from degrees to radians, and vice versa.

2 Explain the "wrapping function," and show how it enables us to establish a one-to-one correspondence between the set of all angles and the set of all real numbers.

3 Discuss in some detail, and with graphs, the periodicity of the six circular (or trigonometric) functions, and explain why the period of 2 sin x is not the same as the period for sin 2x.

4 Discuss the circular functions as many-to-one mappings, and the inverse circular relations as one-to-many mappings over their respective domains. Point out the advantage of using the restricted domains (principal values) in working with inverse circular, or trigonometric, functions.

5 Consider the graphs of the functions $y = \sin x$, $y = \cos x$, $y = \tan x$, and $y = \cot x$. Find for each of these (within the domain of the principal values for that function) the coordinates of the center of symmetry. Discuss.

6 If the graphs of $y = \mathrm{Sin}\ x$ and $y = \mathrm{Sin}^{-1}\ x$ are drawn on the same axes, the composite will be found to have an axis of symmetry. Explain why, and give its equation.

7 Explain why tan $(\mathrm{Cos}^{-1} x) = \sqrt{1 - x^2}/x$, and why $\mathrm{Tan}^{-1} 3 - \mathrm{Tan}^{-1} 4 = \mathrm{Tan}^{-1} (-1/13)$. What special difficulties do you think problems of this sort may hold for students? Discuss.

8 The sine and cosine functions are continuous and bounded over the real numbers, but the other four circular functions have points of discontinuity at which they are undefined. Discuss this.

9 Construct graphs of the sine, cosine, and tangent functions. Then show how these can be used to construct graphs of the cosecant, secant, and cotangent functions, respectively. What values do you see in having high school students do this for, say, the sine and cosecant functions?

10 Construct a graph of $y = \sin x$. Then, using only this graph and geometric methods, construct on the same axes graphs of these functions: $y = 2 \sin x$; $y = \sin 2x$; $y = \sin \frac{1}{2}x$; $y = \frac{1}{2} \sin x$; $y = \sin (2 + x)$; $y = 2 + \sin x$. Explain these constructions as you would to a high school class.

11 Make a table showing the values of the six circular functions of s within the closed interval $[0,\pi]$ if $s = k\pi/6$ ($k = 0, 1, 2, 3, 4, 5, 6$). Then explain how one can write down, by symmetry, the values of the functions of $(\pi + s)$ in the closed interval $[\pi, 2\pi]$.

12 Most tables of trigonometric functions extend only from 0° to 90°, yet it is often necessary to find values of functions not within this domain. Show exactly how you would teach students how to determine from the tables the values, for example, of cos 153°, tan 289°, and sin (−112°). Explain the use of the triangle of reference, and show how it can be helpful in this connection.

13 Using a large-scale graph, determine as closely as you can the value or values of x for which $x = 2 \sin x$, and discuss your graphical solution, bringing out the points you would want to make clear to a high school class.

14 Explain the essential difference between proving a trigonometric identity and solving a trigonometric equation. Illustrate by examples.

15 Show in detail how to develop the formula for cos $(A - B)$, using a unit circle. Then, without using any diagram, show how the following formulas can be derived from this: cos $(A + B)$; sin $(A + B)$; sin $(A - B)$.

16 Explain and illustrate the use of the function hexagon described in this chapter, and show why it is a helpful mnemonic device. Verify each of the twenty-six identities which one can read from it.

17 Using commonly known identities, take ten simple trigonometric expressions and transform them into some other equivalent form. In this way you will have established ten new, or "original," identities, which could then be assigned to your class for proof. This is a good exercise to give to high school students.

18 For what values of x in the interval $0 \leqslant x < 4\pi$ is the statement cos $x < \frac{1}{2}$ valid? For what values of x in this same interval does cos $x = \frac{1}{2}$? Discuss.

19 For what values of x in the interval $(\pi/2) < x \leqslant 5\pi/2$ are the following statements valid? (a) 2 cos $5x = 1$; (b) 2 cos $5x > 1$. What difficulties would you expect high school students to have with such problems as this?

20 Explain how you would find the solution sets for the following equation and inequality in the interval $0 \leqslant x < 2\pi$: (a) sin $x = $ tan x; (b) sin $x < $ tan x. Analysis of part b makes clear the care that is needed in examining inequalities. It suggests also the importance of doing some work with inequalities, and points up the interest which such work can generate.

21 Show and explain all the steps in finding the complete solution set for the equation 6 cot^2 $x = 5$ cot $x - 1$ for the closed interval $[0,\pi]$. Do the same for the equation

$$6 \sec^2 x = 5 \sec x - 1$$

Compare and discuss the two solution sets.

22 Explain how the graph of the function $y = $ sin x could be used also as the graph of the inverse relation $x = $ arcsin y.

23 Explain the relation of polar and rectangular coordinates in a plane, showing how the transformation formulas come about. Then explain how the complex number $a + bi$ can be expressed in polar form (or trigonometric form), and how the complex number $r(\cos \theta + i \sin \theta)$ can be expressed in rectangular form.

24 Explain why the polar coordinates of a point in a plane are not unique, while the rectangular coordinates of the same point are.

25 Using polar coordinates, give a chalk talk showing how to make a graph of the equation $r = 1 - \cos \theta$ over the interval $0 \leqslant \theta < 2\pi$, discussing your procedure as you go, and explaining what happens when $\theta < 0$ and when $\theta > 2\pi$.

26 Consider two complex numbers: $u = a + bi$, $v = c + di$. Explain, using a diagram, how u, v, and their sum $u + v$ can be regarded as vectors in the complex plane. What are the horizontal and vertical components of the sum? Explain.

27 Let u and v be complex numbers, with $u = r(\cos x + i \sin x)$ and

$$v = s(\cos y + i \sin y)$$

where r and s are real numbers. Show in detail why

$$u \times v = rs \ [\cos (x + y) + i \sin (x + y)],$$

and why

$$u^3 = r^3(\cos 3x + i \sin 3x)$$

What parts of the proof do you think might prove troublesome to high school students?

28 Explain in detail how to find the five 5th roots of the complex number $-i$. What points do you think would prove hard for students to understand?

BIBLIOGRAPHY

Allendoerfer, Carl B.: The Method of Equivalence, or How to Cure a Cold, *Mathematics Teacher*, **59** (1966), 531–535.

Biddle, John G.: The Square Function: An Abstract System for Trigonometry, *Mathematics Teacher*, **60** (1967), 121–123.

Bristol, James D.: Construction and Evaluation of Trigonometric Functions of Some Special Angles, *Mathematics Teacher*, **54** (1961), 4–7.

Brother T. Brendon: How Ptolemy Constructed Trigonometry Tables, *Mathematics Teacher*, **58** (1965), 141–149.

Doyle, Thomas: Are We Overemphasizing the Computational Aspects of Trigonometry?, *Mathematics Teacher*, **61** (1968), 271, 277.

Eppenshade, Pamela H.: A Text on Trigonometry by Levi Ben Gerson, *Mathematics Teacher*, **60** (1967), 628–637.

Fraser, Donald G.: A Method for Finding the Period and the Phase Shift of Trigonometric

Functions, *Mathematics Teacher*, **61** (1968), 762–763.

Garfunkel, J.: A Project in Mathematics, *Mathematics Teacher*, **61** (1968), 253–258.

———— and B. Leeds: The Circle of Unit Diameter, *Mathematics Teacher*, **59** (1966), 124–127.

Hailpern, Raoul: The Link Method in Trigonometry, *Mathematics Teacher*, **57** (1964), 469–471.

Kanter, L. H.: Geometric Derivation of the Half-angle Formulas for an Acute Angle, *School Science and Mathematics*, **69** (1969), 300–302.

Maslanka, John S.: Cotangent A in a New Light, *Mathematics Teacher*, **60** (1967), 855.

Mikula, Thomas: The Trigonometry of the Square, *Mathematics Teacher*, **60** (1967), 354–357.

Paisley, David: An Interesting Observation Regarding the Sine Curve, *Mathematics Teacher*, **61** (1968), 391–392.

Schaumberger, Norman: Another Application of De Moivre's Theorem, *Mathematics Teacher*, **61** (1968), 496–497.

Stover, Donald W.: Projectiles, *Mathematics Teacher*, **57** (1964), 317–322.

Thomas, Robert J.: A New Introduction to the Ideas and Methods of Trigonometry, *Mathematics Teacher*, **54** (1961), 427–435.

Troyer, Robert: Rotations, Angles, and Trigonometry, *Mathematics Teacher*, **61** (1968), 123–129.

Wallender, Arnold L.: A Trigonometric Capitulation, *Mathematics Teacher*, **57** (1964), 257–258.

Wegner, Kenneth W.: Trigonometric Excursions and Side Trips, *Mathematics Teacher*, **60** (1967), 33–37.

Willoughby, Stephen S.: "Contemporary Teaching of Secondary School Mathematics" (New York: John Wiley & Sons, Inc., 1967), pp. 323–357.

sixteen

the
teaching
of analytic
geometry

Analytic geometry contributes to the mathematical development
and background of students in at least three important ways: It
embraces a body of subject matter which is interesting and beautiful in its own right. Also, by bringing powerful algebraic concepts
and techniques to bear upon geometrical problems, it links algebra
and geometry together into a new and unified mathematical structure. Finally, it develops formulas and techniques, many of which
are needed for subsequent work in mathematics and the sciences.
It thus provides an important tool for the mathematician and the
scientist. Analytic geometry may be viewed, therefore, as a mathematical structure, as a method, and as a tool.

Perhaps the principal reason for studying analytic geometry
lies in the insight that it affords into the way in which the powerful and exact methods of algebra are invoked for dealing with
geometric problems, and in which geometry provides perfect
space models for algebraic expressions. This fusion, in a new context, of much of the arithmetic, algebra, geometry, and trigonometry studied previously exemplifies the strength and unity of
mathematics. Students should come to see in it not only a fascinating union of much of the mathematics they have already
studied into a new composite, but also a more powerful key than
they have had before for unlocking still other mathematical doors.

Some students find analytic geometry easier than other branches
of mathematics which they have studied, but a good many find it
harder. Since little has been written on the teaching of analytic
geometry, the present chapter undertakes to provide a published
source to which teachers can turn for some discussion of certain
instructional problems related to the subject. Hence consideration
is given in this chapter to some of the key concepts of analytic
geometry and to some of the characteristic difficulties which students often have with the subject.

ANALYTIC GEOMETRY AND THE
HIGH SCHOOL PROGRAM

Up to about the middle of this century analytic geometry was
typically offered as a separate and systematic course in the first
year of college mathematics. There has since been a tendency to

combine analytic geometry and calculus into a single "unified" course of three or four semesters. The argument for such a course has been that time could be saved by confining the work in analytic geometry mainly to those parts which are essential for calculus, so that increased emphasis could be placed on the calculus itself. From this point of view analytic geometry was regarded mainly as a tool needed for the calculus. Many textbooks for such a combined course have been published, and the idea has gained wide, but not universal, acceptance among college teachers. There were, and are, some who did not and do not subscribe to this

Changing
viewpoints

point of view. By the middle 1960s voices were beginning to be heard to the effect that the combined course devoted too little time to analytic geometry, omitting significant parts of it and treating the rest merely as a tool for the calculus, and that as a result students were being shortchanged, and were not being given an adequate picture of analytic geometry as a whole.

Meanwhile, the changes that had taken place and are still taking place in the high school courses in mathematics had brought the former 4-year mathematics program in many high schools within the compass of 3 or 3½ years, leaving a hiatus in the program for the fourth year. Various courses have been proposed for this final part of the high school mathematics program: calculus, probability

Proposals for
twelfth-grade
mathematics

and statistics, analytic geometry, and different courses organized around a variety of mathematical concepts, but in the early 1960s there was no real consensus on what was the best plan. There still is no complete agreement, but a widespread view has been expressed that a systematic course in analytic geometry would be a suitable, feasible, and valuable course for the final year of the high school program.

Small units or chapters on coordinate geometry have come to be accepted and expected in textbooks for tenth-grade geometry, as well as in the second course in algebra. Indeed, in contemporary textbooks for this latter course, one may often find rather good coverage of the straight line and the conics. It now seems reasonable to expect that a whole course in analytic geometry will come to be a regular part of the mathematical curriculum in many high schools. In 1965, at a joint meeting of the Mathematical Association of America and the National Council of Teachers of Mathematics held in Denver, Colorado, a representative of the CUPM strongly implied that committee's approval of such a course. In that same year the School Mathematics Study Group (SMSG) published a textbook for a full course in Analytic Geometry for high school students.

Some arguments
for coordinate
geometry

There is much to recommend such a course. Many college teachers approve it. It would provide students a fuller view of the subject than they would be likely to get in a college course where analytic geometry is combined with, and made subsidiary to, the calculus. It is well within the capacities of the students who would take it, and it would bring into focus the beautiful connections between algebra and geometry, which are the very essence of the course.

SOME ELEMENTARY CONCEPTS

In beginning the study of analytic geometry the students will not encounter immediately any geometric concepts that are essentially new. On the contrary, the introductory work usually consists of a re-examination of the cartesian coordinate system, with which they should already be familiar through their earlier work in algebra and geometry. In many cases, however, this earlier work will have been rather casual and not very systematic. Therefore it is usually advisable at the start to review and freshen the concepts, terms, and notation associated with rectangular coordinates in a two-dimensional system. Along with this introductory refresher work, it will be well to give some attention to the representation of points in 3-space. This should bring into focus the use of three mutually perpendicular planes as reference elements in a three-dimensional coordinate system, instead of just the pair of perpendicular lines used as reference axes in a two-dimensional system, and the need for ordered triples of numbers as coordinates of points, instead of just the ordered pairs needed in plane geometry. Many of the problems of plane analytic geometry have counterparts in 3-space, and it may often be desirable to consider these together. Most students are not adept at making good drawings, and it is harder to make good representations of three-dimensional figures than of two-dimensional figures.

Refresh the students' basic ideas

The concept of *ordered* pairs or triples of numbers should be stressed in connection with representing or reading coordinates of points. It needs to be emphasized that the location of a point in a coordinate system depends, not alone on the numerical values of its coordinate, but also upon their order; that the point whose coordinates are (a,b) or (a,b,c) is not in general the same point as the one whose coordinates are (b,a) or (b,c,a). There is no difficulty involved here, and it would be unnecessary to mention this, except that students sometimes get careless about this convention. It is well, however, to stress the importance of giving conscious and explicit attention both to the concept of order in naming the coordinates of a point and to the conventional notation used. Any carelessness or departure from the accepted notation will induce mistakes in representation and communication. Moreover, it may be pointed out at this time that the modern definition of *function* places emphasis on ordered pairs of elements and that the ordering and its proper representation will be of prime importance throughout all subsequent work in mathematics.

Importance of order and notation

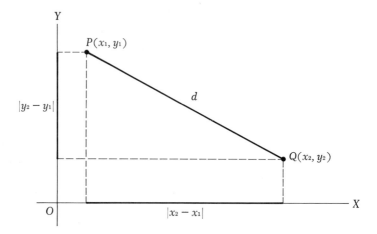

Figure 16-1
Distance between two points in a coordinate plane.

Other matters which probably should be reviewed and clarified in the introductory part of the course include the concept of projections on a line or plane and the notion of directed line segments. Neither of these should require much time or entail any difficulty. The importance of reviewing them at this time lies in the fact that they are basic concepts which must be used continually. Fuzzy conceptions about these terms or the associated notation are likely to lead to fuzzy thinking and uncertainty in their application. It should be emphasized that projections of directed segments are themselves directed segments, and that, on the other hand, the *length* of a projection is always nonnegative. Hence it is important to use the absolute-value signs to denote the length of a projection. If only the squares of the lengths are to be used, the absolute-value notation need not be retained.

Projections; length

Let us consider here this idea of the *length* of a line segment, or *distance* from one point to another. The measure of this distance is made through direct application of the Pythagorean theorem to a right triangle, a concept with which the students are already familiar. In connection with any given line segment in a coordinate plane, no difficulty is involved in showing that an associated right triangle may be formed by taking lines respectively parallel to the axes, one through each end of the given segment, and that the projections of the segment on these lines are the legs of the triangle, the segment itself being the hypotenuse. The very simplicity of this concept may tend to throw teachers off guard. It must be remembered that, while it is very elementary, it is also

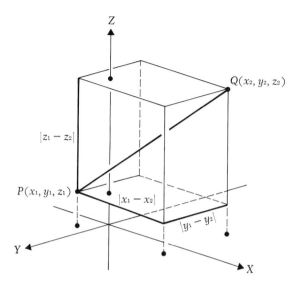

Figure 16-2
Distance between two points in 3-space.

completely fundamental. It needs to be adequately illustrated. Moreover, even after the underlying idea is clearly understood by the students, the general relation needs to be explicitly formulated in terms of the coordinates of the ends of the segment:

$$d = \sqrt{(x_1 - x_2)^2 + (y_1 - y_2)^2} = \sqrt{(x_2 - x_1)^2 + (y_2 - y_1)^2}$$

This is easy to explain and illustrate by a diagram, but it is also the point at which students sometimes begin to become uncertain and confused. Their formulas of synthetic geometry will not usually have involved the use of coordinates, yet from here on they must both make and interpret their formulations in the notation of coordinates. If they can be made to understand both the rationale and the notation of this formula, a long step will have been made in the direction of understanding.

It is doubtless well to develop the general distance formula for 3-space along with that for 2-space, and it is not hard for students to understand. If $P(x_1,y_1)$ and $Q(x_2,y_2)$ are two points in a coordinate plane (see Fig. 16-1), the distance d between them is simply the length of the diagonal of the *rectangle* with sides parallel, respectively, to the coordinate axes, and of which P and Q are a pair of opposite vertexes. In like manner, if $P(x_1,y_1,z_1)$ and $Q(x_2,y_2,z_2)$ are two points in 3-space (see Fig. 16-2), then d is simply the length of a diagonal of the *rectangular prism* whose edges are parallel, respectively, to the coordinate axes, and of which P and Q are a pair of opposite vertexes. This will all seem so simple and clear to the teacher that he may believe (often mistakenly) that it must be equally evident to all the students. Certainly, it is not safe to assume this. The reason why the length of segment $\overline{PQ}$ is given by the formula $d = \sqrt{(x_1 - x_2)^2 + (y_1 - y_2)^2 + (z_1 - z_2)^2}$ should be explained geometrically and in detail, using a clearly drawn diagram (see Fig. 16-2). A few minutes discussion of this, followed immediately by a few simple numerical exercises in determining distances between pairs of given points in 3-space, will pay good dividends, and will be helpful in simplifying subsequent work, such as, for example, work with direction cosines and setting up equations for loci from given geometric conditions.

A key foundation stone

The point-of-division formulas, both for 2-space and 3-space, are examples of formulas of analytic geometry which students often attempt to memorize without having a clear understanding of why they are as they are. Like the distance formula, they depend directly on theorems of high school geometry, and the concept is easily explained on this basis. Students bog down on it, not because the concept is difficult, but because they are unaccustomed to the notation. At this early stage in the course they will not yet have learned either to use or to interpret this notation very readily, and the formulas look forbidding to them. Hence, instead of attempting to interpret the formulas in terms of a figure and then reconstruct them in terms of the new symbols, the students often resort to memorizing the formulas. Usually, it is not the geometric ideas that trouble them. It is the notation which is new. It is fundamental, and it must become the student's tool and servant throughout this and subsequent courses. It is important, therefore, to give a good deal of attention to this matter of notation in the early part of this work. It may even spell the difference between success and failure in the course.

Interpreting the notation readily is a fundamental ability

The mid-point formulas, of course, are merely special cases of the point-of-division formulas, but (again in terms of notation) they are usually stated differently, so that the relation is not immediately apparent. Teachers, on the other hand, may tend to assume that the connection is so obvious as not to require any comment. It is desirable to point out this relation explicitly from a geometric viewpoint, and also to show how the mid-point formulas can be derived analytically from the point-of-division formulas. This not only serves to clarify this particular case, but provides a simple and good illustration of the application of algebraic techniques to geometric problems.

LOCI AND THEIR EQUATIONS

The associated concepts of loci and their equations are central throughout analytic geometry. Here the complete merger of algebra and geometry occurs, for here the geometric conditions or restrictions imposed on the points forming the locus are expressed analytically or algebraically by equations or inequalities which specify particular relations among the coordinates of each point in the locus and for no other points. Frequently, the loci studied in analytic geometry are described verbally in terms of geometric conditions, but before they can be studied analytically, these conditions have to be translated into equations or inequalities.

The first serious difficulty students are likely to encounter stems from this fact. Up to this point they have not been accustomed to identify geometric conditions with algebraic forms. Now they must not only learn to make this identification but go even further. In order to be proficient, they must actually learn to think in terms of these forms. For the common and rather simple loci studied, the form of the equation must come to suggest the associated locus, and conversely, the geometric conception of the locus must come to suggest the form of the associated equation. From the outset it should be made clear and kept continually before the students that there are a duality of form and a dual purpose in analytic geometry. The students should be reminded continually of the complementary interplay between geometry and algebra here. The two fundamental problems of analytic geometry are (1) to learn to associate with each locus studied the characteristic form of its equation and (2) to learn to infer from the type form of the equation the nature and properties of the locus which it represents. These funda-

The two basic problems of analytic geometry

mental considerations are not always made clear to students, yet they form the very foundation of understanding. To learn that the equation $(x - h)^2/a^2 + (y - k)^2/b^2 = 1$ represents an ellipse is certainly necessary, but it is not sufficient. Unless the student understands what the parameters a and b and h and k represent geometrically, he will have little conception of the form or the properties of the ellipse whose equation is given him as $(x - 5)^2/37 + y^2/10 = 1$. And unless he does know this type of equation, he will not be able to write down readily the equation of the ellipse whose center is at $(5,0)$ and whose major and minor axes have lengths of $2\sqrt{37}$ and $2\sqrt{10}$, respectively. Each kind of locus studied in elementary analytic geometry has a characteristic form of equation. The association between the properties of the locus and the form of its type equation needs to be emphasized continually. Indeed, broadly speaking, one may say that this association constitutes one of the fundamental objectives of the course.

The key to real understanding

The moment a student attains real appreciation of how a statement of geometric restrictions can be translated into an equation and of the fact that the one is the counterpart of the other, he has made a major breakthrough. If he really understands what has taken place, it should then be apparent to him that a powerful new instrument has been added to his working equipment. Once the geometric problem has been translated into algebraic terms, he has at his command all the formal rules and procedures of algebra to assist him. He may manipulate the equation formally and at will without, for the moment, giving any thought to the geometric implications. Then, if in the end he can reinterpret the results of his algebraic work back into terms of geometric properties or relations, he will have accomplished his geometric investigation by analytic methods, and these often are more powerful than the direct methods of synthetic geometry.

To some students this concept comes quickly; to others it does not. Yet it is so much the essence of analytic geometry that every effort should be made to ensure that all the students come to appreciate it. Repeated explanations and illustrations will doubtless be necessary, and penetrating questions can often do much to clarify this dual representation and give point to the analytic treatment of geometric problems. Success in this will give the students genuine insight into the method of analytic geometry. Without such insight they may resort to mere profitless memorization and miss the whole point of the course.

INTERSECTING LOCI

Many of the problems of analytic geometry involve the intersection of different loci. This was discussed briefly in Chapter 14, with respect to intersecting straight lines, but it is so pervasive in analytic geometry that it will be well to call attention to it again at this time.

If the solution sets are restricted to the field of real numbers, there need be no difficulty here, provided the students keep themselves alert to the related concepts of the geometrical meaning of the intersection and to the meaning of its algebraic counterpart. They simply need to understand that, geometrically, the intersec-

The central idea: geometric and algebraic analogues

tion of two or more loci, if it exists at all, is precisely the set of points which lie on both (or all) of the loci, and that analytically (algebraically), it is simply the solution set for the system of equations or inequalities which define the loci. But students need to be really sensitive to this relation between the algebraic and geometric meanings of the intersection and to keep it constantly in mind; to feel how the one implies the other. They need to have this dual concept so firmly fixed in mind that without hesitation they will infer from the solution set of the system of equations or inequalities the coordinates of the point or points which make up the intersection of the loci.

This is really all there is to the matter. When students have gained a genuine appreciation of the fact that each equation or inequality is simply the algebraic analog of a geometric locus, then, and not until then, will this geometric interpretation of the algebraic solution set of the system of equations or inequalities be clear to them. To teachers the analogy will be so familiar that it is easy to forget that it may not be equally evident to all the students, but it is not safe to assume that it will be. When work with intersecting loci is taken up, it is wise for the teacher to spend a little time in discussing this matter with the class, to make sure that every student has a clear understanding of why the algebraic work (the solution of a system of simultaneous equations or inequalities) is being done, and of how to reinterpret the solution set into its geometric counterpart. Usually, this will not take long, and the time that it takes will have been spent to good advantage.

DETERMINING THE EQUATION OF A LOCUS

The general problem of setting up the equation of a locus which is described geometrically often implies an ordered sequence of steps. The details are sometimes a bit complicated, but the pattern is not, at least in the case of most of the simpler loci studied in elementary analytic geometry.

A suggested procedure

The first step consists in making a suitable sketch or working drawing. This is done by drawing a pair of axes to represent the coordinate plane, sketching in all given fixed points or lines with their coordinates or equations shown, drawing in a representative point of the locus with variable coordinates (x,y) indicated, and drawing suitable line segments connecting the point (x,y) with the fixed points or lines described in the given conditions. Lengths of these segments may now be denoted (often through their projections on the axes) in terms of the coordinates of the fixed points and the general point of the locus or in terms of the distances of the general point (x,y) from given fixed lines.

Once these details are depicted in a reasonably good sketch, it is not difficult to translate the required conditions from their verbal form into an equation. This equation will always involve the coordinates of the representative point of the locus and the coordinates of some given fixed point or points described in the initial conditions. The actual setting up of the equation in this manner constitutes the second and final step. For the simpler loci it is usually an easy matter. Ordinarily, it will involve distances which will be denoted on the sketch and which are either to be equated to each other or set into an equation with given constants. Once the student has identified these distances on the sketch and has noted their forms in terms of coordinates, it is a simple matter to translate them directly into the required equation.

The essential simplicity of this procedure, however, may not be immediately apparent to the students. Through their very familiarity with the subject, teachers are prone to assume too much on this score. These ideas are still new and unfamiliar to most students, and it cannot be assumed that the students will assimilate and use them successfully without help. A few who have unusual perception and insight will have no difficulty, but for most **Illustrative examples are needed** students the topic will probably require careful and repeated explanation, pointed questions, numerous illustrations, and a considerable amount of supervised practice with well-chosen problems.

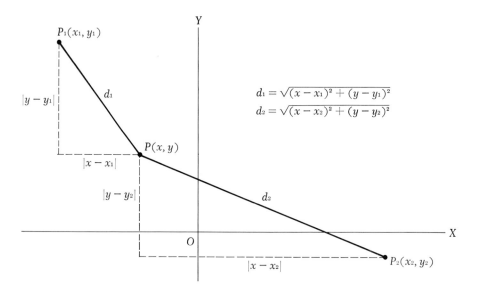

Figure 16-3

Example. Determine the equation of the locus of points the sum of whose distances from two fixed points is 10 units. See Fig. 16-3.

$$\text{Distance from } P_1 + \text{distance from } P_2 \qquad = 10$$
$$d_1 + d_2 = 10$$
$$\sqrt{(x - x_1)^2 + (y - y_1)^2} + \sqrt{(x - x_2)^2 + (y - y_2)^2} = 10$$

Thus the equation is set up without difficulty. To be sure, it is not yet in its simplest form, but the rest is a matter of routine algebraic detail which can be carried on as such without any further immediate concern about geometric considerations.

One matter which may well be clarified at this time is the question, which some student will probably ask: "Why shouldn't we **A legitimate question** write $d_2 = \sqrt{(x_2 - x)^2 + (y - y_2)^2}$ instead of $\sqrt{(x - x_2)^2 + (y - y_2)^2}$?" This often bothers students, and the question is a good one which deserves careful attention. It should be explained that d_1 and d_2 are thought of as undirected distances; so we are concerned only

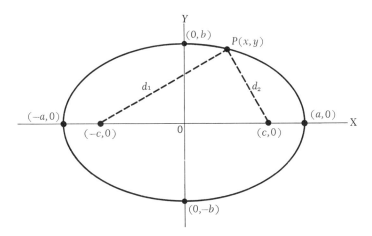

Figure 16-4

with the absolute values of their components, and $|x - x_1| = |x_1 - x|$. In any case, since only the squares of these distances are involved, the order of subscripts would be immaterial, because obviously, $(x - x_2)^2 = (x_2 - x)^2$. Since this is true, by keeping the subscripts in the same order, the form of the equation is made somewhat simpler and easier to remember.

There is one other matter that should be discussed in connection with this problem. It should be pointed out that in Fig. 16-3 the positions of P, P_1, and P_2 were taken essentially at random and so lead to the most general form of the equation. However, unless the coordinates of the fixed point are definitely specified, no harm is done by taking the axes in the most convenient position with respect to the given points. This is usually done in textbooks in developing the type form of the equation for this locus. If the given points P_1 and P_2 are taken on an axis with the origin midway between them, the form of the equation is simplified, and important properties of the locus come to light readily from inspection of the equation.

Thus, by using conventional notation and assuming that d_1 and d_2 are not both zero, the fixed points may be designated as $(c,0)$ and $(-c,0)$, so that the distance between them is $2c$. See Fig. 16-4. Then, if the sum $d_1 + d_2$ is designated as $2a$ for convenience, we immediately have $d_1 + d_2 = 2a$, and unless $d_1 = 0$ or $d_2 = 0$, this means that $2a > 2c$. Then

Simplification without loss of generality

$$d_1 + d_2 = 2a = \sqrt{(x + c)^2 + y^2} + \sqrt{(x - c)^2 + y^2}$$

By straight algebraic manipulation this yields the equation

$$\frac{x^2}{a^2} + \frac{y^2}{a^2 - c^2} = 1$$

and by designating $a^2 - c^2 = b^2$, the equation becomes $x^2/a^2 + y^2/b^2 = 1$.

Not only is this the simplest form for the equation of an ellipse, but the equation itself yields directly some important geometrical information about the locus. If $|a| \neq |c|$ and if $y = 0$, the equation becomes $x^2/a^2 = 1$, which yields the coordinates of the vertexes as $(a,0)$ and $(-a,0)$. If we take $x = 0$, we get $y = \pm b$, and we have the ordinates of the points where the locus intersects the y axis. Thus, with the equation in the form indicated above, the intercepts on the axes are known at a glance, and the coordinates of the foci are immediately determined from the defining relation $c = \sqrt{a^2 - b^2}$. The extent of the locus is readily determined, since if $|x| > |a|$ or if $|y| > |b|$, the values of x and y, respectively, become imaginary. The form of the equation makes it clear that there are no horizontal or vertical asymptotes, and the absence of any odd powers of either variable shows that the locus is symmetrical with respect to both axes, and hence with respect to the origin. Thus this equation provides immediately all information needed to sketch the graph of this locus and locate its foci. It is of interest, in passing, to consider the special case that arises when $c = 0$ and the ellipse becomes a circle, and to notice how easily one reaches this conclusion by merely inspecting the equation.

Geometrical properties are revealed

It is most important, of course, for the students to understand that this simplest form of the equation represents only a very special case, i.e., when the center is at the origin and the major axis lies on the x axis. Under other circumstances the equation will be more complicated and can be thrown into this simple standard form and made to yield the geometrical information which the simple form gives only through the laborious work of referring the coordinates and the equation to a new system of axes with respect to which the curve *is* in standard position.

Practice strengthens insight

In the beginning most students need some supervised practice in setting up equations of loci. A little extra time explicitly on this in the early part of the course can develop insight and appreciation which will pay good dividends later on. The same insight which enables a student to translate geometrical conditions into algebraic equations is likely also to be a powerful aid to him in inferring geometrical conditions when the equations are given.

DETERMINING THE LOCUS OF AN EQUATION

Point-by-point plotting

In beginning coordinate geometry, the locus represented by an equation involving one or two variables is usually found by plotting a considerable number of points whose coordinates satisfy the equation and then drawing a smooth curve through the points.

Students have no trouble with this because they have had some experience with graphing and they understand what they are doing. However, despite the fact that constructing the graph of a given equation is one of the fundamental problems of analytic geometry, this method of point-by-point plotting has severe and fundamental limitations. One of them is that it is tedious and slow, and in general, one can never plot all the points on the locus. Another is that it is inexact, and exactness is often of great importance, as, for example, in determining the coordinates of points of intersection of loci. Thus, by meticulous point-by-point plotting, a student might obtain carefully made graphs of the loci represented by the equations $x^2 + y^2 + 4x - 5 = 0$ and $y = 1 + 2x$. If the graphs are very carefully made to a large scale, he might well conclude that the one represents a circle and the other a straight line. Indeed, he might decide from observation that the circle has its center at about $(-2,0)$, that its radius is about 3 units in length, and that one of its points of intersection with the straight line is at about $(-2,-3)$. He might even make a good estimate of the coordinates of the other point of intersection.

Nobody would question the value of this intuitive observational type of analysis on the part of the students. It should by all means

Limitations be encouraged because it offers a splendid means for clarifying concepts and interpretations and for stimulating interest in the work. But on the other hand, the students must not be left with the impression that this is sufficient. They must be made to realize that even if all these conjectures were exactly correct (and they might well be so in this case), the graph itself could offer no confirmation of such exactness, and that the only way the exact values can be known, or the estimates can be tested for exactness, is through solving simultaneously the equations of the two loci. It should be pointed out also that this observational method cannot bring to light the essential relations between the form of the equation and the general and special properties of the curve.

This is but a single example of the fundamental limitations inherent in this point-by-point plotting of the graphs of equations. Aside from being tedious, slow, and inexact, its fundamental weakness is that it does not utilize algebraic considerations to determine the characteristics of the locus or to relate them to the form of the equation. It should be explained that the objective of the course is to learn how to apply analytic methods which are at the same time less tedious, more powerful, and more revealing

More powerful
methods than those of point-by-point plotting and mere observational analysis of graphs. Such analytic methods can bring to light not only the exact coordinates of intersection points, but also such characteristics as the coordinates of intercepts, limitations on the extent of the locus if such limitations exist, symmetry or lack of symmetry with respect to either or both of the coordinate axes or the origin, and perhaps with respect to other lines or another point, and discontinuities in the case of horizontal or vertical asymptotes.

Most of the loci usually studied in plane analytic geometry belong to a few simple types: the straight line, the circle and the conic sections, and a few of the higher plane curves. Each of these types of locus can be defined in terms of certain characteristic geometric properties, and the type equation of each can be iden-

Associating
geometric and
algebraic
counterparts

tified by certain algebraic characteristics. To infer the type of curve that is represented by one of these equations it is necessary to be familiar with the algebraic characteristics of the equations of the various types of curves. One needs to know, for example, that in a rectangular coordinate system a first-degree equation in two variables is the algebraic representation of a straight line, and that a first-degree equation in one variable ($x = h$ or $y = k$) also represents a straight line, since this is simply a special case of the general equation of a line: $ax + by + c = 0$. One needs to know that a quadratic equation in two variables is to be identified with some type of conic section, the type and specific properties being determined by the form of the equation and by the coefficients of the various terms. In like manner the type equations in polar coordinates of some of the simpler curves must be known if the type of locus is to be inferred from the equation without point-by-point plotting.

Corresponding comments apply to the matter of determining certain characteristics of those three-dimensional loci studied in elementary analytics from the forms of their equations and the coefficients of their several terms. The similarities, for example, of the general equations of the straight line and the plane, of the circle and the sphere, of the conics and the respective conicoids,

Helpful analogies

suggest certain analogies among the two- and three-dimensional loci which are very helpful in associating important properties of the three dimensional loci with corresponding properties of their two-dimensional counterparts.

Teachers need to focus the attention of their students on these considerations, giving numerous illustrations and considerable practice in identifying simple types of curves and determining their properties merely by examination of their equations. It is a matter which deserves more than the scant attention that is too often accorded to it.

THE STRAIGHT LINE

The objectives for the study of the straight line in a two-dimensional coordinate system may be set down as follows:

1 To understand that a straight line is uniquely determined if any of the
following pairs of conditions is specified:
  a. Two fixed points through which it passes
  b. One fixed point through which it passes with a given slope
  c. Its intercepts on the two axes, provided these are not both zero,
     [a special case of (a)]
  d. Its slope and its intercept on one of the axes [a special case of (b)]
  e. Its slope and its directed distance from the origin
2 To know and be able to write or develop the type equation of a
straight line for each of these sets of conditions
3 To recognize and identify the equation of a straight line from the
form and the characteristic constants in its equation
4 To be able to convert the equation of a line from one type form into
another type form

The idea that a line is determined by a point and a direction is
implicit in all five sets of special conditions listed under item 1
above.

From the different sets of sufficient conditions enumerated
under item 1 above, it is easy to set up from diagrams the several
type formulas for the equation of a straight line corresponding to
these several sets of conditions. Thus we have the two-point form,
the symmetric and intercept forms, the point-slope and slope-
intercept forms, and the normal form. Along with these forms attention should probably be given to the parametric equations of a
line in 2-space. The parametric, two-point, intercept, and symmetric equations for a line in 2-space have exact counterparts in
3-space, and the similarities exhibited suggest easy association of
the properties of lines in 2-space and 3-space and interesting generalizations of the equations, as shown in Table 16-1.

TABLE 16-1

Type of equation	2-space	3-space
Parametric	$x = x_1 + k(x_2 - x_1)$ $y = y_1 + k(y_2 - y_1)$	$x = x_1 + k(x_2 - x_1)$ $y = y_1 + k(y_2 - y_1)$ $z = z_1 + k(z_2 - z_1)$
Two-point	$\dfrac{x - x_1}{x_2 - x_1} = \dfrac{y - y_1}{y_2 - y_1}$	$\dfrac{x - x_1}{x_2 - x_1} = \dfrac{y - y_1}{y_2 - y_1} = \dfrac{z - z_1}{z_2 - z_1}$
Symmetric	$\dfrac{x - x_1}{a} = \dfrac{y - y_1}{b}$	$\dfrac{x - x_1}{a} = \dfrac{y - y_1}{b} = \dfrac{z - z_1}{c}$

Understanding the development of the formulas for these different types of equations should occasion little difficulty for students. It is probably advisable for the instructor to give careful
chalk talk explanations of each of them, calling attention to the
reasons why it is desirable to have the different forms, and to the

fact that about all that is involved is the proportionality properties of similar triangles, together with an explanation of what is meant by the slope of a line in 2-space. If the type equations for 2-space and 3-space are developed concurrently, it will be necessary to include some discussion of direction cosines and direction numbers, and this will call for carefully made diagrams or physical models upon which to base the explanations. The advantages of considering the 2- and 3-space cases concurrently are obvious, but it will require more time than that needed for the two-dimensional cases alone, and this must be taken into account in planning the course.

Direction cosines and direction numbers

The importance of the type forms of the equation of a straight line lies not only in setting up specific equations from given geometric conditions, but also in interpreting particular equations in terms of geometric properties of the locus. This consists in identifying certain constants in the equation directly with the particular geometric information which they afford. Thus the equation $y + 7 = (5/9)(x - 4)$ should yield at once the information that this particular line passes through the point $(4,-7)$ and that its slope is $5/9$. Students need practice in this sort of interpretation, but as a rule they get too little of it. Such interpretation can do a great deal to build understanding and appreciation of the geometrical significance of key elements in the equation of a locus, and this is one of the overall objectives of analytic geometry. It need not take a great deal of time, but it does need to be given more attention than it has customarily received in the past.

Practice in interpretation is needed

The normal form for the equation of a straight line will require some special attention to both its derivation and its interpretation. Here a new element, the *normal axis,* is introduced, and along with it the meanings of the *normal intercept* and the *normal angle* (the angle of inclination of the normal axis). Different textbooks exhibit somewhat different methods of deriving the normal equation of a line. Some authors favor using direction cosines here, as the counterpart of the concepts and terminology used in the three-dimensional case for deriving the normal equation of a plane.

The normal form: derivation and interpretation

Derivation of the normal form is not so simple as the derivation of the other four forms. Here the students may experience difficulty even in following some of the details. However, this difficulty again can be traced in large measure to their failing to sense the aim and the plan, i.e., to their failing to see what this form of the equation can tell them that the other forms cannot. This is one of the hard spots in this course, but the normal form is also one of the most important of all the formulas, since it gives the distance from a straight line to a given point. Few students can successfully get all they should about it merely from the discussion in their textbooks. Whether the students are held responsible for redevel-

oping this formula or not, they need to know its form, understand
the geometrical significance of its elements, and understand how
to reduce an ordinary linear equation in two variables to its normal form in order to find the normal angle and the normal intercept of the straight line which it represents. These aims will be
achieved about in proportion to the clearness of the instructor's
explanations and the opportunity afforded to the students for interpretation of particular equations.

THE GENERAL EQUATION OF
THE STRAIGHT LINE

In view of the variety of forms in which the equation of a straight
line in 2-space may be expressed, students may wonder whether
there is any single generalized equation which would encompass
all of these. They should be made and kept aware that there is.
The argument can be substantially as follows.

All straight lines in the coordinate plane fall into three classes:
(1) those which are oblique to the axes and whose type equation
in slope-intercept form is $y = mx + b$ with $m \neq 0$; (2) those that
are parallel to the y axis and whose type equation is $x = k$; and
(3) those that are parallel to the x axis and whose type equation
is $y = h$.

Consider the general equation of the first degree in x and y:
$Ax + By + C = 0$, where A and B are not both zero. If neither is
zero, the solution of this equation is $y = (-A/B)x + (-C)/B$, which
is of the form $y = mx + b$, where $m = -A/B$ and $b = -C/B$. Hence
the general equation $Ax + By + C = 0$ clearly represents a straight
line. If $A \neq 0$ and $B \neq 0$, the line is oblique to the coordinate axes.
Moreover, if $A = 0$ and $B \neq 0$, this equation becomes $y = -C/B$,
which is the equation of the constant function whose graph is a
line parallel to the x axis. Finally, if $B = 0$ and $A \neq 0$, the equation
$Ax + By + C = 0$ becomes $x = -C/A$, which is the graph of the
relation $x = k$. Hence the general equation $Ax + By + C = 0$, with
A and B not both zero, is the general equation of the straight line,
since it subsumes the equation of a line parallel to the y axis (the
graph of a relation), as well as that of any line not parallel to the
y axis (the graph of a function).

FAMILIES OF STRAIGHT
LINES: PARAMETERS

The equation of any straight line, given in one of the standard
forms, contains certain constants, and these constants determine
which one of all the straight lines in the coordinate plane is rep-

resented by that equation. When all the necessary constants are explicitly given, the line is determined uniquely. For example, the equation $y = 7x - 2$ represents the one line whose slope is 7 and whose y intercept is -2. The equation $y = 7x + 1$ represents a different line. It has the same slope as the first one but a different y intercept. Similarly, the equation $y = 4x - 2$ represents still another line. This line has the same y intercept as the first one but a different slope.

The general slope-intercept equation of a line is usually written $y = mx + b$, where m and b are parameters which represent, respectively, the slope and the y intercept of the line. In this general form, however, it is not specified what constant values m and b have. Numerical values may be assigned to m and b at will. By keeping m fixed and assigning different values to b, we can represent arbitrarily many lines having different y intercepts. In other words, we represent a set of parallel lines, one line for each value assigned to b. For example, the equation $y = \frac{1}{2}x + b$ represents the set of all parallel lines in the plane with slope $\frac{1}{2}$. Simi-

Families of lines larly, by keeping b fixed but assigning different values to m, we represent a set of lines all of which have the same y intercept but different slopes. For example, the equation $y = mx + 2$ represents all lines in the plane (except, of course, the y axis, whose slope is undefined) which pass through the point $(0,2)$.

Whenever a slope-intercept equation contains a single parameter, as, for example, $y = 7x + b$ or $y = mx + 5$, it represents a whole *set*, or *system*, or *family* of lines. These lines will all differ in the one characteristic ascribable to that parameter, and they will all be alike in the characteristic determined by the fixed constant. Such a system is a *one-parameter* family of lines. If both m and b are allowed to take on all admissible values, we get a *two-parameter* family of lines which clearly includes every line in the plane except the y axis and those lines parallel to it. No value for m can be ascribed to these lines.

Parameters and generalization Much should be made of this recurring concept of parameters. Here is a fine opportunity to impress students with the fact that parameters are the means whereby equations can be made to represent generalizations, and that by assigning definite numbers to one or more of the parameters, various subsets of the set of all the loci embraced in the general parametric equation can be selected. Exercises in the selection and description of different subsets, for example, of the set of all lines in the coordinate plane, are extremely valuable as means for giving students a clear appreciation of the nature and role of parameters, and at the same time such exercises provide a high order of motivation. It is recommended that there be considerable discussion of parameters both in connection with the equations of the straight line, and subsequently with other two- and three-dimensional loci.

THE LINE AND THE PLANE

The equations of the plane in 3-space exhibit certain similarities to those of the line in 2-space, and these may well be brought to the attention of the students in connection with their study of the straight line. The similarities in the equations not only are useful to students in associating and remembering the equations, but they also suggest analogous properties of the loci or the elements associated with them. Such associations are always helpful in building or suggesting generalizations, sensing unifying elements, and deepening insights. We discuss a few here.

Further analogies Consider, for example, the simplest of all these cases. If a line in 2-space is perpendicular to exactly one of the coordinate axes, its equation will be either $x = a$ or $y = b$ (where a and b are constants). If a plane in 3-space is perpendicular to exactly one of the coordinate axes, its equation will be either $x = a$, $y = b$, or $z = c$ (a, b, and c constants). These sets of equations have exactly the same pattern, the only difference being the number of variables involved in the two cases.

In the more general case in which the line in 2-space intersects both coordinate axes, further similarities between the equations of the plane and the line come to light.

The *intercept equations* are

For a line in 2-space: $\dfrac{x}{a} + \dfrac{y}{b} = 1$

For a plane in 3-space: $\dfrac{x}{a} + \dfrac{y}{b} + \dfrac{z}{c} = 1$

where a, b, and c are the intercepts on the coordinate axes.

The *normal equations* are

For a line in 2-space: $x \cos \alpha + y \cos \beta = p$
For a plane in 3-space: $x \cos \alpha + y \cos \beta + z \cos \gamma = p$

where α, β, and γ are the direction angles of the normal axis, and p is the length of the normal intercept.

The *general equations* are

For a line in 2-space: $ax + by + k = 0$
For a plane in 3-space: $px + qy + rz + d = 0$

where a and b are not both zero, and p, q, and r are not all zero.

Motivate the students to search for patterns The interesting analogies between the equations of the line and the plane may well be brought to the attention of the students. The similarities in form may easily suggest generalizations. Helping and encouraging students to note such patterns as these not only facilitates association and recall, but it spurs the search for generalization. It often stimulates the curiosity of the students, and this in turn can result in conjecture and further inquiry, which is the finest kind of motivation.

THE CIRCLE AND THE SPHERE

Of all the loci studied in elementary analytic geometry, the circle probably offers the least difficulty to students. Once they have grasped the idea of how the equations of loci are set up in terms of coordinates from given geometric conditions, they are not likely to experience difficulty either in setting up the equation from given geometric conditions or in inferring the essential geometric properties of the locus from its equation.

Once the coordinates of the center and the length of the radius are known, a sketch shows clearly that a single application of the distance formula is sufficient to give the equation. The right triangle constructed as shown in Fig. 16-5 yields at once the equation

$$(x - h)^2 + (y - k)^2 = r^2$$

This is the generalized standard form in terms of the three parameters h, k, and r and thus represents a three-parameter family of circles.

Parameters and families again   When a fixed value is assigned to just one of these parameters, say to r, the equation still defines a family of circles in the plane; but this is a two-parameter family of circles because, although r is fixed, both h and k may take on any values whatever. It is the family of all circles lying in the plane and having a fixed radius but arbitrary centers. There are also one-parameter families of circles in the plane. For example, if r is arbitrary while both h and k are fixed, we get the family of concentric circles whose center is at (h,k). Thus, when specific values are assigned to one or two of the three parameters, the family of circles defined by the equation is less inclusive than that defined when all three parameters are left arbitrary. On the other hand, when all three parameters are assigned particular values, a single or unique circle is defined. With this understanding established, it is easy for students to see why the simplest form of all is obtained when both h and k are assigned the value zero.

Three crucial points to be understood   This in turn provides motivation for study of the translation of axes, which may well be undertaken at this time. This isometric, or distance-preserving, mapping should present no serious difficulty to students, provided the instructor makes three things clear: (1) the reason for making the translation (to simplify the equation of the locus), (2) the fact that the general coordinates (x,y) must now be replaced by expressions involving coordinates $(x'y')$ referred to the new axes, and (3) why, in the case of the circle, these replacements are of the form $x = x' + h$, $y = y' + k$, where h and k are the coordinates of the center as referred to the original axes. Once these points are grasped, and with h and k being known, the translation is easily effected and the simplified equation is obtained.

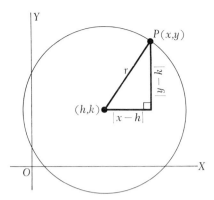

Figure 16-5

Interpreting the
equation

It must be remembered, however, that this is but one side of the coin. Interpretation of the new equation is no less important than its derivation, and there can be little assurance of full understanding unless both receive proper emphasis. Suppose, for example, that the equation of a particular circle is given as $(x - 4)^2 + (y + 1)^2 = 26$ and that through the usual transformation procedures associated with the translation of axes the students arrive at the simpler equation $x'^2 + y'^2 = 26$. Unless they can interpret this new form correctly, little will have been gained. They need to be made to understand that this change in the form of the equation does not imply any change in the characteristics of the circle itself (the location of the center and the length of the radius), because these remain invariant for any particular circle, but merely that $x'^2 + y'^2 = 26$ should be interpreted as $(x' - 0)^2 + (y' - 0)^2 = 26$. In a word, the students must understand that the equation $(x - 4)^2 + (y + 1)^2 = 26$ and $x'^2 + y'^2 = 26$ are merely two representations of the same circle when referred to two sets of respectively parallel axes, one of which has its origin at the center of the circle.

Another form of
the general
equation of a circle

There is a second form of the general equation of a circle with which students should become familiar. If the equation $(x - h)^2 + (y - k)^2 = r^2$ is expanded, it may be written in the form $x^2 + y^2 + ax + by + c = 0$, where a, b, and c are parameters, each with its own individual significance. This significance should be made clear to the students, and there should be abundant practice in converting from one form to the other, as well as giving full analyses of the complete information obtained from each equation. Attention should be called to the fact that, since there are three independent parameters, it requires three independent conditions to be able to determine the equation of any particular circle. Exercises should be given using such conditions as three noncollinear points to find the equation of the circle they determine. Also, opportunity should be provided to discover what happens to the equation when three collinear points are used. What, in work with the equation, reveals that it is impossible to pass a circle through three collinear points? Such questions and exercises lead to enhanced understanding of the circle and its equation.

There are certain problems associated with the study of circles which do sometimes prove troublesome for students. Among those which commonly are included in textbooks may be mentioned the following:

1 Deriving the equation of the circle through three given points not on a line (understanding why it takes three such points to provide the necessary data, why these data are also sufficient, and why the routine work of deriving the equation takes the form it does)
2 Finding the equation of a family of circles through the points of intersection of two given circles
3 Finding the length of a tangent to a given circle from a given point outside the circle

This catalog of associated problems is by no means exhaustive, but it is representative. It may be expected that each of the problems mentioned will prove troublesome to some students. Also, it is almost certain that trouble with such problems stems from lack of insight, i.e., from failure to understand what the problem really is, what the given conditions imply, and what the plan is for using what is known to establish what is required.

To explain the approach to these problems successfully, attention should be focused first on the things of major concern rather than upon details of notation. By rapidly sketching out the problem and the plan of attack in broad, bold strokes, it should be possible to get across to the students a basic understanding of both in a very short time. The explanation may be lacking in elegance, and it may be superficial from the standpoint of rigor and completeness of detail. Elegance and rigor can come later. The important consideration at the moment is that the explanation shall present clearly and as simply as possible the essential considerations and the line of argument leading to the conclusion or solution. Any student who has a modicum of skill in algebraic technique can fill in the necessary details and the proper notation once the essential framework has been built in his mind. Textbooks, however, too seldom use this approach. Authors do not always bother to make clear this framework and plan at the outset, and this is probably responsible for much of the trouble students experience in this subject. Most students can supply necessary detail to complete a proof or to solve a problem when they have the plan of work well in mind more successfully than they can discover the plan by studying the detail.

Sources of students' difficulties

Suggestions to be made to the students

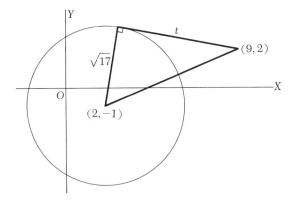

Figure 16-6
Find t.

As a single example of a broad, quick outline of a plan, we shall consider the problem of finding the length of a tangent, say, from the point (9,2) to the circle $(x - 2)^2 + (y + 1)^2 = 17$. A sketch can be quickly made to show that the required distance t is merely one leg of a right triangle (Fig. 16-6). The length of the other leg, being the radius of the circle, is known, and the length of the hypotenuse can be found immediately by use of the distance formula. It is clear, then, that

$$t^2 + (\text{radius})^2 = (\text{hypotenuse})^2$$

and this equation can easily be solved to give the length t which is required.

This explanation can be given in about two minutes at the chalkboard. It involves no subtleties. There is no need for students to ask, "Why do you do it that way?" It lays out the essential plan for attacking this problem in simple, familiar terms, and once the students grasp the plan, they should have no trouble in supplying the details needed for the numerical solution.

The sphere is a three-dimensional analog of the circle. One form of its equation is $(x - h)^2 + (y - k)^2 + (z - t)^2 = r^2$. The similarity between the standard equations of the circle and the sphere suggests that spheres might well be studied concurrently with circles
if time permits so that the two- and three-dimensional analogies could be noted. If this is done, students will quickly come to realize that, once the coordinates of the center are known and the radius is known, the equation of the sphere can be written down just as easily as that of the circle, and conversely, that the standard equations of spheres and circles have analogous interpretations. Other two- and three-dimensional counterparts can be noted quickly,

even if only intuitively: the tangent line to a circle and the tangent plane to a sphere; the 3-parameter equation of a circle and the 4-parameter equation of a sphere; families of circles and of spheres through their respective points of intersection; the radical axis of two circles and the radical plane of two spheres; the sphere as a surface generated by rotating a circle about a diameter.

Further analogous loci

The circular cylinder is another three-dimensional analog of the circle. It is, in fact, a surface of revolution generated by revolving one of two parallel lines (the generatrix) about the other (the axis), the directrix being a circle in any plane perpendicular to the axis of the cylinder, with the axis through its center. Thus *each* right section is a circle. Therefore, if the axis is parallel, say, to the z axis, then the equation of the cylinder will be the same as the equation of its circular trace in the xy plane: $(x - h)^2 + (y - k)^2 = r^2$, because this holds true in every plane perpendicular to the axis of the cylinder regardless of its z coordinate. Such matters are well worth bringing to the attention of students, because of both their mathematical and their motivational value.

THE CONIC SECTIONS

Study of the conic sections has traditionally occupied a place of prominence in analytic geometry. It represents an important class of loci, and the study of these loci affords excellent opportunity for applying analytic methods, as well as for determining the properties of the loci and their equations. The latter should include awareness of both the common characteristics which bind them together in a class and the special characteristics which distinguish them from each other.

If the coordinate axes are chosen to give the equations of these loci in simplest form, if the definitions are given very clearly and are supplemented by good illustrations, and if the geometrical meanings and the notation of the characteristic elements are made perfectly clear, then any intelligent student should attain these

Importance of the teacher's role

objectives without serious difficulty. The explanations of the instructor, however, are very important here, as indeed they are throughout this course. Many students do not read very effectively. Moreover, diagrams in the textbooks are necessary and good as far as they go, but they are static. It is hard even to suggest motion and variation in a textbook diagram. On the other hand, this can be done well by the instructor sketching at the chalkboard and actually building the diagram and discussing it at the same time. In this way he can give the locus a dynamic character and can highlight the things he wants to emphasize much more effectively than an author can simply by placing a ready-made diagram in the textbook. Thus the ability of the instructor to chalk talk effectively is a tremendous asset, and it can do a great deal to promote understanding and facilitate learning.

Defining the conic sections

There is practically complete uniformity among textbooks in their definitions of the parabola, which invariably seem to be in terms of the equality of a point-to-point distance and a point-to-line distance. The ellipse and the hyperbola are initially defined in most textbooks in terms of the sum or difference of two point-to-point distances. But some authors prefer to define first the eccentricity in terms of the *ratio* of a point-to-point distance and a point-to-line distance, and then the parabola, ellipse, and hyperbola in terms of the eccentricity. Doubtless, each of these approaches has its advantages, and it is not possible to state categorically that either is better than any other.

Logically, the two approaches have equal validity. From the viewpoint of the immature learner, some considerations seem to favor the former. Perhaps this is because the sum or difference of two distances can be visualized and apprehended more readily than their ratio. Also, this way of defining these loci stresses the fact, from the outset, that an ellipse or hyperbola has two foci, while a parabola has only one. On the other hand, the directrixes play no part in this definition. In contrast, the second approach ensures that these concepts are established at the outset but gives no hint of the important property upon which the first definition is based. If time permits, it is well, at least for one of these curves, to give derivations from both definitions and to point out that the equations and the properties at which one arrives in the two cases are equivalent.

Some distinguishing characteristics of hyperbolas

Study of the hyperbola involves some features which have to be given special attention. In the ellipse both axes terminate in the curve itself; in the hyperbola they do not. Moreover, in the ellipse the major axis (the line segment joining the vertexes) is always longer than the minor axis; their counterparts (the transverse and conjugate axes) in the hyperbola are not subject to this condition. The length of the conjugate axis can be depicted only by means of an auxiliary rectangle, which in turn is determined by the curve and its asymptotes. The asymptotes themselves and their relation to the locus require special definition and study, and the considerations involved are often troublesome to students. The directrixes of a hyperbola lie between the vertexes, but the vertexes of an ellipse lie between the directrixes. Every hyperbola has associated with it a conjugate hyperbola, but there is no counterpart of this for the ellipse.

Students sometimes forget or confuse these numerous and special characteristics and the conventional notation generally used. It has been found helpful to have them make diagrams, showing these things geometrically in typical form, and actually refer to

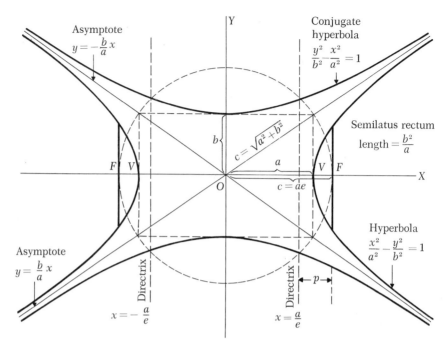

Figure 16-7
Specimen diagram of hyperbola.

these diagrams if they need to do so when working problems. A specimen diagram of this sort is shown in Fig. 16-7.

The general equation of the conics

The general equation of the second degree in x and y takes the form $Ax^2 + Bxy + Cy^2 + Dx + Ey + F = 0$ and always represents a conic section or a degenerate or limiting case of a conic, provided A, B, and C are not all zero. In an equation of this kind the coefficients can reveal much information about the nature of the locus, sometimes even through casual examination, if the students have been taught how to discover it. This fact needs to be emphasized. Thus, if $B = 0$ and $A = C \neq 0$, the curve will be a circle, while if $B = 0$ but A and C are not equal and neither is zero, the curve will be an ellipse or a hyperbola. If A and C have like signs, the curve will be an ellipse; if they have unlike signs, the curve will be a hyperbola. In either case the principal axes of the locus will be parallel to the coordinate axes. If $B = 0$ and either $A = 0$ or $C = 0$ but not both, the curve is a parabola, with its axis parallel to one of the coordinate axes.

Simplifying by translation of axes

If B, D, and E are all zero but A and C are not both zero, then the equation represents a conic in simplest form, with the axis or axes in one or both of the coordinate axes and the center (if neither A nor C is zero) at the origin. If $B = 0$ with $D \neq 0$ or $E \neq 0$, and A and C not both zero, the equation of the locus can be put into this simplest form by a suitable translation of axes, as described in connection with the equation of the circle.

On the other hand, if $B \neq 0$, then the locus is a conic, with its principal axis inclined at some angle θ to the x axis. In such cases the product term can be removed, and the equation correspondingly simplified by the transformation known as "rotation of axes." This is not inherently difficult, but it is a long, laborious process if done by direct substitution of the transformation formulas and the subsequent algebraic work necessary to determine the angle θ for which $B = 0$. The labor of simplifying such equations can be greatly reduced by having the students use the not-too-well-known relation $\tan 2\theta = B/(A - C)$. This should be proved, of course, and most textbooks contain proofs of this theorem, but the relation is often neglected, even though it provides an efficient means for simplifying such equations.

Simplifying by
rotation of axes

With one exception[1] both the translation and rotation of axes have the effect of changing the coordinates of every point on the locus, and consequently of changing the form of the equation of the locus. On the other hand, these transformations do not change the metric or geometrical properties of the locus at all. These properties are said to be *invariant* under the transformations indicated. It is also true that, when the equation is written in the general form

$$Ax^2 + Bxy + Cy^2 + Dx + Ey + F = 0$$

Invariant properties

the values of certain expressions involving some of the coefficients remain unaltered by these transformations. Thus the coefficients of the second-degree terms are invariant under the translation of axes. Under rotation, the sum of the coefficients $A + C$ of the terms in x^2 and y^2 is invariant, and the value of the expression $B^2 - 4AC$ is also invariant under rotation. In view of the fact, noted above, that A, B, and C are individually invariant under translation, it follows that the values of the expressions $A + C$ and $B^2 - 4AC$ are invariants under both transformations.

This rather remarkable fact is interesting, if for no other reason than just because it is so. Additional interest, however, attaches to the invariant $B^2 - 4AC$, because it provides a means of identifying the type of conic represented by the equation. If $B^2 - 4AC < 0$, the function represents an ellipse; if $B^2 - 4AC = 0$, a parabola is indicated; if $B^2 - 4AC > 0$, the locus is a hyperbola. This criterion does not distinguish between the typical conics and their

Identification
of conics

---

[1] The single exception is that the coordinates of the origin are not changed under rotation about the origin.

degenerate or limiting forms, but it is useful anyway, and students should not be left unaware of it.

The ellipse, parabola, and hyperbola can also be distinguished in terms of the eccentricity. When the eccentricity is being studied, it is helpful to students to have their attention called to the following criteria for identification: $0 < e < 1 \rightarrow$ ellipse; $e = 1 \rightarrow$ parabola; $e > 1 \rightarrow$ hyperbola. Indeed, in some textbooks, these criteria are used as definitions of the three types of conic section.

Lack of space makes it impossible to discuss all the important matters or all the interesting problems associated with the conic sections. To mention a few of them, there are the matters of examining the equation for evidence of symmetry, limitations on extent of the locus, axis intercepts, and horizontal and vertical asymptotes; the invariants in the equation under translation and rotation of axes; the interesting correspondence exhibited by the inequalities associated with the invariant $B^2 - 4AC$ and the eccentricity; the polar equations of the conics; and physical applications of the loci.

Each of these topics has its points of difficulty for students. However, the trouble lies not so much in the difficulty of the concepts or considerations themselves, as in the fact that most students cannot readily translate into concepts what they read in their textbooks. The role of the instructor as an expositor in helping to make these ideas emerge and stand out is most important. The instructor who is able to highlight key ideas and help his students crystallize them and make them stand out in their minds will have contributed greatly to their understanding.

The teacher's responsibility

The many interesting aspects and properties of the conics could easily lead one to devote a disproportionate amount of time to their study. It must not be forgotten, however, that there are other parts of the course which are also interesting and important and which must not be neglected. Therefore, in the study of the conic sections, it may be necessary at times to sacrifice the merely interesting to make time for topics that are relatively more important in relation to subsequent work.

It is to be hoped, however, that time can be found to give some attention to the three-dimensional counterparts of the conic sections, especially to the conicoids of revolution. These surfaces are important in calculus, physics, and various applications of mathematics. Without spending a great deal of time on this, students can gain considerable understanding of such matters as algebraic criteria for identification, symmetries of the surfaces, equations of right sections, extent, and traces in planes parallel to the coordinate planes. In their subsequent work in calculus students will benefit largely by having clear concepts of these things. Teachers are urged to try to plan so that some time can be devoted to them in this course.

Related loci in 3-space

FAMILIES OF CONICS

In a previous section attention was called to the fact that the equation of the general linear function, $y = mx + b$, involves two parameters, m and b. Algebraically, this means that there must be two distinct conditions on x and y to give two independent equations which can be solved for unique values of m and b. When specific values are determined and assigned to both parameters, the resulting equation defines one particular line. Geometrically, this means that two distinct points or any equivalent set of two independent conditions determine a unique straight line in the plane. If, however, a specific value is assigned to only one of the parameters, there results an equation which defines an entire family of lines. If m is assigned a value, the resulting equation defines a family of parallel lines, each having the assigned slope. If b is assigned a value, the resulting equation defines the family of lines intersecting in the common fixed point $(0,b)$. Similarly, the general equation of the circle, $(x - h)^2 + (y - k)^2 = r^2$, involves the three parameters h, k, and r. Assignment of a number to any one parameter places one restriction on the set of circles defined by the equation. Assigning a number to a second parameter imposes a second restriction on the set, and if a number is assigned also to the third parameter, this imposes a final restriction on the set, and the equation selects and defines one particular circle out of all the circles in the plane.

Parameters and families of circles

Just as it takes two independent conditions to determine the parameter values for a particular straight line in the plane, so it takes three independent conditions to determine the parameter values for a particular circle in the plane. Geometrically, this means that it takes three noncollinear points, or some equivalent set of three independent conditions, to fix a particular circle in the plane.

Like considerations apply to the equations of all conic sections. The equation of the general conic is $Ax^2 + Bxy + Cy^2 + Dx + Ey + F = 0$, where A, B, and C cannot all be zero. Since all coefficients may be divided by any nonzero coefficient, it is evident that the equation contains five independent constants, or parameters. Assignment of values to any number of these parameters imposes specific restrictions on the characteristics of the conic represented. For example, if $A = C \neq 0$ and $B = 0$, the equation may be written $x^2 + y^2 + px + qy + s = 0$, or in equivalent form, $(x - h)^2 + (y - k)^2 = r^2$.

Parameters and families of conics

Thus it takes five independent conditions to determine the parameter values of a specific conic. Geometrically, this means that it takes five distinct points, no three of which are collinear, or some equivalent set of five independent conditions, to fix a particular conic in the plane. Since a circle may be thought of as a special case of the ellipse, a good question to pose for consider-

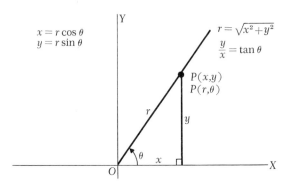

Figure 16-8

ation is: What are the five independent conditions necessary to derive the equation of a particular circle from the general equation of the second degree in two variables?

Too often textbooks and teachers neglect to focus attention deliberately and explicitly on the generalizing effect of the parameters and the restricting effect of replacing any of the parameters by particular constants. The concept of families of curves and of the role of parameters in relation to the descriptions of families of curves is important to a full understanding of analytic geometry. Teachers have a responsibility for bringing this concept out of the shadow of vagueness and for giving their students a clear appreciation of its meaning and its implications.

MORE ON POLAR COORDINATES

In Chapter 15 polar coordinates were defined and discussed in connection with complex numbers and the complex plane. The equations for transforming expressions from rectangular to polar form, and vice versa, were developed, and their use illustrated.

Polar equations are sometimes simpler than rectangular equations

Polar coordinates have an important role in analytic geometry too, because the equations of some loci are simpler in polar form than in rectangular form. Also, some are derived more easily in polar form and yield their implications more easily. Thus $r = 5$ is simpler than $x^2 + y^2 = 25$, though they are equivalent equations of a circle; and $\theta = 126°$ is equivalent to $y = x \tan 126°$. (See Fig. 16-8.)

Work with polar equations involves (1) carefully plotting the graph of the locus; (2) trying to see what, if any, properties of the locus can be inferred from the equation itself (these may include such things as intercepts on the axes, symmetries, extent, asymptotes, and even the form of the locus); (3) noting additional properties, if any, that are revealed by the graph but which were not inferred from the equation; and (4) discussing the locus.

Graphing a polar equation

Typically, constructing a graph requires a point-by-point plotting of enough points to give a good sketch of the locus, and this in turn requires the construction of a table of values of θ and r. Except for the simplest equations, this table may need several columns. For example, let it be required to plot the graph of

$$r = 1 + 4 \cos 2\theta$$

The table should be similar to Table 16-2.

TABLE 16-2

θ	2θ	$\cos 2\theta$	$4 \cos 2\theta$	$1 + 4 \cos 2\theta$
0°	0°	1	4	5
30°	60°	½	2	3
45°	90°	0	0	1
60°	120°	−½	−2	−1

A special caution to students

Many students have to be shown how to plan and construct such a table. Also, they frequently need to be reminded that, as in the present case, even if r is given as a function of 2θ, the values of r must be plotted against the corresponding values of θ itself, not against the values of 2θ. The use of polar-coordinate paper facilitates the actual plotting, though good sketches can often be made by use of a protractor, or even by careful estimates of the sizes of the angles.

Certain additional considerations may be helpful to students in determining characteristics of some loci given in polar coordinates, and they should be emphasized:

Some helpful hints for graphing

1   If r occurs only in the form r^2, then the curve will be symmetrical with respect to the pole.
2   If an equivalent equation is obtained when θ is replaced by $180° - \theta$, then the curve is symmetrical with respect to the 90° axis. An example of this situation occurs with the locus of the equation $r = 3 \sin \theta$. It may be noted that this particular replacement is a sufficient but not a necessary condition for symmetry about the 90° axis, since the same symmetry will result if we replace θ by $540° - \theta$, $900° - \theta$, $-(180° + \theta)$, etc.
3   If an equivalent equation is obtained when θ is replaced by $-\theta$, the curve is symmetrical with respect to the polar axis. Thus the locus of $r = 3 \cos \theta$ is symmetrical in this way. From considerations such as those above, it can be seen that this particular replacement also is a sufficient but not a necessary condition for symmetry about the polar axis.

4   The intercepts on the lines whose equations are $\theta = 0°$, $90°$, $180°$, $270°$, and $360°$ can usually be found readily.

5   Sometimes values of θ for which r becomes infinite can be found easily, and this fact may be very helpful in sketching.

6   Finding maximum and minimum values of r, with the corresponding values of θ, can be helpful in determining the extent of the curve. Limitations on the extent of the curve may also often be determined by solving the equation for r in terms of θ to see whether there are any values of θ that will make r imaginary. Thus, for the locus $r^2 = \cos \theta$, we find that r is imaginary for $90° < \theta < 270°$.

7   Sometimes the form of the locus is revealed by converting the equation from polar to rectangular form. Thus the equation $r = 10 \cos \theta$ becomes $x^2 + y^2 = 10x$, which is clearly the equation of a circle.

Solution sets for simultaneous equations

To determine points of intersection of the graphs of two polar equations, one may solve the equations simultaneously for the two variables, as is done with equations in rectangular form. However, in seeking common solutions for two polar equations, it is always advisable to plot the graphs of the equations. This may suggest at once solutions that can be tested directly in the equations. But even more important, it will sometimes reveal one or more points of intersection that are not brought to light in the algebraic solution of the equations. A simple example of this is the pair of equations $r = 2 \sin \theta$ and $r = 2 \cos \theta$. Algebraic solution gives $\tan \theta = 1$, $\theta = 45°$, $r = \sqrt{2}$. Thus it yields only a single point of intersection, $(\sqrt{2}, 45°)$. The graph will show, however, that the pole also lies on both curves.

PARAMETRIC EQUATIONS

In preceding sections we have discussed parameters as special auxiliary variables used as generalizing agents in the equations of loci. For example, in the equation $x^2/a^2 + y^2/b^2 = 1$, a and b are both parameters. When particular numbers are assigned to both a and b, the equation represents a particular ellipse, but unless values of both a and b are specified, the equation represents a whole family of ellipses.

A new usage for "parameter"

In connection with parametric equations, however, the term "parameter" is used in a somewhat different sense. It is still an auxiliary variable, but here it is used as an "extra" variable, in terms of which the coordinate variables are defined. Consider, for example, the equations $x = 3t - 2$, $y = 2t + 1$. Thus both x and y are functions of t. If the parameter t is eliminated between the two defining equations, the rectangular equation $3y - 2x = 7$ is obtained, and this is immediately identified as the equation of a straight line.

In most of the work which students will have had previously, the equation of a locus will have exhibited a direct and explicit relation between the dependent and independent variables, the one being expressible as a function of the other. It is not at all hard for students to recognize that each of the original variables, say, x and y, may in certain cases be defined as some function of a third variable; it simply is a new idea to which they need to become accustomed. The best way to bring about this feeling of familiarity is by having tables and graphs made for several rather simple cases. Such pairs of equations as $x = t$, $y = 1/t$ or $x = t^2$, $y = 3 + t$ can be used to illustrate how the table of values is to be formed and the corresponding values of x and y are to be used to plot points on the locus.

Eliminating the
parameter

Converting a pair of parametric equations into an equivalent equation in rectangular form by eliminating the parameter is usually interesting to students. It strengthens the feeling of a direct relation between the original variables, even though it may not be apparent in the parametric forms in which they are both expressed. For some loci this rectangular form of the equation may be simple. For example, the parametric equations $x = 5 \cos \theta$, $y = 5 \sin \theta$, yield the equation $x^2 + y^2 = 25$; this equation is recognizable immediately as a circle with center at the origin and radius 5 units. But even though the rectangular form will not always be simple, students should work out a number of such cases as a means of giving explicit form to the implicit relation between the original variables. A useful by-product of this is some excellent incidental practice in algebraic manipulation and equation solving.

Reasons for using
parametric
equations

Students often ask, "Why use the parametric form at all? Why not simply use the rectangular form or the polar form?" In answer to this question it should be pointed out that there may be several possible advantages in using the parametric equations. For one thing, the parametric equations may sometimes convey more information than the rectangular equations, as in the case of the trajectory of a projectile. Thus they are often needed in physics and engineering. Again, in calculus the derivatives of some functions can be obtained more easily from parametric equations of the loci than from the rectangular equations. However, the principal reason for the use of parametric equations in analytic geometry lies in the fact that for certain loci the parametric equations are simpler than the rectangular equations. Indeed, for some loci, parametric equations can be set up directly from the geometrical descriptions of the loci, although it may be impossible to set up the rectangular equations for the loci directly. In such cases the rectangular equation may be derived from the parametric equations if the parameter can be eliminated. The cycloid curves are fairly simple examples of such loci.

SLOW LEARNERS AND FAST LEARNERS
IN ANALYTIC GEOMETRY

It can be expected that most students who get as far in mathematics as analytic geometry will be students who have a considerable amount of native aptitude for mathematics, who have attained a reasonably good command of high school algebra, geometry, and trigonometry, and who are seriously interested in going on to further work in mathematics. One does not expect to find many really poor students in analytic geometry. On the other hand, there are sure to be some to whom concepts and understandings come less readily than to others. For such students, to get full benefit from the course, the teacher needs to exhibit a high degree of pedagogical insight and skill in his teaching. When a student gets bogged down in his work and is unable to get ahead on his own, the teacher needs to be able to diagnose difficulties quickly, and having spotted the key roadblocks and suspected the cause, to lead the student by astute questioning to discover the way to clarification of his understanding. With the proper help, most students can accomplish this in most cases. This heuristic approach can also do much to bolster the student's self-confidence, which in itself is a strong motivating factor.

By contrast, it is not unusual to find some students in an analytic geometry class to whom comprehensions come quickly and easily; who become bored with much routine work and who are capable of, and would enjoy, some independent study of matters associated with the subject but not included among the work expected of the whole class. For example, consider the equations for the distance between two points in 1-space, 2-space, and 3-space. The forms are completely analogous, differing only in the number of variables involved in the three cases. A keen student will quickly note that the number of variables involved in each case is the same as the number of dimensions of the space for which the equation holds. This generalizing thought may easily suggest that similar formulas might be used to define, by analogy, distances in 4-space, 5-space, or n-space. Thus a bright student might be led to discover for himself that an abstraction for which no physical counterpart can be exhibited can still have a mathematical meaning and can make mathematical sense. Understanding this is in itself a worthwhile intellectual achievement.

Moreover, with this as a beginning, it would be strange if a bright student did not become interested in following other variants of this line of thought or pursuing related lines of thought suggested by key concepts. He might decide to see if, by starting with the general equation of a line in 2-space, an analogous equation in three variables would be the general equation of a plane in 3-space, and if so, whether any physical models could be found which are represented by the 4-, 5-, or n-variable analogs of the generalized equation of the line in 2-space. Or since the sphere is a three-dimensional analog of the two-dimensional circle, he might become interested in writing four-, five-, or n-dimensional analogs of the equation of the circle to represent "loci" in four-, five-, and n-dimensional spaces. Also, he might find other analogies which he would be interested in investigating along similar lines.

Eventually, as a result of his investigations and conjectures, the student should be in a position to make an interesting report to the class or to the teacher on, say, some aspects of n-space. Any student who can do this sort of thing through independent study, without neglecting the understandings and skills expected of the class as a whole, will have attained not only a deeper insight into an aspect of mathematics than he would otherwise have gained, but also a powerful motivation for acquiring depth insights into mathematical ideas in general.

Some suitable topics for independent study

Other topics might be suggested to students as being suitable for special independent study in connection with analytic geometry, but space permits listing only some of these here. Among them can be mentioned cylindrical coordinates; spherical coordinates; physical applications of the parabola, ellipse, hyperbola, and catenary; inequalities in analytic geometry; graphs of the rose curves (several); parameters and families of lines, of circles, and of spheres; traces of conicoids and other surfaces in planes parallel to or coincident with the coordinate planes; the rolling curves (cardioid, cycloid, and trochoid, epicycloid, and hypocycloid); and projections on coordinate axes and coordinate planes. These are but suggestive. Other topics appropriate for special independent work will undoubtedly occur to teachers or to students.

EXERCISES

In many of the following exercises you are asked to explain, illustrate, or discuss certain things. The intention is that you should do so as you would with a high school class in analytic geometry, giving special emphasis to those matters you consider most important for students to understand.

1 If (x_1, y_1) and (x_2, y_2) are two points in the coordinate plane and d is the distance between them, then $d^2 = (x_1 - x_2)^2 + (y_1 - y_2)^2$, and also $d^2 = (x_2 - x_1)^2 + (y_2 - y_1)^2$. Explain why the order of the subscripts makes no difference in this case.

2 It has been said that one really understands the method of analytic geometry when he has attained a genuine appreciation of the interrelations between geometric loci and their algebraic or analytic representation. Comment on this.

3 Explain how you would prove to a class that there is no point in the xy plane which lies on all three of the loci defined by these equations: $4x + 7y = 1$; $x = 3y + 5$; $y = 3x^2$.

4 Explain how to set up the equation for the locus of points in the xy plane which are 3 units farther from the point $(2,3)$ than from the point $(9,6)$.

5 Enumerate five types of pairs of sufficient conditions, any pair of which is sufficient to determine a straight line in a coordinate plane; and for each of these pairs explain how to determine the equation of the line. Discuss the advantage of knowing how to interpret and to use these different forms. Be specific.

6 Using well-drawn diagrams, explain how to derive the two-point, symmetric, and

parametric equations of a line in 3-space. Discuss in detail the direction angles, direction cosines, and direction numbers of the line.

7 Describe the 2-space locus represented by each of the following:

$$y = 3 + \tfrac{1}{2}x$$
$$y < 3 + \tfrac{1}{2}x$$
$$y > 3 + \tfrac{1}{2}x$$
$$y \leqslant 3 + \tfrac{1}{2}x$$

8 The following equations are among the type equations of a line in the xy plane:

$$x/a + y/b = 1$$
$$y = mx + b$$
$$x \cos \alpha + y \sin \alpha = p$$

In each of these, identify the parameters and explain what information each parameter gives about the line.

9 Why does the family of lines represented by $y = mx + b$ not include any line perpendicular to the x axis? Does it include all other lines in the plane? Explain.

10 Explain how to derive the normal equation of a plane in 3-space.

11 Let θ be the angle between two rays $\overrightarrow{PR}$ and $\overrightarrow{PQ}$ in 2-space. Show how to derive a formula for $\cos \theta$, and so, by implication, for $m\angle\theta$, in terms of the direction cosines of $\overrightarrow{PR}$ and $\overrightarrow{PQ}$. Repeat, letting $\overrightarrow{PR}$ and $\overrightarrow{PQ}$ be rays in 3-space. What points of difficulty would you expect students to have with these derivations, and why? How would you counter these difficulties?

12 The equation $10x + 3y - 2 = 0$ is the equation of a line in the xy plane. It is also the equation of a certain plane in 3-space. Explain, and tell all you can about this plane.

13 Write the equation of the family of circles in the xy plane whose centers are at $(-3,8)$.

14 Describe the families of circles represented by the following: (a) $(x - 5)^2 + (y - b)^2 = 4$; (b) $(x - a)^2 + (y - b)^2 \neq 12$.

15 Given a circle C and a point P outside the circle, both in the xy plane. Explain how to find the length of a tangent from P to C.

16 What advantage is there in reducing the equations of straight lines, circles, spheres, conic sections, etc., to standard forms? Illustrate and discuss the advantage.

17 The equation $x^2/25 + y^2/9 = 1$ represents an ellipse in the xy plane. What information about the ellipse can be inferred directly from the equation? Be specific. Can the lengths of the latera recta be obtained from this information? The extent of the ellipse? The eccentricity? Discuss.

18 If the equation of an ellipse in the xy plane is $6x^2 + 25y^2 = 400$, explain how to get the equation of the ellipsoid of revolution formed when the curve is revolved (a) about its major axis; (b) about its minor axis. Discuss your procedures fully, and tell all you can about the surfaces generated.

19 For each of the two cases in exercise 18, give the equation of the trace of the surface (a) in each of the coordinate planes; (b) in the plane $z = 3$; (c) in the plane $x = 2$; (d) in the plane $y = 1$. Discuss all these cases fully.

20 The general equation of the second degree in x and y can be written in the form $Ax^2 + Bxy + Cy^2 + Dx + Ey + F = 0$. Give the name of the locus in each of the following cases: $B = 0$, $A > 0$, $C < 0$; $B = 0$, $A = C \neq 0$; $B = 0$, $A > 0$, $C > 0$, $A \neq C$; $B = C = 0$, $A \neq 0$. Are the principal axes of all these curves necessarily parallel to the coordinate axes? Explain.

21 In the general equation of exercise 20, suppose $B \neq 0$ and $0 < A < C$. What information does this provide about the principal axis of the locus? Can the locus be a circle? Explain.

22 Derive and explain the transformation formulas for the translation of axes and for the rotation of axes in a coordinate plane. Explain and illustrate how these transformations can sometimes be used to simplify the equations of certain loci.

23 What is the primary reason for the translation and/or rotation of axes in the study of the conic sections? Be clear, and illustrate by examples.

24 In the general equation of the second degree in two variables, the expression $B^2 - 4AC$ is invariant under translation and rotation of axes. Explain how this invariant provides a means for identifying the kind of conic section represented by any particular second-degree equation in x and y.

25 Transform $r = 5 - 3 \cos \theta$ into rectangular coordinates. Note that the polar equation is the simpler one of the two.

26 Explain how to find several pairs of polar coordinates for the point P whose rectangular coordinates are $(1,1)$.

27 Let two loci be represented, respectively,

by the polar equations $r = \cos \theta$ and $r = \sin \theta$. For $0 \leq \theta \leq 2\pi$, the simultaneous solution of these equations gives $\theta = \pi/4$ and $\theta = 5\pi/4$. These in turn give $r = \sqrt{2}$ and $r = -\sqrt{2}$. Explain why $(\sqrt{2}, \pi/4)$ and $(-\sqrt{2}, 5\pi/4)$ are not two different points of intersection of the loci, and see if you can find another point of intersection not revealed by the simultaneous solution of these polar equations. (*Hint:* Graph the loci.)

28 Explain in detail how to plot in polar coordinates the curves whose equations are, respectively, $r = \cos \theta$ and $r^2 = \cos 3\theta$.

29 Discuss the locus of the equation

$$r = 2/(1 + \cos \theta)$$

as regards (*a*) intercepts on the polar and 90° axes; (*b*) symmetry; (*c*) extent.

30 Prepare or select three good examples which you could use effectively to illustrate how to eliminate the parameter from a pair or triple of parametric equations, and thus obtain the rectangular equation of the locus which they represent. Discuss one of these in detail. Outline your plan

for attacking the problem at the outset, and explain the reasoning on which it is based.

31 Let the points $P(x,y)$ be defined by the parametric equations $x = a \cos t$, $y = b \sin t$. Prove that if either $0 < a < b$ or $0 < b < a$, then the locus defined by these parametric equations is an ellipse. See if you can find a way to construct the locus (both cases) by geometric methods. Describe the locus in case $0 < a = b$.

32 Plot the graph of the locus defined by the parametric equations $x = 3 - 4 \cos \theta$, $y = 1 + 2 \sin \theta$. Then, by eliminating the parameter θ, show that the locus is an ellipse, and discuss it fully.

33 In studying the geometrical properties of objects in 3-space (lines, planes, conicoids, surfaces of revolution), students have trouble in interpreting such things as projections on the coordinate planes; direction angles, direction cosines, and direction numbers of a ray; and equations of traces in the coordinate planes or in planes parallel to these. Do you think this may be largely due to poorly drawn diagrams? Discuss.

BIBLIOGRAPHY

Bradley, James A.: Some Remarks Concerning Families of Circles and Radical Axes, *Mathematics Teacher*, **57** (1964), 533–536.

Byrkit, Donald R.: Distance from a Point to a Line Revisited, *School Science and Mathematics*, **68** (1968), 145–147.

Coxford, Arthur: Classroom Inquiry into the Conic Sections, *Mathematics Teacher*, **60** (1967), 315–322.

Dotson, W. G., Jr.: On the Shape of Plane Curves, *Mathematics Teacher*, **62** (1969), 91–94.

Garfunkel, J.: Exploring Geometric Maxima and Minima, *Mathematics Teacher*, **62** (1969), 85–90.

Gelford, I. M., et al.: The Method of Coordinates (Cambridge, Mass.: The M.I.T. Press, 1967). (Translated and adapted.)

Haddock, Glen, and Donald W. Hight: Geometric Techniques for Graphing, *Mathematics Teacher*, **59** (1966), 2–5.

———— and David Moon: Isometries of Euclidean 1-space, *Bulletin of the Kansas Association of Teachers of Mathematics*, April, 1968, pp. 26–27, 31.

Moser, James M.: Mathematics by Analogy, *Mathematics Teacher*, **61** (1968), 374–376.

Perisho, Clarence R.: The Use of Transformations in Deriving Equations of Common Geometric Figures, *Mathematics Teacher*, **58** (1965), 386–392.

Read, Cecil B.: The Co-ordinate System of Descartes, *Mathematics Teacher*, **54** (1961), 567–569.

Schaff, Mary Ellen: Discovery-type Investigation for Coordinate Geometry Students, *Mathematics Teacher*, **59** (1966), 458–460.

Shuster, Seymour: "Elementary Vector Geometry" (New York: John Wiley & Sons, Inc., 1962).

Sister Maurice Marie Byrne: A Geometric Approach to the Conic Sections, *Mathematics Teacher*, **59** (1966), 348–350.

Sitomer, Harry: Coordinate Geometry with an Affine Approach, *Mathematics Teacher*, **57** (1964), 404–405.

SMSG: "Geometry with Coordinates," parts I and II, (Pasadena, Calif.: A.C. Vroman, Inc., 1965).

_____: "Analytic Geometry" (Pasadena, Calif., A. C. Vroman, Inc., 1965).

Szabo, Steven: Some Results on Quadrilaterals with Perpendicular Diagonals, *Mathematics Teacher*, **60** (1967), 336–338.

"The Twelfth-grade Pre-college Mathematics Program" (Washington, D.C.: National Council of Teachers of Mathematics, 1965), pp. 1–3. (Pamphlet: papers presented at a joint conference of MAA and NCTM, January, 1965.)

Viertel, William K.: Why Not Relate the Conic Sections to the Cone?, *Mathematics Teacher*, **62** (1969), 13–15.

Willoughby, S. S.: Algebraic Geometry for High School Pupils, *American Mathematical Monthly*, **73** (1966), 650–654.

seventeen | the teaching of calculus

In no other area is the ferment of the mathematics curriculum more in evidence than in the role and grade placement of elementary calculus. During this century it has moved from a place in the upper division as the capstone of an undergraduate college program to the sophomore, and finally the freshman, level. One of the strongest factors in the recent "revolution" in secondary school mathematics curriculum was the desire of college and university mathematicians that their students be prepared to enter calculus courses as soon as they entered college.

Pressure to begin the study of calculus earlier

Some of the new curriculums make it possible for the student to cover, by the end of the junior year of the high school, the material formerly covered by the end of grade 12. This is accomplished in part by including in the year of geometry whatever solid geometry is deemed needed, and by including in the second course in algebra the minimum essentials of analytic trigonometry. For good measure, a smattering of analytic geometry is included in one or both of these years. This leaves grade 12 open for experimentation and innovation.

New curriculums leave grade 12 open for innovation in study

A number of one- and two-semester courses have been suggested as appropriate for the twelfth year. Analytic geometry, matrix algebra, modern abstract algebra, elementary functions, and probability and statistics, all have their adherents. But it is inevitable that the one course most certain to be proposed and most certain to cause controversy is calculus.

Suggested twelfth-grade courses

Some issues important to the program of effective instruction in calculus are the problems of organization, presentation, and selecting subject matter. There are arguments, with supporting textbooks, that the first course in calculus should be a coordinated program of calculus and analytic geometry. Just as strong arguments, and with supporting texts, call for a course devoted entirely to the development of calculus concepts and techniques, preceded by a separately organized strong course in analytic geometry. Similarly, there are those who argue for the physical orientation out of which the basic concepts, principles, and techniques of differentiation and integration are shown to evolve. Others argue just as strongly that first one should develop such calculus properties in their theoretical structure and then proceed to the me-

Calculus, or calculus with analytic geometry?

chanics of their physical application. Regardless of which of these two widely different instructional patterns is followed, a strong mixture of an intuitive approach, followed by a rigorous deductive treatment, seems to be the generally accepted pattern of development.

In such a context of debatable issues related to grade placement and instructional pattern, it is not surprising that the present decade finds a professional literature much richer than in previous years in articles dealing with problems related to the teaching of calculus.

CALCULUS IN HIGH SCHOOL

Since the turn of the century, various leaders in mathematical education have advocated that elements of the calculus be introduced in the last year of the senior high school. It was not contemplated that this work should comprise the complete course in differential and integral calculus usually offered in the junior college. It was thought that such a course would require more adequate mastery of algebra, trigonometry, and analytic geometry than could be reasonably expected at the end of the eleventh grade. Rather, the idea was that just as there are certain parts of trigonometry which are simple enough to be understood successfully by junior high school students, so there are certain parts of calculus which can be understood by twelfth-grade students, even if they do not have all the prerequisites for a complete systematic course.

Early recommendations for high school calculus

This position was well stated in the suggestions of the National Committee on Mathematical Requirements regarding calculus in the high school.[1] The committee envisioned the calculus course as one in only "relatively strong schools" and "for a selected group of students." The course was to be limited to algebraic polynomials and was to develop the idea of limit, of slope, and of velocity.

It should also be borne in mind that the suggestion of including elementary calculus is not intended for all schools nor for all teachers in any school. It is not intended to connect in any direct way with college entrance requirements. The future college student will have ample opportunity for calculus later. The capable boy or girl who is not to have the college work ought not on that account to be prevented from learning something of the use of this powerful tool. The applications of elementary calculus to simple concrete problems are far more abundant and interesting than those of algebra. The necessary technique is extremely simple.[2]

---

[1] Report of the National Committee on Mathematical Requirements, "The Reorganization of Mathematics in Secondary Education" (Boston: Houghton Mifflin Company, 1923), pp. 57–59.
[2] *Ibid.*, pp. 54–55.

Recommendations
of the Joint
Commission

This Report of the National Committee gave some impetus to the inclusion of certain concepts and techniques from calculus in the high school program. The attempts, however, were scattered and sporadic, and while a certain amount of interest and success was reported in some instances, there appears to have been little general enthusiasm for the idea. No important subsequent report made any recommendation concerning a course in calculus for the high school until the Joint Commission, in its 1940 report, suggested "introducing study of differentiation, limited to polynomials, with applications to slopes, maxima and minima, rates of change, velocity, acceleration, and related problems" in connection with algebra in the twelfth grade.[3] Much more recently (1959) the College Entrance Examination Board's Commission on Mathematics recommended ". . . that well-staffed schools offer their ablest students a year of college-level calculus and analytic geometry as recommended in the Advanced Placement Program." It also pointed out that few high schools at present are sufficiently well staffed to teach a full course of college-level calculus effectively. The commission deprecated the practice of exposing high school students to formal calculus for a short time.[4] Concurrently with this report the Secondary School Curriculum Committee issued its report in which a college-preparatory program for grades 9 to 12 was proposed. As a portion of the recommendation for the twelfth grade, this sentence occurred:[5] "Some schools might find desirable a strong course in analytic geometry and calculus as preparation for the Advanced Placement examinations." This proposal was received with mixed feelings.[6]

A recent report which deals with this major problem is that of the Cambridge Conference on School Mathematics.[7] In their discussion of the mathematics curriculum for grades 7 to 12 they proposed two topical outlines for the content of the program.[8] Each outline contains "a logically complete course" in analysis (calculus) for grades 11 and 12, with one of them being prefaced on a "heuristic and brief introduction to the calculus in the 9th grade." This entire program for grades 7 to 12 is posited on one

In the left margin:

**CEEB recommends
college-level
calculus for able
students**

**Cambridge Con-
ference proposes
an intuitive course
for grade 9**

---

[3] Joint Commission of the Mathematical Association of America and the National Council of Teachers of Mathematics, "The Place of Mathematics in Secondary Education," *Fifteenth Yearbook* (Washington, D.C.: National Council of Teachers of Mathematics, 1940), pp. 97–98.
[4] College Entrance Examination Board, Report of the Commission on Mathematics (New York: College Entrance Examination Board, 1959), pp. 14–15.
[5] The Secondary Mathematics Curriculum, Report of the Secondary School Curriculum Committee, *Mathematics Teacher*, **52** (1959), 405–406.
[6] See, for example, articles by Allendoerfer, Beninati, Blank, Ferguson, Hildebrandt, McKillip, Neeley, and Rising, listed in the Bibliography of this chapter.
[7] "Goals for School Mathematics," Report of the Cambridge Conference on School Mathematics (Boston: Houghton Mifflin Company, 1963).
[8] *Ibid.*, pp. 43–46.

proposed for the elementary grades (kindergarten through sixth) which is designed to give the student "a thorough grounding in both arithmetic and intuitive geometry." The philosophy supporting this entire program seems to be that the high school program in mathematics should provide: (1) "the foundations upon which applications to the sciences, engineering, and mathematics itself are built"; (2) opportunity for students to become informed in those areas of mathematics which "have become part of what every person should know in order to understand the complex world in which he lives"; and (3) opportunity for students who drop out of the mathematical program of instruction to develop an understanding and appreciation of the structure and usefulness of mathematics.

Twofold aspect of mastery

IMPORTANCE OF EMPHASIZING FUNDAMENTAL CONCEPTS

Both understanding and skill are necessary

Any thorough mastery of the calculus has two fundamental aspects, namely, (1) the understanding of the basic concepts involved in the development of the subject and familiarity with the many special formulas needed and (2) the acquisition of ability and ready facility in the use of these special formulas and methods. Both are fundamental to a balanced mastery of the subject.

Development of meaning is not memorizing formulas and definitions

It is possible for an individual to acquire a high degree of skill in the latter aspect of the work without understanding much about what he is doing or why he is doing it. Indeed, this situation is often found. The relatively enormous amount of formal work that must be done begets a tendency on the part of instructors to emphasize this aspect, often to the detriment of understanding. Many students acquire high proficiency in performing difficult feats of formal differentiation or integration without having any clear conception of the meaning of a derivative or an integral or of the real significance of what they are doing. Proficiency in this mechanical aspect of the work, although it is indispensable, tends to produce complacency on the part of both student and teacher. This is not unnatural, but it is unfortunate. Such a one-sided development indicates not a balanced mastery of the subject, but rather mere proficiency in rote performance. It is precisely the sort of thing against which so much criticism of the teaching of elementary algebra has been directed. The reason we hear so little of this criticism leveled at the teaching of calculus is simply that the matter of improving the teaching of college mathematics has as yet received too little attention, at least in the way of published suggestions.

It should be pointed out that understanding of basic concepts has no necessary relationship to memorizing formal definitions and rigorous proofs. The student's ability to state correctly the delta-epsilon definition of a limit is no guarantee that he knows what a limit is. This part of the work can also become perfunctory and mechanical. In a first course in calculus, major effort should be directed toward development of clear understanding of basic concepts. There are varying degrees of rigor. Mathematics is good mathematics only if the standard of rigor is appropriate to the learner. Fourth-grade arithmetic taught with graduate-school rigor is abominable fourth-grade arithmetic. The level of rigor for a beginning calculus class is too high if and whenever it gets in the way of development of clear and correct, even if intuitive, fundamental concepts.

The level of rigor
must be
appropriate

It is true that most of the actual work of differentiation and integration must be carried on by formal methods and that these must be learned and mastered by the students. At the same time, these formal methods and devices can be developed in such a way as to give them meaning, and this should be regarded as a major responsibility of the instructor. The student who gains a real understanding of the meanings of function,[9] variation, increment, limits,[10] infinitesimals, continuity, derivative, rates, maxima and minima, an integral as an antiderivative and as a summation, indefinite and definite integrals, and other basic concepts will derive a far richer experience and a far more adequate basis for further work in either applied or theoretical mathematics than the student who works by rote alone.

Importance of
understanding

THE TEACHING OF VARIABLES AND LIMITS

Variables, limits, and infinitesimals are primary concepts in calculus, and serious effort should be made to ensure that the students will have a good understanding of their meanings. Normally, the students will have gained considerable familiarity with the meanings of "function" and "variable" through their previous work in trigonometry and algebra. Care should be taken that variables and constants are thought of as symbols, and not as quantities: a *variable* is a symbol which may represent any one of a set of values called its *domain,* or *replacement set;* a *constant* is a symbol which represents the same value throughout a particular discussion, or maybe better said, if the replacement set for a symbol contains only one element, the symbol is called a *constant.*

Variables and
constants are
symbols

The student should become familiar with the concept of a set (domain, range) of values and with the nature of, and the

[9] See "Insights into Modern Mathematics," *Twenty-third Yearbook* (Washington, D.C.: National Council of Teachers of Mathematics, 1957), chap. 8.
[10] *Ibid.,* chap. 7.

Kinds of constants distinction between, *arbitrary constants* (*parameters*) and *absolute constants.*

It is important that a clear distinction between independent and dependent variables be made. Furthermore, when these concepts are used in the context of a defined functional relation, they should Domain and range be associated, respectively, with the domain and the range of the function.

Consider a set of ordered pairs (x,y), and define a function as a rule which specifies the functional relationship between the members of the set of first elements x and the members of the set of second elements y, or which associates with each element of the set of first elements exactly one element from the set of second elements. Then a symbol (in this case x) which may represent any member of the set of first elements is called the *independent variable,* and a symbol (in this case y) which may represent any member of the set of second elements is called the *dependent variable.*

Two conceptions of The function itself (defined above as a rule) may also be thought a function of as the set of ordered pairs (x,y), where for each x in the domain of the function (i.e., each value of the independent variable) the corresponding element y in the range of the function (i.e., the corresponding value of the dependent variable) is determined by the rule which defines the function. Thus the dependent variable represents the set of values of the function over its domain.

In spite of the presumption of familiarity with these notions, it is advisable at the beginning of the course in calculus to review them, giving numerous and varied illustrations involving both algebraic and transcendental functions. It is not anticipated that students will have much difficulty in establishing these concepts, but as a means of ensuring understanding, some practice should be given in identifying independent and dependent variables and in building tables and making graphs to illustrate the variation of each of these and the relationship of functions to their independent variables. The student should also become thoroughly familiar with the generalized functional notation. He should learn to recognize $f(x)$ in all its variations and with all its implications. f(x) has two He should come to think of f in $f(x)$ as a symbol to represent the interpretations rule of correspondence that maps each replacement for the independent variable into its image, an element of the range. In the symbol $f(x)$, the x is simply the independent variable. There are two natural, and complementary, interpretations to be placed on $f(x)$, depending on how one views the role of x. If x is viewed as a symbol representing the domain of the function, $f(x)$ defines a mapping $\overline{X} \to \overline{Y}$, where $\overline{X}$ is the domain and $\overline{Y}$ is the range. But if x is viewed as an arbitrary element of $\overline{X}$, then $f(x)$ represents its image. Thus $\overline{X} \to \overline{Y}$ becomes the set of all mappings $x \to f(x)$. The distinction is sometimes made by referring to $f(x)$ as "f of x" under the first interpretation and as "f at x" under the second.

Under the second interpretation $f(2)$ means the image corresponding to the value $x = 2$. A function consisting of a set of (x,y) pairs is also referred to as a set of $(x,f(x))$ pairs.

Limit is the
foundation stone
of calculus

The concept of a limit,[11] and the application of this concept, is vital to an understanding of the calculus and is indeed the foundation stone upon which the calculus is built. This is the concept which makes the study of calculus fundamentally different from any other areas of study the student may have experienced. It provides the foundation for basic extensions in the domain of mathematical operations and leads to the introduction of the two new inversely related operations, differentiation and integration. As a result the student will not only have to become proficient in the manipulative techniques of these two operations, but also learn the new methods which they provide for attacking problem situations.

The difficulty students most often experience in this connection is not so much in acquiring intuitive concepts of limits as in understanding the technical definitions. The essential concept

Developing the
concept of limit

of a limit can be illustrated by various situations drawn from elementary geometry or algebra. For example, let there be a polygon inscribed in or circumscribed about a circle. As the number of sides is increased, the difference between the length of the perimeter of the polygon and the circumference of the circle obviously becomes less than it was at the outset. As the process is indefinitely continued, the difference between these two lengths becomes and remains less than any value we may care to assign; i.e., the difference approaches zero as a limit. In other words, the length of the perimeter of the polygon becomes always more nearly equal to the circumference of the circle; the one approaches the other as a limit. If one objects to this on the ground that the circumference is defined as a limit, the feeling for the notion of a limit can be increased by both circumscribing and inscribing polygons about the circle and, as Archimedes did, squeezing the circumference in between two perimeters that are constantly getting closer to each other yet never being equal.

Again, let there be a series of terms of the form $\frac{1}{2}^{n-1}$, where $n = 1, 2, 3, 4$, etc. The first term of this series is 1, and if successive terms are added, the sum of the series becomes $1 + \frac{1}{2} + \frac{1}{4} + \frac{1}{8} + \cdots$. The addition of successive terms brings the sum nearer and nearer to 2. No finite number of terms can make the sum equal to 2, but by taking n sufficiently large, the difference between the sum of the series and 2 can be made as small as desired. In fact, the sum of the first n terms, plus the nth term, is always equal to 2. In other words, the sum always differs from 2 by the amount of the last term. Since the final term can be made

[11] *Ibid.*

smaller than any specified number, as the number of terms is indefinitely increased, the sum approaches 2 as a limit. Other series, such as $1 + \frac{1}{2} + \frac{1}{3} + \cdots + 1/n$, should be used as counterexamples to show that it is necessary but not sufficient for the nth term to approach zero if the series is to approach a limit.

The fundamental idea involved in these illustrations is that of a variable difference, diminishing progressively toward zero, between the value of the varying function and the constant which it approaches as a limit. It is not sufficient that the difference can be made less than an arbitrarily small quantity; it must remain less for all subsequent values of the independent variable as it approaches its limit. This idea should be emphasized in all the illustrations that are used, because it is only when it is well understood that the somewhat technical definition of a limit, as it is usually given, takes on real meaning. It was the failure to sense this which prevented the ancients from understanding the real nature of continuous variation, and it is precisely the conception of this distinction that enables us to understand the nature of continuity, and limits, which are the very taproots of calculus.[12]

Limit of a variable

With these concepts clearly in mind, the limit of a variable may now be technically defined as follows: If x is a variable and a is a constant and if it is true that, as the values which x may take so change that $|x-a|$ becomes and remains less than h, where h is an arbitrarily small positive quantity, then x is said to approach a as a limit.[13]

Limit of a function

Evidently, this definition can be extended to define the limit of a function, thus: If $f(x)$ is a function of x, and a and A are constants, and if for any arbitrarily chosen small positive quantity d there exists another small positive quantity h such that, when $|x - a| < h$, it is true that $|f(x) - A| < d$, then $f(x)$ is said to approach A as a limit as x approaches a as a limit.

Every effort should be exerted to make these definitions meaningful to the students. To this end graphic and numerical illustrations should be used in the explanations, which should be more than perfunctory.

Picturing a limit

For example, see Fig. 17-1. When d is chosen, a horizontal band of width $2d$ is determined, with the line $y = A$ as its horizontal axis of symmetry. The definition requires that if $f(x)$ approaches A as x approaches a, there must be a number h such that a vertical strip of width $2h$ exists with the line $x = a$ as its vertical axis of symmetry, and throughout this strip the graph of the function also stays within the horizontal strip. These definitions are of

---

[12] For a discussion of the difficulty the ancients had, see the article by Willerding listed in the Bibliography of this chapter.
[13] The symbol $|x - a|$ is to be read "the absolute value of $x - a$." It is to be interpreted as meaning the difference between x and a without regard to sign.

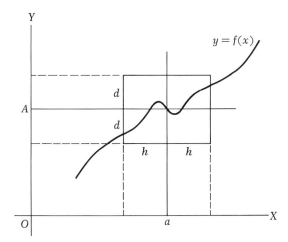

Figure 17-1
Limit of a function.

great importance in that they provide the analytical means of defining the important property of continuity of a function or a variable, as well as the indispensable concept of a derivative.

The students should be made familiar with the customary notation used in connection with limits. They should also become familiar with certain theorems concerning limits. These may be, and usually are, given without proof, but their statements should be accompanied by ample illustrative explanation to ensure that their meanings are really understood by the students.

TEACHING THE MEANING OF A DERIVATIVE AND A DIFFERENTIAL

The late Professor Louis Ingold once said that whoever really understands the meaning of a derivative has learned the most of calculus. He referred, of course, not to operational facility, but rather to the fact that an understanding of the derivative underlies the conception of what calculus is all about. The importance of the concept of a derivative and the associated concept of a differential cannot be too greatly emphasized. Therefore, if calculus is to be taught with the idea of giving the students something more than a rote mastery of its techniques, it is highly important that every effort be made to give them at the outset a clear understanding of these two fundamental concepts.

A derivative might be thought of as the instantaneous rate of change of a function with respect to its independent variable. The usual method of defining the derivative in terms of increments, ratios, and limits, with variation in details, is substantially the same in nearly all textbooks. Like many careful definitions, however, this one is difficult for many students to comprehend.

Derivative is a difficult concept to master
There seems to be something mysterious about the process of passing to the limit and of determining the limiting value of the ratio of the increment of the function to the increment of the independent variable when the latter approaches zero as a limit. The student reasons that, if the one increment approaches zero, the other will also approach zero, and the ratio will be reduced in this way to the form 0/0, which appears meaningless because of the division by zero.

In order to clarify this concept, it is absolutely necessary to make the student understand that the increment of the dependent variable can and must be expressed *in terms of the independent variable and its increment* and that the ratio of the increment of the dependent variable to the increment of the independent variable thus becomes a function of the increment of the independent variable. Furthermore, it should be emphasized that it is the limit of this ratio that is sought, and not the ratio of the limits of the numerator and denominator as separate functions. Thus, let $y = f(x)$ be

The limit of a ratio is not the ratio of the limits of numerator and denominator
a continuous function of x. If x takes on an increment Δx, then y will also take on an increment Δy, such that

$$y + \Delta y = f(x + \Delta x)$$

or $\Delta y = f(x + \Delta x) - y$, or $\Delta y = f(x + \Delta x) - f(x)$. In this way Δy is expressed entirely in terms of x and Δx. Then the ratio $\Delta y/\Delta x$ becomes $[f(x + \Delta x) - f(x)]/\Delta x$, which is reducible in general to a determinate form and should be so reduced *before the limit is taken.* Graphic representations such as are given in nearly all textbooks help greatly in giving concreteness to the concepts of these increments and ratios, and full advantage should be taken of this means of illustrating and clarifying the concepts.

The notation also is confusing to the students, who are puzzled about such questions as these: What is the distinction between Δy and dy and between Δx and dx? Why is it that Δy is not in general equal to dy, while Δx is in general equal to dx? How does Δy become dy? What does dy mean? If dy/dx is defined as the limit of $\Delta y/\Delta x$ as Δx approaches zero, why can it not be thought of as a quotient? Are dy and dx infinitesimals? Are Δy and Δx infinitesimals? What is the distinction between an infinitesimal and an increment and between an increment and a differential?

It is recommended that the notation dy/dx not be used for the derivative until after the concept of differential is developed. A

Fraction notation is a source of confusion
good notation for the derivative of y with respect to x is $D_x y$; similarly, the derivative of $f(x)$ with respect to x would be $D_x f(x)$. There are other good notations that do not introduce the confusion of thinking of a quotient where there is no quotient. For example,

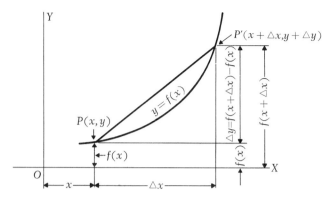

Figure 17-2
Developing the meaning of a differential.

The derivative of a
function is a
function

$f'(x)$ has much to recommend it. The derivative of a function is also a function. Thus $f'(x)$ is a symbol which represents the function derived from $f(x)$. It seems probable that a good deal of the confusion and uncertainty concerning the distinction between increment, differential, and derivative could be avoided if, contrary to custom, at least an intuitive notion of the meaning of a differential were to be developed along with the discussion of the deriv-

Distinction between
derivative and
differential

ative. This can be done easily by means of geometric considerations and an arbitrary definition. In Fig. 17-2, suppose that P is some point (x,y) on the curve $y = f(x)$. If x takes on an increment Δx, then y must take on an increment Δy corresponding to the increment Δx. It should be emphasized to the student that Δx and Δy are corresponding changes in the variables. A change of Δx in x is accompanied by a change of Δy in y. Then the change in y per unit of change in x is $\Delta y/\Delta x$; but this is the average rate of change over the interval Δx, not the instantaneous rate of change at the beginning of the interval. The instantaneous rate of change at any point on the curve is given by the slope of the curve at that point, and the slope of a curve at a given point is defined as the slope of the tangent to the curve at that point. Thus the derivative of a function at a point, which is defined to be $\lim_{\Delta x \to 0} (\Delta y/\Delta x)$ and

The derivative
gives the slope of
the curve

which gives the instantaneous rate of change for the corresponding value of the dependent variable, also gives the slope of the tangent to the curve at that point.

If we draw PT tangent to the curve at $P(x,y)$, the distance dy (Fig. 17-3a) represents the increment which y would have taken if its rate of change with respect to x had become constant exactly at the point $P(x,y)$. As P' moves along the curve to the position of P (Fig. 17-3b), both Δx and Δy approach zero as a limit. If the ratio $\Delta y/\Delta x$ represents the average rate of change for any of the intervals Δx, and the ratio dy/dx the rate of change for the slope of the

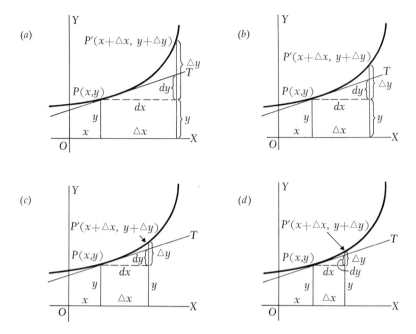

Figure 17-3
Derivative of a function at a point.

tangent line PT, it is evident that $\Delta y/\Delta x$ is changing in value as Δy and Δx approach zero, while dy/dx is remaining constant. For each new position of P' (as in Fig. 17-3c and d), the Δx and dx are the same in value, while Δy and dy differ. Furthermore,

$$\lim_{\Delta x \to 0} \frac{\Delta y}{\Delta x} = \frac{dy}{dx}$$

By agreement we shall call dx, which is the same as Δx, *the differential of x*, and we shall call dy *the differential of y* corresponding to dx. We have shown that the ratio dy/dx of the differentials dy and dx is the same as the *derivative of y with respect to x*. The value of this ratio will vary accordingly as P takes different positions on the curve, but for any particular position of P (i.e., for any given value of x) the value of dy/dx remains constant and is entirely independent of the value of dx.

Now, if we wish to let dx approach zero as a limit, dy will also approach zero as a limit, but the ratio dy/dx remains the same, even in the limit. The differentials may be regarded simply as tangible, finite increments, dx being any arbitrary increment of x, and dy being the increment which y *would take on* if the slope of

The derivative is the ratio of differentials

the curve (or the rate of change of y with respect to x) had become constant at the point $P\ (x,y)$.

It is believed that an approach to the concept of the derivative along with this intuitive notion of the differential as a finite, measurable quantity would dispel much of the mystery and uncertainty so often associated with the meaning of derivatives and differentials. The student's understanding will be strengthened if he is asked to take various curves, select arbitrary values and arbitrary increments for the independent variable, and by drawing and actual measurement, determine dx, $f(x)$, $f(x+\Delta x)$, Δy, and dy. Then by actual division dy/dx, he can get approximations to the values of the derivatives. To develop the rules for differentiation, of course, the usual analytic procedure will need to be employed. However, if a preliminary approach such as has just been described can make this analytic procedure more meaningful to the student, it will be exceedingly worthwhile.

TEACHING THE RULES
FOR DIFFERENTIATION

The student will soon find that the process of finding the derivative of a function by the graphical method gives only approximations at isolated points, and does not give any general expression for the derivative. He will also find that the detailed application of the formula

$$D_x y = \lim_{\Delta x \to 0} \frac{f(x + \Delta x) - f(x)}{\Delta x}$$

Rules for differentiation require analytic procedures

while it does give a general and exact expression for the derivative, is a clumsy and laborious process. The practical limitations of time demand that he learn and use the special rules or formulas which are available for differentiating various kinds of functions.

There are two points of view with regard to the introduction, learning, and use of these rules for differentiation. Considered solely from the standpoint of logical sequence and mathematical consistency, it would seem necessary that each of these formulas should be completely developed and proved before being used.

Importance of rules for differentiation

This is the position taken by the authors of most textbooks on calculus. On the other hand, there are some authors and many teachers who hold that it is a sounder and more economical pedagogical procedure to introduce without proof certain of these rules in which the meaning is clear and to let the students use these empirically for the time being, the proofs being reserved until later, and special attention being given at the time only to the

Rules are to be used empirically

matter of making sure that the concepts involved are understood by the students.[14] Professor E. V. Huntington once expressed this point of view as follows:

Now the simplest function is the polynomial,

$$y = A + Bx + Cx^2 + Dx^3 + \cdots$$

I should begin the second day, therefore, by stating, without proof, the rule for differentiating a polynomial, namely:

$$dy = (B + 2Cx + 3Dx^2 + \cdots) \, dx$$

Equipped with this rule, we can proceed at once to solve a multitude of problems in maxima and minima, which serve better than anything else to convince the student that here is a new tool which is mighty convenient to have at hand. . . .

The study of the polynomial naturally leads to problems involving the quotient of two polynomials, and to problems involving the solution of a quadratic equation. In order to handle such problems, it is well to introduce at this point the statement, without proofs, of the general rules for differentiating a sum, a product, and a quotient, and also the special rules

$$d\left(\frac{1}{x}\right) = -\frac{1}{x^2} \, dx, \qquad d(\sqrt{x}) = \frac{dx}{2\sqrt{x}}$$

in which x may be the independent variable, or itself a function of some other variable. . . .

If the meaning of a theorem is clear, as in the case of the rules for differentiation, the formal proof may often be postponed to advantage, but . . . the meaning of a new concept cannot safely be postponed. . . .[15]

With regard to the subsequent proofs of the rules for differentiation, Huntington continued:

If the time-saving program above outlined has been followed, the student should now have a good working knowledge of the properties of all the elementary functions including the rules for differentiation. If he has a spark of scientific curiosity, he will be interested to know how these rules, whose utility he has come to appreciate, were ever discovered, and how we know they are true. . . .

To indicate how much time can be saved, by taking up the proofs in the most effective order, I may say that the proofs of all the rules for differentiation can easily be disposed of in two classroom periods. First establish the rule for the sine and the rule for the logarithm, for the general case of a function of a function. Then the rules for kx, x^n, e^x, uv, u/v, $\cos x$, $\tan x$, and the inverse functions follow by a turn of the hand.[16]

This will doubtless be regarded by many teachers as an overstatement and an oversimplification of the situation, and it may be that it is. There are also those who will object to it on the grounds that it lacks the sequential rigor of the prove-as-you-go plan, though the basis for this objection may be more apparent than real. However, regardless of whether or not one subscribes wholly to the suggestions made by Huntington, it seems prob-

Differentiation formulas must be thoroughly memorized

[14] See, for example, articles by Kline, Mattuck, and the title "New Directions in Mathematics," listed in the Bibliography of this chapter.

[15] Edward V. Huntington, Teaching the Calculus: Four Papers on the Teaching of Mathematics, *Bulletin* 19 (Lancaster, Pa.: Society for the Promotion of Engineering Education, 1932), pp. 39–41.

[16] *Ibid.*, pp. 46–47.

able that whatever sacrifice of mathematical order they would entail might be largely compensated by increased interest and operational efficiency.

If the student is to use the differentiation formulas with efficiency and dispatch, he will need to memorize them, and memorize them thoroughly. As soon as a rule is given, whether with or without proof, it should be applied immediately, and considerable practice should be given in finding derivatives of functions under this rule. This will do a great deal toward enabling the student to fix the rule in his mind. However, as the number of new formulas increases, the difficulty of keeping them straight becomes greater, and the student will in general have to resort to actual and thorough memorization. Careful inspection of a tabulated list of the formulas will perhaps enable the student to discover certain relationships among them and to set up various mnemonics to aid in remembering them and to avoid confusing them with each other.

Some of the formulas are special cases of others. For example, $D_x(cu)$ is a special case of $D_x(uv)$; $D_x(e^u)$ is a special case of $D_x(a^u)$; and other similar instances may be found. Again, certain similarities may be found among the derivatives of certain related inverse functions. The derivative of the arccos x is the negative of the derivative of the arcsin x; that of the arccot x is the negative of that of the arctan x; and that of the arccsc x is the negative of that of the arcsec x.

These and perhaps other relationships that might be found among the formulas will reduce the amount of sheer memorizing that will need to be done, and the very search for such mnemonic devices is itself an excellent exercise in familiarizing the students with the formulas.

SOME CRITICAL POINTS IN DEVELOPING THE PROOFS OF CERTAIN RULES FOR DIFFERENTIATION

We have already discussed the matter of teaching the meanings of derivative and differential. A clear concept of the meanings of these terms is prerequisite to any real understanding of the proofs of the formulas for the elementary derivatives. These concepts, in turn, involve an understanding of the meanings of increments and limits, which have also been discussed. It is probable that teachers, in developing the formulas for derivatives, are inclined to be too generous in their assumptions regarding the students' mastery of the meanings of these concepts.

The general method of finding a derivative needs to be stressed. Its almost mechanical form and the one-two-three order of its steps, together with the reasons for this order, need to be ex-

Knowing inter-relationships of formulas helps in learning the formulas

Teachers are often too ready to assume mastery of underlying concepts

plained and illustrated, not once but numerous times, until the students are able to apply it independently and with facility to simple functions. It is easy for them to follow and verify, step by step, the illustration of it, but it is by no means equally apparent to them *why* the particular steps are taken in that particular order. Consider the typical order in the general development:

(1) $y = f(x)$

(2) $y + \Delta y = f(x + \Delta x)$

(3) $\Delta y = f(x + \Delta x) - y = f(x + \Delta x) - f(x)$

(4) $\dfrac{\Delta y}{\Delta x} = \dfrac{f(x + \Delta x) - f(x)}{\Delta x}$

(5) $\lim\limits_{\Delta x \to 0} \dfrac{\Delta y}{\Delta x} = \lim\limits_{\Delta x \to 0} \dfrac{f(x + \Delta x) - f(x)}{\Delta x} = D_x y = D_x f(x)$

(by definition)

From a synthetic standpoint it is perfect, each step being a justi-fied consequence of the preceding one. However, it cannot be said that each step *suggests* the following one, and herein lies the rub. The steps and their order suggest themselves only if one has in mind the end toward which he is working. It must be the task of the teacher to point out what this goal is and how and why this particular sequence of steps does lead to it. It is well to carry along this general synthesis with the illustrations of its application to particular functions, while pointing out the parallel development and repeatedly calling attention to the reason for performing each step in its particular place.

The explanation may be somewhat as follows: Let us assume that we have given a variable y which is a function of x. Our task is to find the derivative of y with respect to x, or to find $D_x y$. By definition, $D_x y$ means $\lim\limits_{\Delta x \to 0} (\Delta y / \Delta x)$. We must therefore find some way of getting an expression $\Delta y / \Delta x$ in terms of x and Δx in order that we may determine its limit and thus find the derivative.

General case	*Example*
$y = f(x)$	$y = 3x + 7$
$y + \Delta y = f(x + \Delta x)$	$y + \Delta y = 3(x + \Delta x) + 7$

Since we want to get an expression $\Delta y / \Delta x$, we must first get an expression for Δy itself. This we can do by subtracting y from each member of the above equation.

$\Delta y = f(x + \Delta x) - y$ $\Delta y = 3(x + \Delta x) + 7 - y$

We may now substitute for y its value $f(x)$ (or $3x + 7$) and ex-press Δy entirely in terms of x and Δx.

$\Delta y = f(x + \Delta x) - f(x)$

$\begin{aligned}\Delta y &= 3(x + \Delta x) + 7 - (3x + 7)\\ &= 3x + 3\,\Delta x + 7 - 3x - 7\\ &= 3\,\Delta x\end{aligned}$

The general method does not give insight into why steps are taken

The teacher should supply a motivation for each step in the process

Now in order to get an expression for $\Delta y/\Delta x$, we must divide both members of the equation by Δx.

$$\frac{\Delta y}{\Delta x} = \frac{f(x + \Delta) - f(x)}{\Delta x} \qquad \frac{\Delta y}{\Delta x} = \frac{3\,\Delta x}{\Delta x} = 3$$

Finally, since we want $D_x y$, and since this means $\lim_{\Delta x \to 0} (\Delta y/\Delta x)$, we must take the limit of $\Delta y/\Delta x$ as Δx approaches zero as a limit.

$$D_x y = \lim_{\Delta x \to 0} \frac{\Delta y}{\Delta x} \qquad D_x y = \lim_{\Delta x \to 0} \frac{3\,\Delta x}{\Delta x}$$
$$= \lim_{\Delta x \to 0} \frac{f(x + \Delta x) - f(x)}{\Delta x} \qquad = \lim_{\Delta x \to 0} 3(1)$$
$$= \lim_{\Delta x \to 0} 3 = 3$$

Several illustrations carried through in this manner, with specific attention to the order of procedure and the reasons that each step comes in its particular place, will be extremely helpful to the students. It will go far toward giving them a real understanding of the fundamental meaning and method of finding derivatives and developing the general derivative formulas.

Many students will be puzzled by the fact that in an expression such as $D_x y = \lim_{\Delta x \to 0} (3\,\Delta x/\Delta x)$ it is legal to cancel the Δx's since

Delta process does not involve division by zero

division by zero is prohibited. Of course, if Δx were zero, then, by the same reasoning, division by zero would occur in step 5 of the delta process described on page 546. But as Δx approaches zero as a limit, one value it cannot take is zero. In this connection, every teacher of calculus owes it to himself to read Bishop Berkeley's "The Analyst."[17]

PROOF OF THE FORMULA FOR THE DERIVATIVE OF A LOGARITHM

The general formula is difficult to follow

This is one of the particularly tough spots which students encounter. The method is perfectly general, but the proof involves certain facts and relations with which students often lack familiarity, although presumably they will have encountered them beforehand. We shall give a proof of the general formula and then analyze some of its difficulties.

Let $y = \log_a u$, where u is a function of x (1)

$y + \Delta y = \log_a (u + \Delta u)$ (2)

$\Delta y = \log_a (u + \Delta u) - y$ (3)

$\qquad = \log_a (u + \Delta u) - \log_a u$ (4)

$\qquad = \log_a \dfrac{u + \Delta u}{u}$ (5)

[17] See James R. Newman, "The World of Mathematics," vol. I (New York: Simon and Schuster, Inc., 1956), pp. 288–293.

$$\frac{\Delta y}{\Delta u} = \frac{1}{\Delta u} \log_a \frac{u + \Delta u}{u} \tag{6}$$

$$\frac{\Delta y}{\Delta u} = \frac{1}{\Delta u} \log_a \left(1 + \frac{\Delta u}{u}\right) \tag{7}$$

$$= \frac{1}{u} \times \frac{u}{\Delta u} \log_a \left(1 + \frac{\Delta u}{u}\right) \tag{8}$$

$$= \frac{1}{u} \log_a \left(1 + \frac{\Delta u}{u}\right)^{\frac{u}{\Delta u}} \tag{9}$$

The formula depends on the definition of e

$$D_u y = \lim_{\Delta u \to 0} \frac{\Delta y}{\Delta u} = \frac{1}{u} \log_a \left[\lim_{\Delta u \to 0} \left(1 + \frac{\Delta u}{u}\right)^{\frac{u}{\Delta u}} \right] \tag{10}$$

$$= \frac{1}{u} \log_a e$$

$$= \frac{1}{u} \times \frac{1}{\log_e a} = \frac{1}{u} \times \frac{1}{\ln a} \tag{11}$$

$$D_x y = D_u y \times D_x u = \frac{1}{u \log_e a} \times D_x u = \frac{1}{u \ln a} \times D_x u \tag{12}$$

It must be kept in mind that the proof of this formula necessarily presumes some formal or intuitive justification of the existence[18] of $e = 2.71828 \ldots$ as the limit of $(1 + x)^{1/x}$ as x approaches zero. Although the existence of this limit may reasonably be postulated in a first course in calculus, there should at least be given satisfactory intuitive rationalization of its existence.

The first four steps involve no particular difficulties, but throughout the rest of the proof there are several places where the development is likely to be hard for students to follow. The first of these trouble spots occurs in step 5. Here the student must learn to recognize the application of the principle $\log m - \log n = \log m/n$. The principle itself will be familiar, but there is the possibility that in this unfamiliar dress the student may fail to recognize it unless it is pointed out by the teacher.

There are many specific difficulties

Step 6 then follows naturally in the process of finding $\Delta y/\Delta u$ before passing to the limit. But here we run into trouble. In the present form of the expression on the right we have the problem of finding the limit of a product in which one of the factors becomes infinite and the other approaches 0 as Δu approaches 0. Careful examination of the factors will reveal the fact that if $(u + \Delta u)/u$ is written in the equivalent form $(1 + \Delta u/u)$, this factor has close resemblance to the binomial in the expression $(1 + x)^{1/x}$, for which the limit e exists as x approaches 0. This observation leads to the further investigation of the possibility of converting the expression given in step 7 into a form equivalent to $\lim (1 + x)^{1/x}$. If x is used to represent $\Delta u/u$, then $1/x = u/\Delta u$. The question is then raised as to whether there is any legitimate manipulation which can be used to transform the right side of step 7 into an equivalent expression of the form $(1 + \Delta u/u)^{u/\Delta u}$. Recall-

The limit e

---

[18] For a discussion of this see the article by Pagel listed in the Bibliography of this chapter.

ing the inverse relation between multiplication and division and the logarithmic property that $m \log n = \log (n)^m$, we are led through steps 8 and 9 to step 10. Here we recognize the expression whose limit is e as Δu approaches 0.

Substitution of e for this limit leads to the formula of step 11 for $D_u y$. However, since we are required to find $D_x y$ and since u is a function of x, we must make use of the formula for the derivative of a function of a function: $D_x y = D_u y \times D_x u$. We may assume that this has been previously developed; so in passing to step 12 we need only recall this rule and point out its application in the present situation.

Finally, it should be pointed out that we have developed the formula for the most general case: $y = \log_a u$. If we take e as the base (as a special case of a), then $\log_e a$, in the denominator in step 12, becomes $\log_e e$, and the formula itself becomes

$$D_x(\log_e u) = D_x(\ln u) = \frac{1}{u} \times D_x u$$

since $\log_e e = 1$. This is the form in which it is usually found and in which it is generally used.

We have thus seen that the proof of this formula holds numerous specific difficulties for students. In addition to these, it has the general difficulty of being somewhat long and involving numerous transformations and substitutions, the reasons for which are not immediately obvious to the students. Only a few of the better students will be able to dig it all out for themselves. Whether the majority really get it or not will depend largely upon how skillfully and clearly it is explained by the teacher.

The proof of the formula for the derivative of the exponential $y = a^u$ follows easily after the formula for the derivative of a logarithm has been established. Conversely, if the formula for the derivative of the exponential is independently developed first, as can be done, it may be used to simplify the development of the formula for the derivative of a logarithm. The order varies with different textbooks. Either may be used. In general, it may be said that the one which is developed first, and independently of the other, will be more difficult for the students than the one which makes use of the first. The formulas depend ultimately upon the evaluation of

$$\lim_{x \to 0} \frac{a^x - 1}{x} = \log_e a \qquad \text{or} \qquad \lim_{x \to 0} (1 + x)^{1/x} = e$$

PROOF OF THE FORMULA FOR THE DERIVATIVE OF THE SINE FUNCTION

This is another of the basic derivatives and a proverbial trouble spot for students. The steps in the proof may be given as follows:

1   Let $y = \sin u$, where u is some function of x

2 $y + \Delta y = \sin (u + \Delta u)$

3 $\Delta y = \sin (u + \Delta u) - y$

4 $= \sin (u + \Delta u) - \sin u$

5 $= \sin u \cos \Delta u + \cos u \sin \Delta u - \sin u$

6 $\dfrac{\Delta y}{\Delta u} = \dfrac{\cos u \sin \Delta u}{\Delta u} - \dfrac{\sin u(1 - \cos \Delta u)}{\Delta u}$

7 $= \cos u \dfrac{\sin \Delta u}{\Delta u} - \sin u \dfrac{1 - \cos \Delta u}{\Delta u}$

8 $D_u y = \lim\limits_{\Delta u \to 0} \dfrac{\Delta y}{\Delta u} = \cos u \left(\lim\limits_{\Delta u \to 0} \dfrac{\sin \Delta u}{\Delta u} \right)$

$$- \sin u \left(\lim\limits_{\Delta u \to 0} \dfrac{1 - \cos \Delta u}{\Delta u} \right)$$

9 $= \cos u(1) - (0)$

        $= \cos u$

10 $D_x y = D_u y \times D_x u = \cos u \times D_x u$

The first four steps involve no difficulty whatever. In step 5 there is a substitution to be made, and in steps 6 and 7 there are certain rearrangements of terms and the insertion of the divisor Δu; but these, again, involve no special difficulty so far as the operations themselves are concerned. There is, however, the question *why* these particular substitutions and rearrangements are made, and the reasons should be explained clearly to the students.

Students may have difficulty seeing why

In order to present these reasons, however, one must recall that it is necessary, in setting up the derivative, to evaluate $\lim\limits_{\Delta u \to 0} (\Delta y/\Delta u)$.

It should be explained that, in order to do this, we need to use $\lim\limits_{\Delta u \to 0} [(\sin \Delta u)/\Delta u]$ and $\lim\limits_{\Delta u \to 0} [(1 - \cos \Delta u)/\Delta u]$ because these expressions can be evaluated and their use affords the only way to evaluate $\lim\limits_{\Delta u \to 0} (\Delta y/\Delta u)$. Indeed, the limiting values of these expressions will already have been determined, but as a matter of refreshing the minds of the students on these points, it will be well to review them before substituting them in the formula. As a matter of fact, the two most difficult parts of the whole proof are (1) the preliminary establishment of the limiting values of these two expressions, and (2) sensing the role which they play in the proof. Step 9 merely involves the substitution of the numerical limiting values for these expressions.

It will be noted that this development gives the derivative of y with respect to u, where u is some function of x. In order to get the derivative of y with respect to x, we must again make use of the relation

$$D_x y = D_u y \times D_x u$$

This is done in step 10, which completes the proof.

SUCCESSIVE DIFFERENTIATION;
MAXIMA AND MINIMA

A few illustrations will suffice to make it clear to the students that in general the derivative of a function of x with respect to x is itself a function of x which may in turn be differentiated, and that, by differentiating successive derivatives in this way, there are obtained the so-called higher derivatives of the function. The students should be made acquainted with the various forms of notation for these higher derivatives, and in particular, they should be given an interpretation of the second derivative as the rate at which the first derivative is changing, or graphically, as the rate of change of the slope of the curve. That is, the student should come to understand that, if the second derivative is positive at a given point, it means that the first derivative is increasing at that point; a negative value of the second derivative indicates a decreasing first derivative; and a zero value of the second derivative indicates that the first derivative is neither increasing nor decreasing.

Roles of higher derivatives

The most important immediate application of the second derivative is in connection with the determination of maximum, minimum, and inflection points. It will be obvious to the student from a consideration of the graphs of functions that the first derivative at a maximum or a minimum point must be zero if the function is continuous and has a continuous derivative. Graphs should be used to show why this is not necessarily true if the function or its derivative has a discontinuity. But for continuous functions with continuous derivatives, the converse does not hold. A first-derivative zero does not imply a maximum or minimum. Even if it did, this would not enable one to distinguish between a maximum and a minimum. In order to make a certain test of this, the second derivative must also be employed. The student must be shown that, if $f'(x) = 0$ and is decreasing [i.e., if at the same time $f''(x)$ is negative], then a maximum is indicated at that point, while if $f'(x) = 0$ and is increasing [i.e., if at the same time $f''(x)$ is positive], then a minimum is indicated. If $f'(x) = 0$ and $f''(x) = 0$, also, then at that point the function usually has neither a maximum nor a minimum, but a point of inflection. However, there are exceptions to this. The function $f(x) = x^4$, its first derivative, $f'(x) = 4x^3$, and its second derivative, $f''(x) = 12x^2$, all have zeros at $x = .0$. (Fig. 17-4). Here the first and second derivatives are both zeros, but the function does have a minimum at $x = 0$. The third derivative, $f'''(x) = 24x$, also has a zero at $x = 0$. But $f''(x)$ and $f'''(x)$ are the first and second derivatives, respectively, of $f'(x)$, and $f'(x)$ does have a point of inflection at $x = 0$. Careful explanation of these matters should be given and should be accompanied

First and second derivatives are zero at these critical points

Exceptional cases

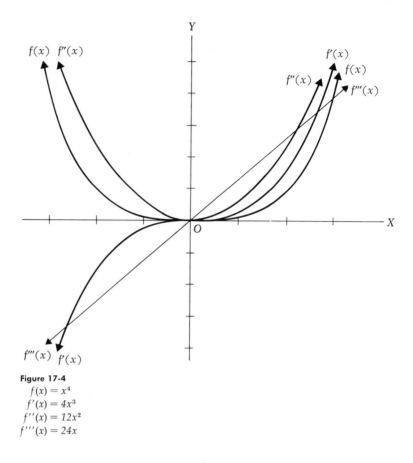

Figure 17-4
$$f(x) = x^4$$
$$f'(x) = 4x^3$$
$$f''(x) = 12x^2$$
$$f'''(x) = 24x$$

by graphic illustrations to ensure that the students understand them clearly.

The students should be warned against concluding wrongly that $f'(x)$ for a certain x, or at a certain point, will necessarily be zero just because $f''(x)$ is zero. Since $f''(x) < 0$ indicates that the curve is *concave downward* and $f''(x) > 0$ indicates it is *concave upward,* it follows that at the point where the sense of concavity changes, $f''(x) = 0$ if it has a value. This point is called a "point of inflection," or "flex point." That these are not sufficient conditions for a flex point may be seen by examining the curves $f(x) = x^4$ and $f(x) = x^{2/3}$. A simple illustration of how $f'(x)$ and $f''(x)$ may be used in graphing a function is the graph of $f(x) = 3x^3 - 2x + 5$ given in Fig. 17-5.

Points of inflection

The study of maxima and minima offers a wealth of interesting applications of the theory to geometrical and physical situations. These problems not only give practice in formal differentiation, but also give to the work a high degree of motivation and afford

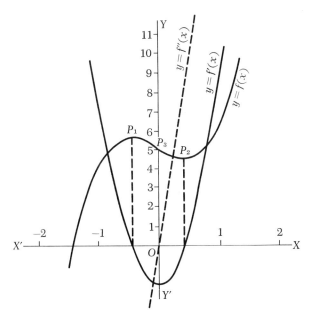

Figure 17-5

$f(x) = 3x^3 - 2x + 5$
$f'(x) = 9x^2 - 2$
$f''(x) = 18x$

excellent training in interpreting geometric and physical situations and in translating these into the formal language of the derivative.

THE INDEFINITE INTEGRAL; ANTIDERIVATIVES

Integral as antiderivative

Up to the present we have considered only matters which are related to derivation and differentiation of functions. We must now give some attention to that part of calculus which is concerned with the inverse problem of finding a primitive function of which the given function is the derivative. It should be pointed out to the students that many of the most important applications of calculus give rise to problems of this nature, particularly those involving definite integrals. No student should have any difficulty in understanding the meaning of integration if it is explained simply as the process of antidifferentiation, i.e., if it is clearly pointed out that in differentiation we are given the function and required to find the derivative, while in integration we are given the derivative and required to find the function. The two processes are absolutely inverse to each other, just as division and multiplication or addition and subtraction are. Either one *un*does the other.

In taking up the study of integration, then, the first task of the instructor should be to make this clear to the students so that their work in integration will not be devoid of meaning. It will help greatly toward achieving this understanding if the instructor and students together work out a few of the fundamental integrals. The finding of a derivative is, of course, a direct process; on the other hand, the finding of an integral form is essentially a matter of trial. In view of the fact that the two processes are exactly inverse to each other, the test for the correctness of an integral is whether or not it can be differentiated to give the original expression.

By using this basic principle, it is possible to take the fundamental formulas for derivatives and, by reversing the reasoning and the notation, arrive at some of the fundamental formulas for integration. A number of these should be set down and tested in this way by the students with the assistance of the instructor. Thus, since $D_x(\sin x) = \cos x$, it is seen at once that $\int(\cos x)\,dx = \sin x + C$, because by applying the test for an integral, it is apparent that the derivative of $\sin x + C$ is $\cos x$. In like manner the integrals corresponding to the other fundamental derivative formulas should be set down, explained, and verified. If this is done, the students can hardly help sensing the relation between derivatives and integrals.

In connection with the development of these integration formulas, the student will note the appearance of the constant of integration. The necessity and meaning of the constant of integration must be carefully explained by the instructor. This may be done by use of the theorem: If two functions have the same derivative, they differ only by a constant; and also its converse. These may easily be illustrated by examples. It should be pointed out that in many of the applications of integration the determination of the constant of integration to satisfy initial conditions is of extreme importance.

Integration is tested by differentiation

Integral formulas from basic differentiation formulas

The constant of integration

USE OF THE TABLE OF INTEGRALS

There are a few fundamental integrals with which the student should become perfectly familiar. The lists of these vary in different textbooks, the number usually being between 12 and 25 and depending mainly upon the author's inclination toward generalization or specialization of the forms. The discussion of these forms in each textbook presumably will be consistent with the author's views in this respect; so the precise number of formulas

Fundamental
integrals should
be memorized
listed in any case is of less consequence than the fact that there *are* certain of these which the student must know thoroughly. These formulas should be tested by differentiation and should be memorized.

In addition to these fundamental integrals, there are many special integrals which are often useful. Textbooks usually contain more or less extensive lists or tables of these special integrals. Separately published tables, much more complete even than those given in the textbooks, are also available. There is no general agreement among instructors on the extent to which students should use these tables of special integrals. Some feel that, since Use of tables of
integrals much of integration is formal anyway, the free use of the tables speeds up the work and allows more to be accomplished without any detriment to the student. Others feel that the student will gain more insight and understanding if he performs most of these integrations for himself by means of the fundamental integrals. Nobody knows just what the optimum is with regard to this question, but it would seem that a middle ground or reasonable balance of these views would perhaps be more defensible than either extreme position. To this end, Huntington's suggestion that "no formula in the table should be used until it has at least been verified by 'differentiating back'"[19] seems appropriate.

In using an extensive table of integrals, the student will need Identification of
types to familiarize himself with the way in which the integrals are classified so that he can readily locate and identify the form corresponding to any given integrand.

Sometimes it may be impossible to find in the table a formula which corresponds to the given integrand. In such cases it is some- Special devices times possible to transform the given expression into usable form through such special devices as resolution of the expression into partial fractions, the substitution of a new variable, application of the rule for integration by parts, or use of the reduction formulas. These special devices involve special procedures the reasons for which, and the real significance of which, will probably not be clear to the students unless the underlying principles and considerations are carefully explained by the instructor. In order that the students may appreciate and become familiar with the nature of these devices, ample illustration and explanation of them should be given. In connection with trigonometric substitutions and the transformation of trigonometric expressions into integrable forms, it may be advisable to give again a brief summary and review of certain of the trigonometric identities, notably the addition formulas and the functions of half angles and double angles. The extreme generality of the reduction formulas makes it desirable that illustrative examples be worked out by the in-

---

[19] Huntington, *op. cit.*, p. 55.

structor to familiarize the students with the precise manner in which these formulas are applied to particular functions and with the effect produced in the integrand through the application of these formulas.

THE DEFINITE INTEGRAL

As in the case of the indefinite integral, many students employ the definite integral without clearly understanding its nature and interpretation. The indefinite integral was defined merely as an antiderivative. The definite integral, on the other hand, is to be interpreted in a different way, namely, as a summation of elements having the characteristic form $f(x) \Delta x$, or more precisely, as the limit of the sum of these elements as Δx approaches zero as a limit. The justification for identifying the limit of such a sum with an integral rests, of course, upon the fundamental theorem for definite integrals, and this must be made clear to the students in due time. Here is a case, however, in which the concept of the definite integral may justifiably be developed, explained, illustrated, defined, associated with its characteristic symbolism, and actually used before proceeding to a proof of the fact that its use is justified.

In general, there are three phases to problems involving definite integrals: (1) setting up the element of integration, (2) performing the formal integration, and (3) substituting limits and evaluating the integral. The third of these is mere labor. The second involves the knowledge and ability required to perform the integration correctly. This presumably will have been developed in connection with the work on indefinite integrals. The first phase, setting up the formula for the element of integration, is the part of the work which is likely to cause students the most difficulty. Since ideas seem to be most readily acquired and assimilated when they are associated with graphic representations, the most effective illustration of the method of setting up the formula for the element of integration is probably in connection with the problem of finding the area under a curve, as in Fig. 17-6. Here it is apparent that the element of area, ΔA or $ABCD$, is approximately equal to the area of the rectangle $ABED$, this area being given by $y \Delta x$, or $f(x) \Delta x$. On passing to the differential notation, we have $dA = f(x) dx$, which is the characteristic form for the differential of area or the element of integration; whence $A = \int dA = \int f(x) dx$. The important thing here is that the element of integration is always of the form $dA = f(x) dx$, and the area itself is given as $A = \int f(x) dx$, or $F(x)$. If $x = a$, we have $A = F(a)$; if $x = b$, we have $A = F(b)$. The area under the curve and *between* the ordinates erected at a and b will evidently be $F(b) - F(a)$, which, as we have seen, is given by

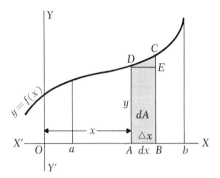

Figure 17-6
Area under a curve.

$$\int_{x=b} f(x)\ dx - \int_{x=a} f(x)\ dx$$

It is to be noted that the constant of integration would appear in both of these integrals but would disappear in the subtraction; so it may be disregarded.

The customary notation for the definite integral $\int_a^b f(x)\ dx$ should be clearly explained, and the student should observe and keep in mind the meaning of every detail of this notation. In particular, the student should be aware of the fact that, for a given function $f(x)$, the value of the definite integral $\int_a^b f(x)\ dx$ depends upon the values of a and b.

The meaning of the definite-integral symbol

The fact that such an integral should produce the measure of the area bounded by the curve, the x axis, and the two specified ordinates is not always completely accepted by a class. This possibly is due to incomplete acceptance of the technique of integration, previously developed and used exclusively as a technique for finding antiderivatives, as having any direct association with the limit of a sum of rectangular strips of area under the curve as their widths approach zero. Help in overcoming this difficulty can be obtained from a pattern of rationalization that consists in creating certain areas which can be computed independently of the definite integral, and then checking this computation against the result obtained by using the definite integral.

Example. (a) Find the area bounded by the straight line $y = 2x + 4$, the x axis, and the line $x = 4$.

If the graph of this line is drawn, the area described will be seen to be that of a right triangle with a base of 6 units and an altitude of 12 units. Its area is therefore 36 square units. From the integral we have

$$A = \int_{-2}^{4} (2x + 4)\ dx = x^2 + 4x + c \Big|_{-2}^{4} = (16 + 16 + c) - (4 - 8 + c) = 36$$

(b) If one desires a more involved illustration of this same type, the example can be that of finding the area of a circle with its center at the origin and with any specified radius. For the area enclosed by the circle $x^2 + y^2 = 25$, we have $A = 25\pi$.

To find the area by integration, first find the area in the first quadrant and then multiply this result by 4.

$$A = 4 \int_0^5 \sqrt{25 - x^2}\, dx$$
$$= 2 \left[x\, \sqrt{25 - x^2} + 25 \sin^{-1} \frac{x}{5} \right]_0^5$$
$$= 2(25 \sin^{-1} 1) = 25\pi$$

It should be pointed out to the student that in general the element of integration for any solid can be readily set up, provided it is possible to get a characteristic expression for the area of all the sections made by planes parallel to a coordinate plane. If the solid is cut into slices of thickness dh by planes parallel to this plane, and if the sections thus made can all be represented by the same algebraic form, then, denoting a typical section by A_i, the element of integration is given by $A_i\, dh$. The meaning of this should be made clear by drawings, as should the fact that, if A_i can now be expressed in terms of h, then a definite integral for the volume can be set up. Probably the most common and simplest application of this is in connection with solids of revolution.

Other forms of the element of integration

Other type forms for the element of integration are encountered in problems involving length of arc, surfaces of solids, plane areas in polar coordinates, moments of mass and inertia, and centroids. Whenever a new type form is to be considered, the instructor should make a special point of explaining and illustrating how the new special form fits into, and in fact derives from, the fundamental concept and definition of an element of integration. If this is done, the student will gradually acquire the ability to interpret problems and set up integrals for himself, and the application of the definite integral will come to have meaning for him, instead of seeming to be merely an assortment of tricks to be learned. If the student once gets a clear concept of the meaning of the element of integration for single definite integrals, the subsequent extension to double, triple, or multiple integrals in general will be plausible and comparatively easy for him.

The place of rigor in an elementary course

The foregoing discussion has dealt mainly with the matter of developing meanings and concepts. The illustrations used have dealt with simple functions, and rigorous treatment has not been attempted. This is not to say that rigorous work has no place in connection with the advanced study of the definite integral. On the contrary, if one is to justify completely the use of this important mathematical tool, it is absolutely necessary that a rigorous proof of the fundamental theorem be given.

Complete justification of the fundamental theorem requires rigorous proof

It should be kept in mind, however, that there is an important distinction between understanding and using a tool and justifying its use. As has been said before, it seems that in this case there is a substantial advantage to be gained by undertaking a thorough development of the concept and application of the definite integral before, perhaps even without, requiring a rigorous analytical proof of the theorem which justifies its use. Indeed, some elementary textbooks make no pretense of giving a rigorous proof of the theorem, but rest the case upon explanations which give understanding and plausibility but which involve a considerable amount of intuition.

All students should be required to understand the line of reasoning which underlies the proof of the fundamental theorem. If the customary geometrical interpretation is used as a basis for the explanation, the problem resolves itself, essentially, into showing that the area bounded by the curve $y = f(x)$, the x axis, and the perpendiculars erected to the x axis at the points $x = a$ and $x = b$ is exactly equal to the area given by the limit of the sum

$$f(x_1)\, \Delta x_1 + f(x_2)\, \Delta x_2 + f(x_3)\, \Delta x_3 + \cdots + f(x_n)\, \Delta x_n$$

as n becomes infinite and each Δx approaches zero as a limit, i.e.,

$\lim\limits_{n \to \infty} \sum\limits_{i=1}^{n} f(x_i)\, \Delta x_i$, where $\Delta x_i \to 0$ as $n \to \infty$. This is done by showing:

1 That a certain area, say A, is given by $F(b) - F(a)$, where a and b are particular values of x and $F(x) = \int f(x)\, dx$

2 That $\lim\limits_{n \to \infty} \sum\limits_{i=1}^{n} f(x_i)\, \Delta x_i$ gives *precisely* this same area A

Thus the students should come to see that the summation process may at any time be replaced by the definite integral and that the symbols $\lim\limits_{n \to \infty} \sum\limits_{i=1}^{n} f(x_i)\, \Delta x_i$ and $\int_{x_1}^{x_2} f(x)\, dx$ may be regarded as interchangeable, provided the function is continuous over the interval.

It should be pointed out that neither the conclusion embodied in the theorem nor the line of reasoning leading to it is limited to or dependent upon geometrical considerations, although a geometrical illustration was used and the problem was set up in terms of the summation of elements of area. This is done (1) because the graphic or geometric representation helps to give tangibility and concreteness to a situation otherwise highly abstract and (2) because functions may be represented graphically and interpreted geometrically even though they refer to nongeometric variables, such as forces, heat, and work. It should be emphasized that the definite integral may be used to determine any kind of magnitude, provided the characteristic function can be set up in conformity with the requirements stated above.

IMPROVEMENT OF PREREQUISITE CONCEPTS AND SKILLS

Prerequisite subjects must be thoroughly mastered

In addition to adding a whole new branch of mathematics to the student's equipment, the study of calculus holds tremendous possibilities for extending and deepening his understanding of the branches previously studied and the perfection of his skills in them. This is especially the case with reference to algebra, trigonometry, and analytic geometry. It has been said that the place where these subjects are really learned is in calculus. That this is more than a mere figure of speech will be evident from a consideration of the completeness with which the concepts and operations peculiar to these branches underlie and permeate the whole structure of calculus. Algebraic processes find application in innumerable connections throughout the course. Indeed, one of the main problems of formal integration is the algebraic transformation of functions into integrable forms. Trigonometric functions, identities, and transformations are also much in evidence, and a good understanding of analytic geometry is certainly a prime requisite, not only in setting up functions and equations for many of the applied problems, but in giving the student tangible geometric interpretations of the fundamental concepts of calculus.

Calculus provides a more meaningful concept of a function

Functions of many kinds are met with and are made the subject of various investigations and operations. Incidentally, it may be noted that calculus gives the student a more comprehensive concept of the nature of a function than he will have been able to get in his previous study. He will already have gained an understanding of the general meaning of a function and will have made some study of the variation of functions, but in calculus, for the first time, he will make a systematic study of a new aspect of functions, namely, the rate of change of a function with respect to its independent variable.

The student who, in taking up a study of calculus, lacks an adequate background in algebra, trigonometry, and analytic geometry will find himself at a great disadvantage. Indeed, it is not improbable that a large share of the difficulty which students experience in calculus may be directly traceable to inadequate mastery of the prerequisite branches. On the other hand, nowhere could there be found a finer opportunity for well-motivated review and application of their concepts and techniques. Every student should be made conscious of this and should be urged as a matter of enlightened self-interest to put forth every effort to perfect himself in these concepts and techniques. For students who have difficulty, the instructor may be able to perform a real service by helping them to diagnose their troubles and suggesting appropriate remedial exercises. The importance of perfecting the skills and having ready mastery of the concepts and relationships of algebra, trigonometry, and analytic geometry is a matter which should receive continual emphasis.

MATHEMATICAL RIGOR IN CALCULUS

The discussion in this chapter has admittedly given special emphasis to the matter of developing concepts and understandings because it has been felt that in general the teaching of calculus more often falls short in this respect than in any other. Intuitive concepts, however, do not provide sufficiently sound mathematical justification for the conclusions upon which much of calculus is based. Moreover, by the time the student has come through a study of calculus, he should have acquired a feeling for the nature of, and the necessity for, mathematical rigor *as such*. There can be no real appreciation of the nature of mathematical thinking, nor any sound basis for the exploration of higher mathematics, apart from an understanding of what is implied by a rigorous examination of the foundations of mathematics, the nature of the processes employed, and the consequences of given conditions.

Calculus stands more or less in the position of a borderline subject with respect to the matter of mathematical rigor. The courses which precede it are concerned mainly with the development of concepts, the acquisition of rules for operation, and the perfection of skills, although at some points there is an approach to real rigor in the treatment of certain theorems. On the other hand, the higher analytical courses are characterized by essentially rigorous and formal treatment of the subject matter. Thus, whether the student expects to "top off" his work in mathematics with calculus or go on into the domain of higher mathematics, it is important that his study of calculus provide him, both as a matter of appreciation and as a matter of training, with some opportunity for really rigorous examination of certain topics.

Calculus is a borderline course as far as rigor is concerned

Calculus offers numerous opportunities for such work in the analytical definitions associated with the concepts of limits, infinitesimals, continuity, differentials, derivatives, and the like, and in the proofs of certain theorems, such as Rolle's theorem, the theorem of the mean, the fundamental theorem of definite integrals, Taylor's theorem, and Maclaurin's theorem.

It is undoubtedly true that many students will be able to do little with this kind of work, but it must not be assumed merely on this account that the course is worthless to them. This, after all, is but one of the objectives of the course; it must not be forgotten that the use of a theorem and the proof of that same theorem are two entirely different matters and that things may often be extremely useful without being completely understood. But the distinction should be maintained between understanding the proof of a theorem and understanding the theorem. Every effort should be made to prevent the student from using a theorem blindly and mechanically. L'Hôpital's rule is a good case in point. The student must understand what the theorem asserts in order for him to apply it even by rote. But it is possible to make the rule plausible even for those students who have difficulty with the rigorous proof. Suppose $f(x)$ and $g(x)$ are such that $f(0) = g(0) = 0$. Then $[f(x)]/[g(x)]$ is indeterminate and L'Hôpital's rule applies. If we think of $f(x)$ and $g(x)$ as representing displacement in time x, then at time a both displacements are zero. But $f'(x)$ and $g'(x)$ give the respective velocities. It seems reasonable that for values close to a the ratio of the velocities $[f'(x)]/[g'(x)]$ should be close to the ratio of the displacements $[f(x)]/[g(x)]$. This does not prove L'Hôpital's rule, but it does make the results of application of the rule seem reasonable.

Geometric demonstrations can be used to make such theorems as the theorem of the mean and Rolle's theorem intuitively evident, and make very clear what the particular theorem is asserting to be true. On the other hand, students who are able to appreciate the significance of the type of analysis necessary for formal proof of such theorems and follow their development will find a satisfying sense of security and finality in their work which must otherwise be lacking. Those who expect to go further in mathematics will find the training afforded in this sort of rigorous treatment of the foundations and theorems of calculus to be of inestimable value to them in their later work.

EXERCISES

1   State and defend your point of view toward teaching calculus in high school. State whether it should be taught in high school, and if it should, what kind of course it should be.

2   It has been contended that if calculus is taught in high school, it should be a course for the non-college-bound. Comment on this. What are the implications of such a position for the nature of the course?

3   The opinion has sometimes been advanced that much of the difficulty students have in calculus is due to inability to handle basic elementary algebra and trigonometric identities with facility and assurance. Comment on this.

4   To what extent do you think students' difficulties in calculus stem from their inability to read and interpret readily the explanations and discussions in their calculus textbooks? Present some examples of material taken from a calculus textbook which you feel might involve difficulty of this nature, and explain what the difficulty is.

5   A recent trend was strongly toward combination courses such as analytic geometry and calculus. Give arguments for and against this practice.

6   Historically, integration preceded differentiation. Usually, but not universally, the order is reversed in teaching calculus today. Suggest possible reasons for this.

7 What do you consider the most serious indictment of the teaching of calculus in colleges and engineering schools?

8 Explain and present illustrations of the following terms: variable, constant, parameter, domain of a variable.

9 What is the rationale for the definition of the slope of a curve at a point as the slope of the tangent to the curve at this point?

10 Many freshman calculus students are positive that by definition the derivative of a function is the slope of the tangent to its graph. How would you proceed to dispel this notion?

11 Give an intuitive explanation or illustration, and also a formal definition, of what is meant by saying that a variable approaches a constant as a limit. What difficulties do students have with the formal definition?

12 Give a formal definition of a derivative, using the notation of the textbook you use. Then explain and clarify this, using various illustrations.

13 If f is a function of x, carefully distinguish between the derivative of f and the differential of f. Give three physical illustrations of the differentials of functions.

14 If $y = f(x)$, explain as you would to a class why it is that $\Delta x = dx$, while in general $\Delta y \neq dy$. Under what circumstances does $\Delta y = dy$?

15 Present arguments to justify or refute the assertion that in calculus the trigonometric identities play a more important role than the solution of triangles.

16 Find a method for approximating e. Use the approximation to find its value to three significant digits.

17 By using the definition and assuming the existence of the number e, present to the class a complete derivation of the formula for $D_x y$, where $y = \log_a x$, and show how this formula is simplified when a is taken to be e. (Note that this is where the number e really comes into the mathematical picture as an important constant.)

18 Show how the formula for the derivative of an exponential follows easily from the formula for the derivative of a logarithm.

19 See if you can find a function whose derivative is equal to its integral.

20 Present to the class a full derivation of the formula for $D_x y$, where $y = \cos x$.

21 By taking u as a function of x and using the formulas for the derivative of sin u and the derivative of a fraction, show how to obtain the formula for the derivative of tan x with respect to x.

22 By using the formulas for the derivatives of the trigonometric functions, show how to obtain the formulas for the derivatives of the inverse trigonometric functions.

23 Give a symbolic statement of the law of the mean. Then, using a diagram, explain and illustrate clearly the meaning of this formula. Give one instance in which this important law is used.

24 Repeat exercise 23 with the law of the mean replaced by Rolle's theorem.

25 Give a clear explanation of the role of first and second derivatives in the matter of locating and classifying critical points (relative maxima and minima and inflection points) on the graph of a function.

26 Explain clearly the meaning of an indefinite integral as an antiderivative. Why must an indefinite integral contain a constant of integration?

27 Explain clearly the meaning of a definite integral as the limit of a summation process. Show that the constant of integration is actually accounted for in the process of evaluating a definite integral.

28 By using the trapezoidal rule, find the approximate area bounded by the curve $y = 3x^2$, the x axis, and the ordinates at $x = 2$ and $x = 7$. Use $\Delta x = 1$. Check your result by integration. Explain your work to the class.

29 Give a clear geometric interpretation of a partial derivative, and explain your diagram in detail. Do the same for a directional derivative.

30 Enumerate five tests for the convergence of infinite series. Explain how and why each of these works and why it is really a test.

31 Cite a problem involving an improper integral, and show how it should be solved.

32 Pick out five things which seemed to you to present special difficulty when you were studying calculus. Try now to locate and identify the precise reasons these caused you difficulty. Then try to devise teaching procedures by which you would hope to make them clear to your own students.

BIBLIOGRAPHY

Allendoerfer, Carl B.: The Case against Calculus, *Mathematical Teacher,* **56** (1963), 482–485.

Anderson, A. G.: The Derivative of cos *x*, *American Mathematics Monthly,* **60** (1953), 255–256.

Apostol, T. M.: Term-wise Differentiation of Power Series, *American Mathematical Monthly,* **59** (1952), 323–326.

Baylock, Adrian: Graphical Interpretation of the Limit of an Intermediate Function, *Mathematics Teacher,* **57** (1964), 104–105.

Beninati, Albert: It's Time to Take a Closer Look at High School Calculus, *Mathematics Teacher,* **59** (1966), 29–30.

Blank, Albert A.: Remarks on the Teaching of Calculus in the Secondary School, *Mathematics Teacher,* **53** (1960), 537–539.

Boyer, Carl B.: "The Concepts of the Calculus" (New York: Columbia University Press, 1939).

Buchanan, Lexton O., Jr.: Opinions of College Teachers of Mathematics Regarding Content of the Twelfth-year Course in Mathematics, *Mathematics Teacher,* **58** (1965), 223–225.

Clair, Harry S.: The Theorem of the Mean and Its Application to Problems of Maxima and Minima, *School Science and Mathematics,* **57** (1957), 468–472.

Coffman, Raphael T.: An Elementary Approach to the Use of the Rate of Change Concept for Solving Problems, *Mathematics Magazine,* **30** (1956), 81–90.

Cummins, Kenneth: A Student Experience-discovery Approach to the Teaching of Calculus, *Mathematics Teacher,* **53** (1960), 162–170.

Cunningham, F., Jr.: Taking Limits under the Integral Sum, *Mathematics Magazine,* **40** (1967), 179–186.

Dubisch, Roy: "The Teaching of Mathematics" (New York: John Wiley & Sons, Inc., 1963), pp. 81–106.

Evans, Trevor, and Bevan K. Youse: "How to Solve Problems in Analytic Geometry and Calculus," vol. I (Englewood Cliffs, N.J.: Prentice-Hall, Inc., 1961).

Ferguson, W. Eugene: Calculus in the High School, *Mathematics Teacher,* **53** (1960), 451–453.

Graesser, R. F.: Notes on the Fundamental Theorem of Integral Calculus, *School Science and Mathematics,* **64** (1964), 523–524.

Hellman, M. J.: On the Evaluation of ∫ sec *x dx* and ∫ cos *x dx*, *Mathematics Teacher,* **59** (1966), 257.

Hight, Donald W.: The Limit Concept in the

Education of Teachers, *American Mathematical Monthly,* **70** (1963), 203–205.

Hildebrand, F. B.: A Simple Problem in Cylindrical Coordinates, *American Mathematical Monthly,* **64** (1957), 194–195.

Hildebrandt, E. H. C.: Remarks on "A Generation of High School Calculus," *American Mathematical Monthly,* **69** (1962), 430–433.

Hoffman, S.: A Classroom Proof of $\lim_{t \to 0} [(\sin t)/t]$, *American Mathematical Monthly,* **67** (1960), 671–672.

Karst, Otto J.: The Limit, *Mathematics Teacher,* **51** (1958), 443–449.

Kline, Morris: First Approach to Calculus through Physical Applications, "The Twelfth-Grade Pre-college Mathematics Program" (Washington: The National Council of Teachers of Mathematics, 1965). (One of a compendium of papers presented in Denver, Colorado, Jan. 30, 1965, at a joint session of the Mathematical Association of America and the National Council of Teachers of Mathematics.)

Leader, S.: On the Definition of ln *a*, *American Mathematical Monthly,* **66** (1959), 622–623.

Mattuck, Arthur P.: Some Remarks about the Calculus Course for Grade Twelve, "The Twelfth-Grade Pre-college Mathematics Program" (Washington: The National Council of Teachers of Mathematics, 1965). (One of a compendium of Papers presented in Denver, Colorado, Jan. 30, 1965, at a joint session of the Mathematical Association of America and the National Council of Teachers of Mathematics.)

McKillip, William D.: The Effects of High School Calculus on Students' First-semester Calculus Grades at the University of Virginia, *Mathematics Teacher,* **59** (1966), 470–472.

Munroe, M. E.: Bringing Calculus Up-to-date, *American Mathematical Monthly,* **65** (1958), 81–90.

Neeley, J. H.: What to Do about a New Kind of Freshman, *American Mathematical Monthly,* **66** (1959), 584–586.

————: The Generation of Calculus, *American Mathematical Monthly,* **68** (1961), 1004–1005.

"New Directions in Mathematics," the Dartmouth College Mathematics Conference (Englewood Cliffs, N.J.: Prentice-Hall, Inc., 1962).

Ogilvy, C. S.: A Calculus Problem with Overtones in Related Fields, *American Mathematical Monthly,* **65** (1958), 765–767.

Pagel, H. Armin: Logarithms, Exponentials, and

Their Integrations: Some Calculus for Chemists, *Journal of Chemical Education,* **36** (1959), 238–241.

Parker, F. D.: Integrals of Inverse Functions, *American Mathematical Monthly,* **62** (1955), 439–440.

Pascual, M. J.: On the $\lim_{\theta \to 0} \cos \theta$, *American Mathematical Monthly,* **62** (1955), 252–253.

———: The Derivatives of the Trigonometric Functions, *Mathematics Magazine,* **31** (1957), 39–40.

Perry, Gary: Alternate Classroom Proof that $(\sin t)/t \to 1$ as $t \to 0$, *American Mathematical Monthly,* **70** (1963), 426–427.

Randolf, John F.: Limits, *Twenty-third Yearbook* (Washington, D.C.: National Council of Teachers of Mathematics, 1957), pp. 220–240.

Ransom, W. R.: The Fundamental Theorem of the Differential Calculus, *American Mathematical Monthly,* **62** (1955), 361–363.

Richmond, D. E.: Calculus: A New Look, *American Mathematical Monthly,* **70** (1963), 415–423.

Rising, Gerald R.: Some Comments on Teaching Calculus in Secondary Schools, *American Mathematical Monthly,* **68** (1961), 287–290.

Thruston, H. A.: A Simple Way of Differentiating Trigonometric Functions and Their Inverses in an Elementary Calculus Course, *American Mathematical Monthly,* **70** (1963), 424.

Walsh, J. L.: "A Rigorous Treatment of Maximum-Minimum Problems in the Calculus" (Boston: D. C. Heath and Company, 1962).

Willerding, Margaret F.: Infinity and Its Presentation at the High School Level, *School Science and Mathematics,* **63** (1963), 463–474.

Willoughby, Stephen S.: Revolution, Rigor, and Rigor Mortis, *Mathematics Teacher,* **60** (1967), 105–108.

Wolfe, James: An Adjusted Trapezoidal Rule Using Function Values within the Range of Integration, *American Mathematical Monthly,* **66** (1959), 125–127.

Wollan, G. N.: Maclaurin and Taylor and Their Series, *Mathematics Teacher,* **61** (1968), 310–312.

Yates, R. C.: The Logarithm and Its Inverse, *Mathematics Teacher,* **51** (1958), 105–106.

———: The Trigonometric Functions, *Mathematics Teacher,* **51** (1958), 191–193.

Zeitlin, David: An Application of the Mean Value Theorem, *American Mathematical Monthly,* **64** (1957), 427.

———: On Plane Area in Polar Coordinates, *American Mathematical Monthly,* **66** (1959), 135–136.

eighteen | the teaching of probability and statistics

There are two kinds of statistics, descriptive statistics and inferential statistics. The former consists of techniques for organizing a mass of data in such a way that they are manageable and interpretable. The latter is concerned with reaching conclusions about a total population based on an examination of a sample of that population. Probability and statistics are used together because probability is essential to statistical inference. The conclusions of statistical inference are stated as probabilities. It should be apparent that conclusions concerning a total population cannot be known with certainty when they are based on a small sample of the population.

Two kinds of statistics

A modicum of descriptive statistics has been taught in the junior high school for years. College algebra, whether in the freshman year of college or the senior year of high school, traditionally contains a unit on probability. Its apparent purpose has been to provide an interesting setting in which to use combination and permutation formulas. But statistical inference as a secondary school course is a relatively new innovation.

Statistical inference in high school is an innovation

In its 1959 Report,[1] the Commission on Mathematics of the College Entrance Examination Board recommended the introduction of a semester course, Introductory Probability with Statistical Applications, as one of the three options for the second semester of grade 12, and sponsored the production of an experimental text for such a course.[2]

In 1959 CEEB recommended introducing a course

The Commission's recommendation was not for a "more elaborate presentation of descriptive statistics" that is commonly found in the junior high school. It was to be "built around concepts of great importance for our modern technological society—the theory of probability."[3] The course has both great practical and great mathematical appeal. The practical appeal of calculus is largely limited to the scientist, the engineer, and the mathematician. But

This course was based on probability

[1] "Report of the Commission on Mathematics" (New York: College Entrance Examination Board, 1959), p. 31.
[2] Commission on Mathematics, "Introductory Probability and Statistical Inference," rev. preliminary edition (New York: College Entrance Examination Board, 1959).
[3] "Report of the Commission on Mathematics," *op. cit.*

Probability has
wide applicability

probability and statistics have utility for practically everyone, since most people have to make decisions based on essentially statistical data.

The course was not
widely accepted

The course has not proved as popular as its advocates had hoped.[4] Its strongest competitor for a place in the curriculum is calculus. High school teachers have shown a decided preference for calculus. Whatever other factors may be involved, the typical high school teacher feels far more competent to teach calculus than statistics.[5] This, in turn, is a reflection of the courses he has taken.

On the other hand, Buchanan has found that college teachers give calculus the lowest mark as a desirable high school subject, with probability and statistics close behind analytic geometry and elementary functions in order of preference.[6]

STATISTICS IN THE JUNIOR HIGH SCHOOL

The need for de-
scriptive statistics

Knowledge of the basic rudiments of statistics is increasingly important for the mathematically literate person in this century. The ability to read and interpret tables, charts, and graphs has become a commonplace necessity. But this is a special kind of reading that requires its own techniques and whose development must not be left to chance.

Statistics for junior
high school
students is not a
separate course

In the junior high school there is not a separate course in statistics. However, an integral part of the mathematics of these grades should include such topics from descriptive statistics as the averages (mean, median, and mode); graphical interpretation of data; the making of frequency distributions, histograms, and polygons; and measures of dispersion.

The emphasis is
on interpretation
of concepts

The mathematical computation required for the statistics in the junior high school is not difficult. Essentially, it provides motivated practice necessary for maintenance of basic skills. The importance of statistical work at this level lies in understanding of concepts and the ability to read and interpret the statistical demonstrations of others. It is more important for the junior high school student to know how to read and interpret a graph than to know how to construct one. This is not to say that construction of graphs should not be studied. On the contrary, the surest road to understanding what a graph reveals is to know how to construct it.

The computation necessary in determining averages is minimal.

[4] Lauren G. Woodby: "Emerging Twelfth Grade Mathematics Programs," U.S. Office of Education Report (Washington: U.S. Government Printing Office, 1965), pp. 25–26.

[5] *Ibid.*, p. 35.

[6] O. Lexton Buchanan, Jr., Opinions of College Teachers of Mathematics Regarding Content of the Twelfth-year Course in Mathematics, *Mathematics Teacher,* **58** (1965), 223–225.

But insight, entirely out of proportion to the difficulty of computation, is required if the student is to know when a particular average is the most appropriate, or how averages can be misused to mislead the reader.

Knowing how to compute measures of dispersion is no guarantee that their significance will be understood.

FREQUENCY DISTRIBUTIONS

A set of statistical data usually consists of a set of measurements of a set of *subjects*. The trait measured is called a *chance variable*, or *statistical variable*. The individual measurements are called *variates*. For example, one might be concerned with the grades a class made on a mathematics test. The students are the subjects, the test grade is the variable, and the individual grades scored are the variates.

A frequency distribution makes a set of scores manageable

If the number of variates is so large that they cannot readily be summarized, they should be grouped in some fashion. The best way to accomplish this is by forming a *frequency distribution*. This is a grouping of all variates into classes according to their size. Since no measurement is exact, placing the variates in a frequency distribution has the effect of increasing the apparent error of the variates. For example, the boys of a school are weighed to the nearest pound, and the weights are separated into *classes*, with a *class width* of 10 pounds. A boy who is measured to weigh 123 pounds has an exact weight somewhere in the range 122.5 to 123.5 pounds. But when he is included in a frequency distribution and falls in a class with *class boundaries* 120 and 130 pounds, the net effect is to indicate his weight as 125 ± 5, rather than 123 ± 0.5.

A frequency distribution increases apparent error of variates

In setting up a frequency distribution certain precautions should be observed. The number of class intervals into which the variates are separated should not be so few that the characteristics of the set of variates are obscured, nor so numerous that little is gained by grouping. A good working rule calls for no fewer than 10 nor more than 25 class intervals. Of course, all class widths should be the same, and the class boundaries should actually separate the variates. The class boundaries should be values that cannot be a variate. For example, if the weights of a set of junior high school boys are obtained to the nearest pound, the class boundaries should be midway between two consecutive integral pounds. In this way no variate can fall on a class boundary. If the boys' weights vary from 50 to 150 pounds, one can use eleven class intervals. A class width of 10 pounds will make it possible for the smallest variate to lie about the middle of its interval, and similarly for the largest variate. This is desirable because there usually are few variates at the extremes of the distri-

How to set up a frequency distribution

No variate should be a class boundary

TABLE 18-1
Weights of junior high school boys

Class boundary	Class mark	Frequency
49.5		
	54.5	1
59.5		
	64.5	2
69.5		
	74.5	23
79.5		
	84.5	74
89.5		
	94.5	118
99.5		
	104.5	113
109.5		
	114.5	83
119.5		
	124.5	50
129.5		
	134.5	20
139.5		
	144.5	13
149.5		
	154.5	3
159.5		

bution. The lowest interval will have boundaries 49.5 and 59.5, and the highest interval will have boundaries 149.5 and 159.5.

Table 18-1 shows a frequency distribution of the weights of 500 junior high school boys. The class mark is midway between the class boundaries. When making computations from a frequency distribution, the identity of the original variate is gone. The new variates are the class marks, and the frequency in each class interval becomes the *weight* of the class mark.

Class marks are new variates

AVERAGES

One of the most important contributions that descriptive statistics can make for junior high school students is understanding of the use and meaning of the measures of *central tendency*, the *averages*. The three most commonly used averages are the mean, the median, and the mode. These measures are called measures of central

"Central tendency" means "most representative variate"

tendency, because each is, from one point of view, the single variate that best represents the total set of variates.

The *mean,* more properly called the *arithmetic mean,* is more frequently called, simply, the *average.* The mean is defined as the sum of all the variates divided by the number of variates.

$$M = \frac{\sum_{i=1}^{n} x_i}{n}$$

The *median* is defined as the mid-variate when the variates are arranged in order of size. The *mode* is defined as the variate that occurs most frequently.

The sense in which
each average is
most representative

Students should come to appreciate the sense in which each measure is the most representative of the set of variates. The mean is not necessarily the most frequently encountered variate; nor is it one such that there is the same number of variates, larger and smaller. It may differ from each of the individual variates. It is the most typical in terms of its size. Imagine the larger variates decreased and the smaller variates correspondingly increased. If this process is continued until all variates are the same size, then each is equal to the mean.

The median can be visualized as a variate such that, if another variate is chosen at random, it is just as likely to be larger as it is to be smaller.

The mode is the most typical variate in the sense that, if a variate is selected at random, the mode is the most likely one to be chosen.

Each average has its peculiar advantages and limitations. Many illustrations should be used to highlight this for the students. Examples should also be used to show how an inappropriate average can be used to leave an incorrect impression concerning the nature of the complete set of variates. For example, it is not at all unusual for the mean to differ from each one of the variates. If the "average man" is an arithmetic average, he very likely is a non-existent man. If the mean is used to describe a dichotomous set of variates, it is completely misleading. For example, if a distribution consists of 50 variates with a measure 10, and 50 variates with measure 100, the mean of the distribution is 55. The only sense in which this typifies the distribution is that it gives an indirect means for finding the aggregate. It is misleading in that it indicates a point of central tendency about which there are clustered no variates.

A useful exercise in developing the significance of the different averages is exploration of such questions as: What can you infer about a set of variates if the mean is greater than the median? Which average is most likely to be affected if additional variates are added to the set? If a large number of variates cluster at one end of the range, what effect does this have on each average?

OTHER MEASURES

The averages are the most important statistical measures studied in the junior high school. But study of the averages should lead to a realization of their inadequacy in describing a mass of data.

The range as a
measure of
dispersion

The range of a set of data is the largest variate minus the smallest. The mean along with the range tells much more about a set of variates than the mean alone. This can be illustrated by an extreme case. Consider two samples taken from Table 18-1. The first consists of 48 of the 113 variates in the interval whose class mark is 104.5. The mean of this sample is 104.5. The second sample consists of 48 variates, 6 from each of the intervals with class marks 74.5 to 144.5. This sample also has 104.5 as its mean. In the first case the mean is 104.5 and the range is 10. In the second case the mean is 104.5 and the range is 80.

Inadequacy of the
range as a measure
of dispersion

The range is easy to find and quite helpful in organizing a mass of data. The range is a measure of *dispersion,* or the extent to which the variates tend to differ from the measure of central tendency. Sometimes the range is inadequate. It is possible for two sets of variates to have the same mean and the same range, yet differ markedly. For example, a third sample could have the same range and mean as the second one described above and yet have its scores concentrated at the ends of the range. There could be 12 variates from the interval with class mark 74.5, 12 variates from the interval with class mark 84.5, 12 variates from the interval with class mark 134.5, and 12 variates from the interval with class mark 144.5. This set of variates will have the same mean, 104.5, and the same range, 80.

STANDARD DEVIATION

Another measure of dispersion, the *standard deviation,* does more than show how far the variates can range. It measures the extent to which the variates tend to cluster around the mean.

The significance of
the standard
deviation depends
on probability
theory

The standard deviation has limited application in the junior high school. The computation of a standard deviation from ungrouped data can be quite a task. Its value as a descriptive statistic is limited until one has studied probability theory and statistical inference.

At whatever level it is studied, it is worthwhile for the student to compute a few standard deviations for ungrouped data. Standard deviation is sometimes called the *root-mean-square deviation.* This name is more indicative of how it is obtained than of how it is interpreted.

How to find the
standard deviation

The standard deviation of a set of variates is the square root of the mean of the squares of the deviations from the mean of the variates. Thus, to find a standard deviation one must:

1 Find the mean of the variates
2 Find the deviation of each variate from the mean of the variates
3 Square each deviation
4 Find the mean of the squares of the deviations
5 Find the square root of the mean of the squares of the deviations

If there is a large number of variates, the required computation is formidable. But if the computation is made from a frequency distribution, it is much shorter.

Computations from a frequency distribution are actually weighted computations of the class marks. Sometimes it is desirable to attach more significance to some variates than to others. For example, in determining a cost-of-living index, the importance of the cost of a given item depends on the quantity of that item consumed. Each item is given a weight to represent its relative significance. The weighted mean of n variates, x_i, each having a weight w_i, is

A weighted mean attaches more significance to some variates than to others

$$W_x = \frac{\sum\limits_{i=1}^{n} x_i w_i}{\sum\limits_{i=1}^{n} w_i}$$

In working from a frequency distribution, the weight assigned to each class mark is the frequency of that class interval.

Table 18-2 contains the same data as Table 18-1. The class boundaries have been omitted; they are implied from the class marks. The column headed f gives the frequency in each class interval. The column headed x gives the new set of variates. They are *deviation scores*, measured from an arbitrarily chosen zero point, with the interval width as unit. In constructing such a

TABLE 18-2

Class mark	f	x	fx	fx^2
54.5	1	−5	−5	25
64.5	2	−4	−8	32
74.5	23	−3	−69	207
84.5	74	−2	−148	296
94.5	118	−1	−118	118
104.5	113	0	0	0
114.5	83	1	83	83
124.5	50	2	100	200
134.5	20	3	60	180
144.5	13	4	52	208
154.5	3	5	15	75
Sum	500		−38	1,424

table it is important for the student to see the full significance of this column. It can be proved that the sum of the weighted deviations of a set of variates from the weighted mean of the set of variates is zero. The column marked fx, which is the product $f \times x$, gives the weighted deviation scores. The sum of the fx column should be zero if the arbitrarily chosen zero class mark is actually the mean of the original variates. But if the sum of the fx column is not zero, this represents a correction to be applied to the mean (zero deviation). The sum -38 is the sum of the weighted deviations from the weighted mean. Then, since there is a total frequency of 500, the correction to be applied to the assumed weighted mean is $-38/500$. If this is to be converted to the original scale, it must be multiplied by the width of the interval. The mean is the arbitrarily chosen class mark plus this correction.

Computation from a frequency distribution

$$M_x = 104.5 + 10 \times \frac{-38}{500}$$

$$= 103.74$$

It is instructive to have the students choose various class marks as assumed means and to compare results. It is also a convincing exercise to have students choose various sizes for the class intervals in making frequency distributions for the same data.

In Table 18-2 the fx^2 column is obtained by multiplying the corresponding elements in the x column and the fx column: $fx^2 = x \times fx$. The sum of this column is the weighted sum of the squares of the deviations from the assumed mean. Then, except for the correction factor resulting from $\Sigma fx \neq 0$, the sum of the fx^2 divided by the total frequency is the square of the standard deviation σ_x. It can be shown that the square of the correction used in finding the mean must be subtracted from $\Sigma fx^2/\Sigma f$. Thus the standard deviation obtained from grouped data is

Class is variate, frequency is weight

$$\sigma_x = \sqrt{\frac{\Sigma fx^2}{\Sigma f} - \left(\frac{\Sigma fx}{\Sigma f}\right)^2}$$

From Table 18-2 we have

$$\sigma_x = \sqrt{\frac{1,424}{500} - \left(\frac{-38}{500}\right)^2}$$

as the standard deviation in interval units. Since the interval width in Table 18-2 is 10 units, the standard deviation in terms of original units is found to be

$$\sigma_x = 10 \sqrt{\frac{1,424}{500} - \left(\frac{-38}{500}\right)^2}$$

It is important for the students to understand the significance of a frequency table like Table 18-2. Many more complicated statistical measures begin with a frequence distribution of this sort.

GRAPHS

Statistical graphs constitute a significant part of the statistics of the junior high school.

Kinds of statistical graphs

The most common types of graphs used for statistical representation are line graphs, bar graphs, and circle graphs or pie charts. All these graphs have one thing in common: they picture a function.

If this is emphasized in developing techniques of construction and interpretation of statistical graphs, a double benefit accrues. The student's conception of function should be sharpened and broadened by contact with functions whose domain is not necessarily a set of numbers. The function approach to graphing should also enhance the student's ability to visualize what the graph really represents.

Values to be derived from work with graphs

In statistical terms, the graph can be described as a pictorial representation of a function relating a set of *subjects* with their respective variates (or measures).

A graph pictures a function

For example, the domain of the graph pictured in Fig. 18-1 is the set of countries, and the range is the set of variates, that is, the measures of the amounts of coffee exported to the United States by each of the eight countries.

In Fig. 18-2 the domain consists of the budget items, and the range is the set of percents devoted to the items. Each sector of the circle represents an ordered pair of the function. The particular budget item is an element of the domain, and the corresponding number of percents is its image in the range.

Advantages of each type of graph

Reading and interpreting graphs should be a major objective in the study of graphs in the junior high school. A necessary ingredient of this is knowing the desirable features of each type of graph. A bar graph such as that in Fig. 18-1 is ideal for comparing any two of the elements involved. If a time function is being graphed, that is, if the domain is a set of times, the bar graph is good for showing trends. But a line graph might serve the purpose better. Figure 18-3 shows a (time, temperature) function. The graph of the function is the set of dots. The lines connecting the dots are an aid in showing the trend. Reading a graph is much like reading a table. One must find the two sets of variables and know how to select an ordered pair, given either the first element or the second element of the pair.

Relationship between a graph and a table

Students should have practice in determining what type of graph to use

Students should have considerable practice in selecting the best type of graph to use to convey the information desired. For example, if it is desirable to compare each element with the whole, as well as element with element, a 100 percent bar graph is more functional than the ordinary bar graph. Figure 18-4 shows a different family budget than Fig. 18-2. The 100 percent bar graph attempts to combine the advantages of the ordinary bar graph and the circle graph.

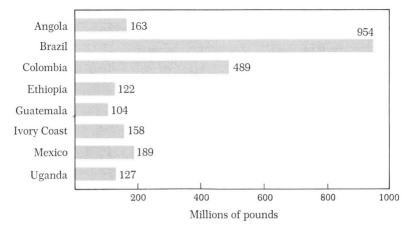

Figure 18-1
Annual imports to the United States of coffee from the eight chief suppliers.

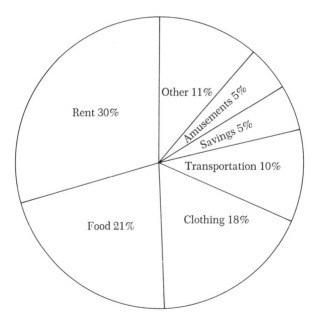

A family budget.

Sometimes a graph is selected on the basis of eye appeal and ease of interpretation. The pictograph is of this sort. Students should be cautioned in constructing pictographs that the comparison must be made in terms of the number of pictures, not the size of the picture; consequently, all the pictures must be of the same size. (See Fig. 18-5.) The same caution applies to bar graphs. All bars should be of the same width.

The pictograph is eye-catching

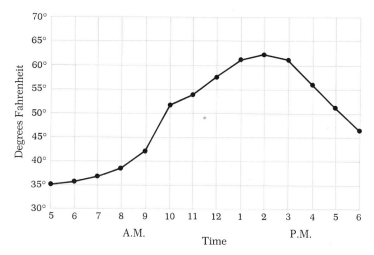

Figure 18-3
Hourly temperature readings, 6 A.M. to 6 P.M.

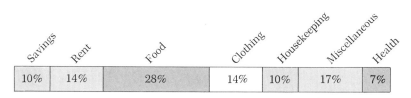

Figure 18-4
Bar graph of a family budget (total = 100 percent).

Figure 18-5
Do students in a certain school like the school? (Each figure represents 100 students.)

One type of graph is especially important to the study of probability and statistical inference. This is the *histogram,* a special kind of bar graph that is used to graph a frequency distribution. In a histogram the bars are placed vertically and there is no space between bars. The width of the bar is the class width of the frequency distribution. The height of each bar is proportional to the frequency in that class interval.

Table 18-3 gives the frequency distribution for 504 junior high school students according to age. The histogram representing this distribution (Fig. 18-6) must have ten bars. Sometimes it is

Histograms are important in studying probability

The use of relative frequency

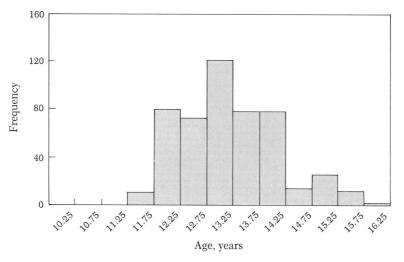

Figure 18-6
Ages of 504 junior high school students.

TABLE 18-3
Ages of 504 junior high school boys

Class boundary (age)	Class mark	Frequency	Relative frequency (percent)
11.25			
	11.50	10	2
11.75			
	12.00	81	16
12.25			
	12.50	75	15
12.75			
	13.00	126	25
13.25			
	13.50	80	16
13.75			
	14.00	80	16
14.25			
	14.50	15	3
14.75			
	15.00	24	5
15.25			
	15.50	12	2
15.75			
	16.00	1	0
16.25			
Total		504	100

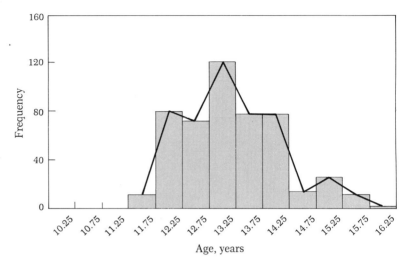

Figure 18-7
A frequency polygon.

desirable for the combined heights of all the bars to equal unity on the vertical scale. When this is done, the relative-frequency column of Table 18-3 is useful.

The idea of a histogram leads to that of a frequency polygon

The histogram of a frequency distribution leads naturally to the idea of a *frequency polygon.* The frequency polygon is the graph of a function whose domain is the set of class marks and whose range is the corresponding set of frequencies; each (class mark, frequency) pair defines a point. The graph (Fig. 18-7) is similar to that in Fig. 18-3, the points being joined by line segments. The polygon may be obtained from the histogram by joining the mid-points of the tops of the bars in the histogram.

A frequency curve may be obtained from a frequency polygon

If the number of variates is increased indefinitely and the class width is decreased in inverse proportion, the frequency polygon will approach a continuous curve, called a *frequency curve.* The frequency curve is the graph of a continuous function which, with the proper choice of unit, becomes a *probability function.*

PROBABILITY AND STATISTICAL INFERENCE IN THE SENIOR HIGH SCHOOL

The senior high school course has little in common with earlier work in statistics

Courses in probability and statistical inference to be offered in the twelfth grade will be in marked contrast to the treatment of statistical topics considered in the junior high school grades. There will be additional concepts to be clarified, and the treatment will be more sophisticated. In the remainder of this chapter we shall turn our attention to a few of the important ideas and strategies that would be involved in such a course.

PROBABILITY

The topic of probability usually requires little motivation. Its relation to betting odds doubtless accounts for some of its fascination. But from the standpoint of developing correct concepts and relating probability to statistical inference, a much better approach to the subject is through the concepts of sample space and probability function.

An *experiment* is a procedure that can be carried to a conclusion. A *trial* consists of carrying out the procedure. An *outcome* is a possible termination of the experiment. To illustrate, a possible experiment consists of drawing a card from a pack of ordinary playing cards. A trial consists of actually making a draw. There are fifty-two outcomes; drawing any specified card of the pack is an outcome.

The set of all possible outcomes of an experiment is a *sample space*. An *event* is any subset of the set of outcomes. In the card-drawing experiment, drawing a black face card is an event. This is a subset of the set of twelve outcomes, three face cards in each of four suits.

If a sample space has a finite number of outcomes, each outcome has a nonnegative number assigned to it as its *probability*. The sum of the probabilities of all the outcomes must equal 1. Thus there is a function relation, with the outcomes as domain and their probabilities as range.

Definition

A probability function of a discrete random variable with finite domain is any function, each element of whose range is equal to or greater than zero, and such that the sum of the elements of the range is 1.

In a probability function each element of the range is the probability of the corresponding element of the domain. The particular number assigned to each outcome depends upon the nature of the experiment. The probabilities may be based on experience, or they may be based on theoretical considerations. If the outcomes are equally likely, and there are n outcomes, the probability of each is $1/n$.

If the foregoing kind of approach to probability is used, such questions as the probability of independent events, of one event followed by another, and of at least one of two mutually exclusive events, become questions concerning subsets of the universal set, the sample space.

PERMUTATIONS AND COMBINATIONS

The study of permutations and combinations is usually carried on in conjunction with the study of probability. Permutation formulas follow readily from the rule for counting successive events.

Rule of counting

If task A can be done in a ways, and after task A has been done, then task B can be done in b ways, both tasks can be done in the specified order in ab ways.

From this rule the formula for the number of permutations of n things r at a time follows immediately.

$$P(n,r) = n(n-1)(n-2) \cdots \text{(to } r \text{ factors)}$$

But the formula that is usually more useful depends on the definition of n factorial for n a nonnegative integer.

$$P(n,r) = \frac{n!}{(n-r)!}$$

From the formula for $P(n,r)$ we have as a special case that $P(r,r) = r!$ Since, by definition, each combination of r things can be arranged in $r!$ ways, the *rule of counting* provides a convenient method to determine the formula for $C(n,r)$, the number of combinations of n things taken r at a time, from the known $P(n,r)$. From the rule of counting we have

The combinations formula is derived from the permutations formula

$$C(n,r) \times P(r,r) = P(n,r)$$
$$C(n,r) = \frac{P(n,r)}{P(r,r)} = \frac{n!}{(n-r)!} \times \frac{1}{r!}$$
$$= \frac{n!}{(n-r)!r!}$$

In its broader application, however, a more meaningful derivation is through the concept of set partition. This approach is more in keeping with the approach to probability that employs the concepts of sample space and a probability function.

A set is *partitioned* when it is divided into two or more disjoint and exhaustive subsets. An *ordered partition* with n cells is a partition with a particular order specified for the n cells. Suppose a clerk has 50 letters to file in three files, 25 in the first file, 15 in the second file, and 10 in the third file. The number of ways this can be done is the number of ordered partitions of 50 things into three cells, 25, 15, and 10 to the first, second, and third cells, respectively. Assume the clerk placed the first 25 letters in file 1, the next 15 in file 2, and the remaining 10 in file 3. The 50 letters can be arranged in 50! ways. But the first 25 can be arranged in 25! ways, and the next 15 can be arranged in 15! ways, and the last 10 in 10! ways for each distinct partition of the 50 letters. Hence the number of partitions is

$$\frac{50!}{25!15!10!}$$

In general, if n objects are partitioned into an ordered partition with t cells, $n_1, n_2, \ldots, n_t$ objects in the first, second, . . . , tth cells, respectively, the number of possible partitions is

$$\frac{n!}{n_1! n_2! \cdots n_t!}$$

The number of ordered partitions into two cells with r objects in one cell and $(n - r)$ in the other is

$$\frac{n!}{r!(n - r)!}$$

Combination as two-cell partition

Of course, the number of ways to partition a set of n elements into two cells, r elements in one of the cells, is exactly the same as the number of ways to select r things from n things, which is the meaning of "number of combinations of n things r at a time."

THE BINOMIAL DISTRIBUTION

Discrete random variable

It can be shown that if p is the probability that an event will occur on a single trial, the probability that it will occur exactly r times in n trials is $C(n,r)p^r q^{n-r}$, where $q = 1 - p$. This is one of the most important probability functions of a discrete variable. To see that it is a probability function it is sufficient to note: (1) $C(n,r)p^r q^{n-r}$ is a positive number for any r, $0 \leqslant r \leqslant n$. Since $C(n,r) > 0$, $p > 0$, $q > 0$, the product is greater than zero. (2) $\sum_{r=0}^{n} C(n,r)p^r q^{n-r} = 1$. This follows immediately if one recognizes that $C(n,r)p^r q^{n-r}$ is the $(n - r)$th term of the expansion of the binomial $(p + q)^n$. The sum of all the terms in the expansion is equal to the value of $(p + q)^n$. If $q = (1 - p)$, we have $(p + 1 - p)^n = 1^n = 1$.

The probability function $C(n,r)p^r q^{n-r}$ is a function of a discrete random variable. The simplest example of this is obtained if $p = q = \frac{1}{2}$ and $n = 2$. It can be shown that for any p and $q(=1 - p)$, if p and q are fixed and n increases without bound, then the histograms of the probability functions $C(n,r)p^r q^{n-r}$ approach the normal probability curve

The normal probability function

$$y = \frac{1}{\sqrt{2\pi}} e^{-x^2/2}$$

provided the histograms are in standard scales, that is, the mean is taken as the zero point and the standard deviation as the unit.

The normal probability function is of great theoretical value. It can be approximated experimentally in a number of ways. Coin-tossing experiments are convincing demonstrations of the normal distribution of error. If each member of the class tosses 10 coins simultaneously for 50 times, recording the number of heads and tails on each toss, and if the results of all members of the class are

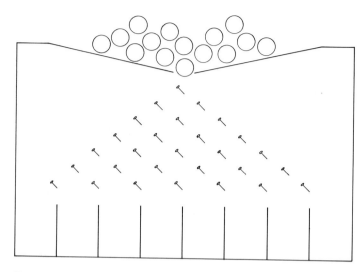

Figure 18-8
A normal-distribution board.

combined, the result is usually a remarkably good approximation to normal distribution predicted by expansion of $(H + T)^{10}$.

Another interesting physical demonstration of normal distribution can be made with a simple device like that pictured in Fig. 18-8. Nails are driven in a pegboard, as indicated and spaced, so that the falling ball must hit and fall on one side or the other of one of the nails in each row. The probability is 1/2 that the ball will fall to the right any time it hits a nail. As a large number of balls are released, they will distribute themselves normally in the lower slots.

Normal distribution of random errors is basic to much of statistical inference. But the teacher should be on guard to dispel the popularly held notion that the measures of any trial obtained from any set of subjects must be normally distributed. Not all probability functions are binomial, and certainly not all distributions are normal.

Probability distribution

Not all distributions are normal

OTHER TOPICS

Statistics has experienced a phenomenal growth during its first century of existence, both in theory and in application. A semester, or year, course in statistical inference in high school can no more exhaust the subject than can a year's study of geometry cover the whole of that subject.

The course should stress basic underlying ideas that permeate the subject. The normal probability curve, sometimes called the

Properties of the
normal curve

curve of error, should be studied from the standpoint of its mathematical properties: bell-shaped; symmetric to the mean; inflection points at plus and minus one standard deviation from the mean; everywhere above the x axis but approaching it asymptotically on each end; area under the curve 1. It should also be studied from the standpoint of its application, its relationship to probability theory.

The student should come to appreciate the fact that all his conclusions from statistical inference are in the form of probabilities. Consequently, he should know of the importance of sound sampling techniques. Opinion polls are a familiar occurrence, but the accuracy with which results from the entire population can be predicted from a minutely small sample is fantastic. Today's students will be interested in learning of the famous poll failure of 1936 and the fact that it failed because of a predictably biased sample.

Opinion polls

Meaning of
correlation

One of the earliest, and still most useful, statistical measures is the measure of correlation. Correlation is a measure of the extent to which two sets of variates obtained from the same set of subjects tend to agree. If the correlation were perfect, the score of a given subject on one trait would be sufficient to predict perfectly his score on the second trait. The measure of correlation, known as a correlation coefficient, is a number r such that $-1 \leqslant r \leqslant 1$. A coefficient -1 means that the subject with the highest score on one trait has the lowest on the other, and so on. If $r = 0$, the two sets of variates are unrelated.

Correlation coefficients cannot be treated quantitatively in the same way as probability. If the probability of event A is .25 and the probability of event B is .50, then B has twice as good a chance of occurring as A has. But if the correlation between two sets of scores is .25 and the correlation between two other sets of similar scores is .50, it cannot be said meaningfully that there is twice as close a relationship between the second pair as between the first. What constitutes a high correlation depends upon the nature of the traits measured. Interpretation of the meaning of correlation coefficients requires much experience.

Interpretation of
correlation requires
experience

There is one misconception that should be dispelled. Correlation has nothing to say about cause and effect, or common causation. Correlation cannot explain the reason for similarity; it can simply measure the extent of its presence or absence.

EXERCISES

1 Distinguish between descriptive statistics and statistical inference. Give illustrations of statistical applications that fall in each category.

2 If class boundaries separate the variates, does this mean that all statistical variables are discrete variables? Discuss,

3 Outline a plan for use with a junior high

school class for distinguishing among mean, median, and mode as measures of central tendency.

4 Give descriptions of situations where only one (the mean, the median, or the mode) is an appropriate measure.

5 Which will be affected the more by addition of extremely high variates, the mean or the median? Why?

6 If additional scores are added to a distribution and the median is increased but the mean is not, what does this indicate about the scores that were added?

7 Make up two sets of variates that have the same mean but markedly different standard deviations.

8 Why would the mean of the deviations of a set of variates not be a good measure of dispersion of the variates?

9 If the standard deviation of a set of variates is zero, what does this tell about the variates?

10 Design a class experiment whose purpose is to illustrate the value of standard deviation.

11 What is the significance of the name "root-mean-square deviation," a synonym for standard deviation?

12 Find in some statistics text the difference between the standard deviation from the mean and the standard error of the mean. Outline the procedure you would use to make the distinction clear to a high school statistics class.

13 Find examples of situations that are likely to require the use of the weighted mean.

14 Describe kinds of situations in which each of the following types of graphs would be preferable: pie chart, pictograph, bar graph, line graph.

15 Do you think the idea of a function should be emphasized in studying statistical graphs? Give reasons for your answer.

16 If the total area of the bars of a histogram is 1 and the width of each bar is 1 on the horizontal axis, what is 1 on the vertical axis? What are the heights of the individual bars?

17 Construct a histogram showing the theoretical number of times no head, one head, and so on to 6 heads will appear when six coins are tossed 64 times.

18 Outline a plan for presenting the concept of sample space to a class.

19 Use the definition of a probability function given on page 579 to show that if an event is certain, its probability is 1.

20 How can the sum of the probabilities of two events from the same sample be greater than 1?

21 In terms of sample space, explain how the probability of an event can be zero.

22 The outcomes of an experiment must be mutually exclusive. Is this inherent in the definition of a probability function?

23 Explain why two events need not be mutually exclusive.

24 The coefficients of the terms of the binomial expansion are frequently given in terms of $C(n,r)$. Outline a method for demonstrating the correctness of this to a class.

25 Explain the difference between a selective sample and a random sample.

BIBLIOGRAPHY

Alder, Henry L.: Mathematics for Today's High School Students, *Teachers College Journal*, **35** (1963), 112–113.

Averill, Edgar W.: Why Offer Elementary Statistics?, *Junior College Journal*, **34** (1963), 21–25.

Barker, J. C.: Not What Can Be Taught, but What Should Be Taught, *American Mathematical Monthly*, **69** (1962), 426–428.

Bishir, John: Probability Theory in the Secondary School, *High School Journal*, **50** (1967), 248–253.

Bridges, Charles M., Jr.: Statistics for Selected Secondary School Students, *Mathematics Teacher*, **54** (1961), 321–323.

Buchanan, O. Lexton, Jr.: Opinions of College Teachers of Mathematics Regarding Content of the Twelfth Year Course in Mathematics, *Mathematics Teacher*, **58** (1965), 223–225.

Byrkit, Donald R.: If Not Calculus, What?, *School Science and Mathematics*, **63** (1963), 545–546.

Fremont, Herbert: "How to Teach Mathematics in Secondary Schools" (Philadelphia: W. B. Saunders Company, 1969), pp. 101–122.

Gross, Benjamin A.: Statistics Made Simple, *Arithmetic Teacher*, **12** (1965), 196–198.

Johnson, Donovan A., and William H. Glenn: "The World of Statistics" (New York: McGraw Hill Book Company, 1961).

Kellogg, Theodore E., and Donovan A. Johnson:

Mathematics in the Secondary School: Current Practice and Trends in Mathematics Curriculums, *Review of Educational Research,* **31** (1961), 272–274.

Leake, Lowell, Jr.: The Status of Three Concepts of Probability in Children of Seventh, Eighth and Ninth Grades, *Journal of Experimental Education,* **34** (1965), 78–81.

Mayer, Joseph: Rudiments of Probability Theory, *School Science and Mathematics,* **60** (1960), 553–566.

Mosteller, Frederick: Continental Classroom's TV Course in Probability and Statistics, *Mathematics Teacher,* **56** (1963), 407–413.

————: What Has Happened to Probability in the High School?, *Mathematics Teacher,* **60** (1967), 824–831.

National Council of Teachers of Mathematics: "Insights into Modern Mathematics," *Twenty-Third Yearbook* (Washington, D.C.: The Council, 1957).

————: "The Growth of Mathematical Ideas, Grades K-12," *Twenty-fourth Yearbook* (Washington, D.C.: The Council, 1959).

O'Connor, Henry A.: Let's Make Educational Statistics More Learnable for Students, *Journal of Educational Research,* **57** (1963), 217–219.

Olander, Clarence E.: Let's Teach Statistics, *Mathematics Teacher,* **51** (1958), 253–260.

Rade, Lennart: Course in Probability Theory for Secondary Schools, *Mathematics Teacher,* **58** (1965), 528–535.

Ranucci, E. R.: Activities for Four Areas in the New Mathematics: Experiments with Probability, *Instructor,* **73** (1964), 63–64.

Rosenberg, H.: Role of Statistics in General Mathematics Courses for College Freshmen, *Mathematics Teacher,* **50** (1957), 343–346.

Streitmatter, Kenneth, and Gerald J. Rockwood: Twelfth-grade High School Mathematics: Calculus or ?, *Mathematics Teacher,* **61** (1968), 39–41.

Stringfellow, Thomas L.: Brief History of Statistics: A Contribution for the Enrichment of High School Mathematics, *School Science and Mathematics,* **61** (1961), 1–4.

Varburg, Dale E.: The Development of Modern Statistics, *Mathematics Teacher,* **56** (1963), 344–348.

Wilkes, S. S.: Teaching Statistical Inference in the Elementary Mathematics Courses, *American Mathematical Monthly,* **65** (1958), 143–153.

Williams, H. E.: Place of Probability and Statistics in the Mathematics Curriculum of the Senior High School and Junior College, *Mathematics Teacher,* **54** (1961), 316–320.

index

Abel, Niels Henrik (1802–1829), 67
Ability grouping, 108–111
Absolute constant, 277
Absolute error, 256
Absolute value, 237, 538
  addition in terms of, 194
Abstract spaces, 70
Academy, curriculum of, 5, 15
Accuracy, 255–257
Achievement tests, 179, 183–185
  criteria for constructing, 185
Addition of directed numbers, 293
Addition and subtraction of rational numbers, 205–208
Advanced Placement Program, 18, 102, 109–110, 533
Aids to instruction, 147–168
  audio-visual devices, 148–149
  computer and school mathematics, 148, 154–155
  equipment and method, 147–148
  laboratory work, 149–152
  media and methods, 147
  planning: for a course, 159
    for daily lessons, 162–165
    for effective learning, 158
  programmed instruction, 148, 152–154
  team teaching, 156–158
  unit planning, 160–162
Algebra:
  basic structure of, 68–69
  in elementary grades, 272
  first course in, 9, 271–275
  fractions, 303–311
    reduction of, 304–305
  graphs, 288–292
  inequalities, 236–239, 296–298
  intermediate, 322–324
  in junior high school, 271–317
  linear equations, 281–286
  matrix, 57
  modern concept of, 56, 67
  nonassociative, 57
  noncommutative, 56
  as a postulational system, 57
  sets, 273–275
  simple equations, 272–273
  special products and factoring, 311–313
  symbols and formulas, 275–277
    goals in studying, 276
  three periods in history of, 68

American Association for the Advancement of Science (AAAS), 21
  Cooperative Committee on the Teaching of Science and Mathematics, 26–27
  Science Teaching Improvement Program (STIP), 34
American Federation of Teachers of the Mathematical and Natural Sciences, 11
American Mathematical Monthly, 20
American Mathematical Society (AMS), 22, 28
Analysis:
  of content of junior high school geometry, 365–367
  of unit on circles, 367–368
Analyst, The, 547
Analytic geometry, teaching of, 493–529
  and calculus, 494, 531
  and the high school program, 493–501
Analytic process, 77–79
Analytic-synthetic process, 76–77, 397–401
Angle:
  general, 462–463
    degree measure, 462
    radian measure, 462–463
    trigonometric functions of, 454–490
Annals of Mathematics, 395
Antiderivative, 553–554
  integral as, 553
Apparent error, 256
Applications:
  significance of, 80–87
  use of, 45
Approximate data, computation with, 257–261
Approximate numbers:
  central concepts of, 258–259
  nature of, 251–253
  need for judgment in use of, 253
Approximativeness, criteria for judging, 253–257
  decimal point, 253
  precision and accuracy, 255–257
  significant digits, 253–254
Arbitrary constant, 277, 509–510, 535–536
Areas, 418–420
Argument, valid, 71
Arithmetic:
  "clock," 246
  early, 5
  modular, 243–246
  number systems of, 193–194
  in secondary school, 192–194

Arithmetic:
  teaching of, 192–267
Arithmetic mean, 239, 570
Arithmetic progression, 347–349
Arithmetic Teacher, The, 21, 358
Army, 28
Assignments, differentiated, 109–111
Assimilation, teaching for, 122–124
Association for Computing Machinery (ACM), 22
Association for Symbolic Logic (ASL), 22
Assumptions:
  contradictory, 78
  role in proof, 55–57, 71–79
Augmented matrix, 328
Averages, 239
  danger in percentage, 241–243
  statistical, 569–570
    arithmetic mean, 570
    measure of central tendency, 569
    mode, 570
    weighted, 240–241, 572
Axes, rotation of, 519
Axis of imaginaries, 486

Ball State Teachers College Experimental Program, 14, 107
Beltrami, E. (1835–1900), 57, 58
Betweenness, 237
Biconditional proposition, 73
Binomial distribution, 581
Board of Regents of the University of the State of New York, 6, 176
Bolyai, Johann (1802–1860), 56
Bolzano, N. (1781–1848), 70
Boole, G. (1815–1864), 70
Borel, E. (ca. 1900), 14
Boston College Mathematics Institute, 14, 107

Calculus, 66–67, 531–565
  and analytic geometry, 494, 531
  fundamental theorem of, 558–559
  in high school, 532–534
  importance of fundamental concepts, 534–535
  inflection points, 552
  maxima and minima, 551–553
  prerequisite skills, 560
  rigor in, 561
  teaching of, 531–565
  variables and limits, 535–539
Cambridge conferences, 35–37, 103, 533
Cancellation, understanding of, 202–204
Cantor, Georg (1845–1918), 58, 70

Carnegie Corporation, 34–35
Carnot, L. N. M. (1753–1823), 65
Cartesian frame of reference, 64, 77, 99
Cartesian product, 193
Carus Monograph Series, 20
Casting out nines, 243–245
Cayley, A. (1821–1895), 57
Central Association of Science and Mathematics Teachers (CASMT), 22, 26
Certification requirements, 26–27, 34–35
Chance variable, 568
Characteristics of a postulate system (*see* Postulate system)
Ciphering, 5
Circles:
  analysis of unit on, 367–368
  families of, 512–513
  general equation of, 513
  and sphere, 512–516
Circular functions, 102, 467–490
Civil Aeronautics Administration, 28
Class boundary, 568
Class interval, 568
Class width, 568
"Clock arithmetic," 246
Clubs and recreations, 143–144
Coefficient matrix, 328
Colburn, Warren (ca. 1825), 7
College Entrance Examination Board (CEEB), 15–18, 92, 109, 176, 364, 533, 566
  Commission on Mathematics of, 18–19, 45, 66, 92, 94, 96, 100, 102, 104, 109, 272, 364, 436, 469, 533, 566
College entrance requirements, change in, 15
College Entrance Requirements, Committee on, 9, 13
Combined course in plane and solid geometry, 100–101
Commission on Examinations in Mathematics, 17
Commission on Post-war Plans, 29–30, 44, 46, 95, 252
Commission on the Teaching of Mathematics, International, 10
Committee, Progressive Education Association, 25–26
Committee on Analysis of Experimental Programs, 107
Committee on Educational Media, 33–34
Committee on Essential Mathematics for Minimum Army Needs, 28*n.*
Committee of Fifteen, National, 11
Committee on Mathematical Requirements, National, 12, 16, 46, 532–533
Committee of Ten, 8, 13

Committee on the Undergraduate Program in Mathematics (CUPM), 32–33
 Panels of, 32, 35, 49, 104–106, 148, 494
Complex numbers, 60–61, 351–353
 definition of operations, 353
 geometric representation, 353
 in trigonometric form, 484–487
  amplitude, 486
  DeMoivre's theorem, 487
  modulus, 486
  vectorial angle, 486
  as vectors, 484–487
Computation with approximate data, 257–261
Computer:
 first mechanical, 66
 offers career opportunities, 141
 and school mathematics, 154–155
Computer-assisted instruction (CAI), 47, 111
 issues associated with, 155
Conant, James Bryant (1893–   ), 48
Conclusion, 72, 74
Conditional clause, 72
Conditional proposition, 72
Congruence, 244–245
Congruence relation, 67
Conic sections, 516–524
 asymptotes, 517–519
 axes, 517–519
 definitions of, 517
 directrixes, 517–519
 foci, 517–519
 general equation, 518–519
  invariant properties of, 519
  simplification of, 518–519
 vertexes, 517–519
Conics, families of, 521–522
Conjecture:
 of Fermat, 79
 of Goldbach, 79
Conjunction, 73
Consequence clause, 72
Constant:
 absolute, 277, 536
 arbitrary, 277, 509–510, 535–536
 function, 292
 of integration, 554
Construction problems, 412–415
 four aspects of, 413
Consumer Education Study, 29
"Continental Classroom," 37
Continuity of a function, 539
Contrapositive proposition, 73, 74, 404–408
Converse proposition, 72, 404–408
Convex figure, 426–429
 supporting lines, 427

Convex set, 427
Convexity, 426–429
Co-operative Committee (AAAS) on the Teaching of Science and Mathematics, 26–27
Cooperative Mathematic Tests, 19
Coordinate geometry, 441–444
Correlation in statistics, 583
Correlation of 2- and 3-dimensional geometry, 410, 418–420, 425, 428–434, 446–447
Counting, rule of, 580
Criteria for judging approximativeness, 253–257
Criteria for test construction, 177–178
Current issues in mathematical education, 91–115
Curriculum change, four sources of, 91
Curriculum problems in mathematics, 91–115
Curve of error, 583

Dedekind, J. W. R. (1831–1916), 58
 postulate of continuity, 76
Deduction:
 patterns of, 71
 techniques of, 71–74
Deductive geometry, structure of, 391–395
Deductive principle, 72
Definite integral, 556–559
 as area, 556
 as limit of a sum, 559
 three steps in use, 556
Degree measure, 462
Demands of technology, 63
DeMoivre's theorem, 487
DeMorgan, Augustus (1806–1871), 56
Denominate numbers, 248–249
Denseness of rationals and reals, 220
Dependence in geometry, 429–432
 two aspects of, 430–431
Dependent variable, 280
Derivative:
 concept of, 539–543
 as limit of a ratio, 540–542
 of logarithmic function, 547–549
 as ratio of differentials, 542–543
 of sine function, 549–550
 as slope of a curve, 541
Desargues, G. (1593–1662), 65
Descartes, René (1596–1650), 64, 65, 68
Descriptive statistics, 566
Detachment, Law of, 72
Diagnosis and remedial teaching, 182
Dichotomy, false, 263
Differential, concept of, 541–543
Differentiated assignments, 109–111

Differentiation, rules of, 543–553
   critical points in developing, 545–547
   successive, 551–552
      inflection points, 552
Digit value, 221
Digits, significant, 253–255
Diophantus (ca. 275), 68
Direct proof, 78
Directed numbers, 292–296
  addition, 293
  division, 296
  multiplication, 294–296
  subtraction, 294
Directing study in mathematics, 123–124
Discipline, mental, 5
Disjunction, 73
Disproof:
  by contradiction, 79
  by counterexample, 79, 440
Distance between two points, 496–497
Divisibility, tests for, 245
Division of directed numbers, 296
Domain:
  of function, 98, 279
  of relation, 280
  of variable, 98, 277
Drill, 129–130
Duality, principle of, 65

Education, 41
  definition of, 42
  general, 41
    (*See also* General education)
  special, 41
Educational Development Center, Inc., 37
Educational Media, Committee on, 33–34
Educational Services, Incorporated, 35
Educational television, four basic uses of, 34
Educational Testing Service, 18, 19
Einstein, Albert (1879–1955), 70
Ellipse, 503
English influence, 6
Enumeration proof, 78–79
Equality, properties of, 195–196, 282
Equations:
  containing fractions, 309–311
  quadratic, 333–344
  simple, 272–273
  simultaneous linear, 290, 298–303, 328–333
  trigonometric, 483–484
Equations and inequalities, 98–99
  simultaneous, 98–99
Equivalence:
  class, 196
  of equations, 283, 298–303, 328–344

Equivalence:
  of propositions, 73
  relation, 196
  of sets, 69, 70
Erlanger Program, 66
Error:
  absolute, 256
  apparent, 256
  percent of, 256
  relative, 256
Estimating, importance of, 261–262
Euclid (ca. 300 B.C.), 76
  elements of, 96
  fifth postulate of, 59
Euclidean geometry, 10, 61, 65, 99, 101
Euclidean method, $10n.$
Euclid's postulates, $10n.$, 394
Euler, Leonhard (1707–1783), 79
Evaluation of instruction, 172–188
  function in learning process, 174
  interpretation and uses of results, 185–186
  nature and purposes of, 172–175
  responsibilities of, 173
  techniques of, 174–178
    steps to effective, 174
Exact numbers, 252
Existence proof, 78–99
Experimental activities, 152
Experimental curriculum and course projects,
    105–108
Experimental groups, 14
Exponential function, 354–355
Exponents and radicals, 322–324

Fermat, Pierre (1601–1665), 66, 79
  last theorem, 79
Field:
  of complex numbers, 220–221
  definition of, 198–199, 284
  ordered number, 198–199
    of rational numbers, 194–219
    of real numbers, 219–220
Field operations, 200, 221
Finite geometries, 448–449
Finite induction, principle of, 60, 197, 349–351
Finite postulational system, 58
Ford Foundation, 33
Foreign influence, 6–8, 34
Formulas, evaluation and solution of, 286–288
Fractions:
  addition and subtraction, 205–208, 302–309
  algebraic operations with, 303–309
  common, 200–208
  decimal, 208–211
    irrational numbers as, 219

Fractions:
  decimal: rational numbers as, 218–219
    real numbers as, 219–220
  difficulties in dealing with, 201
  equations with, 309–311
  goals in studying, 304
  multiplication and division, 203–205, 306
  reduction of, 201–203, 304–305
Fréchet, M. (ca. 1900), 70
French influence, 6
Frequency curve, 578
Frequency distributions, 568–569
Frequency polygon, 578
Function, 65, 277–281
  constant, 292
  definition of, 98, 278
    as a mapping, 279
    as a set of ordered pairs, 65, 536
  domain of, 98, 279
  exponential, 354–355
  linear, 291
  logarithmic, 354–355, 547–549
  quadratic, 335–337
    effect of coefficients on graph, 333–337
  range of, 98, 279
  sine, derivative of, 549–550
  wrapping, 67, 468
  zeros of, 333
Function hexagon, 482
Functions:
  circular, 102, 467–472
  periodic, 102, 467–472
  trigonometric, 453–490
    of acute angle, 455–460
    developing meaning of, 454–456
    of general angle, 463–467
    graphs, 470–472, 476–478
    inverse, 474–476
    of real number, 467–472
    of special angle, 472–474
    of sum or difference of two angles, 478–480
    variation, 470–472
Fund for the Advancement of Education, 18
Fundamental theorem of calculus, 558–559

Galileo (1564–1642), 69
Galois, Évariste (1811–1832), 67
Gauss, Carl Friedrich (1777–1855), 67
General angle, 462–467
General education, mathematics in, 41–53
  basic philosophy, 42–44
  in junior college, 48–51
  in junior high school, 43–46
  objectives, 42
  purposes, 42

General education, mathematics in: in senior
  high school, 46–48
General Electric Educational and Charitable
  Fund, 34
General equation of second degree, 518–519
Gentzen, Gerhard (ca. 1936), 59
Geometric progression, 347–349
Geometry:
  absolute, 64
  analyses of junior high school, 365–367
  analytic, 64–65
    (See also Analytic geometry)
  of Bolyai, 64
  construction problems in, 412–415
  coordinate, 441–444
  dependence in, 429–432
  Descartes' contribution to, 64–65
  euclidean, 10, 61, 65, 99, 101
  finite, 448–449
  generalization in, 416–418
  inequalities in, 402–404
  inversion, 447–448
  in junior college, 493–530
  in junior high school, 363–389
  lobachevskian, 55, 61, 64
  metric, 64
  mirror, 446–447
  modern, concept of, 56
  motivation in, 401–402
  neutral, 64
  before the 19th century, 8
  noneuclidean, 55, 57, 58, 61, 65
  nonmetric, 65
  original exercises in, 399–401
  projective, 65, 99
  recommendations: of Commission on Mathe-
    matics (see Commission on Mathematics)
    of Secondary School Curriculum Committee
    (see Secondary School Curriculum Com-
    mittee)
  riemannian, 55, 57, 58, 64
  in senior high school, 390–452
  structure of deductive, 391–395
  student problems in, 373–374
  symmetries in, 432–436
  synthetic, 64
Geometry Syllabus, National Committee of
  Fifteen on, 11
Gergonne, J. D. (1771–1859), 65
Gifted student:
  characteristics of, 109
  differentiated assignments, 109–111
Gödel, Kurt (1906–   ), 59
Goldbach, C. (1690–1764), 79
Graphs, 217–218, 237–238, 288–292, 333–337
  circle, 575

Graphs:
  histogram, 575–576
  line, 574
  pictograph, 576
  statistical, 574–578
  of trigonometric functions, 470–478
    special functions, 476–478
Grassmann, H. G. (1809–1877), 56
Greater Cleveland Mathematics Program
  (GCMP), 14, 107
Gregory, D. F. (1813–1844), 56
Guidance, prognosis and, 178–181
Guidance pamphlet, 30
Guidelines for teacher education, 35

Hamilton, Sir William Rowan (1805–1865), 56,
  60, 67
Hankel, Hermann (1814–1899), 56
Harvard Committee, Report of, 41, 43
Hilbert, D. (1862–1943), 55, 59
Histogram, 575–576
Hypothesis, 72, 74

Identities, trigonometric, 481–483
Imaginary number, 351–353
Implication, 72
Increment, 540, 545
Indefinite integral, 553–554
Independent variable, 280
Indirect measurement, 454–460, 487–490
Indirect proof, 78, 436–440
  how to construct, 437–440
  student difficulties in, 437
Individual differences, 108–111
Induction:
  dangers of, 80
  mathematical, 348–351
  nature and significance of, 77–80
  principle of finite, 349–351
Inequalities, 98–99, 236–239, 296–298, 344–345
  equivalent, 297–298
  in geometry, 402–404
  in linear programming, 345
  mixed, 237
  operating with, 297
  properties of, 236–237
  solution of, 296–298
  strict, 237
  symbols for, 238
Infinite postulational system, 58
Infinitesimal, 535, 538
Inflection points, 552
Influence:
  English, 6

Influence:
  foreign, 6–7
  French, 6
  of leading mathematicians, 14
  Pestalozzian, 7
Instantaneous rate of change, 54
Institute of Mathematical Statistics (IMS), 22
Instructional problems, analysis of, 191, 371–372
Instructional programs, planning, 191
Integers, domain of, 196
Integral:
  definite, 556–559
  indefinite, 553–554
Integrated courses, 13–14
  criticism of, 14
Integration:
  constant of, 554
  element of, 557
Intermediate algebra, 322–324
International Commission on the Teaching of
  Mathematics, 10
Intervals, indication of, 237–238
Inventory tests, 179–181
Inverse (opposite) proposition, 404–408
Inverse trigonometric functions, 474–476
  notation for, 475–476
  principal values of, 474–475
Inversion, 447–448
Isomorphism, 196
Issues, current, in mathematical education, 91–
  115

Joint Commission of the Mathematical Association of America and the National Council of
  Teachers of Mathematics, 22–24, 46, 94, 533
Joint Committee of the American Society for
  Engineering Education and the Mathematical Association of America, 104
Jordan, C. (1838–1922), 57
Journal for Research in Mathematics Education, 21
Junior college, mathematics in, 15, 103–105, 493–
  565
Junior high school:
  algebra in, 93, 95–96
  arithmetic in, 192–270
  general mathematics in, 94–95
  geometry in, 363–389
  grade nine, 94–96
  grades seven and eight, 92–94
  special problems, 92
  statistics in, 567–568

Klein, Felix (1849–1925), 14, 66, 70
  definition of geometry, 66

Klein, Felix:
  Erlanger program, 66

Latin grammar school, 5, 15
Law of contradiction, 437
Law of excluded middle, 437
Least common denominator (lcd), 207
Legendre, A. M. (1752–1833), 10
Leibniz, Gottfried Wilhelm (1646–1716), 64
Lesson planning, 162–165
Lie, M. S. (1842–1899), 57
Limit, developing concept of, 67, 537
    foundation of calculus, 537
    of a function, 538–539
    of a variable, 538
Limit *e*, the, 548
Linear equations, 281–286, 298–302, 328–333
  equivalent, 283
  simultaneous, 290, 298–303, 328–333
    addition, 302–303
    graphic method, 298–300
    pivotal element, 328–331
    substitution, 300–302
    sweep-out process, 331–333
  solution set, 283
  steps in solving, 283
  truth set, 283
Linear function, 291
Linear relation, 292
Lobachevski, N. J. (1793–1856), 56
Lobachevskian geometry, 55, 61, 64
Locus :
  concept of, 408–412
  equation of, 498–506
  seven basic theorems, 409
Logarithmic functions, 354–355
  derivative of, 547–548
Low achiever, provision for, 265–267, 383–386, 444–446

Madison Project of Syracuse University and Webster College, 14, 106, 107, 363
Maintaining interest in mathematics, 137–138
Maintenance, 132–133
Mappings, 423–426
  composite, 424
  congruence-preserving, 425
  domain of, 423
  into, 423
  invariant of, 425
  many-to-one, 423
  notation of, 424
  one-to-one, 423

Mappings:
  onto, 423
  range, 423
  similarity-preserving, 425–426
Mathematical Association of America, Inc. (MAA), 20–23, 26, 28, 32, 33, 44, 494
Mathematical induction, 348–351
Mathematical learning :
  four fundamental aspects of, 118
  a theory of, 116–136
Mathematical recreations and clubs, 143–144
Mathematics:
  in the academy, 5
  in business, industry, and the professions, 141
  and the changing curriculum, 4
  in consumer education, 29
  criticisms of program, 45, 92
  directing study of, 123–124
  in general education, 30–31, 41–51
  in the junior college, 15, 48–51
  in the junior high school, 13, 43–46
  in the Latin grammar school, 5
  means to effective instruction, 137–171
  modern curriculum problems in, 91–115
  modern program in, 44, 54–90
    new point of view, 55–63
    new recognition of applications, 80–87
    new subject matter, 63–80
  in the public high school, 8
  responsibilities of program, 45
  secondary, evolving program of, 4–40
  in the senior high school, 13, 46–48
  stimulating and maintaining interest in, 137–138
Mathematics Student Journal, The, 21, 127, 143, 265, 358, 449
Mathematics Teacher, The, 21, 358
Matrix:
  augmented, 328
  coefficient, 328
Maxima and minima, 551–553
Measurement, 248–261
  accuracy in, 255–257
  of achievement, 179, 183–185
  important concepts of, 249
  indirect, 101, 454–460, 487–490
  measure, and number, 368–369
  precision in, 255–257
Measurement numbers, 250–251, 368–369
  approximate, 251
Measures, statistical (*see* Statistical measures)
Median, 239, 570
Mental discipline, 5
Metric system, 249
Minnemast, 14

Minnesota Mathematics and Science Teaching
    Project (Minnemast), 14
Mirror geometry, 446–447
Mode, 239, 570
Modular arithmetic, 243–246
Moore, E. H. (1862–1932), 14, 94
Motivation, 138–147
    through applications, 139–141
    in geometry, 401–402
    through intellectual curiosity, 144–146
    through interest in mathematics as a career,
        142–143
    through mathematical recreations and clubs,
        143–144
    through use of multisensory aids and devices,
        138–139
Multiple-track program, 47
Multiplication of directed numbers, 294–296
Multiplication and division of rational numbers,
    203–205
Multisensory aids, 138–139

National Association of State Directors of
    Teacher Education and Certification
    (NASDTEC), 35
National Center for School and College Tele-
    vision, 33
National Committee of Fifteen, 11
National Committee on Mathematical Require-
    ments, 12, 16, 43, 46, 94–95
National Committee of Physicists and Mathe-
    maticians, 28
National Council of Teachers of Mathematics,
    Inc. (NCTM), 21–23, 26, 28, 29, 31, 33, 44,
    106, 107, 148, 149, 364, 436, 494
National Defense Education Act, 37
National Education Association, 11, 14, 21
National Mathematics Magazine, 20
National organizations, 20–22
National Science Foundation, 11, 33, 35, 106–107
Natural number system, 60, 195
Navy, 28
Necessary and sufficient conditions, 285
Negation, 73
New program, shortcomings of, 92
Newton, Isaac (1642–1727), 65
Noneuclidean geometries, 55, 61, 65, 99, 201
    lobachevskian, 55, 57, 58, 61
    riemannian, 55, 57, 58
Normal probability curve, 582–583
Number system:
    bases other than ten, 223–227
        as teaching aids, 223–224
    decimal, 221–223

Number systems of elementary mathematics,
    195
Numbers, approximate, 251
    measurement, 250–251, 368–369
Numerical analysis, 104
Nunn, J. Percy (ca. 1900), 14

Open sentence, 282
Order property, 220
Ordered pairs, 65, 536
Original exercises in geometry, 399–401

Parabola, 517–520
Parallel postulate, 55
Parameter, 277, 509–510, 512–513, 521, 536
Parametric equations, 524–526
    elimination of parameter, 525
    reasons for using, 525
Pascal, B. (1623–1662), 65, 66
Pasch, M. (1843–1931), 55, 76
Pasch's Postulate, 76
Peacock, George (1791–1858), 56
Peano, G. (1858–1932), 55, 58
Pentagon, The, 358
Percent of error, 256
Percentage, 212–218, 241–243
    basic formula, 214–215
    characteristic difficulties, 213
    dangers in averaging per cents, 241–243
    dangers in "three-case" rule, 214
    one-percent method, 215–216
    use of graphs, 217–218
Permutations and combinations, 579–582
Perry, John (ca. 1900), 14, 94
Pestalozzian influence, 7
Pictograph, 576
Pivotal-element method, 328–331
Place value, 208, 221, 223
Plane, straight line and, 511
Polar coordinates, 484–487
    conversion formulas, 485, 522–524
Polar equation:
    graph of, 523–524
    helpful hints, 523
Poncelet, J. V. (1788–1867), 65
Positional value, 208, 221, 223
Postulate system:
    categoricalness, 62
    characteristics of, 57–63
    completeness, 61
    consistency, 57–59, 395
        absolute, 58
        relative, 57–58

Postulate system:
  independence, 59
  redundance, 60
Postulates:
  euclidean, 10*n.*
  nature of, 55, 393–395
Precision, 255–257
President's Scientific Research Board, 27
Primitive terms and statements, 393–395
Principal roots, 327–328
Probability, 66, 102, 104, 579
  event, 579
  experiment, 579
  outcome, 579
  sample space, 579
  trial, 579
Probability and statistics, the teaching of, 566–585
Probability distribution, 582
Probability function, 578–579
  definition of, 579
  normal, 581
Problem solving, 81–87, 229–231
  aids to, 231
  comprehension difficulty, 82–83
  flowchart for, 84–85
  judgment difficulty, 86
  operation difficulty, 86
  proof and, 81
  structure difficulty, 83–86
Problems:
  solvable, unsolvable, and unsolved, 87
  verbal, 228–231
    sources of difficulty, 229
    suggestions for teaching, 229–230, 313–317
Prognosis and guidance, 178–181
Programmed instruction (PI), 111, 152–155
  advantages of, 153
  criticisms of, 153
Progressions, arithmetic and geometric, 347–349
Progressive Education Association, Committee of, 25–26
Proof:
  analytic, 77–78
  analytic-synthetic, 76–77, 397–399
  direct, 78
  by enumeration, 78–79
  existence, 78–79
  indirect, 78, 436–440
  nature of, 74–79
  and problem solving, 81
  reductio ad absurdum, 60
  synthetic, 74–76
  of a theorem, 74
  three basic patterns, 78

Proof:
  three distinct processes, 74–78
Proofs, planning, 397–401
Proposition, 71
  biconditional, 73
  conditional, 72
  contrapositive, 73, 74, 404–408
  converse, 72
Propositional form, 71
Propositions, equivalence of, 73
Public high school, 8

Quadratic equations in one variable, 333–341
  five methods for solving, 333
    completing square, 338
    factoring, 337
    formula, 338–339
      discriminant, 338–339
    graph, 333–337
    inspection, 337
  relation between roots and coefficients, 340–341
  systems in two variables, 341–344
    homogeneous, 343
Quaternions, 61

Radian measure, 462–463
Radicals, exponents and, 322–324
Random variable, 581
Ratio, proportion, and variation, 345–347
  in trigonometric functions, 455–460
Rational numbers:
  as decimal fractions, 218–219
  definition of, 198
  as equivalence classes, 199–200, 304
  field of, 191–219
Rational operations, 221
Real-number line, 220, 238, 293
  addition on, 293
  multiplication on, 294
  order on, 293
  subtraction on, 293
Reasoning:
  deductive, 71–79
  inductive, 79–80
Reductio ad absurdum, 60
Reduction of fractions, 201–203
Relation, 65
  congruence, 67
  domain of, 280
  range of, 280
  set of ordered pairs, 279–280
Relationships, helping students discover, 375–381

Relative error, 256
Remedial teaching, diagnosis and, 182
Replacement set for variable, 277, 535
Residue of n modulo m, 244
Review, 130–132
  incidental, 131
  specialized, 131
Rhind Mathematical Papyrus, 20
Riemann, G. F. B. (1826–1866), 55
Riemannian geometry, 55, 57, 58, 64
Root:
  extraneous, 311
  principal, 327–328
Root-mean-square deviation, 571, 573
Rotation of axes, 519
Rounding off numbers, 254–255
Rule of counting, 580
Rule of signs, 296
Ruler postulate, 395, 424

Sample space, 579
Scholastic Aptitude Test, 18
School Mathematics Study Group (SMSG), 14,
    37, 106, 107, 148, 363, 436, 494
School Science and Mathematics, 22, 143, 358
Science Teaching Improvement Program (STIP),
    34
Scientific American, The, 143
Scientific notation, 259–261
Secondary School Curriculum Committee
    (SSCC), 31–32, 47, 49, 92, 95, 100,
    108, 110, 364, 533
Senior high school:
  algebra in, 98–99, 322–362
  analytic geometry in, 493–501
  calculus in, 531–534
  curricular defects, 96
  geometry in, 99–101, 390–452
  mathematical structure in, 97–98
  modern emphasis, 97–98
  probability and statistics in, 102, 566–585
  statistical inference in, 578–579
  trigonometry in, 101, 453–492
  use of applications, 97
Set:
  concept of, 69–71, 95–96
  finite, 70
  infinite, 70
  ordered partition, 580
  partitioned, 580
Sets, equivalence of, 69, 70
Significant digits, 253–255
Similarity patterns, 126–127
Simple equations, 272–273

Simple Inference Rule, 72
Simultaneous linear equations, 290, 298–303,
    328–333
  pivotal-element method, 328–331
  sweep-out process, 331–333
Slope of line, 291
Slow learner, characteristics of, 108, 265–267,
    383–386, 444, 526–527
Society for Industrial and Applied Mathematics
    (SIAM), 22
Southern Illinois University-Comprehensive
    School Mathematics Project (SIU-CSMP),
    14, 107
Soviet Union, 34
Special education, 41, 46
Special products and factoring, 311–313
Sphere, circle and, 512–516
Square root, 246–248
  principal, 327
Standard deviation, 571
Standard notation, 259–261
Statistical inference, 566
Statistical measures, 569–573
  of central tendency, 569
    arithmetic mean, 570
    median, 570
    mode, 570
    weighted mean, 572
  of dispersion, 571
    deviations, 572
    range, 571
    root-mean-square deviation, 571, 573
    standard deviation, 571, 573
    weighted deviations, 573
Statistical variable, 568
Statistics, 66, 102, 104, 566–579
Stimulating interest in mathematics, 137–138
Straight line, 506–511
  general equation of, 509
  normal form, 508
  and the plane, 511
Straight lines, families of, 509–510
Study in mathematics, directed, 123–124
Subtraction of directed numbers, 294
Successive differentiation, 551–552
  inflection points, 552
  maxima and minima, 551
Superior student, provision for, 263–265, 357–
    359, 381–383, 446–449, 526–527
Sweep-out process, 331–333
Syllogism, Law of the, 72, 73
Symbols and formulas, 275–277, 286–288
  goals in studying, 276
Symmetry, 432–436
  graphs and, 434

Table of integrals, use of, 554–556
Tannery, P. (ca. 1900), 14
Teacher:
  attributes of a good, 48
  need for a well-prepared, 51
Teacher education, guidelines for, 35
Teacher-made tests, 175–176, 184
Teaching:
  for assimilation, 122–123
  developmental, 121–122
  for permanence, 129
  problems of, 119
  for transfer, 124–129
Test construction:
  criteria for, 177–178
  problems to be considered in, 176–177
Tests:
  advantages of oral, 183
  agreement between use and purpose, 178
  as learning aids, 182–183
  precaution in use of timed, 183
  problem-type versus short answer, 177–178
  standardized versus teacher-made, 175–176,
    184
Theorem:
  contrapositive of, 73
  converse of, 72
Three-dimensional geometry, 410, 418–420, 425,
    428–434, 446–447, 495, 497–498, 506–508,
    511–516, 520
Three-track program, 46
Transfer:
  of learning, 125
  teaching for, 124–125
Transformations, 424
Translation of axes, 518
Triangles:
  conditions of solvability of, 488
  solution of, 459–490
  student difficulties, 488
Trichotomy, 60, 197
Trigonometric equations, 483–484
Trigonometric functions:
  or circular functions, 469–470
  developing the meaning of, 454–456
  of general angle, 463–467
  graphs of, 470–472, 476–478
  inverse, 474–476
  ratio definitions of, 464
  of special angles, 472–474
  of sum or difference of two angles, 478–480
    reduction formulas, 480
  two concepts of, 455
  unit circle definitions of, 464–465
  use of, 457–460, 463–467, 481–490

Trigonometric identities, 481–483
Trigonometry, 66–67, 101–102
  in the junior high school, 453–460
  of real numbers, 467–472
  in the senior high school, 461–462
    modern emphasis, 461
  teaching of, 453–492
    change of emphasis, 453
Twelfth-year program, 102
  proposals for, 494, 531, 566
Two-track program, 44, 46, 95

Undefined elements, need for, 56, 393
Understanding of new material, developing,
  119–120
Unitary analysis, 205, 215–216
U.S. Office of Education, 28, 30, 37, 149
University of Illinois Committee on School
  Mathematics (UICSM), 14, 106, 107, 148, 436
University of Maryland Mathematics Project
  (UMMaP), 14, 107

Valid argument, 71
Variable:
  chance, 568
  concept of, 98, 277–281, 535
  dependent, 280, 536
  domain, 277
  independent, 280, 536
  replacement set, 277
  statistical, 568
Variate, 568
Variation, type of, 346–347
Vectors in a plane, 369–371, 434–436, 484–487
Venn diagrams, 274
Verbal problems, 229–230, 313, 317
Volumes, 418–420

War Emergency Committees, 28
War Policy Committee, 28
War Preparedness Committee, 28
World War II, emergency of, 27–28
Wrapping function, 67, 468

Youth, ten imperative needs of, 42

Zero:
  of a function, 333
  as point of reference, 292–293
  significance of, 222